INSTRUCTOR'S GUIDE

FOR

Human Anatomy & Physiology
Laboratory Manual

MAIN VERSION, *SEVENTH EDITION*

CAT VERSION, *EIGHTH EDITION*

FETAL PIG VERSION, *EIGHTH EDITION*

ELAINE N. MARIEB, R.N., Ph.D
Holyoke Community College

LINDA S. KOLLETT, Ph.D
Massasoit Community College

PhysioEx Exercises authored by
Peter Z. Zao, North Idaho College;
Timothy Stabler, Ph.D, Indiana University Northwest;
Greta Peterson, Middlesex Community College

PEARSON

Benjamin
Cummings

San Francisco • Boston • New York
Cape Town • Hong Kong • London • Madrid • Mexico City
Montreal • Munich • Paris • Singapore • Sydney • Tokyo • Toronto

Publisher: Daryl Fox
Executive Editor: Serina Beauparlant
Development Manager: Claire Alexander
PhysioEx® Project Editor: Barbara Yien
Project Editor: Mary Ann Murray
Editorial Assistants: Sarah Kaminker and Alex Streczyn
Managing Editor: Wendy Earl
Production Editor: Leslie Austin
Composition: GTS Graphics
Manufacturing Buyer: Stacey Weinberger
Executive Marketing Manager: Lauren Harp
Cover Designer: Yvo Riezebos

ISBN: 0-8053-5520-0
1 2 3 4 5 6 7 8 9 10—TCS—08 07 06 05 04
www.aw-bc.com

Contents

Part One: Exercises

PREFACE

Organization of this Instructor's Guide

The Instructor's Guide for Human Anatomy & Physiology Laboratory Manual, Cat and Fetal Pig Versions, Eighth Edition and Main Version, Seventh Edition by Elaine N. Marieb continues to feature a wealth of information for the anatomy and physiology laboratory instructor.

Each exercise in this manual includes detailed directions for setting up the laboratory, comments on the exercise (including common problems encountered), some additional or alternative activities, and answers to the questions that appear in the text of the lab manual. (Answers to questions regarding student observations and data have not been included.)

Directions for use of the kymograph have been removed from the laboratory manual but appear in Exercise 16 in the Instructor's Guide. The appendix includes several complete laboratory exercises incorporating PowerLab® and Intelitool® computer data acquisition and compilation systems, which may be duplicated for student use.

 The time allotment at the beginning of each exercise, indicated by the hour glass icon, is an estimate of the amount of in-lab time it will take to complete the exercise, unless noted otherwise. If you are using multimedia, add the running time to the time alloted for a given exercise.

 Suggested multimedia resources, indicated by the computer icon, are listed for each exercise. Format options include, VHS, CD-ROM, and DVD. In addition, the address of the website for the InterActive Physiology® Modules (also available on CD-ROM) is provided. The resources are also listed by system in Multimedia Resources in Appendix F of the guide. Information includes title, format, running time, and distributor. The key to format abbreviations is on the Multimedia Resources page. Street and web addresses of the distributors are listed in Appendix G.

 Each exercise includes directions for preparing needed solutions, indicated by the test tube icon. A complete list of solution preparation instructions may be found in Appendix E of the guide.

 The A.D.A.M.® icon indicates links to A.D.A.M. Interactive Anatomy® in the appendix of the Instructor's Guide.

Trends in Instrumentation includes information about laboratory techniques and equipment, including comments on the use of Intelitool®. (Helpful comments regarding the use of PowerLab® are included in the PowerLab® instructions in Appendix B.) There are some suggestions about additional investigations using techniques and equipment not described in the laboratory manual.

Part Five: PhysioEx® Exercises

Part Six: PhysioEx® Review Sheet Answers   403

Histology Review Supplement   443

Appendices

Human Anatomy and Physiology Laboratory Safety Procedures

1. Upon entering the laboratory, locate exits, fire extinguisher, fire blanket, chemical shower, eye wash station, first aid kit, broken glass containers, and cleanup materials for spills.

2. Do not eat, drink, smoke, handle contact lenses, store food, or apply cosmetics or lip balm in the laboratory. Restrain long hair, loose clothing, and dangling jewelry.

3. Students who are pregnant, taking immunosuppressive drugs, or who have any other medical condition (e.g., diabetes, immunological defect) that might necessitate special precautions in the laboratory must inform the instructor immediately.

4. Wearing contact lenses in the laboratory is inadvisable because they do not provide eye protection and may trap material on the surface of the eye. If possible, wear regular eyeglasses instead.

5. Use safety glasses in all experiments involving liquids, aerosols, vapors, and gases.

6. Decontaminate work surfaces at the beginning and end of every laboratory period, using a commercially prepared disinfectant or 10% bleach solution. After labs involving dissection of preserved material, use hot soapy water or disinfectant.

7. Keep liquids away from the edge of the lab bench to help avoid spills. Liquids should be kept away from the edge of lab benches. Clean up spills of viable materials using disinfectant or 10% bleach solution.

8. Properly label glassware and slides.

9. Use mechanical pipetting devices; mouth pipetting is prohibited.

10. Wear disposable gloves when handling blood and other body fluids, mucous membranes, or nonintact skin, and/or when touching items or surfaces soiled with blood or other body fluids. Change gloves between procedures. Wash hands immediately after removing gloves. (Note: Cover open cuts or scrapes with a sterile bandage before donning gloves.)

11. Place glassware and plasticware contaminated by blood and other body fluids in a disposable autoclave bag for decontamination by autoclaving or place them directly into a 10% bleach solution before reuse or disposal. Place disposable materials such as gloves, mouthpieces, swabs, and toothpicks that come into contact with body fluids into a disposable autoclave bag, and decontaminate before disposal.

12. To help prevent contamination by needle stick injuries, use only disposable needles and lancets. Do not bend needles and lancets. Needles and lancets should be placed promptly in a labeled puncture-resistant leakproof container and decontaminated, preferably by autoclaving.

13. Do not leave heat sources unattended.

14. Report all spills or accidents, no matter how minor, to the instructor.

15. Never work alone in the laboratory.

16. Remove protective clothing and wash hands before leaving the laboratory.

Laboratory Safety Acknowledgment Sheet

I hereby certify that I have read the safety recommendations provided for the laboratory and have located all of the safety equipment listed in Safety Procedure Number 1 of these procedures.

Student's Name _____

Course _____ Date _____

Instructor's Name _____

Adapted from:

Biosafety in Microbiological and Biomedical Laboratories. 1988. U.S. Government Printing Office, Washington, D.C. 20402.

Centers for Disease Control. 1989. "Guidelines for Prevention of Transmission of Human Immunodeficiency Virus and the Hepatitis B Virus to Health-Care and Public-Safety Workers." *MMWR*: 38 (S6).

———. 1987. "Recommendations for Prevention of HIV Transmission in Health-Care Settings." *MMWR*: 36 (2s).

Johnson, Ted, and Christine Case. 1992. *Laboratory Experiments in Microbiology, Brief Version*, Third Edition. Redwood City, CA: Benjamin/Cummings Publishing Co.

School Science Laboratories: A Guide to Some Hazardous Substances. 1984. U.S. Consumer Product Safety Commission. Washington, D.C. 20207.

U.S. Department of Health and Human Services Centers for Disease Control and Prevention and National Institutes for Health, Fourth Edition. May 1999. U.S. Government Printing Office. Washington, D.C. http://www.cdc.gov.od/ohs/manual/labsfty.htm.

Trends in Instrumentation

Robert Anthony and Alan Wade, Triton College
Peter Zao, North Idaho College

This section is designed for instructors interested in incorporating additional laboratory technologies and instrumentation into their anatomy and physiology courses. The following techniques will introduce students to some standard approaches and instrumentation currently used in clinical and research facilities. Although these techniques are used in various biology and chemistry laboratory courses, many students in basic anatomy and physiology are not routinely introduced to these skills. Rather than detailing specific laboratory procedures, this discussion will provide insight into some of the options for bringing technology into the introductory anatomy and physiology laboratory.

One of the standard methods available to medical technicians and researchers is computerized data acquisition. Currently available computer packages can measure and analyze various aspects of cardiac, reflex, muscle, and respiratory physiology. Other standard methods include chromatography, spectrophotometry, and electrophoresis. Applications of available computer data acquisition systems and clinical technologies for use in an anatomy and physiology laboratory are listed on the following pages. Included in each application are relevant exercises in the laboratory manual and a brief description of each possible application. A list of companies offering appropriate products is included at the end of this section.

Computerized Data Acquisition

Computerized equipment is commonly used to monitor patients in today's allied health areas. We have found that students appreciate the brief exposure to computers in our labs and begin to realize that a computer is not an intimidating machine, but a tool that allows them to perform specific tasks. Incorporating computer-based exercises into the lab also generates increased interest because most students realize that they will be using computers in their chosen professions.

Analog-to-digital converters can be used to create customized physiological data collection systems. Easy to use computer data acquisition systems include PowerLab®, BIOPAC®, Intelitool™, and Vernier® systems. The packages are designed for use in college-level courses and require minimal computer experience.

Directions for BIOPAC® are included in the lab manual. The Instructor's Guide includes exercises using PowerLab® and Intelitool®. The Vernier® system can be easily adapted to sections of Exercises 31 and 31A.

General Tips for Computer Data Acquisition Systems Use in the Laboratory

The following ideas are general guidelines designed as an introduction to the operation of computer acquisition systems. Each system contains the software, equipment, and basic instructions needed to conduct the experiments on a computer. Appendices A and B of this Instructor's Guide include complete student exercises for PowerLab® and Intelitool® systems.

Starting the Laboratory

- Prepare the laboratory for a computer assisted data acquisition exercise by connecting the transducers and cables to the computer.

- Run through each exercise yourself so that you have a good idea of how much time is required to complete the activities in the given lab time period.

- You may wish to start the program so that the main menu is visible as the students sit down to work. If computer novices are left to start and prepare the system by themselves, their initial frustration may waste valuable lab time and detract from the experience.

- Once the program menu is up, students should be able to follow the procedures in Appendices A and B exercises without difficulty.

- It may be helpful to have an introductory lab designed to introduce the students to the general operation of the system.

Exercises Based on the PowerLab® system

Laboratory Exercises with PowerLab® instructions have been included in Appendix B for the following laboratory exercices:

Exercise 16A	Skeletal Muscle Physiology: Frog and Human Subjects
Exercise 22	Human Reflex Physiology
Exercise 31	Conduction System of the Heart and Electrocardiography
Exercise 33A	Human Cardiovascular Physiology: Blood Pressure and Pulse Determinations
Exercise 34A	Frog Cardiovascular Physiology: Wet Lab
Exercise 37A	Respiratory System Physiology

Comments and tips specific for each exercise are included in the instructions.

Exercises Based on Intelitool® Systems

Exercise 16i: Muscle Physiology

The Cardiocomp ECG package may be used to investigate electrical aspects of muscle physiology.

This exercise employs the Cardiocomp electrical recording package and the human flexor digitorum muscle to study skeletal muscle activity.

Selecting Real-Time Experiment from the Cardiocomp main menu displays the data collection screen. On the screen, you will see what appears to be random electrical "noise" but what actually is a representation of spontaneous muscle activity. Instruct the subjects to completely relax the muscle being recorded to obtain an accurate spontaneous activity tracing. Have students collect and save data for later analysis if Intelitool® hardware is the limiting factor.

Tips

- Ensure good electrical contact by using disposable electrode pads or plenty of electrode jelly if using standard flat-plate electrodes.

- Clean the electrode placement area with an alcohol pad to enhance electrical contact on subjects with high skin resistance.
- Reassure subjects that this is a recording-only exercise, and that no electrical shock will be delivered.
- Since students will be using Cardiocomp (the ECG recording package) for this exercise, instruct them to substitute "EMG" for the on-screen references to "ECG" to avoid confusion.
- BIOPAC® provides force transducers to record frog gastrocnemius muscle activity.

Exercise 22i: Human Reflex Physiology

Flexicomp replaces the traditional reflex hammer lab exercise. Flexicomp allows the visualization and recording of reflex tracings.

Possible Flexicomp demonstrations include measurement of the magnitude of response in several reflexes (e.g., plantar, patellar); measurement of the intervals between stimulus application, muscle response, and maximum response; facilitation and inhibition; comparisons between opposite limbs; and the difference between involuntary reflex activity and voluntary muscle action in response to an auditory or visual signal.

During analysis, students can measure absolute latent periods and magnitudes of deflection for any of the above-mentioned activities.

Tips
- The Flexicomp hardware uses the computer's game port. The transducer must be calibrated by following the on-screen directions (the calibration process informs the computer of the magnitude of a 90° and 150° deflection). Data values will not be correct if the calibration is not performed when the software is first started.
- Calibration only needs to be performed when the program is first started. It is not necessary to recalibrate between experimental subjects.
- Caution students that the transducer is a delicate piece of electronic equipment and that the chrome thumb screw must be loosened when not actually performing the experiment.
- The experimental subject should be sitting comfortably on the lab bench or a chair tall enough to keep the feet off the floor.

Exercise 31i: Conduction System of the Heart and Electrocardiography

Cardiocomp replaces standard ECG chart recording instrumentation.

Cardiocomp 7 examines leads I, II, III, aVR, aVL, aVF, and an exploratory chest lead. Automatic lead switching; simultaneous data acquisition from leads I, II, and III; and vectorgram capability are additional features.

Computer data acquisition system features include ECG data recording for subsequent study; time and voltage data analysis; automatic QRS, PR, and QT interval analysis; split-screen data review capabilities; and printer plots of all data analysis.

Tips

- If there is a significant amount of electrical interference, ensure good electrical contact by using disposable electrode pads or plenty of electrode jelly if using standard flat-plate electrodes.

- Clean the electrode placement area with an alcohol pad to enhance contact on subjects with high skin resistance.

Exercise 38i: Respiratory System Physiology

This system replaces the typical wet spirometers used to measure lung volumes.

Spirocomp directly records readings of tidal volume, expiratory reserve volume, and vital capacity. If the volume measurement is successfully accomplished, a histogram representing the volume will be displayed. Once all three volumes have been measured, the program will automatically calculate and display:

- Calculated inspiratory reserve volume (cIRV)

- Predicted vital capacity (pVC)

- Timed forced expiratory volume for 1, 2, and 3 seconds (FEVT)

Tips

- Spirocomp should be calibrated using the on-screen directions each time a new group record is started.

- If students have trouble recording the data correctly, adjust either the time period between breaths or the minimum volume necessary to register as a single breath. In some cases, it may be necessary to adjust both.

Exercises in Cell Physiology and Clinical Chemistry

Modern cell physiology lab exercises frequently involve biochemical analysis of cellular components and products. A number of techniques can be used to detect and quantify the constituents of cells and body fluids. Some of the more commonly used clinical and research techniques include chromatography, spectrophotometry, and electrophoresis.[1]

Chromatography

Exercise 4: The Cell: Anatomy and Division Introduce molecular separation techniques when discussing the cell (or macromolecules).

Exercise 29: Blood Separate protein and lipid components during blood analysis.

Application

Chromatographic techniques have a number of applications in cell physiology and chemistry. Chromatography is used for separation and identification of components in mixtures containing amino acids, nucleic acids, sugars, vitamins, steroids, antibiotics, and other drugs.

The major forms of chromatography for the college physiology laboratory include thin-layer, paper, column, gas-liquid, and high-performance liquid chromatography. Descriptions

---

1. Due to the hazards associated with the laboratory use of human body fluids, it may be advisable to avoid using student-drawn blood samples for analysis. There are a wide variety of commercially available blood components, both normal and abnormal, as well as blood component standards.

of these procedures and their clinical applications can be found in a number of clinical method manuals.[2]

Gas and high-performance liquid chromatography offer the greatest sensitivity and quantitative ability, but the high initial investment usually makes these systems prohibitive unless they are already in place.

Thin-layer and paper chromatography are economical, and they can be performed with a minimum of equipment. Both methods can be used as qualitative or semiquantitative screening techniques to detect the presence of both endogenous and exogenous compounds.[3]

An example of a clinically significant screening test is the determination by thin-layer chromatography of abnormal levels of certain amino acids that are associated with genetic diseases affecting metabolism. The disorders phenylketonuria, alkaptonuria, and homocystinuria result in abnormal levels of phenylalanine, homogentisic acid, and methionine, respectively, in the urine and blood. The sample and standards are applied to a thin-layer plate coated with cellulose acetate, or a silica gel, or to a Whatman #4 chromatography paper, and run in a butanol/acetic acid/water solvent. For visualization and identification of amino acids, an indicator such as ninhydrin may be used. The color intensity for the appropriate amino acids can be compared to normal values.

Spectrophotometry

Exercise 29A: Blood Analyze protein or lipid composition, or enzyme hydrolysis.

Exercise 41A: Urinalysis Analyze various substances present in urine.

Exercise 39A: Chemical and Physical Processes of Digestion Quantitative spectrophotometric analysis of enzyme hydrolysis.

Application

Spectrophotometry is a common procedure used in clinical and research settings for determining concentrations of substances in solution, based on the amount of radiant energy transmitted through or absorbed by a substance in solution. Spectrophotometric measurements include total protein, total lipid, cholesterol, lipoprotein, and hemoglobin.

Spectrophotometry can also be used as a quantitative measure of enzymatic hydrolysis using commercially available colorigenic substrates. Most determinations in spectrophotometry utilize wavelengths in visible or ultraviolet ranges. For a more detailed description of the theory of spectrophotometry and use of the equipment, refer to a biochemistry or clinical methods manual.

Diagnostic kits (for specific diseases) include:

1. Bilirubin (liver disease)

2. Total cholesterol and HDL cholesterol (atherosclerosis)

3. Creatine kinase (striated muscle damage)

---

2. A. J. Pesce and L. A. Kaplan. 1987. *Methods in Clinical Chemistry*. C.V. Mosby Co.; M. L. Bishop, J. L. Duben-Von Laufen, E. P. Fody. 1985. *Clinical Chemistry—Principles, Procedures, Correlations*. J.B. Lippincott Co.

3. J. C. Touchstone and M. F. Dobbins. 1983. *The Practice of Thin-Layer Chromatography*. John Wiley and Sons.

4. Hemoglobin (anemia)

5. Creatinine (kidney disease)

Electrophoresis

Exercise 29A: Blood Analyze protein and lipid components of blood.

Exercise 45: Principles of Heredity DNA fingerprinting systems, comparison of adult and sickle cell hemoglobin.

Application

Electrophoretic techniques, which demonstrate the migration and separation of charged solutes in an electrical field, have many important applications in cell and molecular biology. The most commonly used techniques involve zone electrophoresis, in which migration occurs within a semisolid support medium. In a majority of these procedures, agarose, polyacrylamide, or sodium dodecyl sulfate gels are used as the support medium. Sample migration can be horizontal or vertical, depending on the type of apparatus. Directions for agarose gel separation of hemoglobin can be found in Exercise 45 of the laboratory manual.

An increasing number of supply companies are recognizing the importance of studies in molecular biology and their impact on the study of cell physiology and human disease. The companies are becoming involved with biotechnology education by offering lab systems that are designed to introduce the methods of molecular biology and biotechnology to students at the pre-college and college levels. These systems are often in kit form and facilitate hands-on experience with a variety of important procedures. Some of the experimental systems available are:

1. Molecular weight determination (proteins)

2. Separation and identification of serum proteins

3. Cardiac risk assessment—analysis of lipoproteins

4. DNA fingerprinting—restriction fragmentation patterns

Sources of Equipment and Reagents

Supplies for the biochemical techniques described in the above section can be obtained from the following supply houses. The list is by no means complete but includes companies that are familiar to most educators. The Intelitool® products are best obtained directly from the company rather than through another vendor, as delivery times are much quicker.

American Scientific LLC
Biostar Corp.
Carolina Biological Supply
Edvotek, Inc.
Fisher Scientific

Fotodyne, Inc.
Intelitool, Inc.
Modern Biology, Inc.
Sigma Chemical Company
Ward's Natural Science

The Language of Anatomy

If time is a problem, most of this exercise can be done as an out-of-class assignment.

Time Allotment: (in lab): 1/2 hour.

Refer to the lab manual for links to A.D.A.M.® Interactive Anatomy.

Advance Preparation

1. Set out human torso models and have articulated skeletons available.

2. Obtain three preserved kidneys (sheep kidneys work well). Cut one in transverse section, one in longitudinal section (usually a sagittal section), and leave one uncut. Label the kidneys and put them in a demonstration area. You may wish to add a fourth kidney to demonstrate a frontal section.

3. The day before the lab, prepare gelatin or Jell-O® using slightly less water than is called for and cook the spaghetti until it is al dente. Pour the gelatin into several small molds and drop several spaghetti strands into each mold. Refrigerate until lab time.

4. Set out gelatin spaghetti molds and scalpel.

Comments and Pitfalls

1. Students will probably have the most trouble understanding proximal and distal; other than that there should be few problems.

Answers to Questions

Activity 2: Practicing Using Correct Anatomical Terminology (p. 5)

The wrist is *proximal* to the hand.

The trachea (windpipe) is *anterior* or *ventral* to the spine.

The brain is *superior* or *cephalad* to the spinal cord.

The kidneys are *inferior* or *caudal* to the liver.

The nose is *medial* to the cheekbones.

The thumb is *lateral* to the ring finger.

The thorax is *superior* to the abdomen.

The skin is *superficial* to the skeleton.

A dog's nose is *anterior* to its tail.

Activity 4: Identifying Organs in the Abdominopelvic Cavity (p. 7)

Name two organs found in the left upper quadrant: *liver* and *large intestine*

Name two organs found in the right lower quadrant: *liver* and *small intestine*

What organ is sectioned sagittally by the median plane line? *urinary bladder*

Organy Systems Overview

 Time Allotment: 1 1/2 hours (rat dissection—1 hour; human torso model—1/2 hour).

 Multimedia Resources: See Appendix F for a list of multimedia offerings.

Homeostasis (FHS, 20 minutes, VHS, DVD)
Homeostasis: The Body in Balance (HRM, IM, 26 minutes, VHS)
Organ Systems Working Together (WNS, 14 minutes, VHS)
The Incredible Human Machine (CBS, 60 minutes, VHS)

Advance Preparation

1. Make arrangements for appropriate storage and disposal of dissection materials. Check with the Department of Health or the Department of Environmental Protection, or their counterparts, for state regulations.

2. Designate a disposal container for organic debris, set up a dishwashing area with hot soapy water and sponges, and provide lab disinfectant such as Wavicide-01 (Carolina) for washing down the lab benches.

3. Set out safety glasses and disposable gloves for dissection of freshly killed animals (to protect students from parasites) and for dissection of preserved animals.

4. Decide on the number of students in each dissecting group (a maximum of four is suggested, two is probably best). Each dissecting group should have a dissecting pan, dissecting pins, scissors, blunt probe, forceps, twine, and a preserved or freshly killed rat.

5. Preserved rats are more convenient to use unless small mammal facilites are available. If live rats are used, they may be killed a half-hour or so prior to the lab by administering an overdose of ether or chloroform. To do this, remove each rat from its cage and hold it firmly by the skin at the back of its neck. Put the rat in a container with cotton soaked in ether or chloroform. Seal the jar tightly and wait until the rat ceases to breathe.

6. Set out human torso models and a dissected human cadaver if available.

Comments and Pitfalls

1. Students may be overly enthusiastic when using the scalpel and cut away organs they are supposed to locate and identify. Have blunt probes available as the major dissecting

tool and suggest that the scalpel be used to cut only when everyone in the group agrees that the cut is correct.

2. Be sure the lab is well ventilated, and encourage students to take fresh air breaks if the preservative fumes are strong. If the dissection animal will be used only once, it can be rinsed to remove most of the excess preservative.

3. Organic debris may end up in the sinks, clogging the drains. Remind the students to dispose of all dissection materials in the designated container.

Answers to Questions

Activity 5: Examining the Human Torso Model (p. 19)

2. From top to bottom, the organs pointed out on the torso model are: *brain, thyroid gland, trachea, lung, heart, diaphragm, liver, stomach, spleen, large intestine, greater omentum, small intestine*

3. Dorsal body cavity: *brain, spinal cord*

   Thoracic cavity: *aortic arch, bronchi, descending aorta (thoracic region), esophagus, heart, inferior vena cava, lungs, and trachea*

   Abdominopelvic cavity: *adrenal gland, bladder, descending aorta (abdominal region), inferior vena cava, kidneys, large intestine, liver, pancreas, rectum, small intestine, spleen, stomach, ureters*

   Note: The diaphragm separates the thoracic cavity from the abdominopelvic cavity.

4. Umbilical region: *small intestine, large intestine*

   Epigastric region: *stomach, liver, small and large intestine, pancreas*

   Hypogastric region: *small and large intestine (including rectum), bladder*

   Right iliac region: *large intestine*

   Left iliac region: *large intestine*

   Right lumbar region: *large and small intestine*

   Left lumbar region: *large and small intestine*

   Right hypochondriac region: *liver*

   Left hypochondriac region: *stomach, spleen, liver, pancreas*

   Digestive: *esophagus, liver, stomach, pancreas, small intestine, large intestine (including rectum)*

   Urinary: *kidneys, ureters, bladder*

   Cardiovascular: *heart, descending aorta, inferior vena cava*

   Endocrine: *pancreas, adrenal gland*

   Reproductive: *none*

   Respiratory: *lungs, bronchi, trachea*

   Lymphatic/Immunity: *spleen*

   Nervous: *brain, spinal cord, medulla of adrenal gland*

The Microscope

*If students have already had an introductory biology course where the microscope has been intro-
duced and used, there might be a temptation to skip this exercise. I have found that most students
need the review, so I recommend spending this time early in the course to make sure they are all comfortable with the microscope, as it is used extensively throughout the laboratory manual.*

Time Allotment: 2 hours.

Solutions:
Bleach Solution, 10%
Measure out 100 milliliters of household bleach. Add water to a final volume of 1 liter.

Physiologic Saline (Mammalian, 0.9%)
Weigh out 9 grams of NaCl. Add water to a final volume of 1 liter. Make fresh just
prior to experiment.

Advance Preparation

1. Provide each student with a compound microscope, millimeter ruler, bottle of immersion
   oil, lens paper, and millimeter grid slide. A supply of glass cleaner, such as Windex,
   should be available for lens cleaning.

2. Have available slides of the letter *e* and slides of crossed colored threads. Some instructors prefer to have slides for an entire semester available in individual boxes, which can
   be handed out to students. Others prefer to keep the slides on trays to be distributed as
   needed.

3. Set up an area for wet mount supplies, including clean microscope slides and coverslips,
   flat-tipped toothpicks, *physiologic saline*, methylene blue stain, and filter paper, or set
   out prepared slides of cheek epithelial cells.

4. Set up a disposal area containing a beaker of *10% bleach solution* and an autoclave bag.
   Note: Detailed instructions for treatment and disposal of materials used in labs involving
   human tissue and excretions are found in the preface of this Instructor's Guide.

5. If the microscopes are binocular rather than monocular, give additional instructions on focusing.

   a. After the parts of the microscope have been identified, turn on the light and adjust the interpupillary distance so that a single circle of light is visible through the eyepieces. This is difficult for some students, usually because they are moving back and forth and changing their eye position. Have each student record his/her own interpupillary distance for later use.

   b. For a microscope with an adjustable left eyepiece, focus the microscope as directed, using the right eye only.

   c. Focus using the left eyepiece with the right eye closed. Both eyepieces should now be focused on the specimen. (Reverse the directions if the right eyepiece is adjustable.)

6. The directions for perceiving depth (p. 27) are for microscopes with objective lenses that advance and retract during focusing. If the stage moves during focusing, the superior thread will come into focus first if these directions are followed. Alter instructions if necessary.

7. Set out stereomicroscopes for each student.

Comments and Pitfalls

1. Be sure to have the students check the orientation of the letter *e* on the slide before putting the slide on the microscope. If they forget to check, they will miss the point of the exercise.

2. Beware of common focusing problems: dirty lenses, inverted slide, objective lens not securely in place, and wrong lens in position (oil immersion instead of high-power).

3. It is difficult to use a millimeter ruler to measure the working distance of the high-power and oil immersion lenses on some microscopes. A best estimate is usually sufficient.

4. Many students have difficulty with the section on determining the size of the microscope field. The direct measurement is usually no problem, although some students measure area rather than diameter, and some students will have both the letter *e* slide and the grid on the stage at the same time. Emphasize that direct measurement should be done using only one lens. Otherwise, measuring discrepancies cause confusion. The problem is often with the math involved. It is probably worthwhile to stop the class and work through the use of the formula (p. 26) when you see that most students are at this point in the exercise.

5. Clarify what is meant by "detail observed" in the chart on p. 24.

6. Students may forget safety precautions when preparing the wet mount. Emphasize the importance of following directions for safe disposal of toothpicks and proper cleanup of glassware.

7. Many students forget to adjust the iris diaphragm and may end up using the light at its highest intensity, which is hard on the bulb. Remind students that the iris diaphragm should be adjusted so that the field is just filled with light when observed with the ocular lens removed. In practice, it may be necessary to adjust the iris diaphragm for best contrast, although some resolution may be lost.

Answers to Questions

Activity 2: Viewing Objects Through the Microscope (pp. 23–25)

5. Answers will vary depending on the lenses used. The correct answer for total magnification is the product of the objective lens and ocular lens used. The *e* appears upside down and backwards.

6. The image moves toward you. The image moves to the right.

7. and 8. Grains begin to appear and are very visible with the high-power lens.

   Again, total magnification depends on the lenses used.

   The image is much larger.

   The entire *e* is visible with the low-power lens, but less than 1/4 of the letter is probably visible with the high-power lens.

   The field is smaller.

   The object must be centered so that it falls into the field of the higher power lens.

   The light to the field is reduced as the iris diaphragm is closed.

   The light intensity often must be increased when changing to a higher magnification, as the lens has a smaller diameter and therefore lets in less light. In practice, if the microscope does not have a variable light intensity adjustment, the iris diaphragm should be adjusted to obtain the best contrast.

9. Yes. Probably 1000×. It depends on the magnifying power of the lenses.

   The working distance is less than that of the high-power lens. It is desirable to begin focusing with a low-power lens because the field is larger, making it easier to find the specimen on the slide, and the working distance is larger, reducing the chance of hitting the slide with the lens.

Activty 3: Estimating the Diameter of the Microscope Field (pp. 26–27)

3. Answers depend on the field diameter of lenses used. For lenses with field diameters of 1.8 millimeters, 0.45 millimeter, and 0.18 millimeter respectively, the estimated lengths are about 1.2 millimeters, 0.14 millimeter, and 1.8 millimeters.

4. No. The entire length of the object cannot be seen in one field. The estimate should be made with a lower-power objective lens.

Activity 4: Perceiving Depth (p. 27)

2. Answers depend on the order of the threads on the particular slides used.

Activity 5: Preparing and Observing a Wet Mount (pp. 27–28)

8. A cheek epithelial cell is about 80–100 micrometers (0.08–0.1 millimeter) in diameter. Most of the cells are separated from each other rather than in a continuous sheet.

The Cell: Anatomy and Division

The Anatomy of the Composite Cell section can be given as an out-of-class assignment to save time. This might be necessary if audiovisual material is used.

Time Allotment: 2 hours.

Multimedia Resources: See Appendix F for a list of multimedia offerings.

A Journey Through the Cell (FHS, VHS, DVD)
  Cell Functions: A Closer Look (25 minutes)
  Cells: An Introduction (25 minutes)
An Introduction to the Living Cell (CBS, 30 minutes, VHS)
Mitosis and Meiosis (UL, 23 minutes, VHS)

The Cell: Structure, Function, and Process (CE, CD-ROM)
Inside the Cell (CE, CD-ROM)
Inside the Living Cell (WNS, VHS, set of 5)
Mitosis (CE, CD-ROM)

Advance Preparation

1. Set out slides (one per student) of simple squamous epithelium, teased smooth muscle, human blood cell smear, sperm, and whitefish blastulae. Students will also need lens paper, lens cleaning solution, immersion oil, and compound microscopes.

2. Set out a model or a lab chart of a composite cell, and models of mitotic stages.

3. If available, arrange a viewing area for the mitosis video.

Comments and Pitfalls

1. Observing differences and similarities in cell structure often gives students trouble, as many of them have never seen any cells other than epithelial cells. Slides or pictures of these cell types might help.

Answers to Questions

Activity 5: Observing Various Cell Structures (pp. 35–36)

4. Simple squamous epithelial cells are relatively large and irregularly ("fried egg") shaped. Smooth muscle cells are also relatively large, but are long and spindle-shaped. Red blood cells and sperm are both examples of small cells. Red blood cells appear round, while sperm cells are streamlined with long flagella.

Cell shape is often directly related to function. Epithelial cells fit tightly together and cover large areas. Elongated muscle cells are capable of shortening during contraction. The red blood cells are small enough to fit through capillaries, and are actually biconcave in shape, which makes them flexible and increases surface area (not obvious to the students at this point). Sperm cells' streamlined shape and flagella are directly related to efficient locomotion.

The sperm cells have visible projections (flagella), which are necessary for sperm motility. The function of sperm is to travel through the female reproductive system to reach the ovum in the uterine tubes. This requires motility.

None of the cells lack a plasma membrane. Mature red blood cells have no nucleus. Nucleoli will probably be clearly visible in the epithelial cells, and possibly visible in the other nuclei.

No. Identifiable organelles are not visible in most of these cells. Filaments may be visible in the smooth muscle preparations. The details of organelle structure are usually below the limit of resolution of the light microscope. Unless special stains are used, there is no way to see or distinguish the organelles at this level.

The Cell: Transport Mechanisms and Permeability—Wet Lab

This exercise has many parts to it. If students have had an introductory cell biology course, much of it should be review.

Time Allotment:

Brownian movement and diffusion of a dye through an agar gel—90 minutes
Diffusion of a dye through water and osmometer—observations at end of the laboratory session—10 minutes
Diffusion through nonliving membranes—120 minutes
Diffusion through living membranes—25 minutes
Active transport—15 minutes
Observations for diffusion through living membranes, active transport, and filtration can be done while waiting for the results of the other experiments.

Multimedia Resources: See Appendix F for a list of multimedia offerings.

An Introduction to the Living Cell (CBS, 30 minutes, VHS)
Mitosis and Meiosis (IM, UL, 23 minutes)
The Outer Envelope (WNS, 15 minutes, VHS)

The Plasma Membrane and Cellular Transport (CE, CD-ROM)

Solutions:

Agar Gel, 1.5%
Weigh out 15 grams of dried agar. Slowly add 1 liter of distilled water while heating. Bring slowly to a boil, stirring constantly until the agar dissolves. For immediate use, allow the agar to cool to about 45°C. Pour into petri dishes to solidify. Refrigerate in an inverted position. If the plates are to be kept for a longer time (more than one day), autoclave the agar solution in the flask, pour into sterile petri plates, allow the agar to solidify, invert the plates, and store in a refrigerator.

Benedict's Solution
- 173.0 grams sodium citrate
- 100.0 grams sodium carbonate, anhydrous
- 17.3 grams cupric sulfate (pure crystalline)

Add the citrate and carbonate salts to 700–800 milliliters distilled water and heat to dissolve. Add the cupric sulfate to 100 milliliters distilled water and heat to dissolve. Cool the solutions and then combine. Add distilled water to make 1 liter of solution.

Bleach Solution, 10%
Measure out 100 milliliters of bleach and add water to a final volume of 1 liter.

Glucose, 40%
For each 100 milliliters of solution, weigh out 40 grams of glucose and bring to 100 milliliters with distilled water. It may be necessary to heat the mixture to get the glucose into solution. Refrigerate when not in use.

Physiologic Saline (Mammalian, 0.9%)
Weigh out 9 grams of NaCl. Add distilled water to a final volume of 1 liter. Make fresh immediately prior to experiment.

Silver Nitrate (2.9 or 3%)
Weigh out 2.9 grams (for 2.9%) or 3 grams (for 3%) of silver nitrate. **Use caution, this is an oxidizing substance.** Add distilled water to make 100 milliliters of solution. Store in light-resistant bottles. Make fresh for each use.

Sodium Chloride (NaCl), 10%
For each 100 milliliters of solution, weigh out 10 grams of NaCl and bring to 100 milliliters with distilled water. It may be necessary to heat the mixture to get the NaCl into solution.

Sodium Chloride (NaCl), 1.5%
Weigh out 1.5 grams NaCl. Add distilled water to a final volume of 100 milliliters.

Sucrose, 40% (with Congo Red Dye)
For each 100 milliliters of solution, weigh out 40 grams of sucrose and bring to 100 milliliters with distilled water. Add Congo red dye as necessary to color the solution red. It may be necessary to heat the solution to get the sucrose into solution. Refrigerate when not in use.

Yeast Suspension, 10%
Add 5 grams of dried yeast to 50 milliliters of distilled water and gently stir to form a milky solution. After 15 minutes (no more than 30 minutes), stir again. Prepare suspension immediately before use.

Advance Preparation

Note: This lab has many components. Either clearly designate supply areas for each part of the lab, or provide each lab group with its own set of supplies at the outset. The supplies for each part of the exercise are listed separately in case sections of the exercise are omitted. Some equipment is common to several parts of the lab.

1. Set out slides and coverslips. Have compound microscopes available.

2. *Brownian Movement.* Set out blunt-end toothpicks, carmine dye crystals, dropper bottles of water, microscope slides and coverslips. Have compound microscopes available.

3. *Diffusion of a Dye Through an Agar Gel.* Set out 0.1M or 3.5% methylene blue solution (Carolina) and 0.1M or 1.6% potassium permanganate solution (Carolina), 1.5% agar plates (12 milliliters of 1.5% agar per plate, one per group), medicine droppers, and millimeter rulers.

4. *Diffusion of a Dye Through Water (Demonstration).* On the morning of the laboratory session, place some crystals of potassium permanganate in the bottom of a 1000-milliliter graduated cylinder. Slowly and carefully fill the cylinder to the 1000-milliliter mark with water. Record the time at which the demonstration is set up. Set out millimeter rulers.

5. *Osmometer (Demonstration).* At the beginning of the laboratory session, set up an osmometer, using a thistle tube and molasses. Fill the expanded end of the thistle tube with molasses and cover it securely with a differentially permeable membrane. Clamp the thistle tube to a stand and put the broad end into a beaker of distilled water. Mark the level of the molasses in the tube and record the time that the osmometer is set up. Set out millimeter rulers.

6. *Diffusion Through Nonliving Membranes.* For each group, set out four dialysis sacs (Ward's) or 10-centimeter lengths of dialysis tubing (Carolina), five 250-milliliter beakers, a wax marking pencil, 750 milliliters of distilled water, 20 milliliters of *10% NaCl solution*, 20 milliliters of *40% sucrose-Congo red dye solution*, 150 milliliters of *40% glucose solution*, dropper bottles of *Benedict's solution* (Carolina, or see above), *silver nitrate*, four test tubes, a test tube rack, test tube holder, small graduated cylinder, a small funnel, hot plate, and balance. Dialysis sacs can be prepared from cut sections of dialysis tubing. Soak dialysis tubing in a beaker of water for about 15 minutes. Once dialysis tubing has been soaked, open it by rubbing it between the thumb and forefinger until the tubing material separates. Tie the ends with fine twine or close with dialysis tubing closures (Carolina). Small Hefty® "alligator" sandwich bags can also be used to make dialysis bags.

7. *Diffusion Through Living Membranes.* Give each group 6 microscope slides and cover-slips, dropper bottles of distilled water, filter paper, plastic gloves, *physiologic saline*, *1.5% NaCl*, a vial of animal blood, and medicine droppers (one per student). Set out a basin of *10% bleach*, a wash bottle of *10% bleach*, and a disposable autoclave bag.

8. *Active Transport.* Order cultures of *Amoeba proteus* (Carolina) and *Tetrahymena pyriformis* (Carolina) to be delivered as close to the date of the lab as possible. When the cultures arrive, remove the lids and aerate with clean pipettes. Use a different pipette for each culture. Loosely replace the caps and keep in a cool place out of direct sunlight. On the

day of the lab, set out the cultures with pipettes, and a depression slide and coverslip for each student.

Comments and Pitfalls

1. Caution students to keep careful track of time during the diffusion experiments. Lab timers might help. Suggestions for variables include T and different concentrations of solutions.

2. Dialysis sacs may leak. Check to see that they are tightly sealed.

3. You may substitute Clinitest tablets for Benedict's solution.

4. Silver nitrate will stain and possibly damage clothing. Warn students to be careful.

5. Note that the *40% glucose solution* used in sac 1 of the osmosis experiment is not iso-osmotic to the *10% NaCl solution* in sac 3, so caution students about the types of conclusions they may draw from this experiment. Also, sometimes no glucose will be present in the beaker at the end of the hour. You may need to extend the time for this part of the experiment.

6. Advise students to keep the light as low as possible when examining yeast cells.

7. Emphasize the importance of labeling test tubes and slides.

8. Red blood cells in physiologic saline may begin to crenate as the slide begins to dry out. Encourage students to make their observations quickly. If there is still trouble with crenation, use a slightly hypotonic saline solution.

9. Students may have difficulty locating amoebae at first. Instruct them to close down the iris diaphragm for increased contrast. Observations here require patience!

Answers to Questions

Activity 1: Observing Brownian Movement (p. 41)

2. The movement appears random. Increased temperature increases speed of movement, decreasing temperature slows movement.

Activity 2: Observing Diffusion of Dye Through Agar Gel (pp. 42–43)

6. Potassium permanganate (MW 158) diffused more rapidly than methylene blue (MW 320). The smaller the molecular weight, the faster the rate of diffusion. The dye molecules moved because they possess kinetic energy.

Activity 3: Observing Diffusion of Dye Through Water (p. 43)

4. Potassium permanganate diffuses more rapidly through the water. Although the agar gel is largely water, it does contain more solid particles, which hinder free diffusion.

Activity 4: Observing Diffusion Through Nonliving Membranes (pp. 43–45)

5. After 1 hour, sac 1 (originally containing 40% glucose) should have gained weight. Water is moving into the sac by osmosis. Glucose is still present in the sac, and a small amount of glucose may also be present in the beaker. If the Benedict's test is positive, glucose was able to pass through the dialysis membrane.

6. There should be no net weight change in sac 2. Since the concentrations of glucose and water are the same on both sides of the membrane, there is no net movement of water or glucose.

7. Sac 3 will increase in weight, perhaps only by a small amount. There has been a net movement of water into the sac and the weight of the water was not completely offset by the movement of the NaCl out of the sac. The solution in beaker 3 reacts with silver nitrate, indicating the presence of chloride in the beaker. Net dialysis of NaCl occurred.

8. There should be an increase in weight in sac 4. The water color did not turn pink; the dye was not able to diffuse out of the sac.

   The Benedict's test for sugar was negative. Sucrose did not diffuse from the sac to the beaker. The dye and sucrose are too large to diffuse through the pores in the membrane or their rate of diffusion is too slow given the allowed time.

9. Net osmosis occurred in situations 1 and 4.

   Water molecules are very small, and move quickly down a concentration gradient. Na^+ and Cl^- in solution behave like slightly larger molecules, but are smaller than glucose molecules, which move slowly, if at all, through the dialysis tubing. (See item 5 in Comments and Pitfalls.) Note: Students may only be able to conclude that Na^+ and Cl^- in solution and water molecules are small, and glucose, sucrose, and Congo red dye molecules are larger, or that Na^+ and Cl^- in solution and water and glucose molecules are smaller than sucrose molecules.

   The dialysis sac is often compared to the plasma membrane of the cell.

Activity 6: Investigating Diffusion Through Living Membranes—Experiment 1 (p. 45)

5. The dye was not accepted by the unboiled cells but was accepted by the boiled cells. Membrane selectivity is a property of living cells.

Activity 6: Investigating Diffusion Through Living Membranes—Experiment 2 (pp. 45–46)

3. The cells begin to shrink and develop a multipointed star shape.

4. When distilled water is added the cells should begin to revert to their normal shape. Eventually they begin to look very bloated, and finally begin to disappear as their membranes burst open.

Classification of Tissues

 Time Allotment: 2 hours.

 Multimedia Resources: See Appendix F for a list of multimedia offerings.

Histology Slides for Life Science (BC, 35-mm slides)
Histology Videotape Series (UL, 26-part series, 30 minutes each, VHS)

Basic Human Histology (CBS)
Eroschenko's Interactive Histology (UL, CD-ROM)
PhysioEx™: Exercise 6B (BC, CD-ROM)
Ward's Histology Collection (WNS, CD-ROM)

Advance Preparation

1. Set out prepared slides of simple squamous, simple cuboidal, simple columnar, stratified squamous (nonkeratinized), pseudostratified ciliated columnar, stratified cuboidal, stratified columnar, and transitional epithelium.

2. Set out prepared slides of mesenchyme; adipose tissue, areolar connective tissue, dense connective tissue regular (tendon) and irregular (dermis) varieties; elastic connective tissue (wall of large artery); hyaline cartilage, elastic cartilage, and fibrocartilage; bone (cross section); and blood (smear).

3. Set out prepared slides of skeletal, cardiac, and smooth muscle (longitudinal sections) and teased smooth muscle.

4. Set out prepared slide of spinal cord smear.

5. Set out lens paper and lens cleaning solution. Have compound microscopes available.

Comments and Pitfalls

1. Slides of the lung are suggested for simple squamous epithelium and slides of the kidney are suggested for simple cuboidal epithelium.

2. The dense fibrous regular connective tissue slide is sometimes labeled white fibrous tissue.

3. Students may have trouble locating the appropriate tissue on slides with multiple tissue types. Encourage them to consult lab manual Figures 6.3–6.7, available histology texts, and each other for help.

4. A television camera with a microscope adapter and monitor is very useful in this lab. By watching the monitor, students can observe the instructor locating the correct area of tissue on the slide (see item 3 in Comments and Pitfalls). It also makes it easier to answer student questions and share particularly good slides with the class.

5. Constructing a concept map or dichotomous key of tissue types

   Constructing the map or key helps students clarify differences and similarities between tissues based on observations. It provides practice with observation, logical thinking, and grouping—skills that can be applied to material throughout the course.

   The map should also make it much easier for students to identify tissues on the slides.

   a. To construct a map of the tissues, prepare a series of questions that will separate the tissue types in some logical way. Each question should have only "yes" and "no" as possible answers. You will know that a branch of the map is complete when you have separated a group of tissues into single choices. Figure 6.8 in the lab manual suggests a way to begin.

   b. Read through Exercise 6 in the lab manual and note the general characteristics of epithelial, connective, muscle, and nervous tissue. Base the map on things you can *observe* with the microscope. For example, epithelial tissue is mitotic, but this is not something you can observe easily on the slides or pictures.

      Separate out the epithelial tissue pictures. Notice that each of these tissues has a *free edge*.

      A good first question might be, "Is there a free edge?" Note that there are only two possible answers—yes and no. This should separate all of the epithelial tissues from connective, muscle, and nervous tissue.

   c. Continue asking yes and no questions about the epithelial tissues until you have separated each of the epithelial tissue types into a separate category.

   d. Now turn your attention to the pictures in the other ("no") pile. Work on a set of questions that will separate each of these tissue types into a separate category.

Activity 2: Examining Connective Tissue Under the Microscope (p. 56)

All connective tissues consist of cells located within a matrix. Blood is no exception, but its cells float freely in a liquid matrix. The matrix ground substance is the straw-colored fluid called plasma. Its proteins are soluble, rather than fibrous, and include albumin, globulins, and fibrinogen.

The Integumentary System

 Time Allotment: 1¹/2 hours.

 Multimedia Resources: See Appendix F for a list of multimedia offerings. See Exercise 6A for histology listings.

How the Body Works: Skin, Bones, and Muscles (NIMCO, 19 minutes, VHS)
Skin (FHS, 20 minutes, VHS, DVD)
The Skin (NIMCO, 30 minutes, VHS)
The Senses: Skin Deep (FHS, 26 minutes, VHS, DVD)

 Solution:
Lugol's Iodine (IKI)
• 20 grams potassium iodide
• 4 grams iodine crystals
Dissolve potassium iodide in 1 liter distilled water. Add the iodine crystals and stir to dissolve. Store in dark bottles.

Advance Preparation

1. Set out models of the skin, prepared slides of human scalp with hair follicles and skin of palm or sole, lens paper, and lens cleaning solution. Have compound microscopes available.

2. Terminology for layers of the epidermis differs from text to text. Decide on the terminology to be used, and inform the students at the onset of the laboratory session if there is a discrepancy between the laboratory manual and the text.

3. Set out 20# bond paper ruled in 1-centimeter squares, scissors, Betadine swabs, or *Lugol's iodine* (Carolina, or see above), cotton swabs, and adhesive tape.

4. Prepare a data collection sheet for "palm" and "forearm" sweat gland data.

5. Set out 2 × 3 index cards, Parelon® fingerprint pad or portable inking foils, ink cleaner towelettes, and magnifying glasses (all available from Sirchie® Finger Print Laboratories, Inc., 1-800-356-7311 or www.sirchie.com, and Kinderprint Co., Inc., 1-800-227-6020 or www.kinderprint.com.).

Comments and Pitfalls

1. Students may have difficulty finding the arrector pili muscles and sweat glands. Some students will confuse the fibers of the dermis (dense fibrous irregular connective tissue) with smooth muscle.

Answers to Questions

Activity 3: Comparison of Hairy and Relatively Hair-free Skin Microscopically (p. 73)

1. The stratified squamous epithelium of the skin is comprised of several recognizable layers, the outermost of which are keratinized.

   Both types of epithelia are protective, but the skin epithelium also protects against water loss to the external environment, UV damage, and chemical damage in addition to protecting against mechanical damage and bacterial invasion.

2. The thickness of the skin can be attributed to the presence of a fifth epithelial layer, the stratum lucidum, and a thicker stratum corneum and dermis. Thick skin lacks hair follicles, arrector pili, and sebaceous glands that are present on thin skin of the scalp.

Activity 4: Differentiating Sebaceous and Sweat Glands Microscopically (p. 74)

Eccrine sweat glands have long, straight, or undulating ducts with twisted coils at their base. In contrast, sebaceous glands have short ducts leading from a fan-shaped base. Sebaceous glands are usually associated with hair follicles.

Activity 5: Plotting the Distribution of Sweat Glands (p. 75)

6. The palm has a greater density of sweat glands than the forearm.

Activity 7: Taking and Identifying Inked Fingerprints (pp. 75–76)

7. Sometimes it was easy to classify the prints; at other times it was difficult.

   This has to do with the clarity of the prints taken and the fact that more information on fingerprints is necessary to make accurate identifications.

   The same individual would probably affect the fingerprinting process in the same way each time.

Classification of Covering and Lining Membranes

 Time Allotment: 1/2 hour.

 Refer to the lab manual for links to A.D.A.M.® Interactive Anatomy.

Advance Preparation

1. Set out slides of trachea (cross section), esophagus, small intestine (cross section), and a serous membrane such as mesentery (Ward's). If a slide of mesentery is unavailable, use the visceral serosa on a slide of a cross section of the ileum, or substitute a slide of an artery (cross section) and study the endothelium. Have compound microscopes, lens paper, and lens cleaning solution available.

2. Arrange with a butcher or meat packer for a longitudinally cut fresh beef joint. Set out the beef joint and provide disposable gloves at the demonstration area.

Comments and Pitfalls

1. The students have not been introduced to the respiratory or digestive systems yet, and they may have difficulty locating the appropriate tissues. Remind them to look for free surfaces to find epithelium. The intestine slide may be confusing due to the presence of villi in longitudinal and cross sections. A simple diagram on the board may help, or refer students to appropriate exercises later in the lab manual.

2. Start looking early for a butcher who will saw through a beef joint.

Answers to Questions

Activity 1: Examining the Microscopic Structure of Mucous Membranes (p. 79)

Goblet cells are found in both the tracheal and the intestinal epithelia.

The mucous membranes of the trachea and esophagus are mainly protective, while that of the small intestine is specialized for absorption. These membranes protect underlying tissues and the tracheal and intestinal epithelia secrete mucus.

Activity 2: Examining the Microscopic Structure of a Serous Membrane (p. 79)

The serous membranes of the heart and pericardial cavity are the visceral and parietal pericardia.

The membranes of the abdominal viscera and visceral cavity are the visceral peritoneum and parietal peritoneum.

Overview of the Skeleton: Classification and Structure of Bones and Cartilages

exercise

9

 Time Allotment: 45 minutes.

 Multimedia Resources: See Appendix F for a list of multimedia offerings. See Exercise 6A for histology listings.

How the Body Works: Skin, Bones, and Muscles (NIMCO, 19 minutes, VHS)
The Human Skeletal System (IM, 23 minutes, 2001)
Muscle and Bone (NIMCO, 30 minutes, VHS)
Our Flexible Frame (WNS, 20 minutes, VHS)
Skeletal System: The Infrastructure (FHS, 25 minutes, VHS, DVD)
Skeleton: An Introduction (UL, 46 minutes, VHS)
The Skeletal System (WNS, 15 minutes, VHS)

 Solution:
Hydrochloric Acid (HCl), 10%
Add 36 milliliters of 36% HCl to 200 milliliters of distilled water. Add water to a final volume of 360 milliliters.

Advance Preparation

1. If you have a local source, arrange to have a long bone sawed longitudinally. Keep refrigerated or frozen until used. Preserved, sawed long bones can be used instead. Provide disposable gloves at the demonstration area.

2. Bake some long bones (chicken or turkey bones work well) at 250°F for 2 hours or until they are brittle and snap or crumble easily. Prepare these the day before lab observations are to take place.

3. Soak some long bones in *10% hydrochloric acid* or vinegar until flexible. Overnight soaking is usually sufficient for the hydrochloric acid; vinegar will take longer. Prepare well in advance.

4. Prepare numbered samples of long, short, flat, and irregular bones. These can be set out at a station in the lab where students can work on identification.

5. Put out prepared slides of ground bone (cross section), developing long bone undergoing endochondral ossification, hyaline cartilage, fibrocartilage, and elastic cartilage. Also set out lens paper and lens cleaning solution, and have compound microscopes available.

6. Set out models of the microscopic structure of bone.

Comments and Pitfalls

1. Students may initially have some trouble classifying bones by shape; other than that, this lab should cause no problems.

2. Emphasize that all long bones have a long axis, but some long bones are much shorter than others! Long bones include most of the bones of the upper and lower limbs (humerus, radius, ulna, femur, tibia, fibula, metacarpals, metatarsals, phalanges). Short bones include the carpals and the tarsals. Flat bones are thin and include the bones of the roof of the cranial cavity, sternum, scapula, and ribs. Irregular bones include some skull bones, the vertebrae, and possibly bones of the pelvic girdle. Bones included in each of these categories vary from author to author.

Answers to Questions

Activity 3: Examining the Effects of Heat and Hydrochloric Acid on Bones (pp. 84–85)

The treated bones still have the same general shape as the untreated bones, although the acid-soaked bone may appear more fibrous.

The heated bone is very brittle and responds to gentle pressure by breaking.

The acid-treated bone is very flexible.

The acid appears to remove the calcium salts from the bone.

Heating dries out the organic matrix.

The acid-treated bone most closely resembles the bones of a child with rickets.

The Axial Skeleton

Time Allotment: 2^{1}/$_{2}$ hours.

Multimedia Resources: See Appendix F for a list of multimedia offerings.

The Human Skeletal System (IM, 23 minutes, 2001)
The Skull Anatomy Series (UL, 9-part series, VHS)
Thoracic Skeleton, The (UL, 18 minutes, VHS)

Interactive Skeleton: Sports & Kinetic (LP, CD-ROM)

 Refer to the lab manual for links to A.D.A.M.® Interactive Anatomy.

Advance Preparation

1. Set out one intact skull per group.

2. Set out labeled samples of disarticulated vertebrae, an articulated spinal column, a disarticulated skull, and a Beauchene skull.

3. Have articulated skeletons available. There should be a minimum of two, one male and one female.

4. Display X rays of individuals with scoliosis, kyphosis, and lordosis, if available. Students are often willing to bring in X rays for the class to use if none are available.

5. Set out blunt probes or unsharpened pencils with erasers for the students to use while studying the bones. Caution them against marking the bones with pencils or markers.

Comments and Pitfalls

1. Students may have some trouble with the numerous foramina of the skull. You may wish to have them locate all of the foramina at this time, but hold them responsible for identifying a smaller number.

2. The ethmoid bone may cause some problems, especially if the skulls are old and the conchae have begun to crumble. The disarticulated and Beauchene skulls will come in handy here.

3. There is the occasional student who asks whether males have one less rib than females. A trip to the articulated skeletons provides the answer: no.

Answers to Questions

Activity 3: Examining Spinal Curvatures (p. 99)

2. When the fibrous disc is properly positioned, the spinal cord and peripheral nerves are not impaired in any way. If the disc is removed, the intervertebral foramina are reduced in size, and might pinch the nerves exiting at that level.

   Slipped discs often put pressure on spinal nerves, causing pain and/or loss of feeling.

The Appendicular Skeleton

 Time Allotment: 2 hours.

 Multimedia Resources: See Appendix F for a list of multimedia offerings.

Anatomy of a Runner (Structure and Function of the Lower Limb) (UL, 38 minutes, VHS)
Anatomy of the Hand (FHS, 14 minutes, VHS, DVD)
Anatomy of the Shoulder (FHS, 18 minutes, VHS, DVD)
Bones and Joints (FHS, 20 minutes, 1995)
Gluteal Region and Hip Joint (UL, 18 minutes, VHS)
Knee Joint (UL, 16 minutes, VHS)

Interactive Foot and Ankle (LP, CD-ROM)
Interactive Shoulder (LP, CD-ROM)

AIA Refer to the lab manual for links to A.D.A.M.® Interactive Anatomy.

Advance Preparation

1. Have articulated skeletons (male and female) available.

2. Set out disarticulated skeletons. One per group of 3–4 students is ideal.

3. Set out male and female articulated pelves in a demonstration area.

4. Set out blunt probes or unsharpened pencils with erasers for use during bone identification.

5. Set out X rays of bones of the appendicular skeleton.

Comments and Pitfalls

1. Students may have trouble distinguishing between right and left samples of bones. Remind them to review the bone markings before checking the articulated skeleton.

2. Stress the importance of bony landmarks for muscle location and identification.

exercise

The Fetal Skeleton

12

 Time Allotment: 1/2 hour.

Advance Preparation

1. Set out an isolated fetal skull and fetal skeleton in a demonstration area, unless enough are available for each group. If you don't already know it, figure out the approximate age of the fetus, since someone is sure to ask. Developmental charts are usually available in developmental anatomy texts.

2. Have an adult articulated skeleton available.

Answers to Questions

Activity: Examining a Fetal Skull and Skeleton (p. 117)

1. Yes, the fetal and adult skulls have the same bones, although the fetal frontal bone is bipartite as opposed to the single frontal bone seen in the adult skull.

   The fetal face is foreshortened and overshadowed by the cranium; the maxillae and mandible are very tiny.

   In the adult skull the cranium is proportionately smaller and the facial skeleton proportionately larger.

Articulations and Body Movements

 Time Allotment: 1 hour.

 Multimedia Resources: See Appendix F for a list of multimedia offerings.

Anatomy of a Runner (Structure and Function of the Lower Limb) (UL, 38 minutes, VHS)
Bones and Joints (FHS, 20 minutes, VHS, DVD)
Gluteal Region and Hip Joint (UL, 18 minutes, VHS)
Knee Joint (UL, 16 minutes, VHS, DVD)
Movement at Joints of the Body (FHS, 40 minutes, VHS, DVD)
Moving Parts (FHS, 27 minutes, VHS, DVD)
The Skeleton: Types of Articulations (UL, 16 minutes, VHS)

 Refer to the lab manual for links to A.D.A.M.® Interactive Anatomy.

Advance Preparation

1. If you have a local source, obtain a sagittally sawed, fresh diarthrotic beef joint from a butcher or meat packing company. Refrigerate or freeze until use. Preserved joints could be used instead. Have disposable gloves available.

2. Have available the articulated skeleton and isolated skull.

3. Set out any available anatomical charts of joint types, models of joint types, etc., that are available.

4. Display any available X rays of normal and arthritic joints.

5. There are several methods of joint classification. If your text and the lab manual use different systems, decide on the preferred system for your course.

6. Have water balloons and clamps available.

Comments and Pitfalls

1. Some students may have trouble interpreting the movements in Figure 13.6. It may help to have the students perform all of these movements together during lab.

2. Students may be confused by movement at the shoulder joint. Flexion occurs when the arm is moved forward and upward, and extension returns the arm to the anatomical position.

Activity 4: Demonstrating the Importance of Friction-Reducing Structures (p. 123)

4. The fluid-filled sac greatly reduces the friction between the two surfaces. The water balloon represents a synovial cavity, bursae, or tendon sheaths. The fists represent two articulating bones on opposite sides of a synovial cavity. They may also represent muscles, tendons, or ligaments in the case of bursae and tendon sheaths.

Microscopic Anatomy and Organization of Skeletal Muscle

 Time Allotment: 1 1/2 hours.

 Multimedia Resources: See Appendix F for a list of multimedia offerings. See Exercise 6A for histology listings.

Human Musculature Videotape (BC, 23 minutes, VHS)
Muscles (FHS, 20 minutes, VHS, DVD)
Muscles and Joints: Muscle Power (FHS, 26 minutes, VHS)
The New Living Body: Muscles (FHS, 20 minutes, VHS)
The Skeletal and Muscular Systems (IM, 24 minutes, VHS)

 Solution:
Saline Solution, 0.9%
Weigh out 0.9 gram of NaCl. Add distilled water to a final volume of 100 milliliters.

 InterActive Physiology®: Muscular System (BC, CD-ROM, or www.interactivephysiology.com)
      Anatomy Review: Skeletal Muscle
      The Neuromuscular Junction
      Sliding Filament Theory
      Muscle Metabolism
      Contraction of Motor Units
      Contraction of Whole Muscle

Advance Preparation

1. Purchase chicken breasts or thighs from the meat market (one per lab). Refrigerate until used. Cut or tear the meat into small strips just before the lab. Provide gloves.

2. Set out forceps, dissecting needles, *0.9% saline solution* in dropper bottles, and microscope slides and coverslips for each student. Designate an organic matter disposal area.

3. Set out prepared slides of skeletal muscle (longitudinal and cross sections), and slides showing myoneural junctions. (Because the latter slides are expensive, a demonstration microscope is an alternative to providing a slide for each student.) Set out lens paper and lens cleaning solution. Have compound microscopes available.

4. Set out any available models of skeletal muscle cells and myoneural junctions.

Comments and Pitfalls

1. Students may have difficulty observing the muscle banding pattern. This is usually because the light intensity is set too high and the iris diaphragm is not closed down.

2. Emphasize the importance of understanding the organization and terminology of muscle structure. The organization and terminology of the nerves are very similar.

Answers to Questions

Activity 1: Examining Skeletal Muscle Cell Anatomy (pp. 134–135)

4. The banding pattern and limits of the cells are much clearer on the prepared slides.

Gross Anatomy of the Muscular System

 Time Allotment: 2–3 hours in lab plus time outside of lab.

 Multimedia Resources: See Appendix F for a list of multimedia offerings.

Anatomy of a Runner (Structure and Function of the Lower Limb) (UL, 38 minutes, VHS)
Abdomen and Pelvis (UL, 16 minutes, VHS)
Human Musculature Videotape (BC, 23 minutes, VHS)
Lower Extremity (UL, WNS, 28 minutes, VHS)
Major Skeletal Muscles and their Actions (UL, 19 minutes, VHS)
The New Living Body: Muscles (FHS, 20 minutes)
The Skeletal and Muscular Systems (IM, 24 minutes, 1997)
Upper Extremity (UL, WNS, 36 minutes, VHS)

 Refer to the lab manual for links to A.D.A.M.® Interactive Anatomy.

Advance Preparation

1. Set out models of the human torso and upper and lower limbs. It helps to have the muscles labeled on some of the models. Have model keys available.

2. Set out anatomical charts of human musculature.

3. If possible, have a prosected human cadaver available. Be prepared to inform students as to which muscles should be identified.

4. Set out functional knee and hip models available from Ward's Natural Science. (There are two varieties of each model type. Although more expensive, the SOMSO® model is much more flexible and comes with a key.)

Skeletal Muscle Physiology: Frogs and Human Subjects

This exercise may be divided into two parts. The first demonstrates muscle contraction at the cellular level, and the second investigates contraction of the muscle as a whole. If desired, this exercise can be done in conjunction with Exercise 18 (Neurophysiology of Nerve Impulses) to save animals. Alternatively, the instructor may prefer to have the class observe the computer simulation of this material (PhysioEx™ Exercise 16B).

Suggestion for Alternative Equipment

Computerized (Intelitool®) and PowerLab® alternatives to this traditional exercise can be found in Appendix A and B of this instructor's guide.

 Time Allotment:
ATP Muscle Kit: 1 hour+ (depends largely on dissecting dexterity of students).
Muscle Fatigue in Humans: 1/2 hour.
Induction of Contraction in the Frog Gastrocnemius Muscle: 2 hours+.

 Multimedia Resources: See Appendix F for a list of multimedia offerings.

Moving Parts (FHS, 26 minutes, VHS, DVD)
Muscles and Joints: Muscle Power (FHS, 26 minutes, VHS, DVD)
Muscular System: The Inner Athlete (FHS, 25 minutes, VHS, DVD)

Biochemistry of Muscle (ED, CD-ROM)

 InterActive Physiology®: Muscular System (BC, CD-ROM, or www.interactivephysiology.com)
    Anatomy Review: Skeletal Muscle
    The Neuromuscular Junction
    Sliding Filament Theory
    Muscle Metabolism
    Contraction of Motor Units
    Contraction of Whole Muscle

Solution:
Ringer's Solution, Frog
- 6.50 grams sodium chloride
- 0.14 gram potassium chloride
- 0.12 gram calcium chloride
- 0.20 gram sodium bicarbonate

Combine salts in a flask and add distilled water to make 1 liter of solution.

Advance Preparation—ATP Muscle Kit

1. Order the ATP muscle kits (Carolina) to be delivered no more than seven days before the lab. One kit provides generously for eight students. Extra vials of the chemical solutions can be ordered separately (Carolina) and will reduce waiting time. Just before the lab begins, cut the muscle bundles into 2-centimeter lengths and place in a petri dish in the accompanying glycerol.

2. Glass dissecting needles can be made easily from glass stirring rods. Use a Bunsen burner with a flame spreader attachment. Holding a stirring rod with oven mitts, heat the center while turning the rod until the flamed area glows orange. Pull the ends gently but firmly apart until the glass separates. With practice, fine-tipped needles can be made.

Comments and Pitfalls

1. Students may have great difficulty separating the muscle bundles into individual fibers. Often two or three fibers remain together and it is the best they can do.

2. Remind the students to keep the fibers in a pool of glycerol to prevent them from drying out.

3. Sometimes the fibers curl as they contract. Caution the students to measure the uncurled length of the fiber.

4. Occasionally there is great variability in the results (probably due to technical errors). Try rinsing the slides and glass needles in distilled water before use. This is a good exercise to collect class data and have the students compare individual results with the class results. You can discuss the importance of controlled experiments and repeated trials.

Advance Preparation—Frog Gastrocnemius Muscle

1. If animal maintenance facilities are limited, order frogs to be delivered about 2–3 days prior to the date of the lab exercise. Healthy frogs can be maintained for a short time in a clean aquarium with a small amount of chlorinated water that is changed daily. Provide the frogs with a rock extending above the water line. Northern frogs require slightly cooler conditions (10–15°C) than southern frogs (15–20°C). One frog per lab group should be sufficient.

2. Designate a disposal area for the frogs. Have disposable gloves available for handling the frogs.

3. Pith frogs as needed, or if you prefer to have students pith their own frogs, provide them with copies of the pithing instructions on the following page.

4. Set up work stations according to the amount of equipment available. Ideally there should be four students to a group. Each work station should include: a computer and associated equipment or a physiograph and associated equipment, a beaker of *frog Ringer's solution*, a medicine dropper, scissors, a glass needle, cotton thread, forceps, and a glass or porcelain plate.

5. Acquaint students with the operation of the recording equipment. Once the students are comfortable with the equipment, they should proceed with the experiment. Taking time here is worthwhile.

   a. *Physiograph.* There are several different brands of physiographs in use. It is best to consult the manual that comes with your equipment for specific details of operation. Have the students locate the switch regulating paper speed and practice running the paper at different speeds. The paper should then be rewound for future use. The students should also test the time marker at different settings with the paper running, and depress the event marker to observe the response. They should understand that the event marker will be automatically depressed when stimuli are applied to the muscle preparation. Be sure the ink is flowing smoothly through the writing tips, and be sure the tips are adjusted to record on horizontal lines of the paper grid.

   b. BIOPAC®. It is helpful to have experienced student assistants to help with BIOPAC®. Introduce students to the basic features of BIOPAC® use before beginning this lab exercise.

Comments and Pitfalls

1. Students often fail to keep the muscle moist. Someone in the group should be in charge of keeping the muscle moist.

2. If the muscle is not lined up vertically on the equipment, it pulls at an angle.

3. Students may forget to record data. One person in the group should be the designated recorder.

4. Sometimes the ink does not flow smoothly. To help avoid this, test the equipment before beginning the experiment.

5. When determining the effect of load on skeletal muscle, remind students to loosen the afterload screw (if present) on the muscle lever.

6. If the sensitivity control or gain on the physiograph is at its most sensitive setting, you may have electrical interference.

7. If students are having trouble obtaining a muscle response, have them check to be sure that the connections are not loose and that the stimulator electrode is making contact with the muscle.

Answers to Questions

Activity 1: Observing Muscle Fiber Contraction (pp. 168–170)

8. The contracted fiber appears wider and the edges appear scalloped. The I and H zones (or bands) have disappeared.

10. Generally there is little or no contraction with ATP alone. There is no contraction with the salt solutions alone. Maximum contraction occurs in the presence of ATP and the proper concentrations of potassium and magnesium ions.

Activity 2: Demonstrating Muscle Fatigue in Humans (p. 170)

7. As load increases, the period of contraction shortens as the muscle fatigues more quickly.

It is expected that not all groups will obtain exactly the same results. The observed differences may be explained by inadvertent damage occurring to the muscle cells during separation, failure to separate completely to individual cells, and imprecision in measurements.

Activity 3: Inducing Contraction in the Frog Gastrocnemius Muscle (pp. 170–176)

Observing Graded Muscle Response to Increased Stimulus Intensity

4. As the voltage increases, more motor units respond. The name for this is motor unit recruitment.

5. Once maximal stimulus is reached, all the motor units are contracting. Additional voltage has no effect.

Inducing Muscle Fatigue

4. After a period of rest, the muscle contracts again upon stimulation. A physiological basis for this may be that accumulated lactic acid diffuses out of the cells, raising the pH and allowing the enzymes necessary for ATP production to function again and the Na^+/K^+ pump to restore correct ionic distribution.

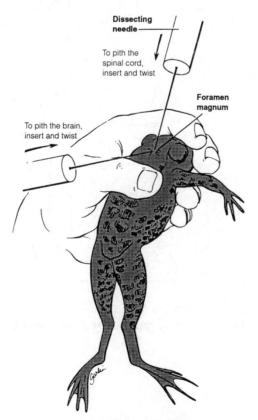

Figure 16A.1
Procedure for pithing a frog

Activity 4: Electromyography in a Human Subject Using BIOPAC® (pp. 176–183)

Part 1: Temporal and Multiple Motor Unit Summation

7. The intensity of each of the values increases with increasing force of muscle contraction.

The maximum voltage is reflective of the number of motor units being activated. The p-p value gradually increases reflecting an increased number of active motor units.

Part 2: Force Measurement and Fatigue

4. There may or may not be a difference in the maximal force between the forearms, but usually the maximal force in the dominant forearm is 10–20% greater than in the non-dominant forearm.

Muscle cells are amitotic. When a muscle gets larger in diameter, it is because of an increase in size (diameter) of the muscle cells, not because of an increase in the number of muscle cells.

One normally observes more rapid fatigue in the non-dominant forearm.

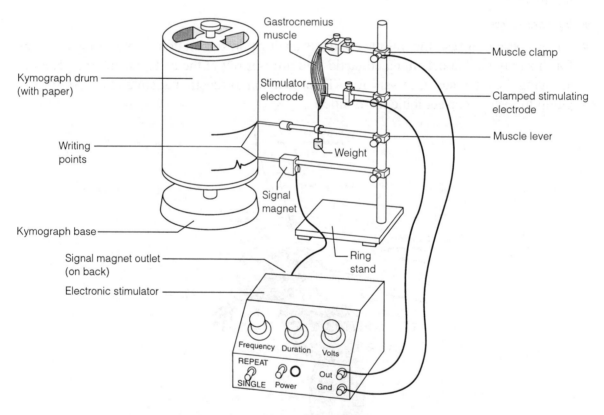

Figure 16A.2
Kymograph setup for frog gastrocnemius experiments.

Advance Preparation for the Kymograph

1. Set up work stations according to the amount of equipment available. Ideally there should be four students to a group. Acquaint students with the operation of the equipment.

2. If smoked paper is to be used for kymograph recording, set up an area in a fume hood for smoking the paper, another hooded area with glazing fluid or fixative, and a line and clips for drying the paper.

Comments and Pitfalls

1. Kymograph paper is smoked in a fume hood using a smoky flame produced by passing natural gas through benzene. Since benzene is a known carcinogen, alternative recording methods should be sought. Muscle levers and signal magnets with ink recording tips can be purchased. If the budget is tight, small right-angled felt-tip markers can be attached to each smoke-writing stylus for satisfactory results. Students should practice putting paper tightly on the drum and lining up the signal magnet and muscle lever writing tips. If the muscle lever is equipped with an afterload screw, have the students adjust it to bring the muscle lever to a horizontal position. Be sure the ink is flowing smoothly (if applicable). Have the students set the signal magnet to deliver one pulse per second, and calculate the drum speed in mm/sec for each setting.

2. Students may brush against the smoked paper before it has been fixed and destroy the recordings. If shellac is used as the glazing fluid, be sure students put paper into the shellac with the smoked side up. Spray lacquers are easier to use.

Histology of
Nervous Tissue

17

 Time Allotment: 1 hour.

 Multimedia Resources: See Appendix F for a list of multimedia offerings. See Exercise 6A for histology listings.

The Human Body Series: Nerves and Nerve Cells (NIMCO, 28 minutes, 1993)
The Living Body: Nerves at Work (FHS, 27 minutes, 1990)
The Nature of the Nerve Impulses (FHS, 15 minutes, 1988)
Nerves and Nerve Cells (CBS, VHS)
Nerves at Work (FHS, 26 minutes, VHS)

IP InterActive Physiology®: Nervous System I (BC, CD-ROM, or www.interactivephysiology.com)
      Nervous I
      Orientation
      Anatomy Review
      Ion Channels
      The Membrane Potential
      The Action Potential

Advance Preparation

1. Set out slides of ox spinal cord smear and teased myelinated fibers, Purkinje cells (cerebellum), pyramidal cells (cerebrum), dorsal root ganglia, and nerve cross section.

2. Set out lens paper, immersion oil, and lens cleaning solution. Have compound microscopes available.

3. Set out models of neurons, if available.

Comments and Pitfalls

1. Students may focus on the wrong cells. Encourage them to use histology atlases and help each other.

2. Students may have difficulty with the connective tissue sheaths. Remind them of the similarities to muscle terminology.

Answers to Questions

Activity 1: Identifying Parts of a Neuron (p. 187)

3. The nodes are at regular intervals. Action potentials will occur at regular intervals along the axon as local currents open voltage-gated sodium channels.

Activity 2: Studying the Microscopic Structure of Selected Neurons (pp. 188–189)

The Purkinje and pyramidal cells are multipolar. The dorsal root neurons are unipolar.

Neurophysiology of Nerve Impulses: Wet Lab

If desired, part of this investigation of the nerve impulse may be done in conjunction with Exercise 16A (Muscle Physiology) to save animals.

 Time Allotment: 1–1½ hours (more if oscilloscope is used).

 Multimedia Resources: See Appendix F for a list of multimedia offerings. See Exercise 6 for histology listings.

Brain and Nervous System: Your Information Superhighway (FHS, 25 minutes, VHS, DVD)
Nerve Impulse Conduction (IM, 29 minutes, VHS)

 IP InterActive Physiology®: Nervous System I and II (BC, CD-ROM, or www.interactivephysiology.com)

Nervous I	Nervous II
Orientation	Orientation
Anatomy Review	Anatomy Review
Ion Channels	Ion Channels
The Membrane Potential	Synaptic Potentials and Cellular Integration
The Action Potential	Synaptic Transmission

 Solutions:

Hydrochloric Acid (HCl), 0.01%
Add 0.27 milliliter of 1N HCl (Carolina) to 90 milliliters of distilled water. Add water to a final volume of 100 milliliters. *Or*, beginning with 37% HCl (d 1.2), prepare a 1N solution by adding 8 milliliters of 37% HCl to 90 milliliters of water. Add distilled water to a final volume of 100 milliliters.

Ringer's Solution, Frog
• 6.50 grams sodium chloride
• 0.14 gram potassium chloride
• 0.12 gram calcium chloride
• 0.20 gram sodium bicarbonate
Combine salts in flask and add distilled water to make a liter of solution.

Tubocurarine, 0.5%
Weigh out 0.125 gram of D-tubocurarine chloride. Add distilled water to make 25 milliliters. **Label: Poison. Use extreme care. Note: Solution should be placed in a serum bottle** (Aldrich) **for use**.

Advance Preparation

1. Order frogs to be delivered 2–3 days prior to the date of the lab, if animal maintenance facilities are limited. Frogs may be pithed just prior to the lab to save time (see Exercise 16A). Each group will need two to three frogs. Have disposable gloves available for handling the frogs.

2. Set out for each group dissecting instruments and tray, safety glasses, two dropper bottles of *frog Ringer's solution* (at room temperature and iced), a small ice bath, thread, several glass rods or glass probes, a laboratory stand and two clamps, several glass slides or glass plates, platinum electrode, stimulator, filter paper, a dropper bottle of *0.01% HCl solution*, NaCl crystals, heat-resistant mitts or a slide holder, a Bunsen burner, absorbent cotton, and a disposable pipet and bulb. Have a small container of ether available. **Note: Ether is highly flammable and should be used with care in a fume hood**.

3. For Claude Bernard's experiment, set out disposable gloves, a frog board, thread, and a 1-cc syringe with small-gauge needle. Have a small container of *0.5% tubocurarine solution* available. **Note: Tubocurarine is extremely toxic. Wear disposable gloves when handling the tubocurarine**.

4. If oscilloscopes are to be used, set out nerve chambers, set up the oscilloscopes, and provide instructions. Allow time for the students to become familiar with the equipment.

Comments and Pitfalls

1. Be sure the muscle nerve preparation is kept moist and not touched by metal dissection equipment. Be careful that the nerve does not get stretched or damaged during dissection and setup.

2. Ether has a very low ignition temperature. Conduct ether experiments in a lab hood. If a hood is not available, do this part of the experiment with the windows open and after all Bunsen burners have been put out. Do not attempt to put out an ether fire with water; use a CO_2 extinguisher. Order ether in small amounts and do not store it for long periods of time. Keep it in an explosion-proof refrigerator when not in use.

3. When performing Claude Bernard's experiment, students may need to increase the stimulus intensity when testing the muscles, as muscle threshold is generally higher than nerve threshold.

Answers to Questions

Activity 1: Eliciting a Nerve Impulse (pp. 193–194)

2. Repeated stimuli should cause the muscle to contract to tetanus.

3. Mechanical stimulation should result in muscle contraction.

4. HCl and NaCl should both cause muscle contraction.

5. Thermal stimulation also results in muscle contraction. These experiments indicate that a variety of stimuli can result in conduction of an impulse.

Activity 2: Inhibiting the Nerve Impulse (pp. 194–195)

2. (Ether) The anesthetized part of the nerve does not respond, but the unanesthetized area distal to the anesthetized area responds to the stimulus, resulting in muscle contraction.

3. (Ether) Ether exerts its blocking effect on the nerve fibers. The muscle was still able to contract when the nerve was stimulated beyond the anesthetized section.

4. (Curare) Eventually the nonligated muscle will show reduced or no contraction in response to the stimulus. Curare travels throughout the frog's circulatory system and eventually finds its way to myoneural junctions. The left muscle is not affected because the ligation cuts off circulation to the tissue in that area. The right muscle does not respond to nervous stimulation because the curare blocks the acetylcholine receptor sites in the myoneural junction.

5. (Curare) Both gastrocnemius muscles should respond to direct stimulation, as direct stimulation of the muscle does not require action at the myoneural junction. The difference between the right and left nerve response is the result of the curare block to the acetylcholine receptor sites. When the muscles are stimulated directly, the stimulus bypasses the chemically gated channels that respond to acetylcholine. Curare acts at the myoneural junction by blocking the acetylcholine receptor sites. **Note: It is beyond the scope of this lab to prove that the nerve to the right muscle is still conducting an impulse.**

Activity 3: Visualizing the Action Potential with an Oscilloscope (pp. 196–197)

7. The amplitude of the action potential will increase until maximal amplitude is reached.

9. The impulse should be conducted in the opposite direction.

Gross Anatomy of the Brain and Cranial Nerves

 Time Allotment: 2 hours.

 Multimedia Resources: See Appendix F for a list of multimedia offerings.

Anatomy of the Human Brain (FHS, 35 minutes, VHS, DVD)
The Brain (FHS, 20 minutes, VHS)
The Brain (NIMCO, 30 minutes, VHS)
Brain Anatomy Series (UL, 6-part series, VHS)
Brain and Nervous System: Your Information Superhighway (FHS, 25 minutes, VHS, DVD)
The Human Brain in Situ (FHS, 19 minutes, VHS, DVD)
The Human Nervous System: Human Brain and Cranial Nerves Videotape (BC, 28 minutes, VHS)
Neuroanatomy (UL, 19 minutes, VHS)
Sheep Brain Dissection (WNS, 22 minutes, VHS)

Animated Neuroscience and the Action of Nicotine, Cocaine, and Marijuana in the Brain (FHS, DVD)

 Refer to the lab manual for links to A.D.A.M.® Interactive Anatomy.

Advance Preparation

1. Make arrangements for appropriate storage, disposal, and cleanup of dissection materials. Check with the Department of Health or the Department of Environmental Protection, or their counterparts, for state regulations.

2. Designate a disposal container for organic debris, and a dishwashing area with hot soapy water, sponges, and a lab disinfectant such as Wavicide-01 (Carolina) for washing down the lab benches.

3. Set out disposable gloves and safety glasses.

4. Set out dissectible human brain models (ideally one per group), and preserved human brains.

5. Set out dissection kits, dissection trays, and sheep brains with meninges and cranial nerves intact.

6. For testing cranial nerve function, set out dropper bottles of oil of cloves and vanilla, eye chart, ophthalmoscope, penlight, safety pins, mall probes (hot and cold), cotton, salty, sweet, sour, and bitter solutions, cotton swabs, ammonia, tuning forks, and tongue depressors. Set out autoclave bag for disposables.

Comments and Pitfalls

1. Students who are not careful readers confuse or do not distinguish between *cerebellar* and *cerebral*.

2. Hasty removal of the meninges removes the pituitary gland before its connection to the brain by the infundibulum can be established; occasionally even the optic chiasma is lost. Encourage the students to go slowly and use the scalpel sparingly.

3. The arachnoid meninx may be hard to identify, as it is usually poorly preserved.

Answers to Questions

Activity 3: Identifying and Testing the Cranial Nerves (p. 211)

3. The trigeminal ganglion is located between the pons and the greater wing of the sphenoid bone and is associated with the trigeminal nerve. The geniculate ganglion is in the inner ear cavity and is associated with the facial nerve. The inferior ganglion is near the parotid salivary gland and is associated with the glossopharyngeal nerve. The superior ganglion is just external to the jugular foramen and is associated with the glossopharyngeal nerve. The spiral ganglion is in the cochlea and is associated with the vestibulocochlear nerve. The vestibular ganglion is in the inner ear and is associated with the vestibulocochlear nerve.

Dissection: The Sheep Brain (pp. 212–216)

1. The sheep's cerebral hemispheres are smaller than those of the human.

Ventral Structures

1. The olfactory bulbs are larger in the sheep. The sense of smell is more important to the sheep than it is to humans for both protection and locating food.

Dorsal Structures

1. The cerebrum is not as deep.

2. The falx cerebelli is not present in the sheep.

4. The corpora quadrigemina are reflex centers for visual and auditory stimuli.

Internal Structures

2. The sheep fornix is large in relation to the size of the sheep's brain when compared to the fornix of the human brain. The fornix links regions of the limbic system, which provides strong emotional response to odors, among other things. Sheep have a more acute sense of smell than humans and rely more on smell to alert them to danger, food sources, etc.

Electroencephalography

 Time Allotment: 30 minutes for each subject. Allow additional time if students are not acquainted with the recording equipment.

Advance Preparation

1. Prepare a set of instructions for the particular recording equipment you will be using. If you are using a physiograph or BIOPAC®, students may be familiar with it from Exercise 16A. Be sure to include instructions on correct calibration of the equipment so that meaningful recordings can be made.

2. Set out recording equipment. This can be either an oscilloscope and EEG selector box, a physiograph and high-gain preamplifier, or BIOPAC® data acquisition unit.

3. Prepare a quiet, dimly lit space with a cot. Have electrodes, electrode leads, electrode gel, and collodion gel available. Long elastic EEG straps or adhesive bandages may be used in place of the collodion.

Comments and Pitfalls

1. It is very important to choose subjects who can relax.

2. Clean the area where the electrode will be attached to provide a better contact.

Answers to Questions

Activity 1: Observing Brain Wave Patterns (p. 220)

5. The frequency of the brain waves should increase and the amplitude should decrease. It may be characterized as a beta rhythm if the amplitude decreases and the frequency is in the range of 15 to 30 cycles per second.

7. Hyperventilation results in alkalosis, which causes overexcitability of the nervous system. The tracings may resemble those of an epileptic seizure.

Activity 4: Electroencephalography Using BIOPAC® (pp. 221–225)

17. The alpha rhythm is observed when the subject is relaxed with the eyes closed, and it usually diminishes when the eyes are open.

    The beta rhythm is usually most pronounced when the eyes are open and attentive, or when the subject is performing mental tasks.

    The delta and theta rhythms are the most varied, especially under these subject conditions. They are most easily observed when the subject makes the transition from mild sleep to deep sleep. It is unlikely that a significant difference can be discerned under these conditions.

Spinal Cord, Spinal Nerves, and the Autonomic Nervous System

 Time Allotment: 1½ hours (1 hour can be completed outside of lab).

 Multimedia Resources: See Appendix F for a list of multimedia offerings. See Exercise 6A for histology listings.

Brain and Nervous System: Your Information Superhighway (FHS, 25 minutes, VHS, DVD)
The Human Nervous System: Spinal Cord and Nerves Videotape (BC, 28 minutes, VHS)
The Peripheral Nervous System (IM, 29 minutes, VHS)

 Refer to the lab manual for links to A.D.A.M.® Interactive Anatomy.

Advance Preparation

1. Make arrangements for appropriate storage, disposal, and cleanup of dissection materials. Check with the Department of Health or the Department of Environmental Protection, or their counterparts, for state regulations.

2. Designate a disposal container for organic debris, and a dishwashing area with hot soapy water and sponges. Provide a lab disinfectant such as Wavicide-01 (Carolina) for washing down the lab benches.

3. Set out disposable gloves and safety glasses.

4. Set out dissection tools, trays, and spinal cord sections from cow specimens or saved from the brain dissection.

5. Set out charts and models of the spinal cord, and red and blue pencils.

6. Set out slides of spinal cord cross section, lens paper, and lens cleaning solution.

7. Set out dissecting microscopes. Have compound microscopes available.

8. Check to be sure that the diagram of the spinal tracts in the text you are using is similar to that in Figure 21.3. If there are differences, decide which you will use and make the appropriate adjustments to the assignment if necessary.

9. Set out equipment and materials for the conduction of the BIOPAC® activity. Introduce your students to the basic features of the equipment prior to beginning the lab activity.

Comments and Pitfalls

1. Students may have trouble distinguishing between gray and white matter in the spinal cord dissection. A drop or two of methylene blue stain with a water rinse may help.

Answers to Questions

Activity 2: Identifying Spinal Cord Tracts (p. 229)

Labels for Figure 21.3

Left (top to bottom) - Ascending Tracts	Right (top to bottom) - Descending Tracts
Fasciculus gracilis	Lateral reticulospinal tract
Fasciculus cuneatus	Lateral corticospinal tract
Posterior spinocerebellar tract	Rubrospinal tract
Anterior spinocerebellar tract	Medial reticulospinal tract
Lateral spinothalamic tract	Anterior corticospinal tract
Anterior spinothalamic tract	Vestibulospinal tract
	Tectospinal tract

Fasciculus gracilis - joint, muscle position sense, fine touch localization (lower trunk and limbs)

Fasciculus cuneatus - same as above (neck, upper trunk and limbs)

Posterior spinocerebellar - proprioception

Anterior spinocerebellar - proprioception

Lateral spinothalamic - pain, temperature, pressure, and coarse touch

Anterior spinothalamic - pain, temperature, pressure, and coarse touch

Lateral corticospinal - cross in medulla, stimuli to skeletal muscles (pyramidal)

Anterior corticospinal - cross at level of synapse, stimuli to skeletal muscles (pyramidal)

Rubrospinal - posture and balance

Tectospinal - posture and balance

Vestibulospinal - posture and balance

Medial reticulospinal - muscle tone and visceral motor functions

Lateral reticulospinal - muscle tone and visceral motor functions

Dissection: Spinal Cord (pp. 229–230)

1. The third meninx is the pia mater, which adheres closely to the surface of the brain and spinal cord.

2. The posterior horns are more tapered than the anterior horns.

3. The central canal is more oval than circular. It is lined with ependymal cells. In a living specimen it contains cerebrospinal fluid. Students may observe that the posterior medial sulcus touches the posterior gray commissure (gray matter) of the spinal cord. Neuron cell bodies can be seen in the ventral horn of the spinal cord. The large neurons are motor neurons; others are association neurons.

Activity 6: Exploring the Galvanic Skin Response within a Polygraph Using BIOPAC® (pp. 241–246)

12. It is likely that the most significant changes will be observed when the face is touched.

   There may or may not be a significant change after each color presentation.

   The responses will vary from student to student depending on the affective nature of the question.

   Colors can affect mood that can be observed through a subsequent change in autonomic activity.

   Specific questions might elicit an emotional response that can be observed through a subsequent change in autonomic activity.

Human Reflex Physiology

Suggestion for Alternative Equipment

Computerized (Intelitool®) and PowerLab® alternatives to this traditional exercise can be found in Appendix A and B of this instructor's guide.

 Time Allotment: 1 hour.

 Multimedia Resources: See Appendix F for a list of multimedia offerings.

Decision (FHS, 26 minutes, VHS, DVD)
Reflexes and Synaptic Transmission (UL, 29 minutes, VHS)

 Solution:
Bleach Solution, 10%
Measure out 100 milliliters of bleach.
Add water to a final volume of 1 liter.

Advance Preparation

1. Fill a large laboratory bucket with *10% bleach solution* and set out an autoclave bag for disposable items. Set out wash bottles of *10% bleach solution.*

2. For each group, set out a reflex hammer, a sharp pencil, a small piece of sterile absorbent cotton, a tongue depressor, a metric ruler, a 12-inch ruler or reaction time ruler, a flashlight, a 100- or 250-milliliter beaker, a 10- or 25-milliliter graduated cylinder, a dropper bottle of lemon juice, and wide-range pH paper.

3. Set out equipment and materials for the conduction of the BIOPAC® activity. Introduce your students to the basic features of the equipment prior to beginning the lab activity.

Comments and Pitfalls

1. Pupillary reflexes are more easily tested on subjects with light-colored irises.

2. Students do not always distinguish between the general term "pupillary reflexes" and the pupillary light reflex. Emphasize that the pupillary light reflex and the consensual response are both examples of pupillary reflexes.

3. Students often erroneously try to catch the ruler with their hands rather than between the thumb and forefinger in the section on Reaction Time of Unlearned Responses. Also, be sure that the same subject does all four parts of this experiment.

Answers to Questions

Activity 1: Initiating Stretch Reflexes (pp. 249–250)

1. The leg swings forward as the quadriceps muscles contract. (The hamstrings are reciprocally inhibited.) The femoral nerve is carrying the impulses.

2. The response is usually greater than the first response. Mental distraction seems to increase the reflex response.

3. The response during other muscle activity is usually more vigorous due to increased facilitation in the spinal cord.

4. Fatigue results in a less vigorous response. Muscle function is responsible. This is probably due to changes in pH, ATP, and Ca^{2+} levels in the muscle. Excitation-contraction coupling is hindered, reducing the response of the muscle cells to nervous stimulation.

5. Plantar flexion due to the contraction of the triceps surae (gastrocnemius and soleus muscles) is the result. Contraction of the gastrocnemius muscle usually results in flexion of the knee.

Activity 2: Initiating the Crossed Extensor Reflex (p. 250)

The subject withdraws the pricked hand by flexion of the elbow. Then the other elbow extends. The extensor part of the reflex is relatively slow, probably due to the fact that many association neurons are involved.

Activity 3: Initiating the Plantar Reflex (p. 251)

The normal response is downward flexion (curling) and adduction of the toes.

Activity 4: Initiating the Corneal Reflex (p. 251)

The subject blinks. The function is to protect the eye. The subject experiences discomfort (if not pain) because the cornea lacks pressure receptors but is richly supplied with pain receptors.

Activity 5: Initiating the Gag Reflex (p. 251)

The posterior pharyngeal walls elevate as pharyngeal muscles contract, and the subject gags.

Activity 6: Initiating Pupillary Reflexes (p. 252)

3. The left pupil contracts (the pupillary light reflex).

4. The right pupil also contracts. The contralateral (consensual) reflex indicates that there is some connection between the pathways for each eye. This is a test of the parasympathetic nervous system. These responses protect the retina from damage by bright light.

Activity 7: Initiating the Ciliospinal Reflex (p. 252)

The left pupil dilates, the right pupil does not. Sympathetic innervation of the irises does not seem to be as closely integrated as parasympathetic innervation since a contralateral response was not observed.

Activity 8: Initiating the Salivary Reflex (pp. 252–253)

3. The volume of saliva is much greater after stimulation with lemon juice. The final saliva pH should be close to the initial reading (usually pH 6–7). It is much less acidic than the reading 10 seconds after the application of lemon juice, as saliva contains sodium bicarbonate. The copious thin watery secretion is the result of parasympathetic stimulation.

Activity 9: Testing Reaction Time for Basic and Acquired Reflexes (pp. 253–254)

3. Addition of a signal word should increase reaction time because it takes time to discriminate the words.

4. The large variation in reaction time is due to the variation in the ability of the subject to formulate a response to the stimulus word.

Activity 10: Measuring Reaction Time Using BIOPAC® (pp. 241–246)

5. It is possible that there will be a difference between Segment 1 and Segment 2. If Segment 2 appears to be faster, this is likely due to the learning that occurred from the experience acquired during Segment 1. Responses may be more rapid during Segment 4 than in Segment 3 for the same reason.

General Sensation

Time Allotment: 1½ hours.

Multimedia Resources: See Appendix F for a list of multimedia offerings.

Mystery of the Senses (IM, VHS) (5-part series)
      Touch (30 minutes)
The Senses of Touch (NIMCO, 28 minutes, VHS)

Advance Preparation

1. Set out prepared slides of Pacinian corpuscles, Meissner's corpuscles, Golgi tendon organs, and muscle spindles. If time is a problem, set these up as a demonstration.

2. Set out lens paper, lens cleaning solution, and immersion oil. Have compound microscopes available.

3. Place half of the mall probes (one per group, Carolina) in a small water bath set at 45°C.

4. Place the remaining mall probes in a beaker containing chipped ice and water.

5. Set out black, red, and blue felt-tipped markers, Von Frey's hairs or sharp pencils, calipers or two-point discriminators or esthesiometers (sometimes called anesthesiometers), and millimeter rulers (one each per group).

6. Have a few nickels or quarters available.

7. For each group, set out three large finger bowls or beakers, a thermometer, and paper towels. Have ice water available.

Comments and Pitfalls

1. Remind the students to use caution when adjusting the width of the calipers or two-point discriminators in the two-point discrimination test. Caution the students against dragging the sharp tips along the surface of the skin. Wooden toothpicks may be substituted for calipers.

2. If a student has Raynaud's disease and is the subject in the Referred Pain experiment, he or she may experience temporary numbness of the hand.

3. Use water-based, felt-tipped pens or have some sort of stain remover available.

4. Adaptation of the hand to ice water may take longer than two minutes. You may wish to warn students that it may be painful to keep their hands in the ice water long enough to experience adaptation.

Answers to Questions

Activity 2: Plotting the Relative Density and Location of Touch and Temperature Receptors (pp. 259–260)

6. Touch receptors and cold receptors are both more abundant than heat receptors. Touch receptors will probably appear to be the most abundant.

Activity 3: Determining the Two-Point Threshold (p. 260)

It would be reasonable to predict that fingertips and lips would have the greatest density of touch receptors.

Activity 4: Testing Tactile Localization (pp. 260–261)

2. The ability to locate the stimulus should not improve with repeated trials because the receptor density remains unchanged.

Activity 5: Demonstrating Adaptation of Touch Receptors (p. 261)

3. The pressure sensation returns when coins are added to the stack. The same receptors are probably being used. Generator potentials are graded and stronger stimuli produce larger potentials and thus increased frequency of nerve impulses.

4. The sensation is greater when the hair springs back. Without adaptation there would be continuous impulses from and awareness of the bending hairs.

Activity 6: Demonstrating Adaptation of Temperature Receptors (pp. 261–262)

1. The water will feel warm to the left hand. After the left hand has been in the warm water for one minute the water will feel much less warm; the water will feel very warm to the right hand. Yes, adaptation has occurred in the left hand.

3. After two minutes the warm water will begin to feel lukewarm to the right hand. The hand in the ice water may hurt and the experiment may have to go longer than two minutes to observe adaptation. Adaptation to the cold seems to take longer. The right hand adapts more quickly.

4. The water feels cool to the right hand and warm to the left hand.

Activity 7: Demonstrating the Phenomenon of Referred Pain (p. 262)

Initially the elbow feels cold and then begins to hurt. After a while a tingling sensation can be felt in the fingers and the palm of the hand. The fingers may then begin to ache. The ulnar nerve serves several hand and finger muscles as well as the skin of a portion of the hand.

Special Senses: Vision

 Time Allotment: 2 hours.

 Multimedia Resources: See Appendix F for a list of multimedia offerings. See Exercise 6A for histology listings.

The Eye: Structure, Function, and Control of Movement (FHS, 54 minutes, VHS, DVD)
The Eye: Vision and Perception (UL, 29 minutes, VHS)
Eyes and Ears (FHS, 28 minutes, VHS, DVD)
Mystery of the Senses (IM, VHS) (5-part series)
       Vision (30 minutes)
Optics of the Human Eye Series (UL, VHS, 4-part series)
The Senses (FHS, 20 minutes, VHS, DVD)
Sheep Eye Dissection (WNS, 15 minutes, VHS)
Visual Reality (NIMCO, 30 minutes, VHS)

 Refer to the lab manual for links to A.D.A.M.® Interactive Anatomy.

Advance Preparation

1. Make arrangements for appropriate storage and disposal of dissection materials. Check with the Department of Health or the Department of Environmental Protection for state regulations.

2. Designate a disposal container for organic debris and a dishwashing area with hot soapy water and sponges. Provide lab disinfectant such as Wavicide-01 (Carolina) for washing down the lab benches.

3. Set out disposable gloves and safety glasses.

4. Set out dissecting kits, dissecting pans, and preserved cow or sheep eyes. Plan for groups of two or individual dissections.

5. Set out dissectible eye models and eye anatomy charts.

6. Set out slides of the eye showing retinal layers (Ward's), lens paper, and lens cleaning

solution. Have compound microscopes available. As an alternative, set up a demonstration slide of the retina.

7. Hang up a Snellen eye chart in a well-lit part of the room. Measure back 20 feet from the chart and mark the distance on the floor with masking tape.

8. Set out Ishihara's color-blindness plates (Carolina).

9. Set out white, red, blue, and green chalk, and a box of common pins. Cut out several 1-inch diameter disks of white, red, blue, and green paper.

10. Set out test tubes, pencils, metric rulers, and meter sticks (one each per group).

11. Set out several laboratory lamps, penlights, or bright flashlights.

12. Set out the ophthalmoscopes (check to be sure ophthalmoscope batteries are working).

13. If there is no flag in the classroom, purchase a picture of the flag, or create a reverse flag with a yellow field and gray stars, and gray and yellow-green stripes (usual flag colors appear as the afterimage).

Comments and Pitfalls

1. Preserved cow eyes are often misshapen, and inexperienced students may need help locating and identifying the cornea at the beginning of the dissection.

2. Some students will have difficulty with the ophthalmoscope. Remind the subject to look straight ahead at a fixed object while the examiner looks through the pupil at a slight angle. Caution the examiner to limit illuminating the retina to *one minute or less*. Switch to the other eye if necessary. *Do not examine the macula for more than one second at a time.*

3. For demonstration of the blind spot, emphasize that the dot disappears when the right eye is tested, and the X disappears when the left eye is tested. Some student is sure to claim that he/she has no blind spot in the left eye as the dot never disappeared!

Answers to Questions

Activity 1: Identifying Accessory Eye Structures (p. 265)

Right eye: medial rectus

Left eye: lateral rectus (and on occasion the superior or inferior oblique)

Activity 4: Predicting the Effects of Visual Pathway Lesions (p. 269)

A lesion in the right optic nerve affects medial and lateral vision of the right eye.

A lesion through the optic chiasma affects medial vision in both eyes.

A lesion in the left optic tract affects left lateral and right medial vision.

A lesion in the visual area of the right cerebral cortex affects right lateral and left medial vision.

Dissection: The Cow (Sheep) Eye (p. 271)

6. The optic disc.

Activity 6: Demonstrating Afterimages (p. 273)

When the eyes are first closed, the field appears bright. Gradually, a dark image of the flag appears against a light background.

Activity 11: Tests for Binocular Vision (p. 275)

It is much easier to put the pencil in the test tube with both eyes open.

Activity 12: Demonstrating Reflex Activity of Intrinsic and Extrinsic Eye Muscles (p. 275)

Photopupillary Reflex

When exposed to bright light, the pupil constricts. The pupil of the opposite eye will also be slightly constricted.

Accommodation Pupillary Reflex

As the eye focuses on printed material, the pupil constricts. This reduces divergent light rays and aids in formation of a sharper image. It also restricts the amount of light entering the eye.

Convergence Reflex

The eyeballs will both move medially to focus on the object. This reflex keeps the image focused on the fovea.

Special Senses: Hearing and Equilibrium

Time Allotment: 1 hour.

Multimedia Resources: See Appendix F for a list of multimedia offerings. See Exercise 6A for histology listings.

The Ear: Hearing and Balance (IM, 29 minutes, VHS)
Eyes and Ears (FHS, 28 minutes, VHS, LV)
Hearing (FHS, 28 minutes, VHS)
The Human Body Series: Balance (NIMCO, 28 minutes, VHS)
Mystery of the Senses (IM, VHS) (5-part series)
　　　　Hearing (30 minutes)
Now Hear This (NIMCO, 30 minutes, VHS)
The Senses (FHS, 20 minutes, VHS, DVD)

Advance Preparation

1. Set out dissectible ear models and ear anatomy charts.

2. Set out slides of the cochlea (Ward's), lens paper, and lens cleaning solution. Have compound microscopes available. Set up a demonstration slide of the crista ampullaris receptor of the semicircular canal.

3. For each group, set out tuning forks (Ward's), rubber mallet, absorbent cotton, a ticking pocket watch or small clock, a piece of white chalk, coins of three sizes, and a metric ruler.

4. If an audiometer is available it can be used instead of the tuning forks to test frequency range of hearing. If necessary, prepare instructions for the use of the audiometer. Set out red and blue pencils.

5. Set out otoscopes, disposable otoscope tips, alcohol swabs, and an autoclave bag.

6. Have a sturdy rotating chair or stool available for the Barany test.

Comments and Pitfalls

1. It is often difficult to find an area quiet enough to get good results with the acuity and sound localization tests. An empty lab or a quiet corner of the hallway might be used.

2. Students should be reminded to simulate conductive deafness while performing the Weber test. Although it is not a specific assignment, they'll be asked for results in the Review Sheets.

3. Remind the students to strike the tuning forks with the rubber mallet and not against the lab bench.

4. Be sure the students understand how to evaluate the direction of nystagmus before the subject spins. Also remind the subject to keep his or her eyes open!

Answers to Questions

Activity 4: Conducting Laboratory Tests of Hearing (p. 282)

Acuity Test

The threshold is indefinite.

Sound Localization

No, the sound is less easily located if the source is equidistant from both ears. Sound arriving from spots equidistant from both ears arrives at each ear at the same time and with equal loudness. This does not provide enough information to adequately locate the position of the source.

Frequency Range of Hearing

Generally, high-frequency sounds are heard less clearly, but results depend on the loudness of each of the tuning forks.

Activity 7: Conducting Laboratory Tests of Equilibrium (p. 286)

Balance Test

1. Nystagmus is not present.
2. The cerebellum integrates input from receptors in the vestibule and semicircular canals, the eyes and somatic receptors, and coordinates skeletal muscle activity and regulates muscle tone.

Barany Test

4. When rotation stops, the direction of nystagmus reverses. If the chair is rotated clockwise, the nystagmus will be counterclockwise.

Romberg Test

2. Gross swaying movements are not usually observed when the eyes are open.
3. Side-to-side movement increases.
4. Front-to-back swaying occurs. The equilibrium apparatus and proprioceptors are probably functioning normally. Visual information is lacking and the result is increased swaying. Equilibrium and balance require input from a number of receptors including proprioceptors, the vestibular apparatus, and the eyes.

Special Senses: Olfaction and Taste

Time Allotment: 1 hour.

Multimedia Resources: See Appendix F for a list of multimedia offerings. See Exercise 6A for histology listings.

Mystery of the Senses (IM, VHS) (5-part series)
    Smell (30 minutes)
    Taste (30 minutes)
The Senses of Smell and Taste (NIMCO, 28 minutes, VHS)
The Senses: Skin Deep (FHS, 26 minutes, VHS, DVD)
Smell and Taste (FHS, 30 minutes, VHS, DVD)
Taste (FHS, 23 minutes, VHS, DVD)
Taste and Smell (NIMCO, 30 minutes, VHS)

Solutions:
Acetic Acid, 1%
Measure out 50 milliliters of 10% acetic acid. Add to a small amount of distilled water. Add water to a final volume of 500 milliliters.

Epsom Salt Solution, 0.1%
Weigh out 0.5 gram of Epsom salts. Add water to a final volume of 500 milliliters.

MSG Solution
Disolve a pinch of MSG crystals in 100 milliliters of distilled water. If you cannot taste the chemical, add more crystals until you can taste the MSG flavor.

Quinine, 0.1%
Weigh out 0.5 gram of quinine sulfate. Add water to a final volume of 500 milliliters.

Sodium Chloride (NaCl), 10%
Weigh out 10 grams of NaCl and bring to 100 milliliters with distilled water. It may be necessary to heat the mixture to get the NaCl into solution.

Sucrose, 5%
Weigh out 5 grams of sucrose. Add distilled water to a final volume of 100 milliliters.

Advance Preparation

1. Set out slides of the tongue and the nasal epithelium, lens paper, and lens cleaning solution. Have compound microscopes available. (Or set up demonstration slides of the tongue and nasal epithelium.) Slides of papillae types can be obtained from Ward's.

2. Set out for each group paper towels, a small mirror, a small dish of granulated sugar, absorbent cotton, four small paper cups or vials for the test solutions, four cotton-tipped swabs, one larger paper cup per person, dropper bottles of oil of cloves and oil of wintergreen and oil of peppermint (or corresponding flavors from the condiment section of the supermarket), a flask of distilled water, a paper plate and chipped ice.

3. Set out bottles of *10% NaCl, 0.1% quinine or Epsom salt solution, 5% sucrose,* and *1% acetic acid.*

4. Set out a disposable autoclave bag, toothpicks, and disposable gloves.

5. Prepare a plate of cubed food items such as cheese, apple, raw potato, dried prunes, banana, raw carrot, and hard-cooked egg white. These foods should be in an opaque container; a foil-lined egg carton works well. Keep covered and refrigerated until used.

6. Set out nose plugs and five numbered vials containing common substances with strong odors (e.g. cinnamon, garlic, ginger, rosemary, lemon peel, etc.).

7. Prepare an answer key for the five vials and have it available.

Comments and Pitfalls

1. Each group should label the four small paper cups or vials and take solution samples to the work area. Each individual in the group can then map his or her tongue, using cotton-tipped swabs dipped in the solutions. Note: There is no one "correct" map of the tongue.

2. Some students dislike putting cotton in their noses. Substitute good nose clips.

3. Some students may have difficulty getting their noses to adapt to the aromatic oil. Be sure they are following directions carefully and are patient.

4. Subjects for the food tests should not be allowed to see the food.

5. Remind students to use toothpicks to select food cubes. Caution students to alert the instructor and group members about food allergies.

Answers to Questions

Localization and Anatomy of Taste Buds (pp. 289–290)

It is easiest to identify fungiform and circumvallate papillae.

Activity 3: Stimulating Taste Buds (p. 291)

Substances must be in aqueous solution to stimulate the taste buds.

Activity 4: Plotting Taste Bud Distribution (p. 291)

5. The center of the tongue seems to lack taste receptors. There is no single "correct" map.

Activity 5: Examining the Combined Effects of Smell, Texture, and Temperature on Taste (pp. 291–293)

No, some foods can be identified fairly easily by texture. The sense of smell is most important when foods do not have an easily recognizable and unique texture. For example, it is hard to differentiate between raw apple and raw potato.

Effect of Olfactory Stimulation

2. It is hard to distinguish the flavor with the nostrils closed.

3. With the nostrils open it is easy to identify the oil.

6. The subject usually identifies the oil held at the nostrils.

7. Smell seems to be more important for identification in this experiment.

Activity 6: Assessing the Importance of Taste and Olfaction in Odor Identification (p. 293)

4. It is much easier to identify odors without the nose clips. There are only four basic tastes. Other taste sensations depend on olfaction.

Activity 7: Demonstrating Olfactory Adaptation (p. 293)

The adapted nostril should be able to detect the new oil. Adaptation is to the particular scent and not to aromatic oils in general.

Functional Anatomy of the Endocrine Glands

 Time Allotment: 1 hour+ (depending on detail required for microscopic study); additional work may be completed outside of lab.

 Multimedia Resources: See Appendix F for a list of multimedia offerings. See Exercise 6A for histology listings.

The Endocrine System (IM, 17 minutes, VHS)
The Endocrine System (UL, 17 minutes, VHS)
The Endocrine System (WNS, 16 minutes, VHS)
Glands and Hormones (NIMCO, 30 minutes, VHS)
Hormonally Yours (FHS, 50 minutes, VHS)
Hormone Heaven? (FHS, 50 minutes, VHS)
Hormone Hell (FHS, 50 minutes, VHS)
The Hypothalamus and Pituitary Glands (UL, VHS)
Hormones: Messengers (FHS, 27 minutes, VHS, LV)
The Neuroendocrine System (IM, 29 minutes, VHS)
The Pancreas (UL, 29 minutes, VHS)
Selected Actions of Hormones and Other Chemical Messengers Videotape (BC, 15 minutes, VHS)

 AIA Refer to the lab manual for links to A.D.A.M.® Interactive Anatomy.

Advance Preparation

1. Set out human torso models and anatomical charts.

2. Set out colored pencils for each student.

3. Set out slides of the anterior pituitary, posterior pituitary, thyroid gland, parathyroid glands, adrenal gland, pancreas tissue, ovaries, and testes. The anterior and posterior pituitary gland slides should be differentially stained, if possible. Set out lens paper and lens cleaning solution. Have compound microscopes available.

Answers to Questions

Activity 2: Examing Microscopic Structure of Endocrine Glands (pp. 298–300)

Pancreas

2. The acinar cells produce digestive enzymes.

Pituitary

4. ADH and oxytocin are the two hormones stored in the posterior lobe. Their source is neurosecretory cells originating in the hypothalamus.

Adrenal Gland

2. The two hormones produced by the adrenal medulla are epinephrine and norepinephrine.

Hormonal Action: Wet Lab

This exercise contains four experiments illustrating hormone function. Each experiment is discussed separately below.

 Multimedia Resources: See Appendix F for a list of multimedia offerings.

Selected Actions of Hormones and Other Chemical Messengers (BC, 15 minutes, VHS)

EFFECT OF THYROID HORMONE ON METABOLIC RATE

 Time Allotment: 1¹/₂ hours.

 Solutions:

Propylthiouracil, 0.02%
Weigh out 0.2 gram of 6-n-propylthiouracil (Aldrich). Add distilled water to make 1 liter of solution. Filter and store in light-resistant containers.
Caution! 6-n-propylthiouracil is a suspected carcinogen. (Note: If it is difficult to dissolve the PTU, add concentrated NaOH to adjust the pH to 8.0.)

Rat Chow with Thyroid Extract
Grind up sufficient regular laboratory rat chow to feed the required number of animals for 2 weeks (approximately 40 grams chow/rat/day). Add 20 grams of desiccated thyroid powder (Carolina) for each 1000 grams of rat chow. Mix thoroughly.

Advance Preparation

1. At least 14 days prior to the date of the lab, obtain young rats (about five weeks old) of the same sex. Six rats per lab session should be sufficient. Keep them in clean, well-ventilated surroundings at room temperature. Divide the rats into three groups. Label one group "Group 1—control," and feed with normal rat chow and water. Label another group "Group 2—experimental group A," and feed with normal rat chow and drinking water containing *0.02% 6-n-propylthiouracil*. Label a third group "Group 3—experimental group B," and feed with *rat chow containing 2% desiccated thyroid* (by weight) and normal drinking water.

2. For each student group, set out a glass desiccator, manometer, 20-milliliter glass syringe, two-hole cork, clamp, T-valve, soda lime, hardware cloth or porcelain platform, 36 inches of rubber tubing, scissors, two 3-inch pieces of glass tubing, and petrolatum. Be sure that the rubber tubing will form a tight seal with the glass tubing and the nib of the syringe. Set out animal balances (Carolina) and heavy animal-handling gloves.

Comments and Pitfalls

1. Leaks in the respirometer will probably be the biggest problem.

2. Be sure that students use the animal-handling gloves when handling the rats to avoid accidental bites. Be sure the animals are handled gently, and avoid squeezing them. Remove rats from their cages by pulling them by their tails. Then hold them firmly by the skin at the back of the neck.

3. When measuring basal rate, discard readings obtained during periods of rat activity.

EFFECT OF PITUITARY HORMONES ON THE OVARY

 Time Allotment: 2 hours (1¹/2 hours of waiting time)

 Solution:
Physiologic Saline (Amphibian, 0.75%)
Weigh out 7.5 grams of NaCl. Add water to a final volume of 1 liter. Make fresh immediately prior to experiment. (Note: 0.7% saline may also be used.)

Advance Preparation

1. Order female frogs (two per group) to be delivered close to the date of the exercise (see preparation for the frog experiment in Exercise 16A). Designate a frog disposal area. Set out disposable gloves.

2. For each group set out two syringes with 20- to 25-gauge needles, two battery jars, wax marking pencils, a small bottle of *amphibian physiologic saline* (Ward's), pond or spring water, and a vial of frog pituitary extract (Carolina).

Comments and Pitfalls

1. Distilled water should be used as a control if the pituitary extract is suspended in water.

2. Injected frogs should be kept in a quiet area.

3. When introducing this exercise, caution students to hold the frog's body firmly and above its hind legs. Demonstrate the holding and carrying procedure.

Answers to Questions

Activity 2: Determining the Effect of Pituitary Hormones on the Ovary (p. 305)

6. Ovulation is induced in the frog that received the pituitary extract injection. LH is the primary hormone stimulus for ovulation.

EFFECTS OF HYPERINSULINISM

 Time Allotment: 1/2 hour.

 Solutions:

Glucose, 10%

Weigh out 100 grams of glucose. Add distilled water to a final volume of 1 liter.

Insulin, 400 IU/100 milliliter H₂O

Weigh out 16 milligrams of zinc-stabilized insulin (25 IU/milligram dry weight— ICN). Re-hydrate in phosphate buffered saline (PBS) to a final volume of 100 milliliters.

Advance Preparation

1. Prepare a solution of *10% glucose* and store it in the refrigerator. Purchase or order enough small fish to supply one per group. Set up an aquarium or large beaker with an air stone to maintain the fish.

2. For each group set out a 250-milliliter bottle of *10% glucose*, a dropper bottle of *insulin*, a glass marking pencil, and two finger bowls.

Comments and Pitfalls

1. The fish may become very agitated and jump out of the bowl or beaker.

2. This exercise may be upsetting to some students, even though the fish recover.

Answers to Questions

Activity 3: Observing the Effects of Hyperinsulinism (pp. 305–306)

2. The fish often becomes very agitated, then loses its sense of balance just before becoming unconscious.

3. The fish will regain consciousness and right itself. The recovery time varies.

EFFECT OF EPINEPHRINE ON THE HEART

 Time Allotment: 1/2 hour.

Solutions:

Ringer's Solution, Frog
- 6.50 grams sodium chloride
- 0.14 gram potassium chloride
- 0.12 gram calcium chloride
- 0.20 gram sodium bicarbonate

Combine salts in flask and add distilled water to make 1 liter of solution.

Epinephrine (adrenaline), 1:1000
Weigh out 0.1 gram of epinephrine (Carolina).
Dissolve in 0.5 milliliter of 1 N HCl.
Add distilled water to a final volume of 100 milliliters.
Caution! Epinephrine is toxic. Label TOXIC.

Advance Preparation*

1. Order frogs (one per group) to be delivered 2–3 days prior to the date of the experiment (see Exercise 16A). Designate a frog disposal area. To save time, frogs may be pithed just before the lab.

2. For each group set out a dissecting pan, disposable gloves, instruments, a dropper bottle of *frog Ringer's solution*, and a dropper bottle of *1:1000 epinephrine*. **Caution! Epinephrine is toxic. Label the bottle TOXIC.**

* If desired, these observations may be deferred and made in conjunction with those in Exercise 34A. This approach also conserves animals.

Comments and Pitfalls

1. Be sure students keep the heart moistened throughout the experiment.

Answers to Questions

Activity 4: Testing the Effect of Epinephrine on the Heart (p. 306)

6. Epinephrine increases the heart rate. Yes, the epinephrine is very active for 10–30 seconds and then there is decreasing activity for one to several minutes.

Blood

Note: For safety reasons, many instructors make the blood tests optional or try to provide alternative experiments. Substituting dog blood, as suggested below, is one option; using prepared slides or artificial blood are others.

Time Allotment: 2 hours.

Multimedia Resources: See Appendix F for a list of multimedia offerings. See Exercise 6 for histology listings.

Bleeding and Coagulation (FHS, 31 minutes, VHS, DVD)
Blood (UL, 22 minutes, VHS)
Blood (FHS, 20 minutes, VHS, DVD)
Blood is Life (FHS, 25 minutes, VHS, DVD)

Blood and Immunity (CE, CD-ROM)

Solutions:
Bleach Solution, 10%
Measure out 100 milliliters of household bleach. Add water to a final volume of 1 liter.

Sodium Citrate, 5%
For 500 milliliters, weigh out 25 grams of sodium citrate. Add water to a final volume of 500 milliliters.

Advance Preparation

1. Set out safety glasses, lens paper, lens cleaning solution, and immersion oil. Have compound microscopes available. Set out any available models and charts of blood cells.

2. Set out prepared slides of macrocytic hypochromic anemia, microcytic hypochromic anemia, sickle-cell anemia, lymphocytic leukemia (chronic), and eosinophilia.

3. Set up the following supply areas (if all tests are to be done). Ideally there should be at least one set of solutions for each lab bench and enough of the other supplies for each student to do each test. If equipment must be shared, it should be washed in hot soapy water and rinsed in *10% bleach solution* after each use.

General supply area:

a. For instructors using student blood samples, set out sterile blood lancets, alcohol wipes, and absorbent cotton balls. Set up a disposable autoclave bag for all disposable items, and a laboratory bucket or battery jar of *10% bleach solution* for glassware. For each lab group, set out a 250-milliliter beaker of *10% bleach solution* (for used slides), spray bottles of *10% bleach solution*, clean microscope slides (two per member of the group), a dropper bottle of Wright stain (Carolina), a dropper bottle of distilled water, wide-range pH paper, test tube and test tube rack, nonhemolyzed plasma obtained fresh from an animal hospital or prepared by centrifuging animal (e.g., cattle or sheep) blood obtained from a biological supply house, timers, and disposable gloves. Set out several sets of pipette cleaning solutions: (1) *10% bleach solution*, (2) distilled water, (3) 70% ethyl alcohol, and (4) acetone.

b. For instructors using heparinized dog blood, set out heparinized dog blood, glass rods, and all the materials listed in paragraph a, except the sterile lancets and alcohol wipes.

c. For instructors using stained smears of human blood, set out prepared slides of human blood stained with Wright stain.

d. Set out slides of WBC pathologies with the labels covered and marked "Unknown sample # ___." Suggestions include eosinophilia, neutrophilia, and various leukemias.

Hematocrit supply area:

Set out heparinized capillary tubes, microhematocrit centrifuge and reading gauge or millimeter ruler, and Seal-ease or capillary tube sealer (Carolina) or modeling clay.

Hemoglobin-determination supply area:

Set out hemoglobinometer and hemolysis applicator or Tallquist scales.

Sedimentation-rate supply area:

Set out Landau Sed-rate pipettes with tubing and rack or use Westergren ESR pipets. *5% sodium citrate* in a wide-mouthed bottle, mechanical suction devices, and millimeter rulers. Supplies for the Westergren ESR method can be ordered from Fisher. To minimize risk, the Sediplast Autozero ESR System, Sediplast racks, and leveling plate are suggested (Fisher).

Coagulation time supply area:

Set out nonheparinized capillary tubes, fine triangular files, and paper towels.

Blood-typing supply area:

Set out blood-typing sera, Rh-typing boxes (if used), wax markers, toothpicks, and blood test cards or slides (Carolina). If you are using Ward's artificial blood, set out simulated blood and antibodies provided with the kit.

Cholesterol-measurement supply area:

Set out cholesterol test cards and color plates (Carolina).

Comments and Pitfalls

1. If human blood samples are provided, disposable gloves and safety glasses should be worn at all times. If student samples are used, be sure students use only their own blood. Emphasize instructions for proper care or disposal of items used in the blood tests (see Anatomy and Physiology Laboratory Safety Procedures in the preface of this Instructor's Guide and p. 308 of the laboratory manual). Be sure that sharp objects such as lancets are discarded in such a way that they will not protrude through the autoclave bag. Petri dishes that can be taped shut or coffee cans with slits cut in the plastic tops can serve this purpose.

2. If student blood samples are used, have the students plan their work so that a minimum number of pricks are necessary. Obtaining enough blood is the usual problem. Be sure that students' hands are warm before trying to obtain blood, and that they follow the advice in the laboratory manual. Emphasize that the capillary tube should be held in a horizontal position with the tip in the drop of blood.

3. It is nearly impossible to prick your own finger to draw blood unless an automatic device such as the Medi-Let Kit (Carolina) is used. Students are often careless with the lancets since they are concentrating on obtaining blood for several different tests. Emphasize the importance of proper disposal. This is particularly important when using the Medi-Let, as it is difficult to distinguish a used lancet with a replaced cap from a new, unused one.

4. Obviously, heparinized blood samples may not be used for the coagulation time experiment.

5. Several problems may arise with the slides. Student-prepared blood smears tend to be too thick; be sure they understand the technique before starting. Warn against allowing the slide to dry with the stain on it. Avoid using old Wright stain, which may develop sediment that interferes with reading the slides.

6. A good color plate of the blood cells will help with identification. It may help to have some prepared slides available for demonstration. Also, point out the typical percentages of each cell type. Many students initially identify large numbers of cells as basophils.

7. Students must clean the Landau Sed-rate pipettes used to draw up blood immediately after use.

8. Emphasize that the coagulation-time test must be started as soon as blood is drawn up into the capillary tube. Have students hold the tubes with paper towels when breaking them to avoid cuts.

9. Blood typing may be done here, but it may be easier to explain if it is done after the immune system has been discussed.

10. If students are unfamiliar with the use of a spectrophotometer, review the use of the distilled water blank to standardize the machine and demonstrate how to read absorbance.

11. Note that directions for electrophoresis of normal and sickle cell hemoglobin can be found in Exercise 45.

Anatomy of the Heart

 Time Allotment: 1½ hours.

 Multimedia Resources: See Appendix F for a list of multimedia offerings. See Exercise 6A for histology listings.

> *The Circulatory System: Two Hearts that Beat as One* (FHS, 28 minutes, VHS, DVD)
> *The Human Body: Work of the Heart* (WNS, 21 minutes, VHS)
> *Human Cardiovascular System: The Heart Videotape* (BC, 25 minutes, VHS)
> *Life Under Pressure* (FHS, 26 minutes, VHS, DVD)
> *The Mammalian Heart* (AIMS, 15 minutes, VHS, DVD)
> *Sheep Heart* (WNS, 14 minutes, VHS)

 InterActive Physiology®: Cardiovascular System (BC, CD-ROM, or www.interactivephysiology.com)
> Anatomy Review: The Heart
> Intrinsic Conduction System

 Refer to the lab manual for links to A.D.A.M.® Interactive Anatomy.

Advance Preparation

1. Make arrangements for appropriate storage, disposal, and cleanup of dissection materials. Check with the Department of Health or the Department of Environmental Protection, or their counterparts, for state regulations.

2. Set out disposable gloves and safety glasses.

3. Set out dissecting kits, dissecting pans, glass probes, and preserved sheep hearts (one for each group).

4. Set out dissectible heart and cardiac muscle models, red and blue pencils, and heart anatomy charts.

5. Set out prepared slides of cardiac muscle (longitudinal section), lens tissue, immersion oil, and lens cleaning solution. Have compound microscopes available.

6. Set out an X ray of the human thorax and an X ray viewing box.

Comments and Pitfalls

1. Some sheep hearts are sold with the pericardial sac removed. If possible, order sheep hearts with intact pericardial sacs (Ward's).

2. Students often confuse the base and apex of the heart.

3. Be sure students have correctly identified the left ventricle of the heart as a landmark before they begin the dissection. As with all dissections, urge students to be cautious with the scalpel.

4. Many preserved hearts have the venae cavae and pulmonary veins completely removed, leaving large holes in the walls of the atria. This will make it difficult for students to answer some of the questions in the lab text. Purchase a dissected pig heart that has all the major vessels intact (Carolina), or refer students to models if necessary.

5. Provide students with extra mall probes to mark vessels as they are identified.

Answers to Questions

Dissection: The Sheep Heart (pp. 328–331)

2. The pericardium is attached to the base of the heart.

3. The visceral pericardium is much thinner than the tough two-layered sero-fibrous parietal pericardium. The visceral pericardium adheres tightly to the heart, while the parietal pericardium forms the outer sac surrounding the pericardial cavity.

8. The lumen of the vena cava is larger. The aorta has thicker walls. The aorta is capable of stretching and elastic recoiling, which helps to maintain pressure in the vessels. This requires strength and resilience. The vena cava is a low-pressure vessel for blood return to the heart, and is not subjected to large pressure fluctuations.

9. The right atrioventricular valve has three flaps.

10. The pulmonary semilunar valve closes when fluid fills the collapsed cuplike valves, causing them to bulge out into the lumen. The atrioventricular valves are flaps that swing closed as pressure in the chamber increases. They are prevented from opening backwards into the atria by the chordae tendineae attached to the papillary muscles.

14. The left ventricular cavity is much narrower than the right ventricular cavity. Papillary muscles and chordae tendineae are present in both cavities. The left atrioventricular valve has two cusps. The sheep valves are very similar to their human counterparts.

Conduction System of the Heart and Electrocardiography

 Time Allotment: about 15 minutes of lab time for each group making ECG recordings.

 InterActive Physiology®: Cardiovascular System (BC, CD-ROM, or www.interactivephysiology.com)
   Anatomy Review: The Heart
   Intrinsic Conduction System
   Cardiac Action Potential
   Cardiac Cycle
   Cardiac Output

Advance Preparation

1. Set out ECG recording apparatus, electrode paste, alcohol swabs, and a cot (or clear a section of the lab bench). Attach the leads to the recorder.

2. If you are using an ECG recording apparatus, turn it on, and allow it to warm up. Set the paper speed at 25 millimeters per second. Test the equipment as instructed by the manufacturer. Most equipment uses heat-sensitive paper. Be sure that the stylus produces a readable tracing. Adjust temperature setting accordingly. Test to see that a 1-millivolt signal causes a 10-millimeter vertical displacement of the stylus, and make any necessary adjustments. If the equipment uses a pen and ink, make sure the ink is flowing smoothly. Be sure the base line of the pen or stylus is on a horizontal line on the paper. If there is electrical interference, use the ground wire. Water or gas pipes are handy points for attachment.

3. Be sure the electrode plates are clean.

4. Set out equipment and materials for the conduction of the BIOPAC® activity. Introduce your students to the basic features of the equipment prior to beginning the lab activity.

Comments and Pitfalls

1. If leg leads are required, select student subjects with bare legs. Nylon stockings interfere with conduction.

2. Since electrode paste can be messy, try using electrode pads.

3. Have someone in the group double-check the arrangements of the electrodes before recording begins.

4. If the ECG is not clear, check to be sure electrodes are secure, remind the subject to remain still, and check the ground wire.

5. It is difficult to obtain good results when the student is running in place and attached to the electrodes. An alternate approach is to have the student run in place for 3 minutes and *then* connect the electrode leads to record the ECG immediately, and 2 and 4 minutes after exercise.

6. It is helpful to use a caliper and millimeter ruler when measuring the waves, intervals, and segments. These can be measured on screen with BIOPAC®.

7. If no ECG recording equipment is available, you can give the students a selection of ECG tracings and ask them to measure the waves, intervals, and segments.

Answers to Questions

Activity 1a: Recording ECGs Using a Standard ECG Apparatus (pp. 335–336)

Recording the ECG after Running in Place

5. The Q-T interval is shortened and the interval between adjacent QRS complexes is shortened (the strength of contraction increases and the length of diastole decreases).

Recording the ECG for Breath Holding

4. The heart rate increases during breath holding. As the CO_2 level in the blood increases, the blood pH decreases, causing cerebral vasodilation. This may increase sympathetic tone, thereby increasing heart rate. There may be some connection between the medullary respiratory and cardiac centers. (Depending on the text you are using, this might be difficult for the students to track down.)

Activity 1b: Electrocardiography Using BIOPAC® (pp. 336–342)

There is not likely to be a significant difference in deltaT between Segment 1 and Segment 3, although if there is a difference, some of the ECG components are likely to be of shorter duration in Segment 3. Post-exercise heart rate should increase, so the bpm of Segment 3 should be greater than Segment 1.

There is an inverse relationship between time between R-waves and heart rate. A shorter interval between R-waves translates into a higher heart rate.

There is likely to be an increase in heart rate as the subject makes the transition from a lying to a sitting state.

Anatomy of Blood Vessels

 Time Allotment: 1 1/2 hours.

 Multimedia Resources: See Appendix F for a list of multimedia offerings. See Exercise 6A for histology listings.

Circulation (IM, 20 minutes, VHS)
The Circulatory System (IM, 23 minutes, VHS)
Circulatory System: The Plasma Pipeline (FHS, 25 minutes, VHS, DVD)
Human Biology (FHS, 58 minutes, VHS, DVD)
Human Cardiovascular System: Blood Vessels Videotape (BC, 25 minutes, VHS)
Life Under Pressure (FHS, 26 minutes)
Pumping Life—The Heart and Circulatory System (WNS, 20 minutes)

 InterActive Physiology®: Cardiovascular System (BC, CD-ROM, or www.interactivephysiology.com)
  Anatomy Review: Blood Vessel Structure and Function

 Refer to the lab manual for links to A.D.A.M.® Interactive Anatomy.

Advance Preparation

1. Set out anatomical charts and/or models of human arteries and veins and the human circulatory system.

2. Set out anatomical charts of special circulations.

3. Set out prepared slides of cross sections of arteries and veins, lens paper, and lens cleaning solution. Have compound microscopes available.

Answers to Questions

Activity 4: Identifying Vessels of the Pulmonary Circulation (pp. 354–355)

Labels for Figure 32.12 (clockwise, starting from the superior vena cava):

Right pulmonary artery, pulmonary trunk, left pulmonary artery, left pulmonary veins, lobar arteries (left lung), left ventricle, left atrium, right ventricle, right atrium, right pulmonary veins, lobar arteries (right lung)

Activity 6: Tracing the Pathway of Fetal Blood Flow (pp. 356–357)

Labels for Figure 32.14a:

ductus arteriosus

foramen ovale

ductus venosus

umbilical vein

umbilical arteries

Activity 7: Tracing the Arterial Supply of the Brain (p. 358)

Labels for Figure 32.15:

middle cerebral artery

1. anterior communicating artery

2. anterior cerebral artery

3. posterior communicating artery

4. posterior cerebral artery

5. basilar artery

Human Cardiovascular Physiology: Blood Pressure and Pulse Determinations

Time Allotment: 2 hours (with some shared small-group data).

Multimedia Resources: See Appendix F for a list of multimedia offerings. A record or audiotape of *Interpreting Heart Sounds* (available on free loan from the local chapters of the American Heart Association).

Human Biology (FHS, 58 minutes VHS, DVD)
Life Under Pressure (FHS, 26 minutes, VHS, DVD)
The Physiology of Exercise (FHS, 15 minutes, DVD)

InterActive Physiology®: Cardiovascular System (BC, CD-ROM, or www.interactivephysiology.com)
      Anatomy Review: Blood Vessel Structure and Function
      Measuring Blood Pressure
      Factors that Affect Blood Pressure
      Blood Pressure Regulation
      Autoregulation and Capillary Dynamics

Refer to the lab manual for links to A.D.A.M.® Interactive Anatomy.

Advance Preparation

1. Set out stethoscopes (both bell and diaphragm) and sphygmomanometers (two per group). Check the valves on the bulbs of the cuffs to be sure that air is released from the cuff when the valves are opened (replacement valves can be ordered). If electronic monitoring equipment is to be used, prepare instructions and distribute.

2. Set out or ask students to bring watches with second hands. Provide each group with a millimeter ruler, alcohol swabs, a felt-tipped pen, a small basin or large finger bowl, and a laboratory thermometer. Have ice available.

3. Set out one 0.4 m (16-inch) high bench (for women) and one 0.5 m (20-inch) high bench (for men). You may have to compromise with a .45 m (18-inch) bench. Set up a cot, if available.

4. If the record or tape is used, set up a phonograph or tape deck.

5. Divide the class into small groups to collect data for Effect of Various Factors on Blood Pressure and Heart Rate. It may be hard to define *well-conditioned* and *poorly conditioned* subjects. A runner or a member of an athletic team might be compared to a more sedentary person (see Comments and Pitfalls, item 4).

6. Set out equipment and materials for the conduction of the BIOPAC® activity. Introduce your students to the basic features of the equipment prior to beginning the lab activity.

Comments and Pitfalls

1. Most students in the health sciences will have no trouble with this lab, and in fact enjoy bringing their own stethoscopes and sphygmomanometers to lab if they are given advance notice.

2. If students have trouble hearing the heart sounds with the bell stethoscope, have them try the diaphragm model. This will be particularly helpful when trying to hear the split sounds. The sounds are louder with the bell stethoscopes, but placement must be more precise.

3. Caution students against overtightening the valve on the sphygmomanometer. If the air in the cuff can't be released, it is very painful to the subject. If the valve does stick, most cuffs can be undone even when filled with air. To avoid problems once the cuff is inflated, have students practice first with the bulb valve.

4. Students performing the Harvard step test should be carefully monitored to be sure that they step completely up and completely down at the prescribed rate. This can be very fatiguing. If the student population is fairly uniform it may be difficult to detect major differences between the *well-conditioned* and *poorly conditioned* individuals. Note: Another well-known test for fitness is the Schneider test (described in G. D. Tharp, *Experiments in Physiology*, 4th edition, Minneapolis, MN: Burgess Publishing Co., 1980). Try to compare people of the same general age and sex, and do not compare a smoker to a nonsmoker. Students who are aware that they have heart problems should be discouraged from acting as subjects.

5. Many fitness tests are designed for people in their early twenties. Several tests that take into account age and gender may be found in the article, "How Fit Are You?" by Tracy Boyd, *The Detroit News*, Tuesday, November 16, 1999.

6. If a person with Raynaud's disease is used as the subject for the cold pressor test, he or she may experience temporary loss of feeling in the hand.

7. Students who are testing the effects of venous congestion should be reminded to keep both arms quietly on the lab bench for the full 5 minutes. Check to be sure pressure is maintained at 40 mm Hg.

Answers to Questions

Activity 1: Auscultating Heart Sounds (pp. 361–362)

3. The interval is about 0.5 second. It is about twice as long as the interval between the first and second heart sounds.

Activity 2: Palpating Superficial Pulse Points (pp. 362–363)

The carotid pulse point has the greatest amplitude, and the dorsalis pedis artery has the least. This is related to distance from the left ventricle of the heart.

Activity 7: Observing the Effect of Various Factors on Blood Pressure and Heart Rate (pp. 367–369)

Exercise

6. Greater elevation of blood pressure is generally noted just after completion of exercise. Increased cardiac output during exercise results in increased systolic pressure. A poorly conditioned individual usually has a higher systolic pressure at the end of exercise, and it usually takes a longer time for the pressure to return to normal. A well-conditioned individual usually has a larger stroke volume and thus can pump more blood with fewer beats per minute than a poorly conditioned individual. Diastolic pressure usually does not increase significantly, as it is the resting pressure of the vessels.

A Noxious Sensory Stimulus (Cold)

Blood pressure changes will be variable. The pulse rate will probably increase.

Activity 8: Examining the Effect of Local Chemical and Physical Factors on Skin Color (pp. 369–371)

Vasodilation and Flushing of the Skin Resulting from Local Metabolites

7. Stopping blood flow causes the hand to turn very pale. Weakness and a tingling sensation may be felt (variable). The skin flushes bright red immediately upon release of pressure and normal color is restored after several minutes or longer. There may be some lingering pain in the forearm region.

Effects of Venous Congestion

2. Slight pressure may be felt in the hand at the end of 5 minutes (variable). The veins are bulging and the hand has a mottled appearance, much darker in color than the control. Upon release of pressure, the veins deflate, and color and feeling return to normal.

3. Intensity of skin color (pink or blue) is related to the volume of blood in the area. The color is determined by the degree of oxygenation of the blood. In this experiment, venous blood gives a blue tint and arterial blood gives a pink tint.

5. Results are variable. The hand usually turns intensely red and a warm tingling sensation may be felt. Redness may last for several minutes.

6. The hand does not become totally ischemic. The second test result is much less dramatic, with much less intense reactive hyperthermia.

7. With only the ulnar artery compressed, the results are intermediate between questions 5 and 6. The ulnar artery has a larger diameter than the radial artery, but they anastomose in the hand to serve the same areas.

Effect of Mechanical Stimulation of Blood Vessels of the Skin

Results will vary. A red streak develops with moderate pressure. With heavy pressure, a wider, darker, longer-lasting streak develops and may swell.

Frog Cardiovascular Physiology: Wet Lab

Time Allotment: 3 hours. (Allow additional time if students must learn to use equipment.)

Solutions:

Ringer's Solution, Frog
- 6.50 grams sodium chloride
- 0.14 gram potassium chloride
- 0.12 gram calcium chloride
- 0.20 gram sodium bicarbonate

Combine salts in flask and add distilled water to make 1 liter of solution.

Test Solutions:

Atropine Sulfate in Frog Ringer's Solution, 5%
Weigh out 5 grams of atropine sulfate. Add frog Ringer's solution to a final volume of 100 milliliters. **Caution! Atropine sulfate is toxic. Label TOXIC.**

Calcium Chloride in Frog Ringer's Solution, 2%
Weigh out 2 grams of calcium chloride. Add frog Ringer's solution to a final volume of 100 milliliters.

Digitalis in Frog Ringer's Solution, 2%
Weigh out 2 grams of digitoxin. Add frog Ringer's solution to a final volume of 100 milliliters.

Epinephrine in Frog Ringer's Solution, 1%
Weigh out 1 gram of epinephrine (Carolina). Dissolve in 0.5 milliliter of 1 N HCl. Add frog Ringer's solution to a final volume of 100 milliliters. **Caution! Epinephrine is toxic. Label TOXIC.**

Histamine in Frog Ringer's Solution, 0.01%
Weigh out 0.01 gram histamine. Add frog Ringer's solution to a final volume of 100 milliliters.

Hydrochloric Acid (HCl) in Frog Ringer's Solution, 0.01 N
Add 0.8 milliliter concentrated HCl to 900 milliliters frog Ringer's solution. Add distilled water to make 1 liter of solution.

Pilocarpine in Frog Ringer's Solution, 2.5%
Weigh out 2.5 grams of pilocarpine chloride. Add frog Ringer's solution to a final volume of 100 milliliters.

Potassium Chloride in Frog Ringer's Solution, 5%
Weigh out 5 grams of potassium chloride. Add frog Ringer's solution to a final volume of 100 milliliters.

Sodium Chloride (NaCl) in Frog Ringer's Solution, 0.7%
Weigh out 0.7 gram of sodium chloride. Add frog Ringer's solution to a final volume of 100 milliliters.

Advance Preparation

1. Order frogs to be delivered close to the date of the lab (see the frog experiment in Exercise 16A). Each group will need one double-pithed frog. If time (or student aversion) is a problem, frogs can be pithed just before the lab begins (see Exercise 16A). Keep the frogs moist with *frog Ringer's solution*.

2. Set out data acquisition equipment (one per group of four). If the equipment has not been used in an earlier experiment, acquaint students with its set-up and use (see Exercise 16A).

    a. BIOPAC®. Set out equipment and materials for the conduction of the BIOPAC® activity, including a computer with BIOPAC® BSL Pro Software installed, tension adjuster, force transducer, and transducer (or ring) stand.

    b. *Physiograph*. For each physiograph, set out paper, ink, transducer stand, myograph transducer, transducer cables, stimulator output extension cable, and electrodes.

    c. *Kymograph*. For each kymograph, set out kymograph paper, ink (if necessary), ring stand, two right-angle clamps, heart lever, signal marker, electronic stimulator, and platinum electrodes. If smoked drums are used, set up a smoking area and a glazing area in fume hoods.

3. Put bottles of *frog Ringer's solution* in a water bath set at 32°C and in a refrigerator set at 5°C. Have a supply bottle of room temperature *frog Ringer's solution* available.

4. Each group should be provided with disposable gloves, a dissecting pan and instruments, a 250-milliliter bottle of *frog Ringer's solution*, two petri dishes, a medicine dropper, a millimeter ruler, thread, sturdy rubber bands, several fine common pins, a frog board with a hole in one end (Carolina), cotton balls, paper towels, and 25-milliliter bottles of *test solutions*. Have supply bottles of the *test solutions* available.

5. Have microscopes, lens paper, and lens cleaning solution available.

6. Designate an appropriate disposal area for the frogs.

Comments and Pitfalls

1. Remind students to keep the tissue moist with *frog Ringer's solution* at all times.

2. Be sure the students have correctly located the vagus nerve and have not invented a nerve from connective tissue.

3. Do not overstretch the heart when attaching it to the recording equipment.

4. If a heart lever is used, be sure that the stylus is horizontal during diastole. If necessary, attach a small counterweight to the lever. Adjust the point of attachment of the thread to the lever to get the best recording height, and be sure the heart is perpendicular to the lever.

5. A Stannius ligature is a simple overhand knot in a loop of thread that can be tightened by pulling on both ends of the thread.

6. See Exercise 16A for additional comments on troubleshooting the recording equipment.

Answers to Questions

Activity 1: Investigating the Automaticity and Rhythmicity of Heart Muscle (p. 373)

4. The heart is contracting rhythmically while the gastrocnemius muscle is not contracting at all.

5. The sinus venosus will continue to beat.

6. Each atrium should continue to beat, as well as the ventricle.

7. The sinus venosus usually displays the most automaticity (contracts at the fastest rate) and the ventricle the least.

Activity 2: Recording Baseline Frog Heart Activity (pp. 374–377)

Preparation of the Frog

4. Yes. The atrium contracts before the ventricle.

Making the Baseline Recording

5. The atrial contraction is much briefer than ventricular contraction.

Activity 3: Investigating the Refractory Period of Cardiac Muscle (p. 377)

3. Extrasystole can only be induced during the pause between contractions (late in ventricular diastole).

4. The heart does not go into tetanus. The heart would be of no value as a pump if it could go into tetanus as a result of rapid repeated stimulation.

Activity 4: Assessing Physical and Chemical Modifiers of Heart Rate (pp. 378–379)

Temperature

5. Warm Ringer's solution speeds up the heart rate. Cold Ringer's solution slows it down.

Vagus Nerve Stimulation

3. Vagal stimulation slows down and eventually stops the heart.

Pilocarpine

Pilocarpine simulates vagal stimulation and slows the heart.

Atropine Sulfate

The heart rate should increase. The atropine effect is *antagonistic* to that of pilocarpine.

Epinephrine

Epinephrine increases heart rate, imitating the sympathetic nervous system.

Digitalis

Digitalis slows and steadies heart contraction.

Various Ions

Ca^{2+} increases strength of contraction; probable induction of spasticity.

Na^+ decreases strength and rate of contraction.

K^+ weakens heart contractions.

Yes. Students may observe arrhythmia with all three ions.

Intrinsic Conduction System Disturbance (Heart Block)

A normal A-V rhythm should reestablish after removing the block.

Activity 5: Investigating the Effect of Various Factors on the Microcirculation (pp. 380–381)

5. RBCs move through capillaries in single file. They are flexible and they may appear "stacked" and slightly curved as they move through. White blood cells resembling monocytes may be seen.

6. Blood flow in the arterioles is rapid and pulsating, while it is slow and steady in the venules. Movement is very slow in the capillaries. The capillaries are much smaller in diameter than the arterioles.

Temperature

Arterioles respond most noticeably to the temperature change. Cold saline causes a reduction in diameter and warm saline an increase in diameter.

Inflammation

HCl causes vasodilation, increasing capillary blood flow. This is a local response to bring more inflammatory cells to the damaged area.

Histamine

Histamine also causes vasodilation and increased blood flow. Epinephrine causes vasoconstriction and reduced blood flow.

The Lymphatic System and Immune Response

exercise

35

Time Allotment: 1 hour.

Multimedia Resources: See Appendix F for a list of multimedia offerings.
See Exercise 6A for histology listings.

Defend and Repair (NIMCO, 30 minutes, VHS)
Organ Systems Working Together (WNS, 14 minutes, VHS)
Internal Defenses (FHS, 28 minutes, VHS, DVD)
The Human Immune System: The Fighting Edge (FHS, 44 minutes, VHS, DVD)

Biochemistry of the Immune System (ED, CD-ROM)
Blood and Immunity (CE, CD-ROM)

Solutions:
Simple Saline Agar
• 2 g agar (Difco Bacto)
• 1 g sodium chloride (NaCl)
• 100 ml distilled water
• 0.1 g sodium azide (optional)
Prepare a clear solution by boiling the mixture gently. Pour while hot to a depth of
3 mm into 100 mm plastic petri dishes, which have been divided into three compart-
ments (7 ml per compartment). Leave open until the gel cools. To store, either steam
sterilize the agar before pouring or add 0.1 g sodium azide per 100 ml.

AIA Refer to the lab manual for links to A.D.A.M.® Interactive Anatomy.

Advance Preparation

1. Set out anatomical charts of the lymphatic system, prepared slides of lymph nodes, lens
paper, and lens cleaning solution. Have microscopes available.

2. Prepare saline agar petri dishes in advance.

3. Set out petri dishes with saline agar (one per group), dropper bottles of red and green food coloring, dropper bottles of goat antibody to bovine serum albumin, horse serum albumin and swine serum albumin, dropper bottles of horse serum albumin, dropper bottles of unknown serum albumin samples diluted to 20%, medicine droppers and wax marking pencils.

Answers to Questions

Activity 3: Using the Ouchterlony Technique to Identify Antigens (pp. 388–390)

5. Horse serum albumin is the antigen.

7. a.   Goat antibody to horse serum albumin reacts with the antigen in section II.

   b.   A white precipitin line forms between wells 1 and 2.

8. A white precipitin line forms between wells 1 and 4.

9. No reaction. The antibodies are specific to horse, bovine, and swine albumins.

Anatomy of the Respiratory System

36

 Time Allotment: 1 hour.

 Multimedia Resources: See Appendix F for a list of multimedia offerings. See Exercise 6A for histology listings.

Breath of Life (FHS, 26 minutes, VHS, DVD)
Dissection of the Thorax Series, The (UL, VHS)
      Part I. The Thoracic Wall (23 minutes)
      Part II. Pleurae and Lungs (24 minutes)
Human Respiratory System Videotape (BC, 25 minutes, VHS)
Lungs (Revised) (AIMS, 10 minutes, VHS)
The Respiratory System (UL, 26 minutes, VHS)
Respiratory System: Intake and Exhaust (FHS, 25 minutes, VHS, DVD)
Thorax (UL, 22 minutes, VHS)

 InterActive Physiology®: Respiratory System (BC, CD-ROM, or www.interactivephysiology.com)
      Anatomy Review: Respiratory Structures

 Refer to the lab manual for links to A.D.A.M.® Interactive Anatomy.

Advance Preparation

1. Set out human torso models, respiratory organ system model, larynx model, and/or charts of the respiratory system.

2. Set out a sheep pluck (fresh if possible), or set up an inflatable swine lungs kit (Nasco), and disposable gloves.

3. Arrange for a source of compressed air, or provide cardboard mouthpieces and a 2-foot length of rubber tubing. Set out an autoclave bag for disposal of the mouthpieces, if used.

4. Set out prepared slides of the trachea, normal lung tissue, and pathological lung tissue exhibiting conditions such as bronchitis, pneumonia, emphysema, or lung cancer; lens paper; and lens cleaning solution. Have compound microscopes and stereomicroscopes available.

Comments and Pitfalls

1. Many prepared slides of the trachea also include the esophagus. Remind the students that the trachea is held open by cartilaginous rings, while the esophagus is not. Showing a 35-millimeter slide or videodisc image of the section might be useful.

2. When using a preserved sheep pluck with a compressed air supply, be careful to avoid overinflation (leading to an explosion of preserved tissue)!

3. The inflatable swine lungs kit includes an inflation rack and tray, inflatable swine lungs, and a section of dried swine lung. The inflatable lungs will last for several years and give a much more dramatic response than that usually seen with the preserved lungs of the sheep pluck. An inflatable diseased lung is also available from Nasco and is excellent for comparison to a healthy lung.

Respiratory System Physiology

Time Allotment: 2 hours (allow an additional half hour if students are unfamiliar with the recording apparatus).

Multimedia Resources: See Appendix F for a list of multimedia offerings.

Breath of Life (FHS, 26 minutes, VHS, DVD)
Breathing (FHS, 20 minutes, VHS, DVD)
The Physiology of Exercise (FHS, 15 minutes, VHS, DVD)
Respiration (FHS, 15 minutes, VHS)
Respiratory System: Intake and Exhaust (FHS, 25 minutes, VHS, DVD)

IP InterActive Physiology®: Respiratory System (BC, CD-ROM, or www.interactivephysiology.com)
      Anatomy Review: Respiratory Structures
      Pulmonary Ventilation
      Gas Exchange
      Gas Transport
      Control of Respiration

Solution:

Hydrochloric Acid (HCl), 0.01 M
Add 0.8 milliliter concentrated HCl to 900 milliliters distilled water. Add distilled water to make 1 liter of solution; *or* dilute 10 milliliters of 1 N HCl to a final volume of 1 liter with distilled water.

Sodium Hydroxide (NaOH), 0.05 M
Weigh out 2 g. of NaOH and add to distilled water to make 1 liter of solution.

Advance Preparation

1. Set out the model lung.

2. For each group set out a tape measure, clear adhesive tape, nose clips, spirometer, disposable mouthpieces (enough for each member of the group), alcohol swabs, a paper

bag, a physiograph with a pneumograph and recording attachments, or PowerLab® unit and cable, computer with Chart® software installed, respiratory belt transducer and cable, paper, and a stethoscope. See the frog experiment in Exercise 16A for further directions for the physiograph. If a wet spirometer is used, be sure it is filled with distilled water according to the manufacturer's instructions. Set out a battery jar of 70% ethanol.

4. Set out equipment and materials for the conduction of the BIOPAC® activity. Introduce your students to the basic features of the equipment prior to beginning the lab activity.

5. For each group set out a pH meter standardized with a buffer of pH 7, five 250-milliliter beakers, two 50-milliliter beakers, a 100-milliliter graduated cylinder, a dropper bottle of concentrated HCl, a dropper bottle of concentrated NaOH, 300 milliliters of standard buffer solution (pH 7), 500 milliliters of distilled water, a wash bottle of distilled water, a dropper bottle of *0.01 M HCl*, a glass stirring rod, and animal plasma.

6. Set up a disposable autoclave bag.

7. Draw a class data chart on the blackboard to record TV (V_t), IRV, ERV, and VC.

8. Set out bottles of 0.05 *M* NaOH, dropper bottles of phenol red, distilled water, 100-ml beakers, and straws for each group.

Comments and Pitfalls

1. If a dry spirometer is used, the tidal volume readings are not very accurate. Somewhat better readings are obtained if the student exhales three times into the spirometer and divides the result by three.

2. Students will have to adjust the pneumograph until a good recording can be made. Be sure that it fits comfortably around the chest. Check all connections for a good fit, and if a tambour is used, be sure the rubber is intact. (This can be easily replaced using rubber sheeting. Use a good adhesive to reattach the clip.)

3. When using the pneumograph, be sure that students can correctly interpret the tracings. On some equipment, inspiration results in a downward deflection of the pointer (opposite the direction noted on the spirometer tracing in Figure 37A.2).

4. Students may be confused about hyperventilation. The forced hyperventilation here results in a decreased breathing rate. Hyperventilation during psychological stress can produce a positive feedback situation, resulting in further hyperventilation. As hypocapnia increases, cerebral vessels constrict and increasingly acidotic conditions in the brain stimulate the medullary respiratory centers. Rebreathing breathed air in the latter case raises blood P_{CO_2}, reverses the cerebral vessel constriction, and stops the hyperventilation.

5. For the experiment in Role of the Respiratory System in Acid-Base Balance of Blood, if you wish to avoid using concentrated acid and base and conserve pH buffer, you can scale down the experiment by using 1 *M* NaOH, 1 *M* HCl, and 50 milliliters of pH 7 buffer.

Answers to Questions

Activity 1: Operating the Model Lung (p. 400)

4. The walls of the human thorax expand and collapse bringing about changes in thoracic volume. In the model, the bottle walls are rigid. All changes in thoracic volume are realized only by the diaphragm. In real lungs, the intrapleural cavity is a fluid-filled space with pleural fluid maintaining the lungs expanded against the rib cage. In the model, this cavity is air filled though sealed. Consequently, the simulation of a pneumothorax is not as significant as would occur in the biologic system.

Activity 5: Visualizing Respiratory Variations (pp. 409–412)

Using the Physiograph-Pneumograph Apparatus

4. During breath holding, the subject has the desire to expire. After a deep and forceful exhalation, the urge is to inspire. This may be explained by the Hering-Breuer reflex. Stretch receptors in the lungs are sensitive to extreme inflation and extreme deflation of the lungs. Impulses to the medulla oblongata initiate expiration or inspiration respectively.

5. The hyperventilation tracing should be similar in height and depth to the vital capacity tracing, but with an increased rate. After hyperventilation, the breathing rate slows down.

6. Breath-holding time increases after hyperventilation.

7. After 3 minutes of rebreathing breathed air, the ventilation rate increases. It is much faster than the breathing rate after hyperventilating.

9. Forced expiration results in dilation of the neck and face veins. Increased intrathoracic pressure reduces blood flow back to the heart, decreasing cardiac output. This results in increased cardiac rate (seen here as increased pulse rate).

Measuring Respiratory Volumes Using BIOPAC®

11. Generally, the taller and larger a subject is, the larger will be the vital capacity. This is because a larger person requires more oxygen for cellular respiration. Other factors that can affect vital capacity include: aerobic conditioning of the subject, chronic obstructive pulmonary diseases, smoking, etc.

Activity 6: Demonstrating the Reaction Between Carbon Dioxide in Exhaled Air and Water (p. 417)

3. Carbon dioxide in the exhaled air combines with water to form carbonic acid, lowering the pH of the solution.

Activity 7: Observing the Operation of Standard Buffers (p. 417)

The buffer system should resist change in pH. The contrast between the pH change with water alone and the pH change with buffer should be clear.

Activity 8: Exploring the Operation of the Carbonic Acid–Bicarbonate Buffer System (p. 417)

4. When testing the plasma carbonic acid–bicarbonate buffer system, it is the bicarbonate that counteracts the change in pH.

Anatomy of the Digestive System

38

 Time Allotment: 2 hours.

 Multimedia Resources: See Appendix F for a list of multimedia offerings. See Exercise 6A for histology listings.

Digestive System: Your Personal Power Plant (FHS, 25 minutes, VHS, DVD)
The Food Machine (NIMCO, 30 minutes, VHS)
The Guides to Dissection Series (UL, VHS)
   Group V. The Abdomen (6 parts) 88.5 minutes total
Digestive System (WNS, 14 minutes, VHS)
The Human Digestive System (AIMS, 18 minutes, VHS)
Human Digestive System Videotape (BC, 33 minutes, VHS)

 Refer to the lab manual for links to A.D.A.M.® Interactive Anatomy.

Advance Preparation

1. Set out the dissectible torso model and anatomical charts of the human digestive system.

2. Set out models of a villus and the liver, if available; a jaw model; and/or a human skull.

3. Set out slides of liver, mixed salivary glands, pancreas; longitudinal sections of the gastroesophageal junction and a tooth; cross sections of the stomach, duodenum, and ileum; lens paper and lens cleaning solution. Have compound microscopes and hand lenses available.

Answers to Questions

Activity 2: Studying the Histological Structure of Selected Digestive System Organs (p. 424)

Stomach

The extra layer of smooth muscle produces the churning movement because of the additional planes in which contraction can take place.

Gastroesophageal Junction

The esophagus is lined with stratified squamous epithelium, while the stomach is lined with simple columnar epithelium. The esophagus is designed to handle abrasion. The stomach lining has secretory and some absorptive functions.

Activity 3: Observing the Histological Structure of the Small Intestine (p. 427)

Duodenum

Simple columnar epithelium lines the duodenum.

Ileum

Peyer's patches are lymphatic tissue.

Chemical and Physical Processes of Digestion: Wet Lab

 Time Allotment: 3 hours. (Two parts of the exercise require 2-hour incubations.)

 Muiltimedia Resources: See Appendix F for a list of multimedia offerings.

Breakdown (FHS, 28 minutes, VHS, DVD)
Digestion: Eating to Live (FHS, 27 minutes, VHS)
The Food Machine (NIMCO, 30 minutes, VHS)
Digestive System (WNS, 14 minutes, VHS)
The Human Digestive System (AIMS, 18 minutes, VHS)
Passage of Food Through the Digestive Tract (WNS, 8 minutes, VHS)

 Solutions:

Alpha-Amylase, 1%
Weigh out 1 gram of alpha-amylase. Add distilled water to a final volume of 100 milliliters. For best results, be sure that the enzyme is not standardized with maltose.

BAPNA, .01%
Weigh out .01 gram BAPNA. Add distilled water to a final volume of 100 milliliters.

Benedict's Solution
• 173.0 grams sodium citrate
• 100.0 grams sodium carbonate, anhydrous
• 17.3 grams cupric sulfate (pure crystalline)
Add the citrate and carbonate salts to 700–800 milliliters distilled water. Heat to dissolve. Add the cupric sulfate to 100 milliliters distilled water and heat to dissolve. Cool the solutions and then combine. Add distilled water to make 1 liter of solution.

Hydrochloric Acid (HCl), 0.1 N
Add 8 milliliters concentrated HCl to 900 milliliters distilled water. Add distilled water to a final volume of 1 liter; *or* dilute 100 milliliters of 1 N HCl to a final volume of 1 liter with distilled water.

Litmus Cream
Add powdered litmus to fresh cream to achieve a blue color.

Lugol's Iodine (IKI)
• 20 grams potassium iodide
• 4 grams iodine crystals
Dissolve potassium iodide in 1 liter distilled water. Add the iodine crystals and stir to dissolve. Store in dark bottles.

Maltose, 1%
Weigh out 1 gram maltose. Add distilled water to a final volume of 100 milliliters.

Pancreatin, 1%
Weigh out 1 gram pancreatin. Dissolve in distilled water to a final volume of 100 milliliters.

Starch Solution, Boiled, 1%
Add 1 gram of starch to 100 milliliters distilled water. Boil just until it changes from cloudy to translucent. Cool and filter. Add a pinch of NaCl. Prepare fresh daily. For best results, use potato starch from a biological supply house.

Trypsin, 1%
Weigh out 1 gram trypsin. Add distilled water to a final volume of 100 milliliters.

Advance Preparation

1. Put a chart on the board for recording class results.

2. Decide how to divide the class into groups to do the experiments.

3. Set up five supply areas.

General supply area (for a class of 24, divided into six groups of four each):

144 test tubes, 6 test tube racks, and 6 wax marking pencils, hot plates, 250-milliliter beakers, ice water bath, 37°C water bath, boiling chips (Carolina), and dropper bottles of distilled water.

Supply area 1 (for each group of four students):

Dropper bottles of *1% boiled starch solution*, freshly prepared, *1% amylase solution*, *1% maltose solution*, *Lugol's solution* (Carolina or see above), *Benedict's solution* (Carolina or see above), and spot plates.

Supply area 2 (for each group of four students):

Dropper bottles of *1% trypsin* (Sigma) and *.01% BAPNA* (Sigma).

Supply area 3 (for each group of four students):

Bile salts, parafilm, and dropper bottles of *1% pancreatin solution, 0.1 N HCl*, vegetable oil, and *litmus cream* (litmus powder—Carolina).

Supply area 4 (for each group of four students):

Pitcher of water, four paper cups, a stethoscope, disposable autoclave bag, and alcohol swabs.

4. Set up a VHS viewing area with the tape *Passage of Food Through the Digestive Tract* (Ward's) to allow independent viewing by students. This is an 8-minute film.

Comments and Pitfalls

1. This lab requires a great deal of organization and coordination on the part of the students. Emphasize the need for careful labeling and record keeping.

2. If a 37°C water bath is not available, incubate the tubes at room temperature and double the incubation time.

3. Enzyme activity can vary. Enzyme solutions should be prepared just before the lab and adjusted for appropriate activity.

Answers to Questions

Activity 3: Demonstrating the Emulsification Action of Bile and Assessing Fat Digestion by Lipase (pp. 439–440)

2. Emulsification occurs in the tubes containing bile salts.

Activity 6: Observing Movements and Sounds of Digestion (p. 441)

3. Movement of the larynx ensures that its passageway is covered by the epiglottis.

Anatomy of the Urinary System

40

 Time Allotment: 1 hour.

 Multimedia Resources: See Appendix F for a list of multimedia offerings. See Exercise 6A for histology listings.

Human Urinary System Videotape (BC, 23 minutes, VHS)
Kidney Functions (AIMS, 5 minutes, VHS, DVD)
The Kidney (FHS, 15 minutes, VHS)
The Urinary Tract: Water! (FHS, 28 minutes, VHS, DVD)

 IP InterActive Physiology®: Urinary System (BC, CD-ROM, or www.interactivephysiology.com)
        Anatomy Review
        Glomerular Filtration
        Early Filtrate Processing
        Late Filtrate Processing
InterActive Physiology®: Fluids and Electrolytes (BC, CD-ROM, or www.interactivephysiology.com)
        Introduction to Body Fluids
        Water Homeostasis
        Electrolyte Homeostasis
        Acid/base Homeostasis

 AIA Refer to the lab manual for links to A.D.A.M.® Interactive Anatomy.

Advance Preparation

1. Make arrangements for appropriate storage, disposal, and cleanup of dissection materials. Check with the Department of Health, the Department of Environmental Protection, or their counterparts for state regulations.
2. Set out disposable gloves and safety glasses.
3. Set out dissecting kits, dissecting pans, and pig or sheep kidneys.

4. Set out slides of longitudinal sections of the kidney and cross sections of the bladder; lens paper; and lens cleaning solution. Have compound microscopes available.

5. Set out the dissectible human torso and/or any anatomical charts and models of the urinary system, kidney, and nephron.

Answers to Questions

Activity 3: Studying Bladder Structure (p. 450)

5. Both organs have an internal mucosa, a layer of smooth muscle, and an external adventitia. The ureter has only two layers of smooth muscle.

Urinalysis

Time Allotment: 1 hour.

Solutions:

Barium Chloride, 10%
Weigh out 10 grams of barium chloride. Add water to a final volume of 100 milliliters.

Bleach Solution, 10%
Measure out 100 milliliters of household bleach. Add water to a final volume of 1 liter.

Hydrochloric Acid (HCl), Dilute, 3 N
Add 258 milliliters of 36% HCl to 700 milliliters distilled water. Add distilled water to a final volume of 1 liter.

Nitric Acid (HNO$_3$), Dilute, 3 N
Add 183 milliliters of 69% HNO3 to 700 milliliters distilled water. Add distilled water to a final volume of 1 liter.

Silver Nitrate, 3%
Weigh out 3 grams of silver nitrate. **Use caution: This is an oxidizing substance**. Add distilled water to make 100 milliliters of solution. Store in light-resistant bottles. Make fresh for each use.

Urine, Artificial Normal Human*
- 36.4 grams urea
- 15 grams sodium chloride
- 9.0 grams potassium chloride
- 9.6 grams sodium phosphate
- 4.0 grams creatinine
- 100 milligrams albumin

Add urea to 1.5 liters of distilled water. Mix until crystals dissolve. Add sodium chloride, potassium chloride, and sodium phosphate. Mix until solution is clear. The pH should be within the 5 to 7 pH range for normal human urine. Adjust pH, if necessary, with 1 *N* HCl or 1 *N* NaOH. Place a urine hydrometer in the solution and dilute with water to a specific gravity within the range of 1.015 to 1.025. This stock solution may be refrigerated for several weeks or frozen for months. Before use, warm to room temperature and add 4.0 grams creatinine and 100 milligrams of albumin for each 2 liters of solution.

*Urine, Glycosuria**

For a minimally detectable level of glucose, add a minimum of 600 milligrams of glucose to 1 liter of "normal" urine solution. For moderate to high glycosuria, add 2.5 to 5.0 grams of glucose to each liter of solution.

*Urine, Hematuria**

Add 1 milliliter of heparinized or defibrinated sheep blood to 1 liter of "normal" urine solution.

*Urine, Hemoglobinuria**

Add 2 milligrams of bovine hemoglobin to 1 liter of "normal" urine solution.

*Urine, Hyposthenuria**

Add distilled water to a sample of "normal" urine until the specific gravity approaches 1.005.

*Urine, Ketonuria**

Add a minimum of 100 milligrams of acetoacetic acid or at least 1 milliliter of acetone to 1 liter of "normal" urine solution.

*Urine, Leukocyte Presence**

Add 100 to 200 units of pork or rabbit liver esterase to 100 milliliters of the "normal" urine solution. This test must be performed immediately after adding the enzyme.

*Urine, pH Imbalance**

Adjust "normal" urine to a pH of 4.0 to 4.5 with 1 *N* HCl for acid urine. Adjust "normal" urine to a pH of 8 to 9 with 1 *N* NaOH for alkaline urine.

*Urine, Proteinuria**

Add 300 milligrams or more of albumin per liter of "normal" urine solution. For severe renal damage, add 1 gram of albumin to each liter of solution.

*Urine, Whole Spectrum Pathological Artificial Human**

Mix appropriate amounts of abnormal condition reagents to 1 liter of "normal" urine solution.
Diabetes mellitus: glycosuria and ketonuria
Glomerular damage: proteinuria, hemoglobinuria, and hematuria

* From B. R. Shmaefsky, "Artificial Urine for Laboratory Testing," *American Biology Teacher* 52 (3), March 1990, pp. 170–172 (Reston, VA: National Association of Biology Teachers). Reprinted with permission.

Advance Preparation

1. Prepare *"normal" artificial urine* (about 1 liter for a class of 30 students) and *"pathological" artificial urine* samples and number them.

2. Set out two laboratory buckets containing *10% bleach solution*, and a disposable auto-clave bag. Put a flask of *10% bleach solution* and a sponge at each lab bench.

3. For each student in the class set out disposable gloves, five test tubes, a glass stirring rod, a test tube rack, a medicine dropper, a urinometer cylinder and float, microscope slides, coverslips, individual reagent strips (Clinistix, Ketostix, Hemastix, Bilistix—all available from Fisher), or combination strips (Chemstrip—Carolina or Multistix—Fisher), Clinitest tablets (Fisher), a 10-milliliter graduated cylinder, a wax marking pencil, Ictotest reagent tablet and mat (Fisher). Have compound microscopes, lens paper, and lens cleaning solution available.

4. For each group set out wide-range pH paper, a bottle containing 100 milliliters of *10% barium chloride*, a bottle containing 100 milliliters of dilute ammonium molybdate (LabChem, a hot plate, a 500-milliliter beaker, and dropper bottles of *dilute HCl, dilute HNO$_3$*, freshly prepared *3.0% silver nitrate*, and concentrated HNO$_3$.

5. Set up a demonstration slide of urine sediment stained with Sedi-stain (Fisher). To prepare the slide, centrifuge a 5-milliliter sample of urine at 2000 to 2500 rpm for 5 to 6 minutes. Decant the supernatant and add one or two drops of Sedi-stain to the pellet. Put stained material onto a slide and cover with a coverslip.

Comments and Pitfalls

1. When preparing pathological samples, do not substitute sucrose for glucose. Vitamin C contamination will give false positive glucose tests. The artificial urine is suitable for test strips, but not for use with clinical analyzers (Shmaefsky, 1990).

2. Urge students to use extreme caution when using the concentrated HCl and HNO$_3$ solutions.

3. Because students are usually very interested in the crystals, cells, and casts in urine, have additional references available for them.

Answers to Questions

Activity 1: Analyzing Urine Samples (pp. 453–454)

Determination of Inorganic Constituents of Urine

Sulfates are usually present in urine in small amounts.

Anatomy of the Reproductive System

Time Allotment: 1 hour.

Multimedia Resources: See Appendix F for a list of multimedia offerings. See Exercise 6A for histology listings.

The Guides to Dissection Series (UL, VHS)
   Group VI. The Pelvis and Perineum (4 parts) 64 minutes total
Human Biology (FHS, 58 minutes, VHS, DVD)
The Human Female Reproductive System (UL, 29 minutes, VHS)
The Human Male Reproductive System (UL, 29 minutes, VHS)
Human Reproductive Biology (FHS, 35 minutes, VHS, DVD)
Human Reproductive System Videotape (BC, 32 minutes, VHS)
Reproduction: Shares in the Future (FHS, 26 minutes, VHS, DVD)

Refer to the lab manual for links to A.D.A.M.® Interactive Anatomy.

Advance Preparation

1. Set out slides of the penis, epididymis, uterine tube, and uterus showing endometrium (proliferative phase). Set out lens paper and lens cleaning solution, and have compound microscopes available.

2. Set out models and anatomical charts of the male and female reproductive systems.

Comments and Pitfalls

1. If you are not planning to do Exercise 44, you may wish to include the microscopic studies of the testis and ovary described there in this laboratory session.

Answers to Questions

Activity 2: Examining the Penis Microscopically (p. 461)

The epithelium is stratified columnar epithelium. Its basic function is protection of underlying tissues.

Activity 4: Examining the Epididymis Through the Microscope (p. 462)

The smooth muscle rhythmically contracts under sympathetic stimulation during emission and ejaculation. The peristaltic movements propel sperm/seminal fluid from the epididymis through the vas deferens, ejaculatory duct, and urethra.

Activity 5: Conducting a Microscopic Study of Selected Female Reproductive Organs (p. 465)

Wall of the Uterus

During the birth process the myometrium contracts, pushing the baby toward the cervical canal, and exerting pressure on the amniotic sac.

Physiology of Reproduction: Gametogenesis and the Female Cycles

 Time Allotment: 1¹/₂ hours.

 Multimedia Resources: See Appendix F for a list of multimedia offerings. See Exercise 6A for histology listings.

Coming Together (FHS, 28 minutes, VHS, DVD)
Human Biology (FHS, 58 minutes, VHS, DVD)
Highlights of Reproduction and Prenatal Development (UL, 16 minutes, VHS)
Human Reproductive Biology (FHS, 35 minutes, VHS)
Meiosis: The Key to Genetic Diversity (WNS, 30 minutes, VHS)
Sex (WNS, 30 minutes, VHS)

Advance Preparation

1. Set out models illustrating meiosis, spermatogenesis, and oogenesis.

2. Set out prepared slides of testis, ovary, human sperm, and uterine endometrium (showing menses, proliferative, and secretory stages). Set out lens paper and immersion oil. Have compound microscopes available.

3. Set up five microscopes in a demonstration area with the following slides of stages of oogenesis in *Ascaris megalocephala* (Carolina): (1) primary oocyte with fertilization membrane, sperm nucleus, and aligned tetrads apparent; (2) formation of first polar body; (3) secondary oocyte with dyads aligned; (4) formation of ovum and second polar body; and (5) fusion of the male and female pronuclei to form the fertilized egg.

4. Set out sets of colored "pop-it" beads (two colors) and magnetic centromeres (Ward's).

Comments and Pitfalls

1. If students have trouble counting chromosomes, have them count centromeres.

Answers to Questions

Activity 2: Examing Events of Spermatogenesis (pp. 469–470)

3. Tetrads may be visible. Evidence of crossing over may be difficult to see, but the tetrads may appear to have chromatids wrapped around each other. Tetrads are in primary spermatocytes, which are closer to the spermatogonia than to the lumen.

Activity 5: Comparing and Contrasting Oogenesis and Spermatogenesis (p. 473)

A human oocyte is 0.1–0.15 mm in diameter while the head of a sperm is just 0.004–0.005 mm wide. This means the egg is about 20× larger than the sperm. (Note: Sea urchin eggs are 200,000 larger than the sperm.) Oocytes contain a substantial volume of cytoplasm and all the organelles of a cell. The head of a spermatozoa, in contrast, consists of not much more than a nucleus and acrosome.

Gametogenesis in both males and females results in the production of haploid gametes.

Male gametogenesis results in four equally sized cells. In females, three polar bodies degenerate leaving one large primary oocyte. This oocyte is arrested at meiosis I until ovulation. No such arrested development occurs in the male process. Finally, spermatogenesis is spatially organized such that it proceeds from the walls of the seminiferous tubules inwards toward the lumen. In contrast, oogenesis occurs randomly throughout the ovarian cortex (contrary to the apparent circular sequence illustrated in many illustrations and models).

Survey of Embryonic Development

 Time Allotment: 2 hours.

 Multimedia Resources: See Appendix F for a list of multimedia offerings. See Exercise 6A for histology listings.

A Human Life Emerges (FHS, 33 minutes, VHS, DVD)
A New Life (FHS, 28 minutes, VHS, DVD)
Dozen Eggs, A: Time-Lapse Microscopy of Normal Development (IM, 46 minutes, VHS)
Human Embryology Series (UL, VHS)
       Highlights of Reproduction and Prenatal Development (16 minutes)
       Fertilization, Cleavage and Implantation (17 minutes)
Human Reproductive Biology (FHS, 35 minutes, VHS)
In the Womb (NIMCO, 30 minutes, VHS)
Into the World (FHS, 28 minutes, VHS, DVD)
Introduction to Development (IM, 22 minutes, VHS)
Miracle of Life (CBS, 60 minutes, VHS, DVD)

Advance Preparation

1. Order *A Colour Atlas of Life Before Birth: Normal Fetal Development*, London, England: Wolfe Medical Publications, Ltd. 1983. This book can be ordered from DGi Denoyer-Geppert International.

2. Set out lens paper, lens cleaning solution, and slides of sea urchin development (zygote to larval stages) and of a placenta tissue. Have compound microscopes available.

3. Set out models of human development and pregnant human torso.

4. Obtain a fresh or formalin-preserved placenta from a clinical agency.

5. Set out a pregnant cat, rat, or pig uterus, disposable gloves, safety glasses, and dissecting equipment.

Comments and Pitfalls

1. Students may have difficulty with the questions in the text. Additional reference material (developmental biology or embryology books) might be helpful.

Answers to Questions

Activity 1: Examining the Stages of Human Development (pp. 478–481)

5. The chorionic villi look like feathery projections. Areas of the brain and the heart appear very early in development. Development is rostral to caudal and proximal to distal. Spontaneous movement in utero can be felt by the mother. The fetus, attached to the placenta by the umbilical cord, may resemble an astronaut on a "space walk" connected to life support systems on a space ship. The vernix caseosa covers the fetus and consists mainly of sebaceous secretions and dead epidermal cells. It may act as a lubricant and protect the growing fetus from chafing injuries. Lanugo is a downy coat of fetal hairs that appears at about the fifth month of development and is usually lost at birth or shortly thereafter.

Activity 2: Identifying Fetal Structures (p. 481)

1. The placenta of the pig is diffuse with villi distributed over the surface of the chorion. In the cat, the villi form a belt around the fetus (zonary placenta). The rat has a discoidal placenta similar to the human placenta. The umbilical cord connects the placenta to the fetus. Amniotic fluid is usually clear and watery and fetal skin is relatively thin. If it is a very young fetus, the skin may be almost transparent.

2. The human placenta is discoidal in shape. Implantation usually occurs in the upper part of the uterus. One problem that may occur with lower implantation is placenta previa. The placenta may irritate the cervix, resulting in contractions and spontaneous abortion. A feet-first position is not as desirable as head-first. The head is the largest structure and if it is delivered first, the rest of the baby is delivered easily. It is also possible to suction and deliver oxygen to a baby in a head-first position if difficulties are encountered.

Activity 3: Studying Placental Structure (p. 482)

1. The fetal side is the smooth side. The ragged side was united with maternal tissue. The umbilical vein delivers relatively oxygen-rich blood to the fetus from the placenta. The umbilical arteries carry blood from the fetus to the placenta. If any fetal membranes are still attached, one may be the amnion.

Principles of Heredity

 Time Allotment: 2 hours+ with gel electrophoresis and if Punnett squares are done outside of lab.

 Multimedia Resources: See Appendix F for a list of multimedia offerings.

Genetics: A Popular Guide to the Principles of Human Heredity (FHS, VHS, DVD)
    Understanding the Basic Concepts of Genetics (30 minutes)
    Genetic Discoveries, Disorders, and Mutations (26 minutes)
    Practical Applications and the Risks of Genetic Science (24 minutes)
Reproduction: Shares in the Future (FHS, 26 minutes, VHS, DVD)

Genetics (FHS, CD-ROM)

 Solutions:
Agarose gel, 1.2%
Weigh out 0.9 gram of agarose and add 1XTris-Borate-EDTA buffer (ICN) to a volume of 75 ml. Boil on a hot plate or in a microwave oven until the agarose melts, stirring periodically.

Bleach Solution, 10%
Measure out 100 milliliters of household bleach. Add water to a final volume of 1 liter.

Advance Preparation

1. For each student set out PTC taste strips (Carolina), sodium benzoate taste strips (Carolina), pennies, wax markers, lancets, cotton, alcohol preps, and toothpicks and clean microscope slides, or blood mixing sticks and test cards (Carolina).

2. Set out anti-A and anti-B blood typing sera, beakers of *10% bleach solution*, and a disposable autoclave bag.

3. Prepare a chart on the blackboard for tabulation of class data.

4. Preparations for agarose gel electrophoresis:

    a. Prepare the casting tray. Place a clean glass slide into the gel casting tray and seal both ends of the tray with duct tape. Be sure the tray is tightly sealed.

b. Prepare four gels. Pour 15 ml of the melted 1.2% agarose solution onto the glass slide in the casting tray. Insert the well comb into the slots on the casting tray, and press down. Cool the gel for about 15 minutes and then carefully remove the tape and lift the comb straight up out of the gel. To store for later use, leave the comb in place, wrap the gel with comb in plastic wrap or a baggie and refrigerate.

c. Prepare the sample buffer. The hemoglobin samples should be prepared as 10%–20% solutions in TBE solubilization buffer with bromophenol blue (ICN). HbA and HbS can be purchased from Sigma. Solutions can be mixed to make a heterozygous sample. Label the samples AA, AS, SS, and unknown sample.

5. Set out gel electrophoresis equipment, power supplies, micropipets, or variable automatic micropipets (2–20 μl) with tips, and 1.2% agarose gels.

6. Set out Coomassie blue stain (Carolina), staining tray, destaining solution (Carolina), and plastic baggies.

7. Set out hemoglobin samples, TBE buffer pH 8.4, 100-ml graduated cylinders, millimeter rulers, goggles, and disposable gloves.

Comments and Pitfalls

1. Some students will have difficulty with the Punnett squares. It might be best to have these as an out-of-class assignment, and go over the solutions with the class.

2. Using Phenotype to Determine Genotype is usually fun for the students and provides material for them to construct a genetic family tree.

3. Practice using micropipets to fill wells in the agarose gel.

Answers to Questions

Activity 1: Working Out Crosses Involving Dominant and Recessive Genes (pp. 484–485)

1. a. 50% Tt, 50% tt; 50% tall, 50% dwarf

   b. 25% TT, 50% Tt, 25% tt; 75% tall, 25% dwarf

2. a. 50% Rr, 50% RR; 100% rough coated, 0% smooth

   b. 50% Rr, 50% rr; 50% rough, 50% smooth

   c. 100% Rr; 100% rough, 0% smooth

Activity 2: Working Out Crosses Involving Incomplete Dominance (pp. 485–486)

1. a. 100% Rr; 100% pink

   b. 50% Rr, 50% rr; 50% pink, 50% white

   c. 25% RR, 50% Rr, 25% rr; 25% red, 50% pink, 25% white

2. a. 100% Ss; 100% sickle-cell trait

   b. 25% SS, 50% Ss, 25% ss; 25% normal hemoglobin, 50% sickle-cell trait, 25% sickle-cell anemia

   c. 50% Ss, 50% ss; 50% sickle-cell trait, 50% sickle-cell anemia

Activity 3: Working Out Crosses Involving Sex-Linked Inheritance (p. 487)

1. 50% will be color blind. 50% of the females and 50% of the males will be color blind. 25% will be carriers. The carriers are females.

2. 50% of the males, 0% of the females. 50% neither exhibit nor carry the allele for hemophilia. 25% of the individuals (50% of the females) will be carriers. The carriers are female.

Activity 4: Exploring Probability (p. 488)

1. b. The tosses are independent and do not influence each other.

   c. The probability of two heads is 25%; one head and one tail, 50%; and two tails, 25%.

2. The probability of a male is 50%; the probability of a female is 50%.

3. Dad's chances are 1/512 or 0.19%. (He should teach his daughters to play!)

Surface Anatomy Roundup

 Time Allotment: 2 hours for a thorough review.

Advance Preparation

1. Have articulated skeletons and skeletal muscle charts and models available.

2. Set out washable markers, hand mirrors, stethoscopes, and alcohol swabs.

Comments and Pitfalls

1. Muscles and other landmarks on the posterior aspect of the body trunk are difficult for students to palpate on themselves. If necessary, ask for volunteers (you may wish to select males) to act as subjects.

Answers to Questions

Activity 1: Palpating Landmarks of the Head (pp. 493–495)

Cranium

3. Scalp wounds bleed profusely. However, because the scalp is so well vascularized, these wounds heal quickly.

Activity 2: Palpating Landmarks of the Neck (pp. 495–497)

Triangles of the Neck

2. They result from damage to the cervical plexus and accessory nerve, which supply these skin regions and muscles.

Activity 3: Palpating Landmarks of the Trunk (pp. 497–499)

The Back: Muscles

1. This action draws the scapula anteriorly and enlarges the triangle of auscultation as much as possible.

Activity 5: Palpating the Landmarks of the Upper Limb (pp. 502–506)

Forearm and Hand

2. In this fracture, the physician can feel that the styloid process of the radius has moved proximally from its normal position.

The Language of Anatomy

Surface Anatomy

1. Match each of the following descriptions with a key equivalent, and record the key letter or term in front of the description.

Key: a. buccal   c. cephalic   e. patellar
      b. calcaneal   d. digital   f. scapular

a; buccal _____ 1. cheek

d; digital _____ 2. pertaining to the fingers

f; scapular _____ 3. shoulder blade region

e; patellar _____ 4. anterior aspect of knee

b; calcaneal _____ 5. heel of foot

c; cephalic _____ 6. pertaining to the head

2. Indicate the following body areas on the accompanying diagram by placing the correct key letter at the end of each line.

Key:

a. abdominal
b. antecubital
c. axillary
d. brachial
e. cervical
f. crural
g. femoral
h. fibular
i. gluteal
j. inguinal
k. lumbar
l. occipital
m. oral
n. popliteal
o. pubic
p. sural
q. thoracic
r. umbilical

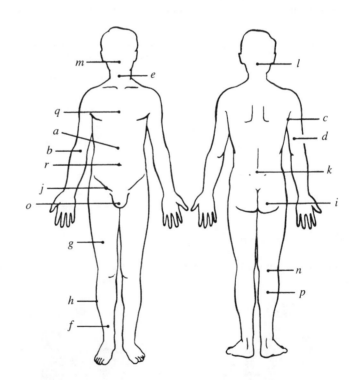

3. Classify each of the terms in the key of question 2 above into one of the large body regions indicated below. Insert the appropriate key letters on the answer blanks.

b, c, d, f, g, h, n, p _____ 1. Appendicular

a, e, i, j, k, l, m, o, q, r _____ 2. Axial

Body Orientation, Direction, Planes, and Sections

4. Describe completely the standard human anatomical position. _Standing erect, feet together, head and toes pointed_

forward, arms hanging at sides with palms forward.

5. Define _section:_ _A cut made along a body plane._

6. Several incomplete statements are listed below. Correctly complete each statement by choosing the appropriate anatomical term from the key. Record the key letters and/or terms on the correspondingly numbered blanks below.

> Key: a. anterior   d. inferior   g. posterior   j. superior
>   b. distal   e. lateral   h. proximal   k. transverse
>   c. frontal   f. medial   i. sagittal

In the anatomical position, the face and palms are on the __1__ body surface; the buttocks and shoulder blades are on the __2__ body surface; and the top of the head is the most __3__ part of the body. The ears are __4__ and __5__ to the shoulders and __6__ to the nose. The heart is __7__ to the vertebral column (spine) and __8__ to the lungs. The elbow is __9__ to the fingers but __10__ to the shoulder. The abdominopelvic cavity is __11__ to the thoracic cavity and __12__ to the spinal cavity. In humans, the dorsal surface can also be called the __13__ surface; however, in quadruped animals, the dorsal surface is the __14__ surface.

If an incision cuts the heart into right and left parts, the section is a __15__ section; but if the heart is cut so that superior and inferior portions result, the section is a __16__ section. You are told to cut a dissection animal along two planes so that the kidneys are observable in both sections. The two sections that meet this requirement are the __17__ and __18__ sections. A section that demonstrates the continuity between the spinal and cranial cavities is a __19__ section.

1. _a; anterior_

2. _g; posterior_

3. _j; superior_

4. _f; medial_

5. _j; superior_

6. _e; lateral_

7. _a; anterior_

8. _f; medial_

9. _h; proximal_

10. _b; distal_

11. _d; inferior_

12. _a; anterior_

13. _g; posterior_

14. _j; superior_

15. _i; sagittal_

16. _k; transverse_

17. _c; frontal_

18. _k; transverse_

19. _i; sagittal_

7. Correctly identify each of the body planes by inserting the appropriate term for each on the answer line below the drawing.

(a)

median (mid-sagittal) plane

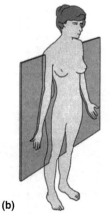

(b)

frontal plane

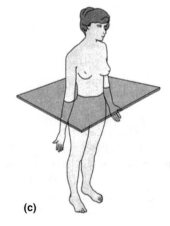

(c)

transverse plane

8. Draw a kidney as it would appear sectioned in three different planes.

frontal section

sagittal section

transverse section

9. Correctly identify each of the nine areas of the abdominal surface by inserting the appropriate term for each of the letters indicated in the drawing.

a. *epigastric region*

b. *right hypochondriac region*

c. *left hypochondriac region*

d. *umbilical region*

e. *right lumbar region*

f. *left lumbar region*

g. *hypogastric (pubic) region*

h. *right iliac region*

i. *left iliac region*

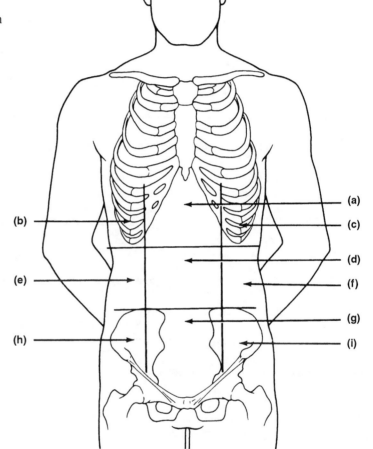

Body Cavities

10. Which body cavity would have to be opened for the following types of surgery? (Insert letter of key choice in same-numbered blank. More than one choice may apply.)

Key: a. abdominopelvic   c. dorsal   e. thoracic
      b. cranial   d. spinal   f. ventral

1. surgery to remove a cancerous lung lobe
2. removal of the uterus or womb
3. removal of a brain tumor
4. appendectomy
5. stomach ulcer operation
6. delivery of pre-operative "saddle" anesthesia

1. *e*
2. *a*
3. *b*
4. *a*
5. *a*
6. *d*

11. Name the muscle that subdivides the ventral body cavity. *diaphragm*

12. Which organ system would not be represented in any of the body cavities? *Skeletal, muscular, integumentary*

13. What are the bony landmarks of the abdominopelvic cavity? *Dorsally, the vertebral column; laterally and anteriorly,*

    the pelvis

14. Which body cavity affords the least protection to its internal structures? *Abdominal*

15. What is the function of the serous membranes of the body? *The serous membranes produce a lubricating fluid that reduces*

    friction as organs slide across one another or against the cavity walls during their functioning.

16. A nurse informs you that she is about to take blood from the antecubital region. What portion of your body should you present to her? *Your arm (the anterior surface of the elbow joint).*

17. The mouth, or oral cavity, and its extension, which stretches through the body to the anus, is not listed as an internal body cavity. Why is this so? *The cavity (lumen) of this digestive tube is continuous with the external environment.*

18. Using the key choices, identify the small body cavities described below.

    Key: a. middle ear cavity   c. oral cavity   e. synovial cavity
           b. nasal cavity   d. orbital cavity

    d; orbital cavity 1. holds the eyes in an anterior-facing position

    c; oral cavity 2. contains the tongue

    e; synovial cavity 3. lines a joint cavity

    a; middle ear cavity 4. houses three tiny bones involved in hearing

    b; nasal cavity 5. contained within the nose

19. On the incomplete flow chart provided below:

    • Fill in the cavity names as appropriate to each box.
    • Then, using either the box numbers or the name of the cavity, identify the descriptions on the following page. (Some may require more than one choice.)

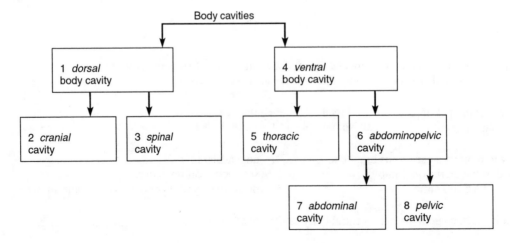

1; dorsal ____ a. contained within the skull and vertebral column

8; pelvic ____ b. contains female reproductive organs

2; cranial ____ c. the most protective body cavity

4; ventral ____ d. its name means belly

5; thoracic ____ e. contains the heart

7; abdominal ____ f. contains the small intestine

5; thoracic ____ g. bounded by the ribs

6; abdominopelvic ____ h. its walls are muscular

Organ Systems Overview

1. Use the key below to indicate the body systems that perform the following functions for the body. Then, circle the organ systems (in the key) that are present in all subdivisions of the ventral body cavity.

Key: a. (cardiovascular)   d. integumentary   g. (nervous)   j. skeletal
      b. digestive   e. (lymphatic/immune) h. reproductive   k. urinary
      c. endocrine   f. muscular   i. respiratory

k; urinary _____ 1. rids the body of nitrogen-containing wastes

c; endocrine _____ 2. is affected by removal of the thyroid gland

j; skeletal _____ 3. provides support and levers on which the muscular system acts

a; cardiovascular _____ 4. includes the heart

c; endocrine (h; reproductive) 5. causes the onset of the menstrual cycle

d; integumentary _____ 6. protects underlying organs from drying out and from mechanical damage

e; lymphatic/immune _____ 7. protects the body; destroys bacteria and tumor cells

b; digestive _____ 8. breaks down ingested food into its building blocks

i; respiratory _____ 9. removes carbon dioxide from the blood

a; cardiovascular _____ 10. delivers oxygen and nutrients to the tissues

f; muscular _____ 11. moves the limbs; facilitates facial expression

k; urinary _____ 12. conserves body water or eliminates excesses

c; endocrine _____ and _h; reproductive_ _____ 13. facilitate conception and childbearing

c; endocrine _____ 14. controls the body by means of chemical molecules called hormones

d; integumentary _____ 15. is damaged when you cut your finger or get a severe sunburn

2. Using the above key, choose the *organ system* to which each of the following sets of organs or body structures belong:

e; lymphatic/immune 1. thymus, spleen, lymphatic vessels

j; skeletal 2. bones, cartilages, tendons

c; endocrine 3. pancreas, pituitary, adrenals

i; respiratory 4. trachea, bronchi, alveoli

k; urinary 5. kidneys, bladder, ureters

h; reproductive 6. testis, vas deferens, urethra

b; digestive 7. esophagus, large intestine, rectum

a; cardiovascular 8. arteries, veins, heart

3. Using the key below, place the following organs in their proper body cavity.

Key: a. abdominopelvic   b. cranial   c. spinal   d. thoracic

a; abdominopelvic 1. stomach   _a; abdominopelvic_ 4. liver   _d; thoracic_ 7. heart

d; thoracic 2. esophagus   _c; spinal_ 5. spinal cord   _d; thoracic_ 8. trachea

a; abdominopelvic 3. large intestine   _a; abdominopelvic_ 6. urinary bladder   _a; abdominopelvic_ 9. rectum

4. Using the organs listed in question 3 above, record, by number, which would be found in the abdominal regions listed below:

_3, 7, 11_ 1. hypogastric region   _1, 3, 5_ 4. epigastric region

_3_ 2. right lumbar region   _3_ 5. left iliac region

_3_ 3. umbilical region   _1, 3, 4_ 6. left hypochondriac region

5. The levels of organization of a living body are chemical, _cell_ , _tissue_ ,

organ , _organ system_ , and organism.

6. Define *organ*: _A body part (or structure) that is made up of two or more tissue types and performs a specific body function, e.g._

the stomach, the kidney.

7. Using the terms provided, correctly identify all of the body organs provided with leader lines in the drawings shown below. Then name the organ systems by entering the name of each on the answer blank below each drawing.

Key:

blood vessels	heart	nerves	spinal cord	urethra
brain	kidney	sensory receptor	ureter	urinary bladder

(a) _nervous system_   (b) _cardiovascular system_   (c) _urinary system_

8. Why is it helpful to study the external and internal structures of the rat? _Many of the external and internal structures are_

similar to those in the human. Studying the rat can help you to understand your own structure.

The Microscope

Care and Structure of the Compound Microscope

1. Label all indicated parts of the microscope.

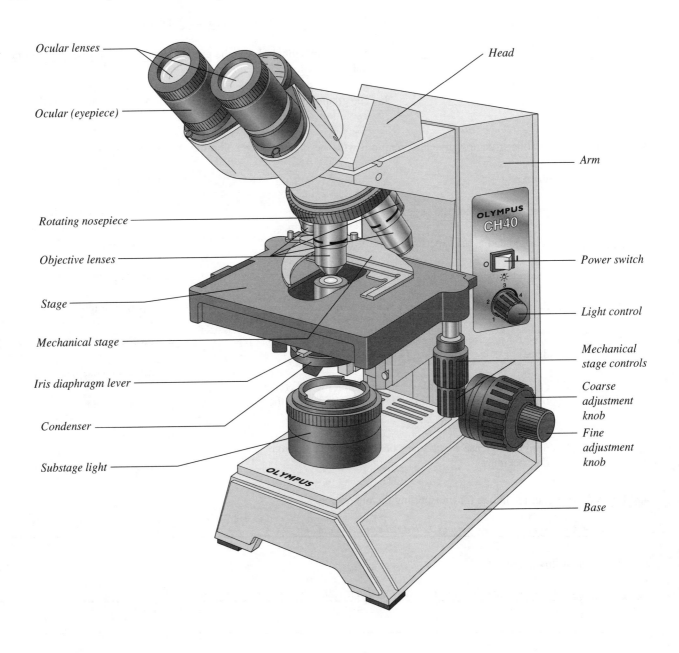

Ocular lenses

Ocular (eyepiece)

Rotating nosepiece

Objective lenses

Stage

Mechanical stage

Iris diaphragm lever

Condenser

Substage light

Head

Arm

OLYMPUS
CH40

Power switch

Light control

Mechanical
stage controls

Coarse
adjustment
knob

Fine
adjustment
knob

Base

OLYMPUS

2. The following statements are true or false. If true, write *T* on the answer blank. If false, correct the statement by writing on the blank the proper word or phrase to replace the one that is underlined.

with grit-free lens paper _____ 1. The microscope lens may be cleaned <u>with any soft tissue.</u>

with l.p. and scanning objectives only _____ 2. The coarse adjustment knob may be used in focusing <u>with all objective lenses.</u>

low-power or scanning _____ 3. The microscope should be stored with the <u>oil immersion</u> lens in position over the stage.

T _____ 4. When beginning to focus, the <u>lowest power</u> lens should be used.

away from _____ 5. When focusing, always focus <u>toward</u> the specimen.

T _____ 6. A coverslip should always be used <u>with wet mounts and the high-power and oil lenses.</u>

greater _____ 7. The greater the amount of light delivered to the objective lens, the <u>less</u> the resolution.

3. Match the microscope structures given in column B with the statements in column A that identify or describe them.

Column A

i _____ 1. platform on which the slide rests for viewing

h _____ 2. lens located at the superior end of the body tube

e _____ 3. secure(s) the slide to the stage

b _____ 4. delivers a concentrated beam of light to the specimen

c _____ 5. used for precise focusing once initial focusing has been done

f _____ 6. carries the objective lenses; rotates so that the different objective lenses can be brought into position over the specimen

d _____ 7. used to increase the amount of light passing through the specimen

Column B

a. coarse adjustment knob

b. condenser

c. fine adjustment knob

d. iris diaphragm

e. mechanical stage or spring clips

f. movable nosepiece

g. objective lenses

h. ocular

i. stage

4. Explain the proper technique for transporting the microscope.

Carry with two hands—one supporting the base, the other holding the arm. _____

5. Define the following terms.

real image: *An image that is inverted, reversed from left to right, and smaller than the object.* _____

_____

virtual image: *An image that is erect and appears to be where it is not.* _____

_____

total magnification: <u>*Magnification of the ocular lens × magnification of the objective lens in use, e.g. h.p. (45×) × ocular (10×) =*</u>

<u>*450×.*</u>

resolution: <u>*Ability to discriminate two closely situated objects as separate.*</u>

Viewing Objects Through the Microscope

6. Complete, or respond to, the following statements:

<u>*working distance*</u>   1. The distance from the bottom of the objective lens in use to the specimen is called the _____.

<u>*100*</u>   2. The resolution of the human eye is approximately _____ μm.

<u>*field*</u>   3. The area of the specimen seen when looking through the microscope is the _____.

<u>*95*</u>   4. If a microscope has a 10× ocular and the total magnification at a particular time is 950×, the objective lens in use at that time is _____ ×.

<u>*increases contrast*</u>   5. Why should the light be dimmed when looking at living (nearly transparent) cells?

<u>*parfocal*</u>   6. If, after focusing in low power, only the fine adjustment need be used to focus the specimen at the higher powers, the microscope is said to be _____.

<u>*0.75*</u>   7. If, when using a 10× ocular and a 15× objective, the field size is 1.5 mm, the approximate field size with a 30× objective is _____ mm.

<u>*0.4*</u>   8. If the size of the high-power field is 1.2 mm, an object that occupies approximately a third of that field has an estimated diameter of _____ mm.

<u>*to the left*</u>   9. Assume there is an object on the left side of the field that you want to bring to the center (that is, toward the apparent right). In what direction would you move your slide?

<u>*away from you*</u>   10. If the object is in the top of the field and you want to move it downward to the center, you would move the slide _____.

7. You have been asked to prepare a slide with the letter *k* on it (as below). In the circle below, draw the *k* as seen in the low-power field.

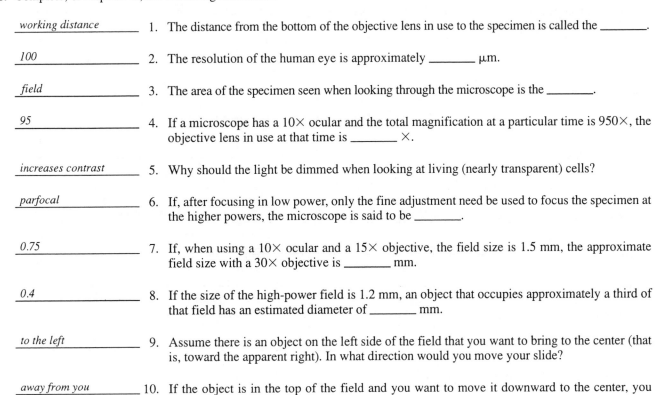

8. The numbers for the field sizes below are too large to represent the typical compound microscope lens system, but the relationships depicted are accurate. Figure out the magnification of fields 1 and 3, and the field size of 2. (*Hint:* Use your ruler.)

1. 5 mm <u>50</u> ×   **2.** <u>2.5</u> mm 100×   **3.** 0.5 mm <u>500</u> ×

9. Say you are observing an object in the low-power field. When you switch to high-power, it is no longer in your field of view.

Why might this occur? <u>*The field decreases proportionately as magnification increases. Therefore, unless the object is centered at*</u>

<u>*low power, it might be outside the higher-power field.*</u>

What should be done initially to prevent this from happening? *Center the object that you wish to view.*

10. Do the following factors increase or decrease as one moves to higher magnifications with the microscope?

resolution *increases (to a point)*   amount of light needed *increases*

working distance *decreases*   depth of field *decreases*

11. A student has the high-dry lens in position and appears to be intently observing the specimen. The instructor, noting a working distance of about 1 cm, knows the student isn't actually seeing the specimen.

How so? *The working distance for the h.p. lens is closer to 1 mm.*

12. Why is it important to be able to use your microscope to perceive depth when studying slides?

So that you can determine the number of cell layers in a tissue specimen and differentiate different cell types.

13. Describe the proper procedure for preparing a wet mount.

Place the specimen on the slide with a medicine dropper. Hold a coverslip with forceps so that the coverslip touches one side of the spec-

*imen drop, and then **slowly** and **carefully** lower the angled coverslip onto the specimen.*

14. Give two reasons why the light should be dimmed when viewing living or unstained material.

Living or unstained material is nearly transparent. Decreasing the light increases contrast. Also, a component of light is heat; therefore,

bright light will "kill" living material.

15. Indicate the probable cause of the following situations arising during use of a microscope.

a. Only half of the field is illuminated: *The lens is not correctly rotated into place.*

b. Field does not change as mechanical stage is moved: *The slide is not correctly positioned in the clamp on the mechanical*

stage and does not move when the mechanical stage moves.

16. Under what circumstances is the stereomicroscope used to study biological specimens? *It is used to view objects that are too*

small to see clearly with the unaided eye, and too large to view with the compound microscope.

The Cell: Anatomy and Division

Anatomy of the Composite Cell

1. Define the following:

    organelle: _Highly organized intracellular structure that performs a specific (metabolic) function(s) for the cell._ _____

    _____

    cell: _The basic structural and functional unit of living organisms._ _____

2. Although cells have differences that reflect their specific functions in the body, what functions do they have in common?

    Ability to metabolize, to reproduce, to grow (increase in mass), to respond to a stimulus, and move. _____

3. Identify the following cell parts:

plasma membrane	1. external boundary of cell; regulates flow of materials into and out of the cell; site of cell signaling
lysosome	2. contains digestive enzymes of many varieties; "suicide sac" of the cell
mitochondria	3. scattered throughout the cell; major site of ATP synthesis
microvilli	4. slender extensions of the plasma membrane that increase its surface area
inclusions	5. stored glycogen granules, crystals, pigments, and so on
Golgi apparatus	6. membranous system consisting of flattened sacs and vesicles; packages proteins for export
nucleus	7. control center of the cell; necessary for cell division and cell life
centrioles	8. two rod-shaped bodies near the nucleus; direct formation of the mitotic spindle
nucleolus	9. dense, darkly staining nuclear body; packaging site for ribosomes
microfilaments	10. contractile elements of the cytoskeleton
rough ER	11. membranous system; involved in intracellular transport of proteins and synthesis of membrane lipids
ribosomes	12. attached to membrane systems or scattered in the cytoplasm; synthesize proteins
chromatin threads	13. threadlike structures in the nucleus; contain genetic material (DNA)
peroxisome	14. site of free radical detoxification

4. In the following diagram, label all parts provided with a leader line.

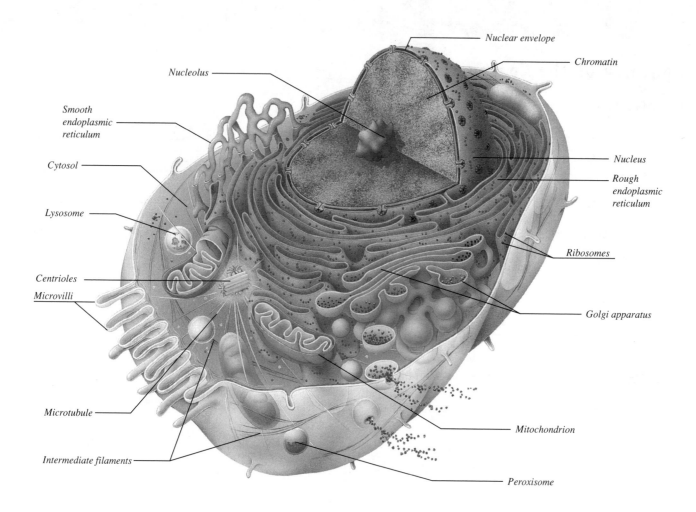

Differences and Similarities in Cell Structure

5. For each of the following cell types, list (a) *one* important structural characteristic observed in the laboratory, and (b) the function that the structure complements or ensures.

squamous epithelium   a. *cells fit closely together like floor tiles*

                       b. *often a lining or covering tissue*

sperm   a. *has a tail or flagellum*

                       b. *allows sperm to propel itself to an egg*

smooth muscle   a. *cells have an elongated shape*

                       b. *a long axis allows a greater degree of shortening*

red blood cells   a. _anucleate, disc-shaped_

b. _large surface area; more "room" to carry hemoglobin_

6. What is the significance of the red blood cell being anucleate (without a nucleus)? _Limited existence. The nucleus is gone;_

therefore, the cell cannot manufacture new proteins, etc.

Did it ever have a nucleus? _Yes_   If so, when? _Before its release into the bloodstream._

7. List the four cells observed from largest to smallest. _(student data)_ _____ _____ _____

Cell Division: Mitosis and Cytokinesis

8. Identify the three phases of mitosis in the following photomicrographs.

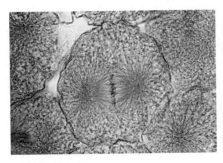   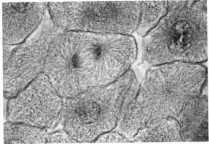   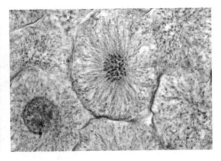

1. _metaphase_   2. _anaphase_   3. _prophase_

9. What is the importance of mitotic cell division? _Provides cells for body growth and for repair of damaged tissue._

10. Draw the phases of mitosis for a cell with a diploid (2N) number of 4.

11. Complete or respond to the following statements:

    Division of the __1__ is referred to as mitosis. Cytokinesis is division of the __2__. The major structural difference between chromatin and chromosomes is that the latter is __3__. Chromosomes attach to the spindle fibers by undivided structures called __4__. If a cell undergoes mitosis but not cytokinesis, the product is __5__. The structure that acts as a scaffolding for chromosomal attachment and movement is called the __6__. __7__ is the period of cell life when the cell is not involved in division. Two cell populations in the body that do not undergo cell division are __8__ and __9__. The implication of an inability of a cell population to divide is that when some of its members die, they are replaced by __10__.

1. _nucleus_

2. _cytoplasm_

3. _coiled/condensed_

4. _centromeres_

5. _a binucleate cell_

6. _spindle_

7. _interphase_

8. _neurons_

9. _skeletal and cardiac muscle cells_

10. _scar (connective) tissue_

12. Using the key, categorize each of the events described below according to the phase in which it occurs.

Key: a. anaphase   b. interphase   c. metaphase   d. prophase   e. telophase

_d_____ 1. Chromatin coils and condenses, forming chromosomes.

_a_____ 2. The chromosomes are V-shaped.

_e_____ 3. The nuclear membrane re-forms.

_e_____ 4. Chromosomes stop moving toward the poles.

_c_____ 5. Chromosomes line up in the center of the cell.

_d_____ 6. The nuclear membrane fragments.

_d_____ 7. The mitotic spindle forms.

_b_____ 8. DNA synthesis occurs.

_b_____ 9. Centrioles replicate.

_d_____ 10. Chromosomes first appear to be duplex structures.

_d_____ 11. Chromosomal centromeres are attached to the kinetochore fibers.

_e_____ 12. Cleavage furrow forms.

_a_____, _d_____ 13. The nuclear membrane(s) is absent.

13. What is the physical advantage of the chromatin coiling and condensing to form short chromosomes at the onset of mitosis?

_Short, compact bodies are mechanically much easier to manipulate during mitosis than are long chromatin threads._____

_____

The Cell: Transport Mechanisms and Permeability—Wet Lab

Choose all answers that apply to items 1 and 2, and place their letters on the response blanks to the right.

1. Molecular motion _a, d_____

    a. reflects the kinetic energy of molecules.   c. is ordered and predictable.
    b. reflects the potential energy of molecules.   d.. is random and erratic.

2. Velocity of molecular movement _b, c_____

    a. is higher in larger molecules.   d. decreases with increasing temperature.
    b. is lower in larger molecules.   e. reflects kinetic energy.
    c. increases with increasing temperature.

3. The following refer to Activity 4, the laboratory experiment using dialysis sacs to study diffusion through nonliving membranes:

Sac 1: 40% glucose suspended in distilled water

    Did glucose pass out of the sac? _yes_____

    Test used to determine presence of glucose: _Benedict's test_____

    Did the sac weight change? _yes_____

    If so, explain the reason for its weight change: _Glucose was passing out of the sac (simple diffusion), but, more_____

    _importantly, water was moving into the sac (osmosis) to the area of its lower concentration._____

Sac 2: 40% glucose suspended in 40% glucose

    Was there net movement of glucose in either direction? _no_____

    Explanation: _Net movement occurs only when there is a concentration gradient._____

    Did the sac weight change? _no_____ Explanation: _Water concentration on both sides of the_____

    _membrane was the same; thus, no net osmosis occurred._____

Sac 3: 10% NaCl in distilled water

    Was there net movement of NaCl out of the sac? _yes_____

    Test used to determine the presence of NaCl: _silver nitrate for the presence of Cl^-_____

    Direction of net osmosis: _into the sac_____

Sac 4:   Sucrose and Congo red dye in distilled water

       Was there net movement of dye out of the sac? _*no*_____

       Was there net movement of sucrose out of the sac? _*no*_____

       Test used to determine sucrose movement from the sac to the beaker and rationale for use of this test: _*Upon boiling,*_

       some of the sucrose bonds are hydrolyzed, releasing glucose and fructose. Using Benedict's test then indicates the presence of

       glucose if sucrose passed through the membrane.

       Direction of net osmosis: _*into the sac*_____

4. What single characteristic of the differentially permeable membranes used in the laboratory determines the substances that

can pass through them? _*Size of pores*_____

In addition to this characteristic, what other factors influence the passage of substances through living membranes?

    Solubility in the lipid portion of the membrane and/or presence of membrane "carriers" for the substance(s).

_____

5. A semipermeable sac containing 4% NaCl, 9% glucose, and 10% albumin is suspended in a solution with the following composition: 10% NaCl, 10% glucose, and 40% albumin. Assume that the sac is permeable to all substances except albumin. State whether each of the following will (a) move into the sac, (b) move out of the sac, or (c) not move.

   glucose: _*a; moves into sac*_____   albumin: _*c; does not move*_____

   water: _*b; moves out of sac*_____   NaCl: _*a; moves into sac*_____

6. The diagrams below represent three microscope fields containing red blood cells. Arrows show the direction of net osmosis.

Which field contains a hypertonic solution? _*c*_____ The cells in this field are said to be _*crenated*_____.

Which field contains an isotonic bathing solution? _*b*_____ Which field contains a hypotonic solution? _*a*_____ What is

happening to the cells in this field? _*Hemolysis; they are bursting as excessive water entry occurs.*_____

_____

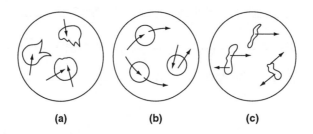

        (a)   (b)   (c)

7. Assume you are conducting the experiment illustrated in the next figure. Both hydrochloric acid (HCl) with a molecular weight of about 36.5 and ammonium hydroxide (NH_4OH) with a molecular weight of 35 are volatile and easily enter the gaseous state. When they meet, the following reaction will occur:

$$HCl + NH_4OH \rightarrow H_2O + NH_4Cl$$

Ammonium chloride (NH₄Cl) will be deposited on the glass tubing as a smoky precipitate where the two gases meet. Predict which gas will diffuse more quickly and indicate to which end of the tube the smoky precipitate will be closer.

a. The faster diffusing gas is _NH₄OH_____.

b. The precipitate forms closer to the _HCl_____ end.

8. What determines whether a transport process is active or passive? _Whether or not the cell must provide ATP for the process;_

if so, the process is active.

9. Characterize membrane transport as fully as possible by choosing all the phrases that apply and inserting their letters on the answer blanks.

Passive processes: _a, c, e_____   Active processes: _b, d, f_____

a. account for the movement of fats and respiratory gases through the plasma membrane
b. explain solute pumping, phagocytosis, and pinocytosis
c. include osmosis, simple diffusion, and filtration
d. may occur against concentration and/or electrical gradients
e. use hydrostatic pressure or molecular energy as the driving force
f. move ions, amino acids, and some sugars across the plasma membrane

10. For the osmometer demonstration (Activity 5), explain why the level of the water column rose during the laboratory session.

The thistle tube was immersed in a dialysis sac which, in turn, was immersed in water. Since water will move down its concentration

gradient if it is able, water diffused from the beaker into the sac, where its concentration was much lower. As a result, the fluid column

(molasses and entering water) rose in the thistle tube.

11. Define the following terms:

diffusion: _Movement of molecules from a region of their higher concentration to an area where they are in lower concentration._

osmosis: _Diffusion of water through a semipermeable or differentially permeable membrane._

simple diffusion: *Diffusion of solutes through a semipermeable membrane.*

filtration: *Passage of substances across a membrane from an area of higher hydrostatic pressure to an area of lower hydrostatic pressure.*

active transport: *A transport system that requires that the cell provide ATP. One such system moves substances across the cell membrane attached to a carrier molecule called a solute pump.*

phagocytosis: *Engulfment of extracellular particles by pseudopod formation. "Cell eating."*

bulk-phase endocytosis: *Intake of extracellular fluids by vesicle formation. "Cell drinking."*

Classification of Tissues

Tissue Structure and Function—General Review

1. Define *tissue:* _A group of cells similar to one another in structure and function._

2. Use the key choices to identify the major tissue types described below.

Key: a. connective tissue   b. epithelium   c. muscle   d. nervous tissue

b; epithelium _____ 1. lines body cavities and covers the body's external surface

c; muscle _____ 2. pumps blood, flushes urine out of the body, allows one to swing a bat

d; nervous c; muscle _____ 3. transmits electrochemical impulses

a; connective _____ 4. anchors, packages, and supports body organs

b; epithelium _____ 5. cells may absorb, secrete, and filter

d; nervous _____ 6. most involved in regulating and controlling body functions

c; muscle _____ 7. major function is to contract

b; epithelium _____ 8. synthesizes hormones

a; connective _____ 9. the most durable tissue type

a; connective _____ 10. abundant nonliving extracellular matrix

a; connective _____ 11. most widespread tissue in the body

d; nervous _____ 12. forms nerves and the brain

Epithelial Tissue

3. Describe five general characteristics of epithelial tissue. _The cells fit closely together, forming sheetlike membranes. Little_

intercellular material between the cells. Avascular; the membrane has a free edge. Generally has a high regenerative capacity.

4. On what bases are epithelial tissues classified? _Cellular arrangement and cell shape._

5. List the six major functions of epithelium in the body, and give examples of each. *(a) Protection—stratified squamous epithe-*

lium (epidermis) of skin and ciliated epithelium of the trachea; (b) absorption and (c) secretion—mucosa of digestive tract;

(d) filtration and (e) excretion— kidney tubule epithelium; (f) sensory reception—free dendritic endings of sensory neurons.

_____

_____

_____

_____

6. How is the function of epithelium reflected in its arrangement? *Stratified epithelia are usually present where increased*

protection is necessary or stretching occurs. Simple epithelia generally have absorptive or secretory functions.

_____

7. Where is ciliated epithelium found? *Lining of the respiratory tract and of the male and female reproductive tracts (vas deferens*

and uterine tubes, respectively).

What role does it play? *In the respiratory tract, it acts to sweep mucus superiorly away from the lungs. In the reproductive tract, it*

acts to propel sperm or ova (male and female tracts respectively) along the tract.

_____

8. Transitional epithelium is actually stratified squamous epithelium, but there is something special about it.

How does it differ structurally from other stratified squamous epithelia? *The surface cells are "plump" rather than flattened.*

_____

How does this reflect its function in the body? *The surface cells have the ability to slide over one another, increasing the internal*

volume of the organ (e.g. bladder) as it fills.

_____

9. How do the endocrine and exocrine glands differ in structure and function? *Endocrine glands are ductless glands. They*

produce hormones, which are liberated directly to the blood. Exocrine glands maintain their ducts and manufacture secretions of

various types (perspiration, oil, digestive enzymes, etc.), which are ducted to the body (or membrane) surface.

_____

10. Respond to the following with the key choices.

Key: a. pseudostratified ciliated columnar   c. simple cuboidal   e. stratified squamous
       b. simple columnar   d. simple squamous   f. transitional

e; stratified squamous _____   1. lining of the esophagus _b; simple columnar_   2. lining of the stomach

d; simple squamous   3. alveolar sacs of lungs

c; simple cuboidal   4. tubules of the kidney

e; stratified squamous   5. epidermis of the skin

f; transitional   6. lining of bladder; peculiar cells that have the ability to slide over each other

d; simple squamous   7. forms the thin serous membranes; a single layer of flattened cells

Connective Tissue

11. What are three general characteristics of connective tissues? _Connective tissue is composed of many diverse cell types. The bulk of most connective tissue is nonliving extracellular material (matrix) produced by the cells and then extruded to their exterior. The matrix provides the strength and supportive function associated with connective tissues. Most types are well vascularized._

12. What functions are performed by connective tissue? _Protection, support, and the binding together of other body tissues._

13. How are the functions of connective tissue reflected in its structure? _Living cells are soft and fragile. The large amount of nonliving matrix (containing fibers) seen provides the strength needed for the normal functions of connective tissues._

14. Using the key, choose the best response to identify the connective tissues described below.

c; dense   1. attaches bones to bones and muscles to bones

a; adipose   2. acts as a storage depot for fat

c; dense   3. the dermis of the skin

e; fibrocartilage   4. makes up the intervertebral discs

h; osseous   5. forms your hip bone

b; areolar   6. composes basement membranes; a soft packaging tissue with a jellylike matrix

g; hyaline cartilage   7. forms the larynx, the costal cartilages of the ribs, and the embryonic skeleton

d; elastic cartilage   8. provides a flexible framework for the external ear

g; hyaline cartilage   9. firm, structurally amorphous matrix heavily invaded with fibers; appears glassy and smooth

h; osseous   10. matrix hard owing to calcium salts; provides levers for muscles to act on

a; adipose   11. insulates against heat loss

Key:
a. adipose connective tissue
b. areolar connective tissue
c. dense connective tissue
d. elastic cartilage
e. fibrocartilage
f. hematopoietic tissue
g. hyaline cartilage
h. osseous tissue

15. Why do adipose cells remind people of a ring with a single jewel? _They contain a large fat-filled vacuole occupying most of the cell volume. The nucleus is pushed to the periphery, giving the cell a "signet ring" appearance._

Muscle Tissue

16. The three types of muscle tissue exhibit similarities as well as differences. Check the appropriate space in the chart to indicate which muscle types exhibit each characteristic.

Characteristic	Skeletal	Cardiac	Smooth
Voluntarily controlled	✓		
Involuntarily controlled		✓	✓
Striated	✓	✓	
Has a single nucleus in each cell		✓	✓
Has several nuclei per cell	✓		
Found attached to bones	✓		
Allows you to direct your eyeballs	✓		
Found in the walls of the stomach, uterus, and arteries			✓
Contains spindle-shaped cells			✓
Contains branching cylindrical cells		✓	
Contains long, nonbranching cylindrical cells	✓		
Has intercalated discs		✓	
Concerned with locomotion of the body as a whole	✓		
Changes the internal volume of an organ as it contracts		✓	✓
Tissue of the heart		✓	

Nervous Tissue

17. What two physiological characteristics are highly developed in neurons (nerve cells)? _Irritability and conductivity._

18. In what ways are neurons similar to other cells? _They contain a nucleus and the usual organelles._

How are they different? _Their cytoplasm is drawn out into long processes._

19. Sketch a neuron, recalling in your diagram the most important aspects of its structure. Below the diagram, describe how its particular structure relates to its function in the body.

Neurons conduct impulses over relatively long distances in the body. This is facilitated by their long cytoplasmic extensions.

For Review

20. Label the following tissue types here and on the next pages, and identify all major structures—cell types, matrix (ground substance and fibers), fat vacuole, basement membrane—if present.

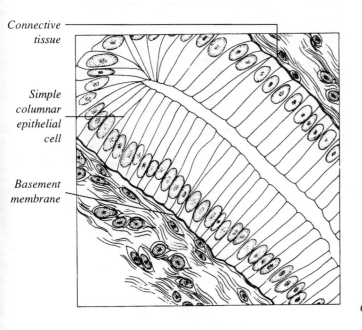

Connective tissue

Simple columnar epithelial cell

Basement membrane

(a) _Simple columnar epithelial_

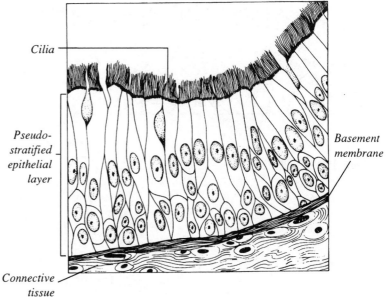

Cilia

Pseudo-stratified epithelial layer

Basement membrane

Connective tissue

(b) _Pseudostratified ciliated columnar epithelial_

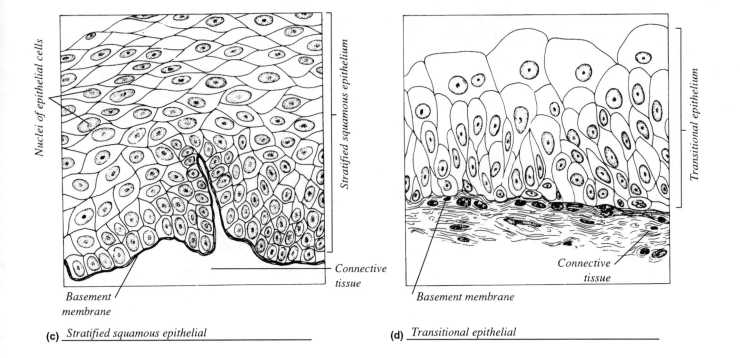

Nuclei of epithelial cells

Stratified squamous epithelium

Connective tissue

Basement membrane

(c) _Stratified squamous epithelial_

Transitional epithelium

Connective tissue

Basement membrane

(d) _Transitional epithelial_

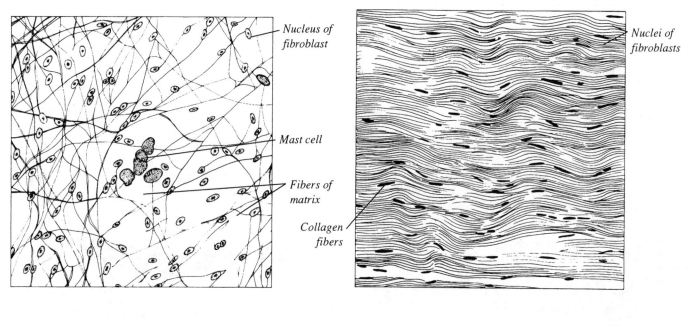

Nucleus of fibroblast

Mast cell

Fibers of matrix

Nuclei of fibroblasts

Collagen fibers

(e) _Areolar connective tissue_

(f) _Dense fibrous connective_

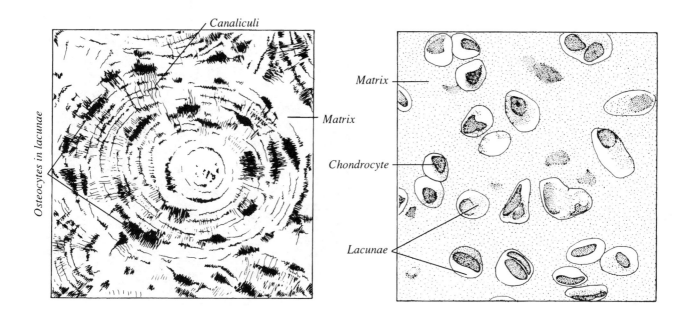

(g) _Osseous tissue_

(h) _Hyaline cartilage_

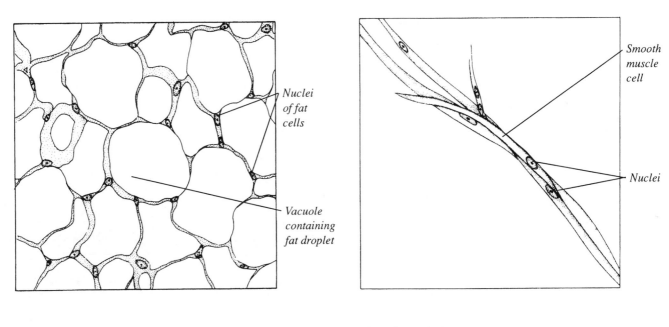

(i) _Adipose tissue_

(j) _Smooth muscle tissue_

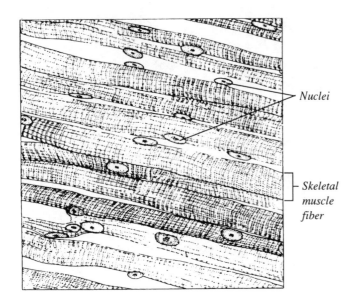

Nuclei

Skeletal
muscle
fiber

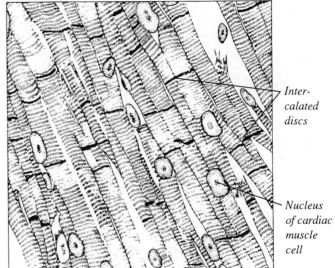

Inter-
calated
discs

Nucleus
of cardiac
muscle
cell

(k) Skeletal muscle tissue

(l) Cardiac muscle tissue

The Integumentary System

Basic Structure of the Skin

1. Complete the following statements by writing the appropriate word or phrase on the correspondingly numbered blank:

The two basic tissues of which the skin is composed are dense irregular connective tissue, which makes up the dermis, and __1__, which forms the epidermis. The tough water-repellent protein found in the epidermal cells is called __2__. The pigments melanin and __3__ contribute to skin color. A localized concentration of melanin is referred to as a __4__.

1. *stratified squamous epithelium*

2. *keratin*

3. *carotene*

4. *freckle*

2. Four protective functions of the skin are *Prevents dessication, protects against thermal damage, prevents bacterial invasion, and*

protects against UV radiation. .

3. Using the key choices, choose all responses that apply to the following descriptions.

Key: a. stratum basale
       b. stratum corneum
       c. stratum granulosum

       d. stratum lucidum
       e. stratum spinosum
       f. papillary layer

       g. reticular layer
       h. epidermis as a whole
       i. dermis as a whole

d; stratum lucidum　　　　1. translucent cells in thick skin containing keratin fibrils

b & d; strata corneum and lucidum　　　2. dead cells

f; papillary layer　　　　3. dermis layer responsible for fingerprints

i; dermis (or f, g)　　　　4. vascular region

h; epidermis　　　　5. major skin area that produces derivatives (nails and hair)

a; stratum basale　　　　6. epidermal region exhibiting the most rapid cell division

b; stratum corneum　　　　7. scalelike dead cells, full of keratin, that constantly slough off

e; stratum spinosum　　　　8. mitotic cells filled with intermediate filaments

i; dermis (or g)　　　　9. has abundant elastic and collagenic fibers

a; stratum basale　　　　10. location of melanocytes and Merkel cells

e; stratum spinosum　　　　11. area where weblike prekeratin filaments first appear

f; papillary layer　　　　12. region of areolar connective tissue

4. Label the skin structures and areas indicated in the accompanying diagram of thin skin. Then, complete the statements that follow.

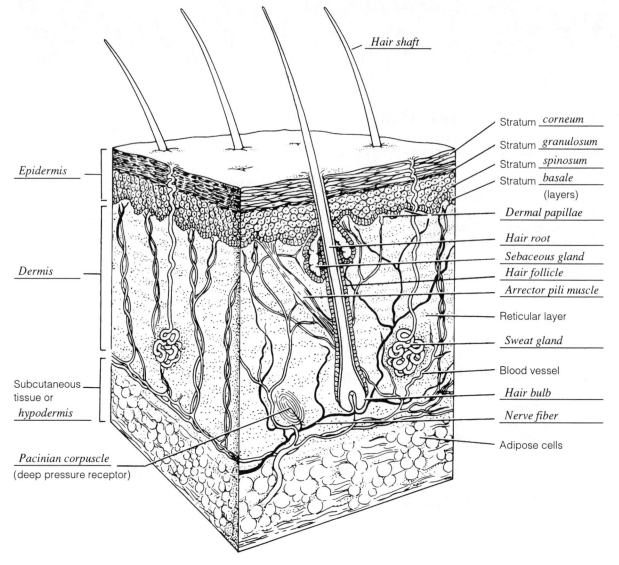

Hair shaft

Stratum *corneum*
Stratum *granulosum*
Stratum *spinosum*
Stratum *basale*
(layers)

Epidermis

Dermal papillae

Hair root
Sebaceous gland
Hair follicle
Arrector pili muscle

Dermis

Reticular layer

Sweat gland

Blood vessel

Subcutaneous tissue or *hypodermis*

Hair bulb

Nerve fiber

Adipose cells

Pacinian corpuscle
(deep pressure receptor)

a. <u>*Laminated (or lamellated)*</u> granules extruded from the keratinocytes prevent water loss by diffusion through the epidermis.

b. Fibers in the dermis are produced by <u>*fibroblasts*</u>.

c. Glands that respond to rising androgen levels are the <u>*sebaceous (and apocrine sweat)*</u> glands.

d. Phagocytic cells that occupy the epidermis are called <u>*Langerhans' cells*</u>.

e. A unique touch receptor formed from a stratum basale cell and a nerve fiber is a <u>*Merkel disc*</u>.

f. What layer is present in thick skin but not in thin skin? <u>*Stratum lucidum*</u>

g. What cell-to-cell structures hold the cells of the stratum spinosum tightly together? <u>*Desmosomes*</u>

5. What substance is manufactured in the skin (but is not a secretion) to play a role elsewhere in the body?

<u>*Vitamin D*</u>

6. List the sensory receptors found in the dermis of the skin. *Pain, pressure, touch, heat, and cold.*

7. A nurse tells a doctor that a patient is cyanotic. Define cyanosis. *A blue cast to the skin.*

What does its presence imply? *Inadequate oxygenation of the blood.*

8. What is the mechanism of a suntan? *When exposed to UV radiation, the melanocytes produce more protective melanin and the skin becomes more brown in color.*

9. What is a bedsore (decubitus ulcer) ? *Localized area of tissue necrosis and death.*

Why does it occur? *Pressure areas (points of increased pressure over bony areas) restrict the blood supply to the area.*

10. Some injections hurt more than others. On the basis of what you have learned about skin structure, can you determine why this is so? *It depends on the relative number of pain receptors stimulated.*

Appendages of the Skin

11. Using key choices, respond to the following descriptions.

Key: a. arrector pili   d. hair follicle   g. sweat gland—apocrine
       b. cutaneous receptors   e. nail   h. sweat gland—eccrine
       c. hair   f. sebaceous glands

f; sebaceous glands   1. produces an accumulation of oily material that is known as a blackhead

a; arrector pili   2. tiny muscles, attached to hair follicles, that pull the hair upright during fright or cold

h; sweat gland—eccrine   3. perspiration glands with a role in temperature control

d; hair follicle   4. sheath formed of both epithelial and connective tissues

g; sweat gland—apocrine   5. less numerous type of perspiration-producing gland; found mainly in the pubic and axillary regions

f; sebaceous glands   6. found everywhere on body except palms of hands and soles of feet

c, e; hair, nail   7. primarily dead/keratinized cells

b; cutaneous receptors   8. specialized nerve endings that respond to temperature, touch, etc

f; sebaceous glands   9. its secretion is a lubricant for hair and skin

e; nail   10. "sports" a lunula and a cuticle

12. Describe two integumentary system mechanisms that help in regulating body temperature. *(1) When capillary blood flow to the skin is enhanced (by nervous system controls), heat radiates from the skin surface; restriction of blood flow conserves body heat. (2) Activity of sweat glands, i.e., when perspiration evaporates from the skin surface, heat is lost.*

13. Several structures or skin regions are listed below. Identify each by matching its letter with the appropriate area on the figure.

a. Adipose cells

b. Dermis

c. Epidermis

d. Hair follicle

e. Hair shaft

f. Sloughing stratum corneum cells

Plotting the Distribution of Sweat Glands

14. With what substance in the bond paper does the iodine painted on the skin react? *The starch*

15. Based on class data, which skin area—the forearm or palm of hand—has more sweat glands? *Palm*

Was this an expected result? *Yes* Explain. *For most people, hands sweat more than the forearm.*

Which other body areas would, if tested, prove to have a high density of sweat glands? *Face, axillae*

16. What organ system controls the activity of the eccrine sweat glands? *Nervous system (sympathetic division)*

Dermography: Fingerprinting

17. Why can fingerprints be used to identify individuals?

Everyone's fingerprints are genetically distinct.

18. Name the three common fingerprint patterns.

loops , *arches* , and *whorls*

Classification of Covering and Lining Membranes

Classification of Body Membranes

1. Complete the following chart:

Membrane	Tissue types: membrane composition (epithelial/connective)	Common locations	General functions
cutaneous	*epithelial, connective*	*The skin*	*Secretion (oil, sweat) Waterproofing (keratin) Bacteriostatic (acid mantle and sebum) Protection against chemical and mechanical damage (keratinization and continuity)*
mucous	*epithelial, connective (lamina propria)*	*Lining of the digestive, respiratory, and urogenital tracts*	*Secretion (mucus) Absorption Ciliated for movement of substances*
serous	*epithelial, connective*	*Lining of closed ventral body cavities*	*Secretion (serous fluid); decreases friction*
synovial	*connective tissue*	*Lining of joint cavities of freely movable joints*	*Secretion (synovial fluid); decreases friction*

2. Respond to the following statements by choosing an answer from the key.

Key: a. cutaneous   b. mucous   c. serous   d. synovial

_d_ 1. membrane type in joints, bursae, and tendon sheaths

_c_ 2. epithelium is always simple squamous epithelium

_a_, _d_ 3. membrane types *not* found in the ventral body cavity

_b_ 4. the only membrane type in which goblet cells are found

_a_ 5. the dry membrane with keratinizing epithelium

_b, c, d_ 6. "wet" membranes

_b_ 7. adapted for absorption and secretion

_c_ 8. has parietal and visceral layers

3. Using terms from the list above the figure, identify specifically the different types of body membranes (cutaneous, mucous, serous, and synovial) by writing in the terms at the end of the appropriate leader lines.

a. cutaneous membrane (skin)
b. esophageal mucosa
c. gastric mucosa
d. nasal mucosa
e. oral mucosa
f. mucosa of lung bronchi

g. parietal pericardium
h. parietal pleura
i. synovial membrane of joint
j. tracheal mucosa
k. visceral pericardium
l. visceral pleura

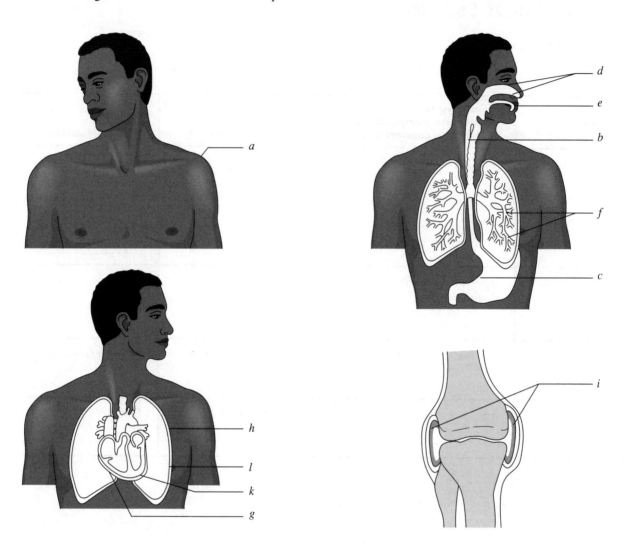

4. Use the terms in question 3 to make a list of the two types of membranes below.

The mucous membranes are ___*b, c, d, e, f, j*___

_____

The serous membranes are ___*g, h*___

_____

5. a. The serous membranes covering the lungs are the _visceral_ and _parietal pleurae_ .

    b. The serous membranes covering the heart are the _visceral_ and _parietal pericardium_ .

    c. The serous membranes covering the organs of the abdominopelvic cavity are the _visceral_ and _parietal peritoneums_ .

6. Knowing that *-itis* is a sufix meaning "inflammation of," what do peritonitis, pleurisy, and pericarditis (pathological conditions) have in common? _All are inflammations of serous membranes._

7. Why are these conditions accompanied by a great deal of pain? _When serous membranes become inflamed, insufficient serous fluid may be produced. As a result, friction increases and adhesions may form._

Overview of the Skeleton: Classification and Structure of Bones and Cartilages

Bone Markings

1. Match the terms in column B with the appropriate description in column A:

Column A		Column B
l; spine	1. sharp, slender process*	a. condyle
n; tubercle	2. small rounded projection*	b. crest
b; crest	3. narrow ridge of bone*	c. epicondyle
o; tuberosity	4. large rounded projection*	d. fissure
g; head	5. structure supported on neck†	e. foramen
j; ramus	6. armlike projection†	f. fossa
a; condyle	7. rounded, convex projection†	g. head
d; fissure	8. narrow depression or opening‡	h. meatus
h; meatus	9. canal-like structure‡	i. process
e; foramen	10. opening through a bone‡	j. ramus
f; fossa	11. shallow depression†	k. sinus
k; sinus	12. air-filled cavity	l. spine
m; trochanter	13. large, irregularly shaped projection*	m. trochanter
c; epicondyle	14. raised area of a condyle*	n. tubercle
i; process	15. projection or prominence	o. tuberosity

* A site of muscle attachment.
† Takes part in joint formation.
‡ A passageway for nerves or blood vessels.

Classification of Bones

2. The four major anatomical classifications of bones are long, short, flat, and irregular. Which category has the least amount of spongy bone relative to its total volume? _Long_

3. Classify each of the bones in the next chart into one of the four major categories by checking the appropriate column. Use appropriate references as necessary.

	Long	Short	Flat	Irregular
humerus	✓			
phalanx	✓			
parietal			✓	
calcaneus		✓		
rib			✓	
vertebra				✓
ulna	✓			

Gross Anatomy of the Typical Long Bone

4. Use the terms below to identify the structures marked by leader lines and braces in the diagrams (some terms are used more than once).

Key A: a. articular cartilage
        b. compact bone
        c. diaphysis
        d. endosteum

        e. epiphyseal line
        f. epiphysis
        g. medullary cavity
        h. nutrient artery

        i. periosteum
        j. red marrow cavity
        k. trabeculae of spongy bone
        l. yellow marrow

Key B: b. compact bone
        d. endosteum
        i. periosteum
        l. yellow marrow

Key C: b. compact bone
        i. periosteum
        k. trabeculae of spongy bone

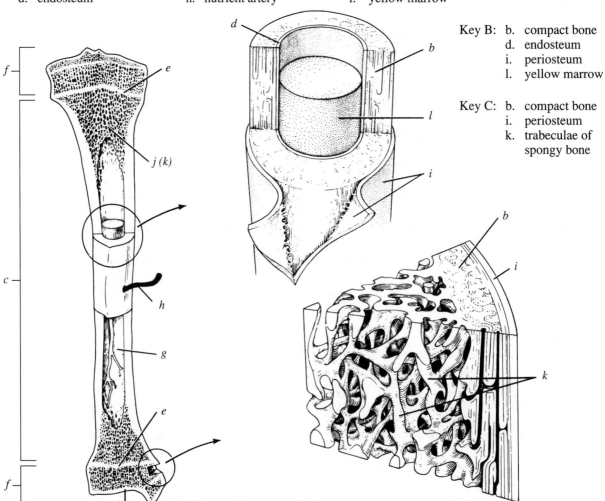

5. Match the terms in question 1 with the information below.

_f_ ____ 1. contains spongy bone in adults   _c_ ____ 5. scientific term for bone shaft

_c_ ____ 2. made of compact bone   _g (l)_ ____ 6. contains fat in adult bones

_j_ ____ 3. site of blood cell formation   _e_ ____ 7. growth plate remnant

_d_ ____, _i_ ____ 4. major submembranous site of osteoclasts   _i_ ____ 8. major submembranous site of osteoblasts

6. What differences between compact and spongy bone can be seen with the naked eye? _Compact bone appears homogeneous;_ _spongy bone has obvious spaces._

7. What is the function of the periosteum? _Protects the bone and is the structure from which blood vessels and nerves enter bone._

Microscopic Structure of Compact Bone

8. Trace the route taken by nutrients through a bone, starting with the periosteum and ending with an osteocyte in a lacuna.

Periosteum ___→_____ _perforating canal_ ___→_____

___central (Haversian) canal_____ ___→___ _canaliculus_ ___→___ osteocyte

9. Several descriptions of bone structure are given below. Identify the structure involved by choosing the appropriate term from the key and placing its letter in the blank. Then, on the photomicrograph of bone on the right (208×), identify all structures named in the key and bracket an osteon.

Key: a. canaliculi   b. central canal   c. concentric lamellae   d. lacunae   e. matrix

_c_ ____ 1. layers of bony matrix around a central canal

_d_ ____ 2. site of osteocytes

_b_ ____ 3. longitudinal canal carrying blood vessels, lymphatics, and nerves

_a_ ____ 4. minute canals connecting osteocytes of an osteon

_e_ ____ 5. inorganic salts deposited in organic ground substance

Ossification: Bone Formation and Growth in Length

10. How does the appearance of the chondrocytes in the transformation zone differ from those in the growth zone?

Those in the transformation zone are much larger (hypertrophied).

11. Compare and contrast events occurring on the epiphyseal and diaphyseal faces of the epiphyseal plate.

Epiphyseal face: _Cartilage matrix is being laid down._

Diaphyseal face: _Cartilage matrix is being eroded and replaced by bone matrix._

Chemical Composition of Bone

12. What is the function of the organic matrix in bone? *To provide flexibility (and strength).*

13. Name the important organic bone components. *Collagenic and elastic fibers and ground substances; cells.*

14. Calcium salts form the bulk of the inorganic material in bone. What is the function of the calcium salts?

To provide hardness and strength.

15. Baking removes *water* from bone. Soaking bone in acid removes *calcium salts*.

16. Which is responsible for bone structure? (circle the appropriate response)

inorganic portion   organic portion   (both contribute)

Cartilages of the Skeleton

17. Using key choices, identify each type of cartilage described (in terms of its body location or function) below.

Key: a. elastic   b. fibrocartilage   c. hyaline

a; elastic   1. supports the external ear

b; fibrocartilage   2. between the vertebrae

c; hyaline   3. forms the walls of the voice box (larynx)

a; elastic   4. the epiglottis

c; hyaline   5. articular cartilages

b; fibrocartilage   6. meniscus in a knee joint

c; hyaline   7. connects the ribs to the sternum

b; fibrocartilage   8. most effective at resisting compression

a; elastic   9. most springy and flexible

c; hyaline   10. most abundant

18. Identify the two types of cartilage diagrammed below. On each, label the *chondrocytes in lacunae* and the *matrix.*

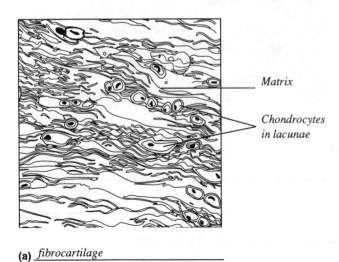

— Matrix

— Chondrocytes in lacunae

(a) *fibrocartilage*

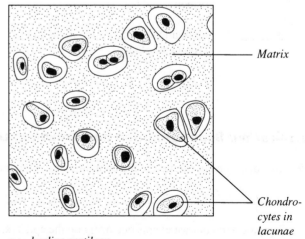

— Matrix

— Chondrocytes in lacunae

(b) *hyaline cartilage*

The Axial Skeleton

The Skull

1. The skull is one of the major components of the axial skeleton. Name the other two:

vertebral column _____ and _bony thorax_ _____

What structures do each of these areas protect? _The vertebral column protects the spinal cord. The bony thorax protects the heart,_

lungs, esophagus, and great vessels (aorta and venae cavae) of the thorax. The skull protects the brain.

_____

2. Define *suture*: _Fibrous joint between skull bones._ _____

3. With one exception, the skull bones are joined by sutures. Name the exception. _Joint(s) between the mandible and temporal_

bones. _____

4. What are the four major sutures of the skull, and what bones do they connect?

a. _Sagittal suture: Parietal bones._ _____

b. _Coronal suture: Parietal bones and frontal bone._ _____

c. _Squamous suture: Parietal bone and temporal bone._ _____

d. _Lambdoidal suture: Parietal bones and occipital bone._ _____

5. Name the eight bones of the cranium.

frontal _____ _occipital_ _____ _right parietal_ _____ _left parietal_ _____

sphenoid _____ _ethmoid_ _____ _right temporal_ _____ _left temporal_ _____

6. Give two possible functions of the sinuses. _(1) Lighten the skull, (2) resonance chambers for speech._

_____

7. What is the orbit? _Bony socket for the eye._ _____

What bones contribute to the formation of the orbit? _Ethmoid, lacrimal, frontal, sphenoid, zygomatic, maxillary, palatine_

_____

8. Why can the sphenoid bone be called the keystone of the cranial floor? _It articulates with all of the other cranial bones._

_____

9. What is a cleft palate? *An opening in the palate resulting in a continuity between the oral and nasal cavities due to the failure of the*

palatine bones or palatine processes of the maxillary bones to fuse properly.

10. Match the bone names in column B with the descriptions in column A.

Column A

Column B

b; frontal _____ 1. forehead bone

n; zygomatic _____ 2. cheekbone

a. ethmoid

e; mandible _____ 3. lower jaw

b. frontal

g; nasal _____ 4. bridge of nose

c. hyoid

i; palatine _____ 5. posterior bones of the hard palate

d. lacrimal

j; parietal _____ 6. much of the lateral and superior cranium

e. mandible

h; occipital _____ 7. most posterior part of cranium

f. maxilla

k; sphenoid _____ 8. single, irregular, bat-shaped bone forming part of the cranial floor

g. nasal

d; lacrimal _____ 9. tiny bones bearing tear ducts

h. occipital

f; maxilla _____ 10. anterior part of hard palate

i. palatine

a; ethmoid _____ 11. superior and medial nasal conchae formed from its projections

j. parietal

l; temporal _____ 12. site of mastoid process

k. sphenoid

k; sphenoid _____ 13. site of sella turcica

l. temporal

a; ethmoid _____ 14. site of cribriform plate

m. vomer

e; mandible _____ 15. site of mental foramen

n. zygomatic

l; temporal _____ 16. site of styloid processes

a; ethmoid _____, *b; frontal* _____, *f; maxilla* _____, and

k; sphenoid _____ 17. four bones containing paranasal sinuses

h; occipital _____ 18. condyles here articulate with the atlas

h; occipital _____ 19. foramen magnum contained here

c; hyoid _____ 20. small U-shaped bone in neck, where many tongue muscles attach

l; temporal _____ 21. middle ear found here

m; vomer (a; ethmoid) _____ 22. nasal septum

a; ethmoid _____ 23. bears an upward protrusion, the "cock's comb," or crista galli

e; mandible _____, *f; maxilla* _____ 24. contain alveoli bearing teeth

11. Using choices from the numbered key to the right, identify all bones and bone markings provided with leader lines in the two diagrams below.

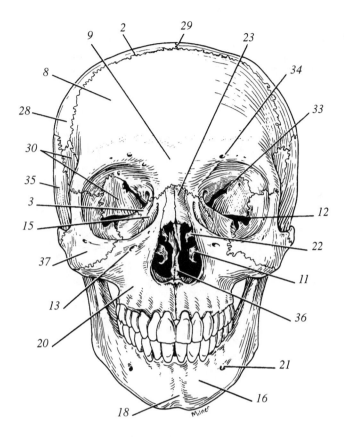

1. carotid canal
2. coronal suture
3. ethmoid bone
4. external occipital protuberance
5. foramen lacerum
6. foramen magnum
7. foramen ovale
8. frontal bone
9. glabella
10. incisive fossa
11. inferior nasal concha
12. inferior orbital fissure
13. infraorbital foramen
14. jugular foramen
15. lacrimal bone
16. mandible
17. mandibular fossa
18. mandibular symphysis
19. mastoid process
20. maxilla
21. mental foramen
22. middle nasal concha of ethmoid
23. nasal bone
24. occipital bone
25. occipital condyle
26. palatine bone
27. palatine process of maxilla
28. parietal bone
29. sagittal suture
30. sphenoid bone
31. styloid process
32. stylomastoid foramen
33. superior orbital fissure
34. supraorbital foramen
35. temporal bone
36. vomer
37. zygomatic bone
38. zygomatic process of temporal bone

The Vertebral Column

12. Using the key, correctly identify the vertebral parts/areas described below. (More than one choice may apply in some cases.) Also use the key letters to correctly identify the vertebral areas in the diagram.

Key: a. body
   b. intervertebral foramina
   c. lamina

   d. pedicle
   e. spinous process
   f. superior articular process

   g. transverse process
   h. vertebral arch
   i. vertebral foramen

<u>*i*</u> 1. cavity enclosing the nerve cord

<u>*a*</u> 2. weight-bearing portion of the vertebra

<u>*e, g*</u> 3. provide levers against which muscles pull

<u>*a, g*</u> 4. provide an articulation point for the ribs

<u>*b*</u> 5. openings providing for exit of spinal nerves

<u>*a, h*</u> 6. structures that form an enclosure for the spinal cord

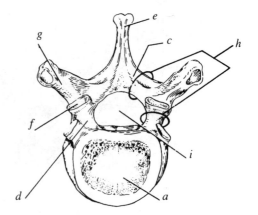

13. The distinguishing characteristics of the vertebrae composing the vertebral column are noted below. Correctly identify each described structure/region by choosing a response from the key.

Key: a. atlas
   b. axis
   c. cervical vertebra—typical

   d. coccyx
   e. lumbar vertebra

   f. sacrum
   g. thoracic vertebra

<u>*c; cervical (also a & b)*</u> 1. vertebral type containing foramina in the transverse processes, through which the vertebral arteries ascend to reach the brain

<u>*b; axis*</u> 2. dens here provides a pivot for rotation of the first cervical vertebra (C_1)

<u>*g; thoracic*</u> 3. transverse processes faceted for articulation with ribs; spinous process pointing sharply downward

<u>*f; sacrum*</u> 4. composite bone; articulates with the hip bone laterally

<u>*e; lumbar*</u> 5. massive vertebrae; weight-sustaining

<u>*d; coccyx*</u> 6. "tail bone"; vestigial fused vertebrae

<u>*a; atlas*</u> 7. supports the head; allows a rocking motion in conjunction with the occipital condyles

<u>*c; cervical (also a & b)*</u> 8. seven components; unfused

<u>*g; thoracic*</u> 9. twelve components; unfused

14. Identify specifically each of the vertebra types shown in the diagrams below. Also identify and label the following markings on each: transverse processes, spinous process, body, superior articular processes.

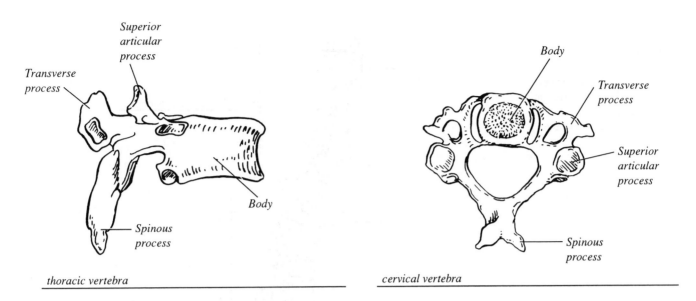

Superior articular process

Transverse process

Body

Spinous process

thoracic vertebra

Body

Transverse process

Superior articular process

Spinous process

cervical vertebra

15. Describe how a spinal nerve exits from the vertebral column. _Via the intervertebral foramina found between the pedicles of_

adjacent vertebrae.

16. Name two factors/structures that allow for flexibility of the vertebral column.

Intervertebral discs and _curvatures_

17. What kind of tissue composes the intervertebral discs? _Fibrocartilage_

18. What is a herniated disc? _A ruptured disc in which a portion of the disc protrudes outward._

What problems might it cause? _It might compress a nerve, leading to pain and possibly paralysis._

19. Which two spinal curvatures are obvious at birth? _Thoracic_ and

sacral

Under what conditions do the secondary curvatures develop? _The cervical curvature develops when the baby begins to raise its_

head independently. The lumbar curvature forms when the baby begins to walk (assumes upright posture).

20. On this illustration of an articulated vertebral column, identify each curvature indicated and label it as a primary or a secondary curvature. Also identify the structures provided with leader lines, using the letters of the terms listed below.

a.   atlas
b.   axis
c.   a disc
d.   two thoracic vertebrae
e.   two lumbar vertebrae
f.   sacrum
g.   vertebra prominens

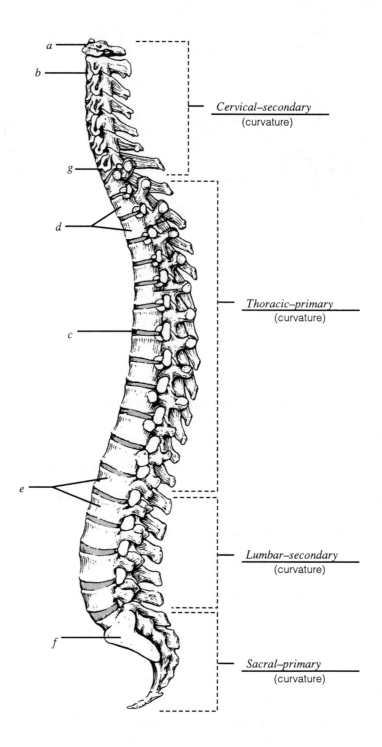

Cervical–secondary
(curvature)

Thoracic–primary
(curvature)

Lumbar–secondary
(curvature)

Sacral–primary
(curvature)

21. Diagram the abnormal spinal curvatures named below. (Use posterior or lateral views as necessary and label the views shown.)

Lordosis	Scoliosis	Kyphosis
Lateral view	*Posterior view*	*Lateral view*

P ⎰ *A*

Arrows indicate area(s) of exaggerated curvature

The Bony Thorax

22. The major components of the thorax (excluding the vertebral column) are the <u>ribs</u>

and the <u>sternum</u>.

23. Differentiate between a true rib and a false rib. <u>A true rib has its own costal cartilage attachment to the sternum; a false rib at-</u>

<u>taches indirectly or not at all.</u>

Is a floating rib a true or a false rib? <u>False</u>

24. What is the general shape of the thoracic cage? <u>Inverted cone shape</u>

25. Provide the more scientific name for the following rib types.

a. True ribs <u>Vertebrosternal ribs</u>

b. False ribs (not including c) <u>Vertebrochondral ribs</u>

c. Floating ribs <u>Vertebral ribs</u>

26. Using the terms at the right, identify the regions and landmarks of the bony thorax.

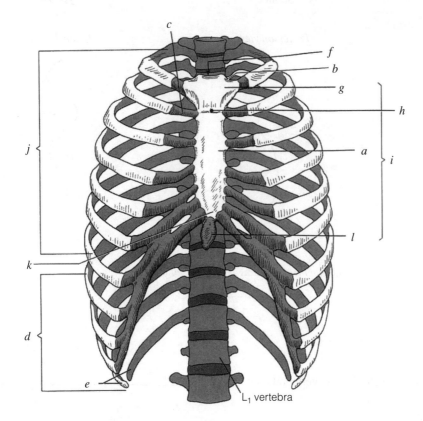

L₁ vertebra

a. body

b. clavicular notch

c. costal cartilage

d. false ribs

e. floating ribs

f. jugular notch

g. manubrium

h. sternal angle

i. sternum

j. true ribs

k. xiphisternal joint

l. xiphoid process

The Appendicular Skeleton

Bones of the Pectoral Girdle and Upper Extremity

1. Match the bone names or markings in column B with the descriptions in column A.

Column A

g; deltoid tuberosity 1. raised area on lateral surface of humerus to which deltoid muscle attaches

i; humerus 2. arm bone

d; clavicle , _p; scapula_ 3. bones of the shoulder girdle

o; radius , _t; ulna_ 4. forearm bones

a; acromion 5. scapular region to which the clavicle connects

p; scapula 6. shoulder girdle bone that is unattached to the axial skeleton

d; clavicle 7. shoulder girdle bone that transmits forces from the upper limb to the bony thorax

h; glenoid cavity 8. depression in the scapula that articulates with the humerus

e; coracoid process 9. process above the glenoid cavity that permits muscle attachment

d; clavicle 10. the "collarbone"

s; trochlea 11. distal condyle of the humerus that articulates with the ulna

t; ulna 12. medial bone of forearm in anatomical position

b; capitulum 13. rounded knob on the humerus; adjoins the radius

f; coronoid fossa 14. anterior depression, superior to the trochlea, which receives part of the ulna when the forearm is flexed

t; ulna 15. forearm bone involved in formation of the elbow joint

c; carpus 16. wrist bones

m; phalanges 17. finger bones

j; metacarpus 18. heads of these bones form the knuckles

p; scapula , _q; sternum_ 19. bones that articulate with the clavicle

Column B

a. acromion

b. capitulum

c. carpals

d. clavicle

e. coracoid process

f. coronoid fossa

g. deltoid tuberosity

h. glenoid cavity

i. humerus

j. metacarpals

k. olecranon fossa

l. olecranon process

m. phalanges

n. radial tuberosity

o. radius

p. scapula

q. sternum

r. styloid process

s. trochlea

t. ulna

2. Why is the clavicle at risk to fracture when a person falls on his or her shoulder? *It is a slender, lightweight bone that with-*

stands trauma poorly.

3. Why is it generally no problem for the arm to clear the widest dimension of the thoracic cage?

The clavicle acts as a strut to hold the glenoid cavity of the scapula (therefore the arm) laterally away from the narrowest dimension of

the rib cage.

4. What is the total number of phalanges in the hand? *14*

5. What is the total number of carpals in the wrist? *8*

Name the carpals (medial to lateral) in the proximal row. *pisiform, triangular, lunate, scaphoid*

In the distal row, they are (medial to lateral) *hamate, capitate, trapezoid, trapezium*

6. Using items from the list at the right, identify the anatomical landmarks and regions of the scapula.

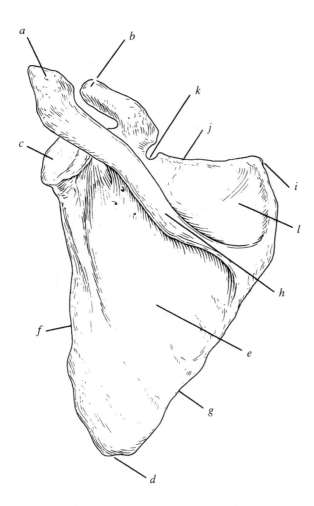

a.   acromion

b.   coracoid process

c.   glenoid cavity

d.   inferior angle

e.   infraspinous fossa

f.   lateral border

g.   medial border

h.   spine

i.   superior angle

j.   superior border

k.   suprascapular notch

l.   supraspinous fossa

7. Match the terms in the key with the appropriate leader lines on the drawings of the humerus and the radius and ulna. Also decide whether these bones are right or left bones.

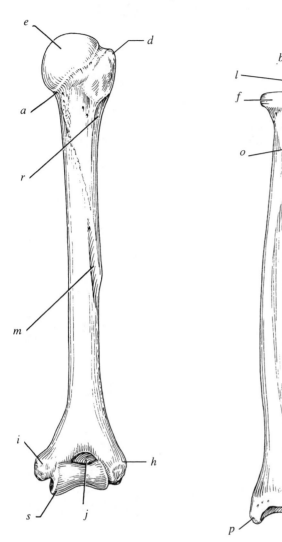

Key:

a. anatomical neck

b. coronoid process

c. distal radioulnar joint

d. greater tubercle

e. head of humerus

f. head of radius

g. head of ulna

h. lateral epicondyle

i. medial epicondyle

j. olecranon fossa

k. olecranon process

l. proximal radioulnar joint

m. radial groove

n. radial notch

o. radial tuberosity

p. styloid process of radius

q. styloid process of ulna

r. surgical neck

s. trochlea

t. trochlear notch

The humerus is a _right (posterior view)_ bone; the radius and ulna are _right (anterior view)_ bones.

Bones of the Pelvic Girdle and Lower Limb

8. Compare the pectoral and pelvic girdles by choosing appropriate descriptive terms from the key.

Key: a. flexibility most important
      b. massive
      c. lightweight

d. insecure axial and limb attachments
e. secure axial and limb attachments
f. weight-bearing most important

Pectoral: _a_ , _c_ , _d_   Pelvic: _b_ , _e_ , _f_

9. What organs are protected, at least in part, by the pelvic girdle? _Uterus (female), bladder, small intestine, rectum_

10. Distinguish between the true pelvis and the false pelvis. _The true pelvis is the region inferior to the pelvic brim, which is encircled_

by bone. The false pelvis is the area medial to the flaring iliac bones and lies superior to the pelvic brim.

11. Use letters from the key to identify the bone markings on this illustration of an articulated pelvis. Make an educated guess as to whether the illustration shows a male or female pelvis and provide two reasons for your decision.

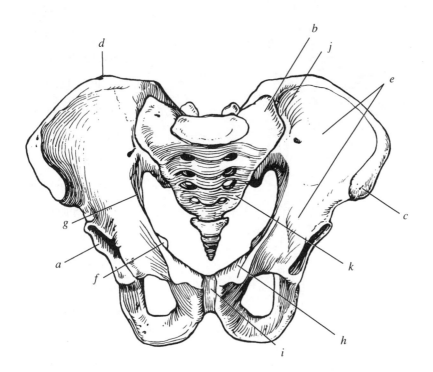

Key:

a. acetabulum

b. ala

c. anterior superior iliac spine

d. iliac crest

e. iliac fossa

f. ischial spine

g. pelvic brim

h. pubic crest

i. pubic symphysis

j. sacroiliac joint

k. sacrum

This is a _male_ (female/male) pelvis because:

Acetabula are close together; pubic angle/arch is less than 90°; narrow sacrum, heart-shaped pelvic inlet.

12. Deduce why the pelvic bones of a four-legged animal such as the cat or pig are much less massive than those of the human.

The pelvic girdle does not have to carry the entire weight of the trunk in the quadruped animal.

13. A person instinctively curls over his abdominal area in times of danger. Why? _Abdominal area organs receive the least protection from the skeletal system._

14. For what anatomical reason do many women appear to be slightly knock-kneed? _The pelvis is broader and the acetabula and ilia are more laterally positioned. Thus, the femur runs downward to the knee more obliquely than in the male._

15. What does _fallen arches_ mean? _A weakening of the tendons and ligaments supporting the arches of the foot._

16. Match the bone names and markings in column B with the descriptions in column A.

Column A

_i; ilium_____, _k; ischium_____, and

_t; pubis_____ 1. fuse to form the coxal bone

_k; ischium_____ 2. inferoposterior "bone" of the coxal bone

s; pubic symphysis 3. point where the coxal bones join anteriorly

_h; iliac crest_____ 4. superiormost margin of the coxal bone

_a; acetabulum_____ 5. deep socket in the coxal bone that receives the head of the thigh bone

u; sacroiliac joint 6. joint between axial skeleton and pelvic girdle

_c; femur_____ 7. longest, strongest bone in body

_d; fibula_____ 8. thin lateral leg bone

_x; tibia_____ 9. heavy medial leg bone

_c; femur_____, _x; tibia_____ 10. bones forming knee joint

y; tibial tuberosity 11. point where the patellar ligament attaches

_r; patella_____ 12. kneecap

_x; tibia_____ 13. shin bone

o; medial malleolus 14. medial ankle projection

l; lateral malleolus 15. lateral ankle projection

_b; calcaneus_____ 16. largest tarsal bone

_w; tarsals_____ 17. ankle bones

_p; metatarsals_____ 18. bones forming the instep of the foot

q; obturator foramen 19. opening in hip bone formed by the pubic and ischial rami

e; gluteal tuberosity and _g; greater and lesser trochanters_ 20. sites of muscle attachment on the proximal femur

_v; talus_____ 21. tarsal bone that "sits" on the calcaneus

_x; tibia_____ 22. weight-bearing bone of the leg

_v; talus_____ 23. tarsal bone that articulates with the tibia

Column B

a. acetabulum

b. calcaneus

c. femur

d. fibula

e. gluteal tuberosity

f. greater sciatic notch

g. greater and lesser trochanters

h. iliac crest

i. ilium

j. ischial tuberosity

k. ischium

l. lateral malleolus

m. lesser sciatic notch

n. linea aspera

o. medial malleolus

p. metatarsals

q. obturator foramen

r. patella

s. pubic symphysis

t. pubis

u. sacroiliac joint

v. talus

w. tarsals

x. tibia

y. tibial tuberosity

17. Match the terms in the key with the appropriate leader lines on the drawings of the femur and the tibia and fibula. Also decide if these bones are right or left bones.

Key:

a. distal tibiofibular joint

b. fovea capitis

c. gluteal tuberosity

d. greater trochanter

e. head of femur

f. head of fibula

g. intercondylar eminence

h. intertrochanteric crest

i. lateral condyle

j. lateral epicondyle

k. lateral malleolus

l. lesser trochanter

m. medial condyle

n. medial epicondyle

o. medial malleolus

p. neck of femur

q. proximal tibiofibular joint

r. tibial anterior crest

s. tibial tuberosity

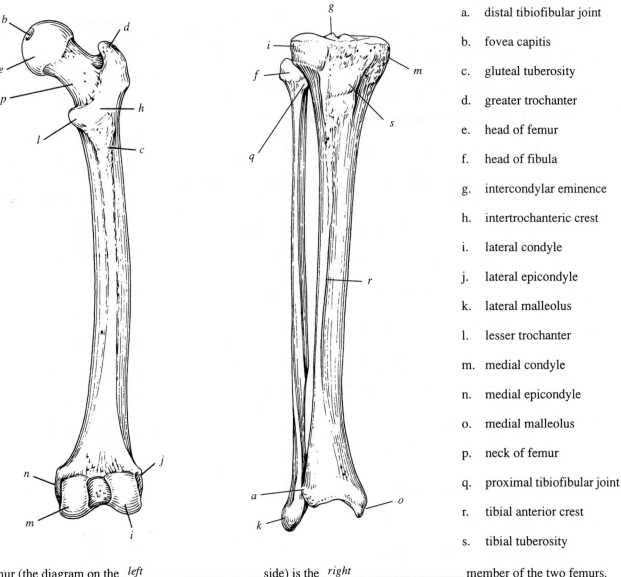

The femur (the diagram on the ___left___ side) is the ___right___ member of the two femurs.

The tibia and fibula (the diagram on the ___right___ side) are ___right leg___ bones.

Summary of Skeleton

18. Identify all indicated bones (or groups of bones) in the diagram of the articulated skeleton on the following page.

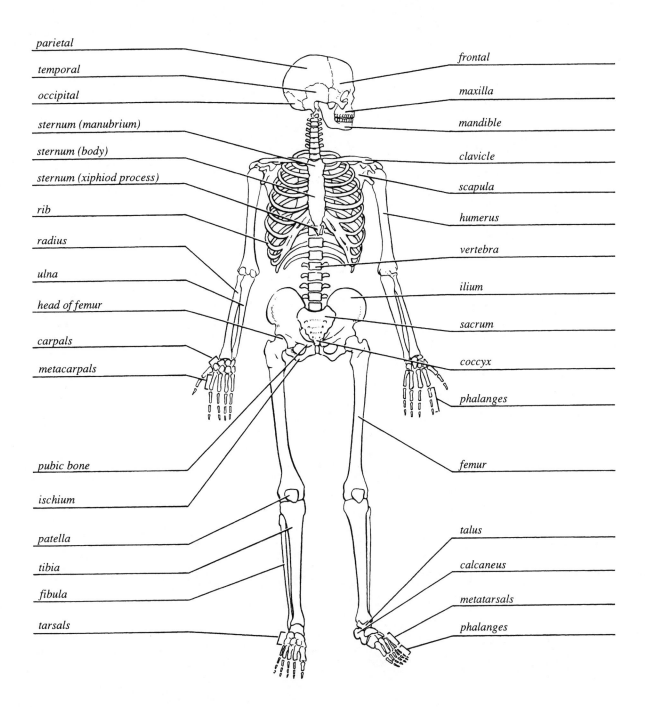

parietal

temporal

occipital

sternum (manubrium)

sternum (body)

sternum (xiphiod process)

rib

radius

ulna

head of femur

carpals

metacarpals

pubic bone

ischium

patella

tibia

fibula

tarsals

frontal

maxilla

mandible

clavicle

scapula

humerus

vertebra

ilium

sacrum

coccyx

phalanges

femur

talus

calcaneus

metatarsals

phalanges

The Fetal Skeleton

1. Are the same skull bones seen in the adult found in the fetal skull? *Yes* _____

2. How does the size of the fetal face compare to its cranium? *Face is foreshortened, overshadowed by the large cranium. Maxillae*

   and mandible are very tiny. _____

   How does this compare to the adult skull? *In the adult the cranium is proportionately smaller and the facial bones are proportion-*

   ately larger and more prominent.

   _____

3. What are the outward conical projections in some of the fetal cranial bones? *These are growth areas.* _____

   _____

4. What is a fontanel? *A fibrocartilage membrane connecting fetal skull bones.* _____

   What is its fate? *Progressively ossified; replaced by a suture.* _____

   What is the function of the fontanels in the fetal skull? *Allow fetal skull to be compressed slightly during birth passage; allow for*

   fetal brain growth. _____

5. Describe how the fetal skeleton compares with the adult skeleton in the following areas:

   vertebrae *In the fetus, only the primary curvatures are present; the bones of the sacrum and coccyx are unfused.* _____

   _____

   os coxae *In the fetus the ilium, ischium, and pubis are separate bones. In the adult they form the composite os coxa.* __

   _____

   carpals and tarsals *Not ossified in the fetus.* _____

   sternum *Its component parts are not fused in the fetus.* _____

   frontal bone *Bipartite superiorly in the fetus; fused in the adult.* _____

   patella *May be absent in the fetus; if present, is unossified.* _____

   rib cage *Compressed laterally forming a pointed anterior rib cage surface in the fetus.* _____

   _____

6. How does the size of the fetus's head compare to the size of its body? _The head is disproportionately large._

_____

7. Using the terms listed, identify each of the fontanels shown on the fetal skull below.

    a. anterior fontanel   b. mastoid fontanel   c. posterior fontanel   d. sphenoidal fontanel

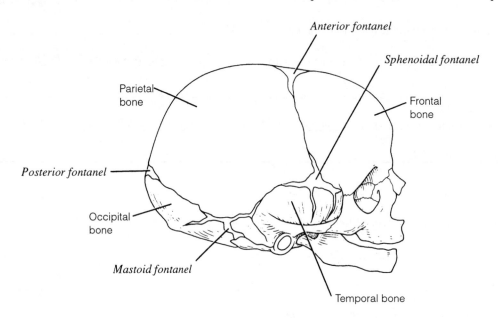

Articulations and Body Movements

Fibrous, Cartilaginous, and Synovial Joints

1. Use key responses to identify the joint types described below.

   Key: a. cartilaginous   b. fibrous   c. synovial

   a; cartilaginous _____ 1. typically allows a slight degree of movement

   a; cartilaginous _____ 2. includes joints between the vertebral bodies and the pubic symphysis

   b; fibrous _____ 3. essentially immovable joints

   b; fibrous _____ 4. sutures are the most remembered examples

   a; cartilaginous _____ 5. characterized by cartilage connecting the bony portions

   c; synovial _____ 6. all characterized by a fibrous articular capsule lined with a synovial membrane surrounding a joint cavity

   c; synovial _____ 7. all are freely movable or diarthrotic

   b; fibrous _____ 8. bone regions are united by fibrous connective tissue

   c; synovial _____ 9. include the hip, knee, and elbow joints

2. Describe the structure and function of the following structures or tissues in relation to a synovial joint and label the structures indicated by leader lines in the diagram.

   ligament *Dense fibrous connective tissue; attaches bones*
   together; reinforces joints

   tendon *Dense fibrous connective tissue; reinforces the*
   joint capsule as it spans a joint

   articular cartilage *Hyaline cartilage; reduces friction where*
   bones articulate

   synovial membrane *Loose connective tissue; produces*
   synovial fluid which decreases friction within the joint capsule

   bursa *Fluid-filled synovial sac which cushions the tendon where it crosses the bone*

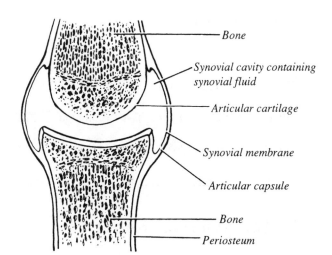

Bone

Synovial cavity containing synovial fluid

Articular cartilage

Synovial membrane

Articular capsule

Bone

Periosteum

3. Match the joint subcategories in column B with their descriptions in column A, and place an asterisk (*) beside all choices that are examples of synovial joints.

Column A		Column B
g; suture	1. joint between skull bones	a. ball and socket
e; pivot*	2. joint between the axis and atlas	b. condyloid
a; ball and socket*	3. hip joint	c. gliding
c; gliding*	4. intervertebral joints (between articular processes)	d. hinge
b; condyloid*	5. joint between forearm bones and wrist	e. pivot
d; hinge*	6. elbow	f. saddle
d; hinge*	7. interphalangeal joints	g. suture
c; gliding*	8. intercarpal joints	h. symphysis
d; hinge*	9. joint between tarsus and tibia/fibula	i. synchondrosis
b; condyloid*	10. joint between skull and vertebral column	j. syndesmosis
d; hinge*	11. joint between jaw and skull	
b; condyloid*	12. joints between proximal phalanges and metacarpal bones	
i; synchondrosis	13. epiphyseal plate of a child's long bone	
a; ball and socket*	14. a multiaxial joint	
b; condyloid* , _f; saddle*_	15. biaxial joints	
d; hinge* , _e; pivot*_	16. uniaxial joints	

4. When considering movement,

What do all uniaxial joints have in common? _They allow movement in only one plane._

What do all biaxial joints have in common? _They allow movement in two planes._

What do all multiaxial joints have in common? _They allow all angular movement and rotation._

5. What characteristics do all joints have in common? _All consist of bony regions separated by fibrous or cartilaginous connective tissue._

Selected Synovial Joints

6. Which joint, the hip or the knee, is more stable? _Hip_

Name two important factors that contribute to the stability of the hip joint.

Deep socket for femur and _strongly reinforced articular capsule_

Name two important factors that contribute to the stability of the knee.

The menisci and _intracapsular cruciate ligaments_

7. The diagram shows a frontal section of the hip joint. Identify its major structural elements by using the key letters.

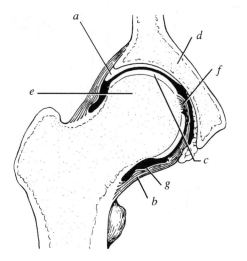

Key:

a. acetabular labrum

b. articular capsule

c. articular cartilage

d. coxal bone

e. head of femur

f. ligamentum teres

g. synovial cavity

8. Describe how the structure of the temporomandibular joint (TMJ) allows us to chew hard candy and hazel nuts.

The superior compartment of the synovial cavity causes

the mandible to glide forward, distributing forces to the

stronger articular tubercle (to prevent breakage of the

mandibular fossa).

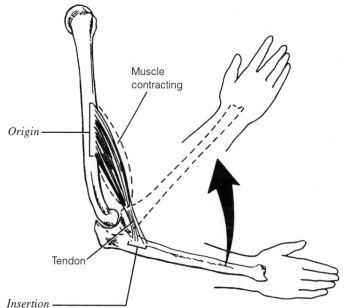

Movements Allowed by Synovial Joints

9. Label the *origin* and *insertion* points on the diagram below and complete the following statement:

During muscle contraction, the _insertion_

moves toward the _origin_ .

10. Complete the statements below the stick diagrams by inserting the missing words in the answer blanks.

1. _pronation_

2. _rotation_

3. _circumduction_

4. _flexion_

5. _flexion_

6. _abduction_

7. _adduction_

8. _hyperextension_

9. _dorsiflexion_

10. _extension_

11. _inversion_

(continues on next page)

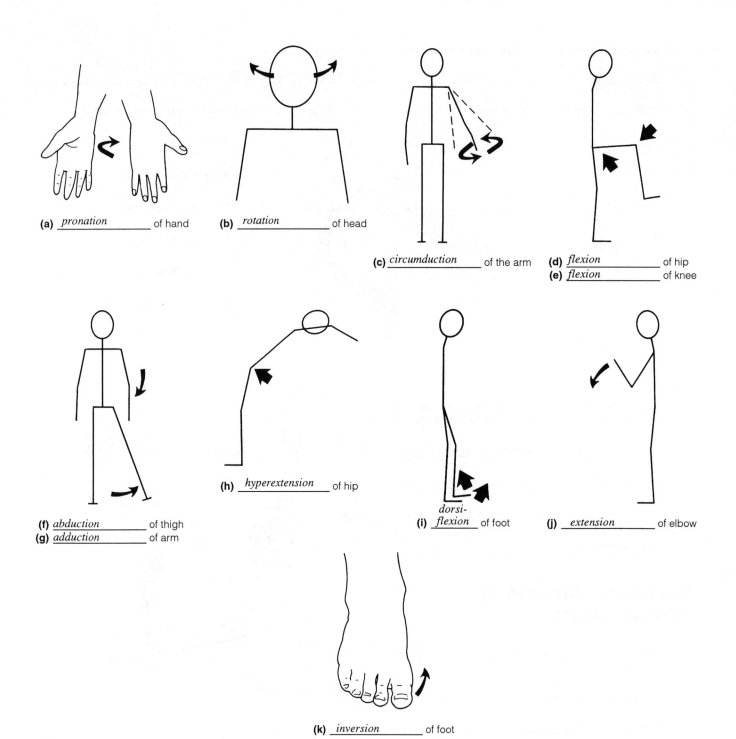

(a) _pronation_ of hand

(b) _rotation_ of head

(c) _circumduction_ of the arm

(d) _flexion_ of hip
(e) _flexion_ of knee

(f) _abduction_ of thigh
(g) _adduction_ of arm

(h) _hyperextension_ of hip

(i) _dorsi-flexion_ of foot

(j) _extension_ of elbow

(k) _inversion_ of foot

Joint Disorders

11. What structural joint changes are common to the elderly? _Degenerative changes (adhesions and bone spurs) begin to "sprout up"_

in diarthrotic joints; intervertebral discs begin to degenerate. These changes lead to increased joint stiffness and pain.

12. Define:

sprain _Ligaments reinforcing a joint are damaged by excessive stretching, or torn away from the bony attachment._

dislocation _Bones are forced out of their normal positions in a joint cavity._

Microscopic Anatomy and Organization of Skeletal Muscle

Skeletal Muscle Cells and Their Packaging into Muscles

1. What capability is most highly expressed in muscle tissue? *contractility* _____

2. Use the items on the right to correctly identify the structures described on the left.

    g; perimysium _____ 1. connective tissue ensheathing a bundle of muscle cells

    c; fascicle _____ 2. bundle of muscle cells

    i; sarcomere _____ 3. contractile unit of muscle

    d; fiber _____ 4. a muscle cell

    a; endomysium _____ 5. thin reticular connective tissue investing each muscle cell

    h; sarcolemma _____ 6. plasma membrane of the muscle fiber

    f; myofibril _____ 7. a long filamentous organelle with a banded appearance found within muscle cells

    e; myofilament _____ 8. actin- or myosin-containing structure

    k; tendon _____ 9. cord of collagen fibers that attaches a muscle to a bone

    a. endomysium

    b. epimysium

    c. fascicle

    d. fiber

    e. myofilament

    f. myofibril

    g. perimysium

    h. sarcolemma

    i. sarcomere

    j. sarcoplasm

    k. tendon

3. Why are the connective tissue wrappings of skeletal muscle important? (Give at least three reasons.)

    The connective tissue wrappings (a) bundle the muscle fibers together, increasing coordination of their activity; (b) add strength to the

    muscle; and (c) provide a route for entry and exit of blood vessels and nerves to the muscle fibers.

    _____

    _____

4. Why are indirect—that is, tendinous—muscle attachments to bone seen more often than direct attachments?

    They conserve space (less bulky than fleshy muscle attachments) and are more durable than muscle tissue where bony prominences

    must be spanned.

    _____

5. How does an aponeurosis differ from a tendon? *An aponeurosis is a sheet of white fibrous connective tissue; a tendon is a band or*

    cord of the same tissue. Both serve to attach muscles to bones (or to other muscles).

    _____

6. The diagram illustrates a small portion of a muscle myofibril. Using letters from the key, correctly identify each structure indicated by a leader line or a bracket. Below the diagram make a sketch of how this segment of the myofibril would look if contracted.

Key: a. actin filament   d. myosin filament
     b. A band   e. sarcomere
     c. I band   f. Z disc

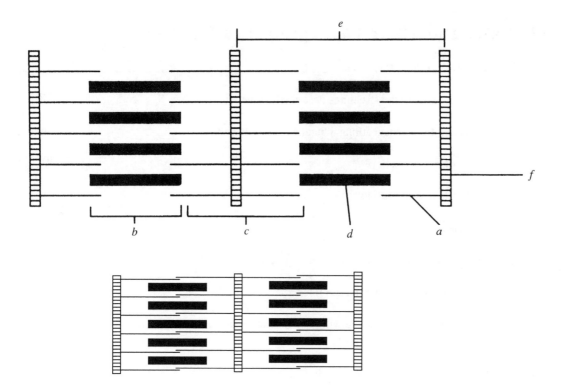

7. On the following figure, label blood vessel, endomysium, epimysium, fascicle, muscle cell, perimysium, and tendon.

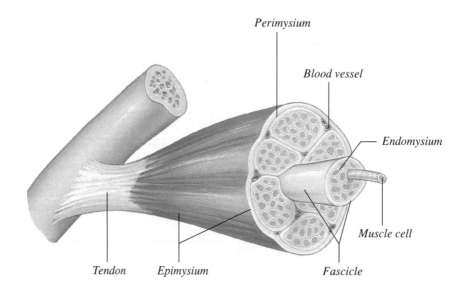

Perimysium

Blood vessel

Endomysium

Muscle cell

Tendon   *Epimysium*   *Fascicle*

The Neuromuscular Junction

8. Complete the following statements:

    The junction between a motor neuron's axon and the muscle cell membrane is called a neuromuscular junction or a __1__ junction. A motor neuron and all of the skeletal muscle cells it stimulates is called a __2__ . The actual gap between the axonal terminal and the muscle cell is called a __3__ . Within the axonal terminal are many small vesicles containing a neurotransmitter substance called __4__ . When the __5__ reaches the ends of the axon, the neurotransmitter is released and diffuses to the muscle cell membrane to combine with receptors there. The combining of the neurotransmitter with the muscle membrane receptors causes the membrane to become permeable to both sodium and potassium. The greater influx of sodium ions results in __6__ of the membrane. Then contraction of the muscle cell occurs. Before a muscle cell can be stimulated to contract again, __7__ must occur.

1. *myoneural*

2. *motor unit*

3. *synaptic cleft*

4. *acetylcholine*

5. *nerve impulse (action potential)*

6. *depolarization*

7. *repolarization*

9. The events that occur at a neuromuscular junction are depicted below. Identify by labeling every structure provided with a leader line.

Key:

a. ACh molecules

b. ACh receptor

c. axonal terminal

d. ion channel

e. mitochondrion

f. muscle fiber

g. myelinated axon

h. sarcolemma

i. sodium ion

j. synaptic cleft

k. synaptic vesicle (exocytosing)

l. T tubule

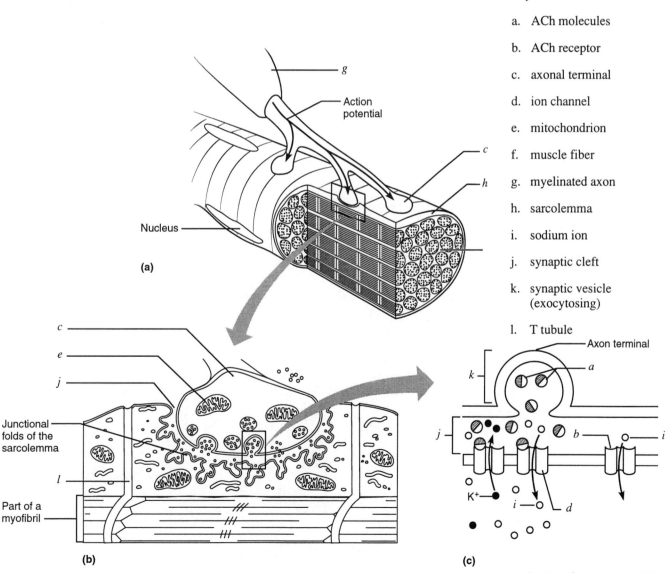

Gross Anatomy of the Muscular System

Classification of Skeletal Muscles

1. Several criteria were given relative to the naming of muscles. Match the criteria (column B) to the muscle names (column A). Note that more than one criterion may apply in some cases.

Column A

_e, g_   1. gluteus maximus

_a, g_   2. adductor magnus

_d, e_   3. biceps femoris

_e, f_   4. transversus abdominis

_a, c, e_   5. extensor carpi ulnaris

_b_   6. trapezius

_e, f_   7. rectus femoris

_e, f_   8. external oblique

Column B

a. action of the muscle

b. shape of the muscle

c. location of the origin and/or insertion of the muscle

d. number of origins

e. location of the muscle relative to a bone or body region

f. direction in which the muscle fibers run relative to some imaginary line

g. relative size of the muscle

2. When muscles are discussed relative to the manner in which they interact with other muscles, the terms shown in the key are often used. Match the key terms with the appropriate definitions.

Key: a. antagonist   b. fixator   c. prime mover   d. synergist

c; prime mover   1. agonist

b; fixator   2. postural muscles, for the most part

a; antagonist   3. reverses and/or opposes the action of a prime mover

d; synergist   4. stabilizes a joint so that the prime mover may act at more distal joints

d; synergist   5. performs the same movement as the prime mover

b; fixator   6. immobilizes the origin of a prime mover

Muscles of the Head and Neck

3. Using choices from the list at the right, correctly identify muscles provided with leader lines on the diagram.

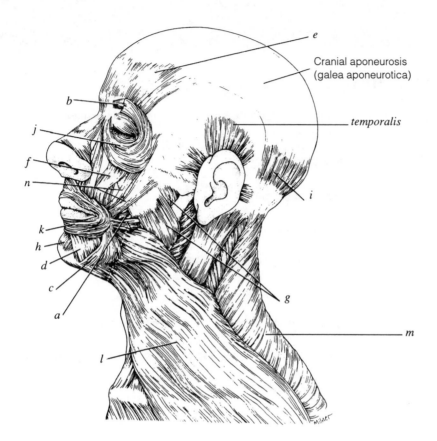

Cranial aponeurosis
(galea aponeurotica)

temporalis

a. buccinator

b. corrugator supercilii

c. depressor anguli oris

d. depressor labii inferioris

e. frontalis

f. levator labii superioris

g. masseter

h. mentalis

i. occipitalis

j. orbicularis oculi

k. orbicularis oris

l. platysma

m. trapezius

n. zygomaticus major
and minor

4. Using the terms provided above, identify the muscles described next.

   n   1. used in smiling

   a   2. used to suck in your cheeks

   j   3. used in blinking and squinting

   c   4. used to pout (pulls the corners of the mouth downward)

   e   5. raises your eyebrows for a questioning expression

   b   6. used to form the vertical frown crease on the forehead

   k   7. your "kisser"

   g   8. prime mover to raise the lower jawbone

   l   9. tenses skin of the neck during shaving

Muscles of the Trunk

5. Correctly identify both intact and transected (cut) muscles depicted in the diagram, using the terms given at the right. (Not all terms will be used in this identification.)

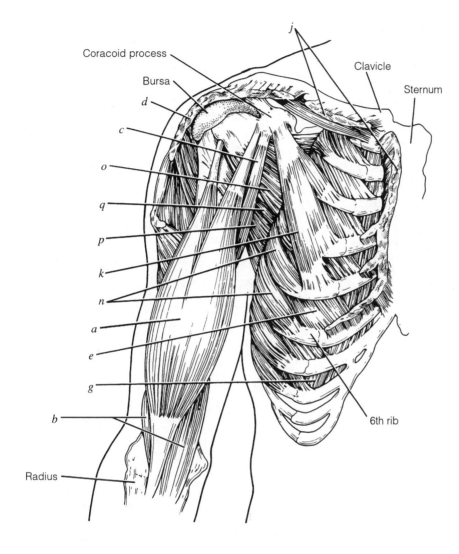

a. biceps brachii

b. brachialis

c. coracobrachialis

d. deltoid (cut)

e. external intercostals

f. external oblique

g. internal intercostals

h. internal oblique

i. latissimus dorsi

j. pectoralis major (cut)

k. pectoralis minor

l. rectus abdominis

m. rhomboids

n. serratus anterior

o. subscapularis

p. teres major

q. teres minor

r. transversus abdominis

s. trapezius

6. Using the key provided in question 5 above, identify the major muscles described next.

_l_ 1. a major spine flexor

_i_ 2. prime mover for pulling the arm posteriorly

_j_ 3. prime mover for shoulder flexion

_f, h, r_ 4. assume major responsibility for forming the abdominal girdle (three pairs of muscles)

_i_ 5. pulls the shoulder backward and downward

_d_ 6. prime mover of shoulder abduction

_i, j_ 7. important in shoulder adduction; antagonists of the shoulder abductor (two muscles)

_n_ 8. moves the scapula forward and downward

_e_ 9. small, inspiratory muscles between the ribs; elevate the ribs

_s_ 10. extends the head

_m_ 11. pull the scapulae medially

Muscles of the Upper Limb

7. Using terms from the list on the right, correctly identify all muscles provided with leader lines in the diagram. (Note that not all the listed terms will be used in this exercise.)

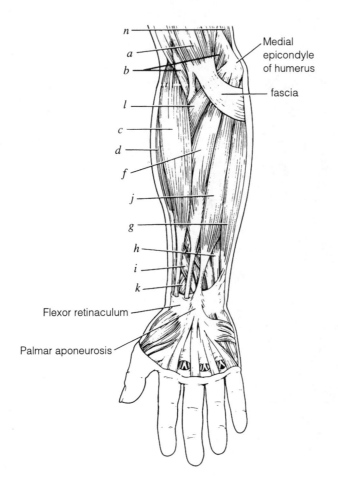

a. biceps brachii

b. brachialis

c. brachioradialis

d. extensor carpi radialis longus

e. extensor digitorum

f. flexor carpi radialis

g. flexor carpi ulnaris

h. flexor digitorum superficialis

i. flexor pollicis longus

j. palmaris longus

k. pronator quadratus

l. pronator teres

m. supinator

n. triceps brachii

8. Use the terms provided in question 1 to identify the muscles described next.

_a, m_ 1. places the palm upward (two muscles)

_a_ 2. flexes the forearm and supinates the hand

_b, c_ 3. forearm flexors; no role in supination (two muscles)

_n_ 4. elbow extensor

_f_ 5. power wrist flexor and abductor

_h_ 6. flexes wrist and middle phalanges

_k, l_ 7. pronate the hand (two muscles)

_i_ 8. flexes the thumb

_d_ 9. extends and abducts the wrist

_e_ 10. extends the wrist and digits

_j_ 11. flat muscle that is a weak wrist flexor

Muscles of the Lower Limb

9. Using the terms listed to the right, correctly identify all muscles provided with leader lines in the diagram below. (Not all listed terms will be used in this exercise.)

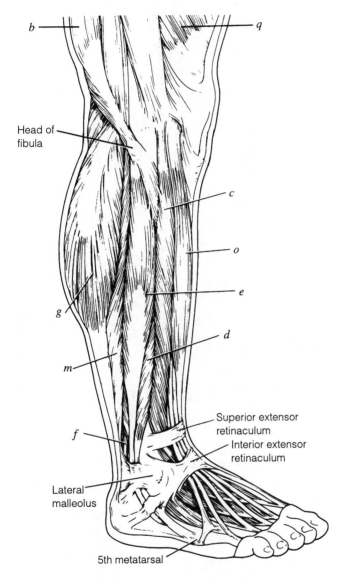

a. adductor group

b. biceps femoris

c. extensor digitorum longus

d. fibularis brevis

e. fibularis longus

f. flexor hallucis longus

g. gastrocnemius

h. gluteus maximus

i. gluteus medius

j. rectus femoris

k. semimembranosus

l. semitendinosus

m. soleus

n. tensor fasciae latae

o. tibialis anterior

p. tibialis posterior

q. vastus lateralis

10. Use the key terms in exercise 9 to respond to the descriptions below.

_f_____ 1. flexes the great toe and inverts the ankle

_d, e_____ 2. lateral compartment muscles that plantar flex and evert the ankle (two muscles)

_i, n_____ 3. move the thigh laterally to take the "at ease" stance (two muscles)

_h_____ 4. used to extend the hip when climbing stairs

_g, m_____ 5. prime movers of ankle plantar flexion (two muscles)

_p_____ 6. major foot inverter

_o_____ 7. prime mover of ankle dorsiflexion

_a_____ 8. allow you to draw your legs to the midline of your body, as when standing at attention

_c_____ 9. extends the toes

_b, k, l_____ 10. extend thigh and flex knee (three muscles)

_j_____ 11. extends knee and flexes thigh

General Review: Muscle Recognition

11. Identify the lettered muscles in the diagram of the human anterior superficial musculature by matching the letter with one of the following muscle names:

jj 1. adductor longus

g 2. biceps brachii

i 3. brachioradialis

e 4. deltoid

s 5. extensor digitorum longus

ee 6. external oblique

r 7. fibularis longus

j 8. flexor carpi radialis

l 9. flexor carpi ulnaris

u 10. frontalis

ll 11. gastrocnemius

kk 12. gracilis

m 13. iliopsoas

ff 14. internal oblique

cc 15. latissimus dorsi

b 16. masseter

v 17. orbicularis oculi

x 18. orbicularis oris

k 19. palmaris longus

n 20. pectineus

aa 21. pectoralis major

c 22. platysma

h 23. pronator teres

dd 24. rectus abdominis

o 25. rectus femoris

ii 26. sartorius

bb 27. serratus anterior

mm 28. soleus

z 29. sternocleidomastoid

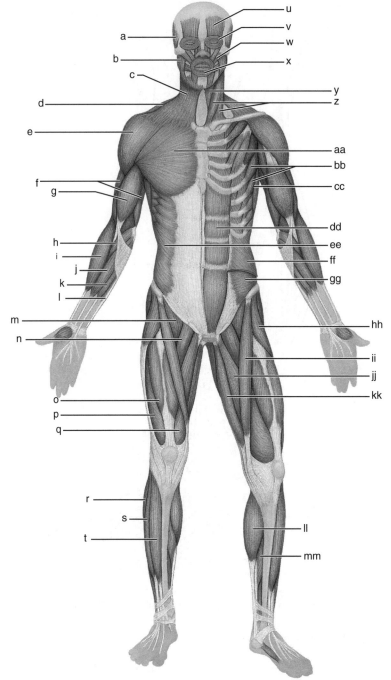

y 30. sternohyoid

a 31. temporalis

hh 32. tensor fasciae latae

t 33. tibialis anterior

gg 34. transversus abdominis

d 35. trapezius

f 36. triceps brachii

p 37. vastus lateralis

q 38. vastus medialis

w 39. zygomaticus

12. Identify each of the lettered muscles in this diagram of the human posterior superficial musculature by matching its letter to one of the following muscle names:

_t_____ 1. adductor magnus

_u_____ 2. biceps femoris

_b_____ 3. brachialis

_c_____ 4. brachioradialis

_m_____ 5. deltoid

_d_____ 6. extensor carpi radialis longus

_f_____ 7. extensor carpi ulnaris

_g_____ 8. extensor digitorum

_q_____ 9. external oblique

_e_____ 10. flexor carpi ulnaris

_i_____ 11. gastrocnemius

_s_____ 12. gluteus maximus

_r_____ 13. gluteus medius

_v_____ 14. gracilis

_h_____ 15. iliotibial tract (tendon)

_n_____ 16. infraspinatus

_p_____ 17. latissimus dorsi

_j_____ 18. occipitalis

_x_____ 19. semimembranosus

_w_____ 20. semitendinosus

_k_____ 21. sternocleidomastoid

_o_____ 22. teres major

_l_____ 23. trapezius

_a_____ 24. triceps brachii

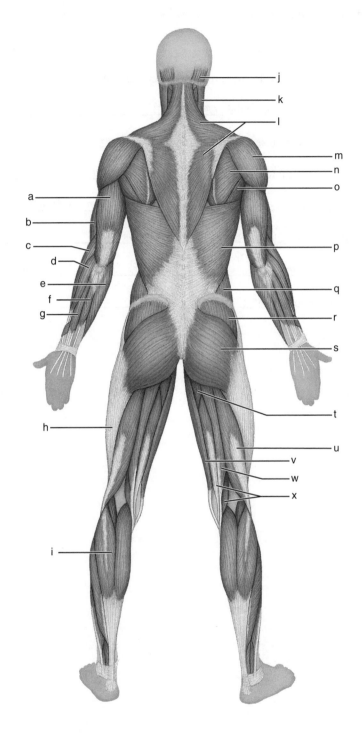

General Review: Muscle Descriptions

13. Identify the muscles described below by completing the statements:

1. The _deltoid_____, _vasti_____, and _gluteus maximus and medius_____

   are commonly used for intramuscular injections (three muscles).

2. The insertion tendon of the _quadriceps_____ group contains a large sesamoid bone, the patella.

3. The triceps surae insert in common into the _calcaneal_____ tendon.

4. The bulk of the tissue of a muscle tends to lie _proximal_____ to the part of the body it causes to move.

5. The extrinsic muscles of the hand originate on the _humerus, radius, and ulna_____.

6. Most flexor muscles are located on the _anterior_____ aspect of the body; most extensors

   are located _posteriorly_____. An exception to this generalization is the extensor-flexor

   musculature of the _knee_____.

Skeletal Muscle Physiology:
Frogs and Human Subjects

Muscle Activity

1. The following group of incomplete statements refers to a muscle cell in the resting or polarized state just before stimulation. Complete each statement by choosing the correct response from the key items below.

Key: a. Na^+ diffuses out of the cell
        b. K^+ diffuses out of the cell
        c. Na^+ diffuses into the cell
        d. K^+ diffuses into the cell
        e. inside the cell
        f. outside the cell
        g. relative ionic concentrations on the two sides of the membrane

        h. electrical conditions
        i. activation of the sodium-potassium pump, which moves K^+ into the cell and Na^+ out of the cell
        j. activation of the sodium-potassium pump, which moves Na^+ into the cell and K^+ out of the cell

There is a greater concentration of Na^+ _f_____; there is a greater concentration of K^+ _e_____. When the stimulus

is delivered, the permeability of the membrane at that point is changed; and _c_____, initiating the depolarization of the

membrane. Almost as soon as the depolarization wave has begun, a repolarization wave follows it across the membrane.

This occurs as _b_____. Repolarization restores the _h_____ of the resting cell membrane. The _g_____ is (are) reestab-

lished by _i_____.

2. Number the following statements in the proper sequence to describe the contraction mechanism in a skeletal muscle cell. Number 1 has already been designated.

   _1_____   Acetylcholine is released into the neuromuscular junction by the axonal terminal.

   _4_____   The action potential, carried deep into the cell by the T system, triggers the release of calcium ions from the sarcoplasmic reticulum.

   _7_____   The muscle cell relaxes and lengthens.

   _2_____   Acetylcholine diffuses across the neuromuscular junction and binds to receptors on the sarcolemma.

   _5_____   The calcium ion concentrations at the myofilaments increase; the myofilaments slide past one another, and the cell shortens.

   _3_____   Depolarization occurs, and the action potential is generated.

   _6_____   The concentration of the calcium ions at the myofilaments decreases as they are actively transported into the sarcoplasmic reticulum.

3. Muscle contraction is commonly explained by the sliding filament hypothesis. What are the essential points of this hypothesis? *The sliding of the actin filaments past the myosin filaments results in the shortening of each sarcomere, thus in the shortening of the muscle cell as a whole.*

4. Relative to your observations of muscle fiber contraction (pp. 168–170):

   a. What percentage of contraction was observed with the solution containing ATP, K^+, and Mg^{2+}? *(stu)* %

      With *just* ATP? *(stu)* % With *just* Mg^{2+} and K^+? *(stu)* %

   b. Did your data support your hypothesis?

   c. *Explain* your observations fully. *Optimal muscle contraction requires Mg^{2+}, K^+, and ATP. Without ATP (the energy source) no contraction can occur once energy stores are exhausted. Mg^{2+} and K^+ are necessary for ATPase activity.*

   d. What zones or bands disappear when the muscle cell contracts? *I bands and H zones*

   e. Draw a relaxed and a contracted sarcomere below.

   Relaxed   Contracted

Induction of Contraction in the Frog Gastrocnemius Muscle

5. Why is it important to destroy the brain and spinal cord of a frog before conducting physiological experiments on muscle contraction? *Renders the frog unable to feel pain and prevents reflex movements that would confuse experimental results.*

6. What sources of stimuli, other than electrical shocks, cause a muscle to contract? *Extremes of pH, heat, some chemicals (e.g. salt).*

7. What is the most common stimulus for muscle contraction in the body? *Electrochemical*

8. Give the name and duration of each of the three phases of the muscle twitch, and describe what is happening during each phase:

   (a) *latent* , _____ sec., *electrical/chemical changes preparatory to contraction, i.e. depolarization, release of Ca^{2+}*

   (b) *contraction* , _____ sec., *muscle shortens due to sliding of myofilaments*

   (c) *relaxation* , _____ sec., *Ca^{2+} is reabsorbed by the sarcoplasmic reliculum, the muscle cells lengthen and relax.*

9. Use the terms given on the right to identify the conditions described on the left:

d; tetanus _____ 1. sustained contraction without any evidence of relaxation

c; subthreshold _____ 2. stimulus that results in no perceptible contraction

e; threshold stimulus _____ 3. stimulus at which the muscle first contracts perceptibly

f; treppe _____ 4. increasingly stronger contractions in the absence of increased stimulus intensity

g; wave summation _____ 5. increasingly stronger contractions owing to stimulation at a rapid rate

b; multiple motor unit summation 6. increasingly stronger contractions owing to increased stimulus strength

a; maximal stimulus _____ 7. weakest stimulus at which all muscle cells in the muscle are contracting

a. maximal stimulus

b. multiple motor unit summation

c. subthreshold stimulus

d. tetanus

e. threshold stimulus

f. treppe

g. wave summation

10. With brackets and labels, identify the portions of the tracing below that best correspond to three of the phenomena listed in the preceding key.

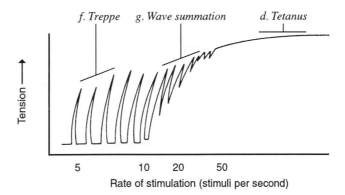

f. Treppe   *g. Wave summation*   *d. Tetanus*

Tension →

Rate of stimulation (stimuli per second)

5   10   20   50

11. Complete the following statements by writing the appropriate words on the correspondingly numbered blanks at the right.

When a weak but smooth muscle contraction is desired, a few motor units are stimulated at a __1__ rate. Treppe is referred to as the "warming up" process. It is believed that muscles contract more strongly after the first few contractions because the __2__ become more efficient. If blue litmus paper is pressed to the cut surface of a fatigued muscle, the paper color changes to red, indicating low pH. This situation is caused by the accumulation of __3__ in the muscle. Within limits, as the load on a muscle is increased, the muscle contracts __4__ (more/less) strongly. The relative refractory period is the time when the muscle cell will not respond to a stimulus because __5__ is occurring.

1. *very rapid* _____

2. *enzyme systems* _____

3. *lactic acid* _____

4. *more* _____

5. *repolarization* _____

12. During the experiment on muscle fatigue, how did the muscle contraction pattern change as the muscle began to fatigue?

The distance of the contraction peak from the baseline continued to decrease.

How long was stimulation continued before fatigue was apparent? *(student data)*

If the sciatic nerve that stimulates the living frog's gastrocnemius muscle had been left attached to the muscle and the stimulus had been applied to the nerve rather than the muscle, would fatigue have become apparent sooner or later?

Sooner

Explain your answer. *Fatigue of the neuromuscular junctions generally occurs before a muscle becomes fatigued and unable to*

contract.

13. Explain how the weak but smooth sustained muscle contractions of precision movements are produced.

Only a few motor units are stimulated, but at a very high frequency.

14. What do you think happens to a muscle in the body when its nerve supply is destroyed or badly damaged?

The muscle becomes flaccid, paralyzed, and eventually atrophies. Nerve stimulation is necessary for viable muscles.

15. Explain the relationship between the load on a muscle and its strength of contraction. *Strength of contraction increases as*

the load increases until the load becomes excessive.

16. The skeletal muscles are maintained in a slightly stretched condition for optimal contraction. How is this accomplished?

By the manner in which they are attached to the skeleton.

Why does overstretching a muscle drastically reduce its ability to contract? (Include an explanation of the events at the level

of the myofilaments.) *Overstretching prevents myosin cross-bridge interaction since the myofilaments no longer overlap. If the*

cross bridges cannot make contact, no sliding force (contraction) can be generated.

17. If the length but not the tension of a muscle is changed, the contraction is called an isotonic contraction. In an isometric contraction the tension is increased but the muscle does not shorten. Which type of contraction did you observe most often

during the laboratory experiments? *Isotonic*

What is the role of isometric contractions in normal body functioning? *Seen primarily in postural and antigravity muscle*

functioning, e.g. when standing, the quadriceps muscle group is contracting.

Electromyography in a Human Subject Using BIOPAC®.

18. If you were a physical therapist applying a constant voltage to the forearm, what might you observe if you gradually increased the *frequency* of stimulatory impulses, keeping the voltage constant each time?

One is likely to observe an increase in the duration of motor units activation.

19. Describe what is meant by the term *motor unit recruitment*.

Motor unit recruitment refers to the process by which an increasing number of motor units in a muscle are activated by gradually increasing levels of stimulation (e.g., voltage).

20. Describe the physiological processes occurring in the muscle cells that account for the gradual onset of muscle fatigue.

A deficit in ATP, an accumulation of lactic acid, and ionic imbalances all contribute to muscle fatigue.

21. Given that most subjects use their dominant forearm far more than their non-dominant forearm, what does this indicate about degree of activation of motor units and these factors: muscle fiber diameter, maximum muscle fiber force, and time to muscle fatigue?

Generally, since people use their dominant forearm more, the muscle fibers in that arm are activated for more prolonged periods. Thus, increase in muscle diameter (muscular hypertrophy) usually results allowing for increased force. Increased activity generally leads to increased respiratory and contractual efficiency resulting in a greater time to muscle fatigue.

22. Define *dynamometry*.

Dynamometry is the process of measuring force.

23. How might dynamometry be used to assess patients in a clinical setting?

Dynamometry can assist the clinician in the assessment of muscle function allowing for the study of contractual deficits and the recovery of muscle function.

Histology of Nervous Tissue

1. The cellular unit of the nervous system is the neuron. What is the major function of this cell type?

To generate and transmit nerve impulses. _____

2. Name four types of neuroglia in the CNS, and list at least four functions of these cells. (You will need to consult your textbook for this.)

Types

a. *microglia* _____

b. *oligodendrocytes* _____

c. *astrocytes* _____

d. *ependymal cells* _____

Functions

a. *phagocytosis of debris (dead cells, bacteria, etc.)* _____

_____

b. *package (myelinate) neuron processes in the CNS* _____

_____

c. *support the neurons; may serve nutritive function and help regulate*

the chemical environment of the neurons _____

d. *line cavities of the brain (and spinal cord); aid in circulation of*

cerebrospinal fluid _____

3. Match each statement with a response chosen from the key.

Key:
a. afferent neuron
b. association neuron
c. central nervous system
d. efferent neuron

e. ganglion
f. neuroglia
g. neurotransmitters
h. nerve

i. nuclei
j. peripheral nervous system
k. synapse
l. tract

_c_ 1. the brain and spinal cord collectively

_f_ 2. specialized supporting cells in the CNS

_k_ 3. junction or point of close contact between neurons

_l_ 4. a bundle of nerve processes inside the central nervous system

_b_ 5. neuron serving as part of the conduction pathway between sensory and motor neurons

_j_ 6. spinal and cranial nerves and ganglia

_e_ 7. collection of nerve cell bodies found outside the CNS

_d_ 8. neuron that conducts impulses away from the CNS to muscles and glands

_a_ 9. neuron that conducts impulses toward the CNS from the body periphery

_g_ 10. chemicals released by neurons that stimulate or inhibit other neurons or effectors

Neuron Anatomy

4. Match the following anatomical terms (column B) with the appropriate description or function (column A).

Column A

*c*____ 1. region of the cell body from which the axon originates

*b*____ 2. secretes neurotransmitters

*d*____ 3. receptive region of a neuron

*e*____ 4. insulates the nerve fibers

*g*____ 5. is site of the nucleus and the most important metabolic area

*f*____ 6. may be involved in the transport of substances within the neuron

*h*____ 7. essentially rough endoplasmic reticulum, important metabolically

*a*____ 8. impulse generator and transmitter

Column B

a. axon

b. axonal terminal

c. axon hillock

d. dendrite

e. myelin sheath

f. neurofibril

g. neuronal cell body

h. Nissl bodies

5. Draw a "typical" neuron in the space below. Include and label the following structures on your diagram: cell body, nucleus, nucleolus, Nissl bodies, dendrites, axon, axon collateral branch, myelin sheath, nodes of Ranvier, axonal terminals, and neurofibrils.

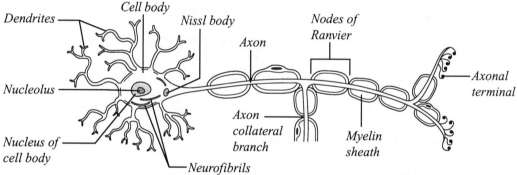

6. How is one-way conduction at synapses ensured? *Generally speaking, neurotransmitters are relased by axonal endings.*

____

7. What anatomical characteristic determines whether a particular neuron is classified as unipolar, bipolar, or multipolar?

The number of processes issuing from the cell body.

____

Make a simple line drawing of each type here.

Unipolar neuron   Bipolar neuron   Multipolar neuron

8. Correctly identify the sensory (afferent) neuron, association neuron (interneuron), and motor (efferent) neuron in the figure below.

Which of these neuron types is/are unipolar? *Sensory neuron*

Which is/are most likely multipolar? *Motor neuron, interneuron*

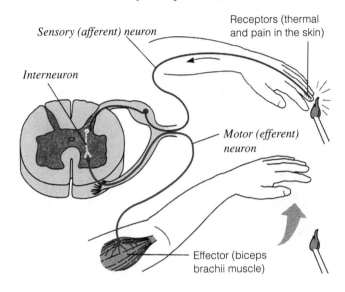

9. Describe how the Schwann cells form the myelin sheath and the neurilemma encasing the nerve processes. (You may want to diagram the process.)

Schwann cells lie against the axon and then begin to wrap themselves around it jellyroll fashion, thus forming a tight coil of

membranous material which forms the myelin sheath. The neurilemma is the outermost (exposed) Schwann cell membrane.

Structure of a Nerve

10. What is a nerve? *A bundle of neuron processes wrapped in connective tissue wrappings. Extends from the CNS to structures of the*

body viscera or periphery.

11. State the location of each of the following connective tissue coverings:

endoneurium: *Surrounds the neuron process.*

perineurium: *Surrounds a bundle of neuron processes.*

epineurium: *Surrounds all of the neuron processes contributing to a nerve.*

12. What is the value of the connective tissue wrappings found in a nerve? *To protect and insulate the delicate nerve fibers.*

13. Define *mixed nerve:* <u>*Nerve containing both motor (efferent) and sensory (afferent) fibers.*</u>

14. Identify all indicated parts of the nerve section.

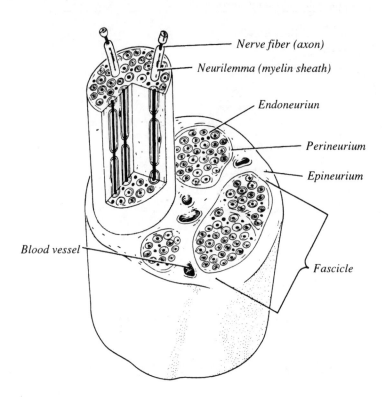

Nerve fiber (axon)

Neurilemma (myelin sheath)

Endoneuriun

Perineurium

Epineurium

Fascicle

Blood vessel

Neurophysiology of Nerve Impulses: Wet Lab

The Nerve Impulse

1. Match each of the terms in column B to the appropriate definition in column A.

Column A

_b_ ____ 1. period of depolarization of the neuron membrane during which it cannot respond to a second stimulus

_c_ ____ 2. reversal of the resting potential owing to an influx of sodium ions

_e, d_ ____ 3. period during which potassium ions diffuse out of the neuron owing to a change in membrane permeability

_a_ ____ 4. self-propagated transmission of the depolarization wave along the neuronal membrane

_f_ ____ 5. mechanism in which ATP is used to move sodium out of the cell and potassium into the cell; restores the resting membrane voltage and intracellular ionic concentrations

Column B

a. action potential

b. absolute refractory period

c. depolarization

d. relative refractory period

e. repolarization

f. sodium-potassium pump

2. Respond appropriately to each statement below either by completing the statement or by answering the question raised. Insert your responses in the corresponding numbered blanks on the right.

1. The cellular unit of the nervous system is the neuron. What is the major function of this cell type?

2–3. What characteristics are highly developed to allow the neuron to perform this function?

4. Would a substance that decreases membrane permeability to sodium increase or decrease the probability of generating a nerve impulse?

1. _to transmit nerve impulses_

2. _irritability_

3. _conductivity_

4. _decrease_

3. Why don't the terms *depolarization* and *action potential* mean the same thing? (*Hint:* Under which conditions will a local depolarization *not* lead to the action potential?) _Depolarization (reduction of negative membrane potential) may be only a short-lived local change in membrane potential if the stimulus is subthreshold. An action potential is a large depolarization including a reversal of membrane polarity that occurs when the membrane depolarizes to threshold._

4. Below is a drawing of a section of an axon. Complete the figure by illustrating the resting membrane potential, an area of depolarization and local current flow. Indicate the direction of the depolarization wave.

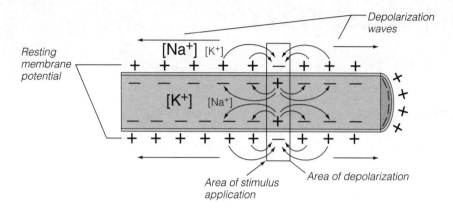

5. A nerve generally contains many thickly myelinated fibers that typically exhibit nodes of Ranvier. An action potential is generated along these fibers by "saltatory conduction." Use an appropriate reference to explain how saltatory conduction differs from conduction along unmyelinated fibers.

In saltatory conduction, the depolarization wave "jumps" from node to node along the fiber rather than passing down the entire

axolemma. Saltatory conduction is much faster.

Physiology of Nerve Fibers: Eliciting and Inhibiting the Nerve Impulse

6. Respond appropriately to each question posed below. Insert your responses in the corresponding numbered blanks to the right.

1–3. Name three types of stimuli that resulted in action potential generation in the sciatic nerve of the frog during the laboratory experiments.

4. Which of the stimuli resulted in the most effective nerve stimulation?

5. Which of the stimuli employed in that experiment might represent types of stimuli to which nerves in the human body are subjected?

6. What is the usual mode of stimulus transfer in neuron-to-neuron interactions?

7. Since the action potentials themselves were not visualized with an oscilloscope during this initial set of experiments, how did you recognize that impulses were being transmitted?

1. *electrical shock*

2. *chemical (acid or salt)*

3. *thermal (heat) or mechanical (pinching)*

4. *electrical shock*

5. *all of them*

6. *electrochemical*

7. *contraction of the gastrocnemius muscle*

7. Describe the observed effects of ether on nerve-muscle interaction. *Decreased reaction, lack of muscle response.*

Does ether exert its blocking effects on nerve *or* muscle? *Nerve* What observations made during the experiment support your conclusion? *Inability to stimulate the muscle by stimulating the nerve beyond the ether-soaked pad.*

8. At what site did the tubocurarine block the impulse transmission? _ACh receptor site of the muscle_ Provide evidence from the experiment to substantiate your conclusion. _Direct stimulation of the gastrocnemius muscle in the non-ligated muscle was successful in inducing the contraction._

Why was one of the frog's legs ligated in this experiment? _As a control to prevent the tubocurarine (in the blood) from reaching that muscle._

Visualizing the Action Potential with an Oscilloscope

9. What is a stimulus artifact? _A vertical deflection on the screen of an oscilloscope generated by an electrical impulse delivered to the muscle by the stimulating electrodes._

10. Explain why the amplitude of the action potential recorded from the frog sciatic nerve increased when the voltage of the stimulus was increased above the threshold value. _More and more muscle fibers were being recruited (multiple motor unit summation)._

11. What was the effect of cold temperature (flooding the nerve with iced Ringer's solution) on the functioning of the sciatic nerve tested? _Cold temperature increases the threshold for excitation and may result in complete inexcitability of the nerve._

12. When the nerve was reversed in position, was the impulse conducted in the opposite direction? _No_
How can this result be reconciled with the concept of one-way conduction in neurons? _In the body, nerve impulses are initiated by local currents created when sensory receptors are adequately stimulated or neurotransmitters (released by presynaptic axons) bind to receptors on the postsynaptic neuron. Action potentials only travel away from the point of their initiation because a repolarization wave follows the depolarization wave along the membrane._

Gross Anatomy of the Brain and Cranial Nerves

The Human Brain

1. Match the letters on the diagram of the human brain (right lateral view) to the appropriate terms listed at the left:

_h_____ 1. frontal lobe

_b_____ 2. parietal lobe

_j_____ 3. temporal lobe

_f_____ 4. precentral gyrus

_c_____ 5. parieto-occipital sulcus

_a_____ 6. postcentral gyrus

_i_____ 7. lateral sulcus

_g_____ 8. central sulcus

_e_____ 9. cerebellum

_l_____ 10. medulla

_d_____ 11. occipital lobe

_k_____ 12. pons

2. In which of the cerebral lobes would the following functional areas be found?

auditory area _temporal_____

primary motor area _frontal_____

primary sensory area _parietal_____

olfactory area _temporal_____

visual area _occipital_____

Broca's area _frontal_____

3. Which of the following structures are not part of the brain stem? (Circle the appropriate response or responses.)

(cerebral hemispheres)   pons   midbrain   (cerebellum)   medulla   (diencephalon)

4. Complete the following statements by writing the proper word or phrase on the corresponding blanks at the right.

A(n) __1__ is an elevated ridge of cerebral tissue. The convolutions seen in the cerebrum are important because they increase the __2__. Gray matter is composed of __3__. White matter is composed of __4__. A fiber tract that provides for communication between different parts of the same cerebral hemisphere is called a(n) __5__, whereas one that carries impulses to the cerebrum from, and from the cerebrum to, lower CNS areas is called a(n) __6__ tract. The lentiform nucleus along with the amygdaloid and caudate nuclei are collectively called the __7__.

1. _gyrus_____

2. _surface area_____

3. _neuron cell bodies_____

4. _myelinated fibers_____

5. _association tract_____

6. _projection_____

7. _basal nuclei_____

5. Identify the structures on the following sagittal view of the human brain by matching the numbered areas to the proper terms in the list.

_18_   a. cerebellum

_15_   b. cerebral aqueduct

_1_   c. cerebral hemisphere

_14_   d. cerebral peduncle

_10_   e. choroid plexus

_13_   f. corpora quadrigemina

_2_   g. corpus callosum

_4_   h. fornix

_16_   i. fourth ventricle

_6_   j. hypothalamus

_8_   k. mammillary bodies   _7_   n. optic chiasma   _17_   q. pons

_5_   l. massa intermedia   _12_   o. pineal body   _3_   r. septum pellucidum

_19_   m. medulla oblongata   _9_   p. pituitary gland   _11_   s. thalamus

6. Using the terms from item 5, match the appropriate structures with the descriptions given below:

_j_   1. site of regulation of body temperature and water balance; most important autonomic center

_c_   2. consciousness depends on the function of this part of the brain

_f_   3. located in the midbrain; contains reflex centers for vision and audition

_a_   4. responsible for regulation of posture and coordination of complex muscular movements

_s_   5. important synapse site for afferent fibers traveling to the sensory cortex

_m_   6. contains autonomic centers regulating blood pressure, heart rate, and respiratory rhythm, as well as coughing, sneezing, and swallowing centers

_g_   7. large commissure connecting the cerebral hemispheres

_h_   8. fiber tract involved with olfaction

_b_   9. connects the third and fourth ventricles

_s_   10. encloses the third ventricle

7. Embryologically, the brain arises from the rostral end of a tubelike structure that quickly becomes divided into three major regions. Groups of structures that develop from the embryonic brain are listed below. Designate the embryonic origin of each group as the hindbrain, midbrain, or forebrain.

   *forebrain*_____ 1. the diencephalon, including the thalamus, optic chiasma, and hypothalamus

   *hindbrain*_____ 2. the medulla, pons, and cerebellum

   *forebrain*_____ 3. the cerebral hemispheres

8. What is the function of the basal nuclei? *They are involved in the regulation, modulation, and refinement of voluntary motor*_____

   *activity.*_____

9. What is the corpus striatum, and how is it related to the fibers of the internal capsule? *The fibers of the internal capsule*_____

   *pass between the basal nuclei, giving them a striped appearance; therefore, a striped body or corpus striatum.*_____

   _____

10. A brain hemorrhage within the region of the right internal capsule results in paralysis of the left side of the body.

    Explain why the left side (rather than the right side) is affected. *Because most of the motor fibers cross over to the opposite*_____

    *side at the level of the medulla oblongata.*_____

11. Explain why trauma to the base of the brain is often much more dangerous than trauma to the frontal lobes. (*Hint:* Think about the relative functioning of the cerebral hemispheres and the brain stem structures. Which contain centers more vital to life?)

    *Trauma to the base of the brain might damage the medulla oblongata, which contains vital respiratory, cardiac, and vasomotor*_____

    *centers. Also, the reticular activating system, which helps to maintain consciousness, spans the length of the brain stem.*_____

    _____

12. In "split brain" experiments, the main commissure connecting the cerebral hemispheres is cut. First, name this commissure:

    *Corpus callosum*_____

    Then, describe what results (in terms of behavior) can be anticipated in such experiments. (Use an appropriate reference if you need help with this one!)

    *The disconnection of verbal naming and mathematical functions of the left side of the brain from the spatial recognition abilities*_____

    *of the right side (i.e. associating names with faces); some patients report that they no longer dream; isolated patients are mute for*_____

    *a brief time after surgery and have difficulty controlling the left side of the body.*_____

    _____

    _____

Meninges of the Brain

13. Identify the meningeal (or associated) structures described below:

dura mater _____ 1. outermost meninx covering the brain; composed of tough fibrous connective tissue

pia mater _____ 2. innermost meninx covering the brain; delicate and highly vascular

arachnoid villi _____ 3. structures instrumental in returning cerebrospinal fluid to the venous blood in the dural sinuses

choroid plexus _____ 4. structure that forms the cerebrospinal fluid

arachnoid mater _____ 5. middle meninx; like a cobweb in structure

dura mater _____ 6. its outer layer forms the periosteum of the skull

falx cerebri _____ 7. a dural fold that attaches the cerebrum to the crista galli of the skull

tentorium cerebelli _____ 8. a dural fold separating the cerebrum from the cerebellum

Cerebrospinal Fluid

14. Fill in the following flowchart by delineating the circulation of cerebrospinal fluid from its formation site (assume that this is one of the lateral ventricles) to the site of its reabsorption into the venous blood:

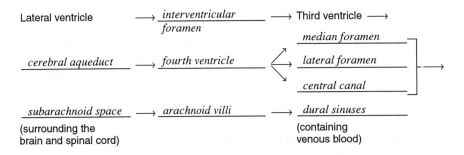

Lateral ventricle $\longrightarrow$ *interventricular foramen* $\longrightarrow$ Third ventricle $\longrightarrow$

cerebral aqueduct $\longrightarrow$ *fourth ventricle* $\Big\langle$ *median foramen* / *lateral foramen* / *central canal* $\Big]$ $\longrightarrow$

subarachnoid space $\longrightarrow$ *arachnoid villi* $\longrightarrow$ *dural sinuses*
(surrounding the brain and spinal cord)   (containing venous blood)

Now label appropriately the structures involved with circulation of cerebrospinal fluid on the accompanying diagram. (These structures are identified by leader lines.)

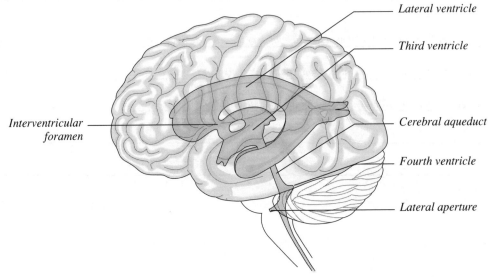

Lateral ventricle

Third ventricle

Interventricular foramen

Cerebral aqueduct

Fourth ventricle

Lateral aperture

Cranial Nerves

15. Using the terms below, correctly identify all structures indicated by leader lines on the diagram.

a. abducens nerve (VI)

b. accessory nerve (XI)

c. cerebellum

d. cerebral peduncle

e. decussation of the pyramids

f. facial nerve (VII)

g. frontal lobe of cerebral hemisphere

h. glossopharyngeal nerve (IX)

i. hypoglossal nerve (XII)

j. longitudinal fissure

k. mammillary body

l. medulla oblongata

m. oculomotor nerve (III)

n. olfactory bulb

o. olfactory tract

p. optic chiasma

q. optic nerve (II)

r. optic tract

s. pituitary gland

t. pons

u. spinal cord

v. temporal lobe of cerebral hemisphere

w. trigeminal nerve (V)

x. trochlear nerve (IV)

y. vagus nerve (X)

z. vestibulocochlear nerve (VIII)

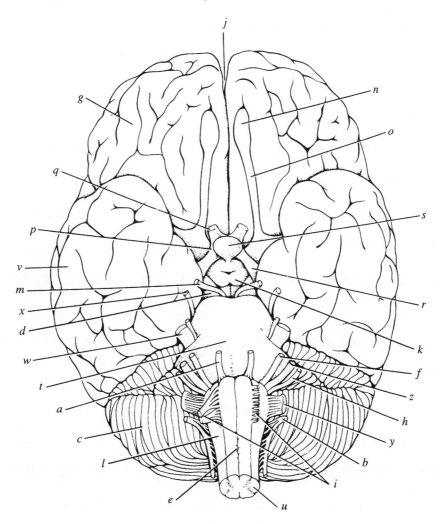

16. Provide the name and number of the cranial nerves involved in each of the following activities, sensations, or disorders:

accessory (XI) _____ 1. shrugging the shoulders

olfactory (I) _____ 2. smelling a flower

oculomotor (III) _____ 3. raising the eyelids; focusing the lens of the eye for accommodation; and pupillary constriction

vagus (X) _____ 4. slows the heart; increases the mobility of the digestive tract

facial (VII) _____ 5. involved in Bell's palsy (facial paralysis)

trigeminal (V) _____ 6. chewing food

vestibulocochlear (VIII) _____ 7. listening to music; seasickness

facial (VII) _____ 8. secretion of saliva; tasting well-seasoned food

III, IV, VI _____ 9. involved in "rolling" the eyes (three nerves—provide numbers only)

trigeminal (V) _____ 10. feeling a toothache

optic (II) _____ 11. reading *Mad* magazine

I, II, VIII _____ 12. purely sensory in function (three nerves—provide numbers only)

Dissection of the Sheep Brain

17. In your own words, describe the firmness and texture of the sheep brain tissue as observed when cutting into it.

    Very soft; much like thickened oatmeal in consistency. _____

    Because formalin hardens all tissue, what conclusions might you draw about the firmness and texture of living brain

    tissue? *It must be very soft and fragile.* _____

18. Compare the relative sizes of the cerebral hemispheres in sheep and human brains? *The cerebral hemispheres are*

    much larger in humans. _____

    What is the significance of these differences? *Evolution of the cerebral hemispheres in humans has encompassed higher*

    functions; i.e. speech, reasoning, etc. _____

19. Compare the sizes of the brain stems in sheep and human brains. *They are similar in size.* _____

    What is the significance? *The brain stem is responsible for automatic behavior necessary for survival. These functions are similar in*

    sheep and humans. _____

20. Why are the olfactory bulbs much larger in the sheep brain than in the human brain? *The sense of smell is an important*

    survival sense (food finding, recognition of predators) in sheep. This is not true in humans.

Electroencephalography

Brain Wave Patterns and the Electroencephalogram

1. Define *EEG*. *A record of the electrical activity of the brain.* _____

2. What are the four major types of brain wave patterns? *Alpha, beta, delta, theta* _____

   Match each statement below to a type of brain wave pattern:

   delta _____ below 4 Hz; slow, large waves; normally seen during deep sleep

   alpha _____ rhythm generally apparent when an individual is in a relaxed, nonattentive state with the eyes closed

   beta _____ correlated to the alert state; usually about 15 to 25 Hz

3. What is meant by the term *alpha block*? *A change from an alpha rhythm to increased frequency waves as a result of increased*

   alertness, mental concentration, excitement, etc. _____

   _____

4. List at least four types of brain lesions that may be determined by EEG studies. _____

   Epileptic foci, infections, tumors, abscesses, blood clots

5. What is the common result of hypoactivity or hyperactivity of the brain neurons? *Unconsciousness* _____

Observing Brain Wave Patterns

6. How was alpha block demonstrated in the laboratory experiment? *By clapping your hands, which caught the attention of the*

   subject. _____

7. What was the effect of mental concentration on the brain wave pattern? *(Should have) increased the frequency of the brain*

   waves from the level of the alpha rhythm. _____

   _____

8. What effect on the brain wave pattern did hyperventilation have? *Produced a fast, irregular pattern.* _____

   Why? *Alkalosis increases neuronal irritability and results in a brain wave pattern resembling that of an epileptic seizure.*

   _____

Electroencephalography Using BIOPAC®

9. Observe the average frequency of the waves you measured for each rhythm. Did the calculated average fall within the specified range indicated in the introduction to Exercise 20?

The average should fall within the normal range.

10. Suggest the possible advantages and disadvantages of using electroencephalography in a clinical setting.

EEG is a useful tool in the clinical setting to assess cerebral activity in generalized brain regions. Because EEG is indirectly recording,

via the scalp, the activity of millions of nerve cells simultaneously, it is less effective in assessing the function of very specific regions of

the brain.

Spinal Cord, Spinal Nerves, and the Autonomic Nervous System

Anatomy of the Spinal Cord

1. Match the descriptions given below to the proper anatomical term:

Key: a. cauda equina   b. conus medullaris   c. filum terminale   d. foramen magnum

  _d_   1. most superior boundary of the spinal cord

  _c_   2. meningeal extension beyond the spinal cord terminus

  _b_   3. spinal cord terminus

  _a_   4. collection of spinal nerves traveling in the vertebral canal below the terminus of the spinal cord

2. Match the key letters on the diagram with the following terms.

  _m_   1. anterior (ventral) horn   _n_   6. dorsal root of spinal nerve   _c_   11. posterior (dorsal) horn

  _k_   2. arachnoid mater   _j_   7. dura mater   _f_   12. spinal nerve

  _a_   3. central canal   _o_   8. gray commissure   _i_   13. ventral ramus of spinal nerve

  _h_   4. dorsal ramus of spinal nerve   _d_   9. lateral horn   _e_   14. ventral root of spinal nerve

  _g_   5. dorsal root ganglion   _l_   10. pia mater   _b_   15. white matter

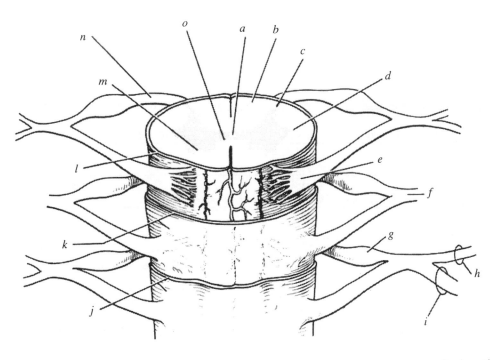

3. Choose the proper answer from the following key to respond to the descriptions relating to spinal cord anatomy.

Key: a. afferent   b. efferent   c. both afferent and efferent   d. association

    _d_   1. neuron type found in posterior horn   _b_   4. fiber type in ventral root

    _b_   2. neuron type found in anterior horn   _a_   5. fiber type in dorsal root

    _a_   3. neuron type in dorsal root ganglion   _c_   6. fiber type in spinal nerve

4. Where in the vertebral column is a lumbar puncture generally done? _Between the third and fourth lumbar vertebrae._

Why is this the site of choice? _The spinal cord ends at the level of L_2; thus there is little chance of damaging it below that level._

5. The spinal cord is enlarged in two regions, the _cervical_ and the _lumbar_ regions.

What is the significance of these enlargements? _Nerves serving the limbs issue from these regions of the spinal cord._

6. How does the position of the gray and white matter differ in the spinal cord and the cerebral hemispheres?

In the spinal cord, the white matter surrounds the gray matter. In the cerebral hemisphere, there is an outer "rind" of gray matter and

deep to that is white matter with a few scattered islands of gray matter.

7. From the key to the right, choose the name of the tract that might be damaged when the following conditions are observed. (More than one choice may apply.)

    _e, f, g_   1. uncoordinated movement

    _c, d_   2. lack of voluntary movement

    _e, f, g_   3. tremors, jerky movements

    _h_   4. diminished pain perception

    _a, b, i_   5. diminished sense of touch

Key: a. fasciculus gracilis
           b. fasciculus cuneatus
           c. lateral corticospinal tract
           d. anterior corticospinal tract
           e. tectospinal tract
           f. rubrospinal tract
           g. vestibulospinal tract
           h. lateral spinothalamic tract
           i. anterior spinothalamic tract
           j. posterior spinocerebellar tract
           k. anterior spinocerebellar tract

8. Use an appropriate reference to describe the functional significance of an upper motor neuron and a lower motor neuron:

upper motor neuron _Pyramidal cells of the motor cortex and neurons in subcortical motor nuclei that give rise to descending_

motor pathways.

lower motor neuron _Anterior horn motor neuron that stimulates voluntary muscle._

Will contraction of a muscle occur if the lower motor neurons serving it have been destroyed? _No_ If the upper motor

neurons serving it have been destroyed? _Yes_ Using an appropriate reference, differentiate between flaccid and spastic

paralysis and note the possible causes of each. _Flaccid paralysis occurs when anterior horn neurons are destroyed (e.g. spinal_ *cord transection in an auto accident). The muscle receives no stimulation; thus, it becomes flaccid and atrophies. Spastic paralysis*

occurs as a result of upper motor neuron damage (e.g. from brain hemorrhage). Voluntary motor activity is lost, but reflex movements

initiated by spinal cord neurons still occur. The muscle does not become limp (flaccid), but instead becomes more tense and shows

hyperactive and uncontrolled movement.

Spinal Nerves and Nerve Plexuses

9. In the human, there are 31 pairs of spinal nerves, named according to the region of the vertebral column from which they issue. The spinal nerves are named below. Indicate how they are numbered.

cervical nerves $C_1 - C_8$ sacral nerves $S_1 - S_5$

lumbar nerves $L_1 - L_5$ thoracic nerves $T_1 - T_{12}$

10. The ventral rami of spinal nerves C_1 through T_1 and T_{12} through S_4 take part in forming *plexuses* ,

which serve the *limbs and anterior trunk* of the body. The ventral rami of T_2 through T_{12} run

between the ribs to serve the *intercostal muscles* . The dorsal rami of the spinal nerves

serve *the posterior body trunk* .

11. What would happen if the following structures were damaged or transected? (Use key choices for responses.)

Key: a.   loss of motor function   b.   loss of sensory function   c.   loss of both motor and sensory function

  b   1.   dorsal root of a spinal nerve   *c*   3.   anterior ramus of a spinal nerve

  a   2.   ventral root of a spinal nerve

12. Define *plexus*: *A complex network of joining and diverging nerves.*

13. Name the major nerves that serve the following body areas:

cervical   1.   head, neck, shoulders (name plexus only)

phrenic   2.   diaphragm

sciatic   3.   posterior thigh

common fibular, tibial, sural, medial and lateral plantar   4.   leg and foot (name two)

median ulnar   5.   anterior forearm muscles (name two)

radial, musculocutaneous   6.   arm muscles (name two)

lumbar   7.   abdominal wall (name plexus only)

femoral   8.   anterior thigh

ulnar   9.   medial side of the hand

Dissection of the Spinal Cord

14. Compare and contrast the meninges of the spinal cord and the brain. _Both the spinal cord and the brain have three meninges: pia mater, arachnoid mater, and dura mater. In the brain the dura mater has two layers—periosteal and meningeal. The spinal cord has only the meningeal layer._

15. How can you distinguish between the anterior and posterior horns? _The anterior horns are wider than the posterior horns. The posterior horns extend closer to the edge of the spinal cord._

16. How does the position of gray and white matter differ from that in the cerebral hemispheres of the sheep brain? _White matter is deep to the gray matter of the cerebral cortex, and superficial to the gray matter of the spinal cord._

The Autonomic Nervous System

17. For the most part, sympathetic and parasympathetic fibers serve the same organs and structures. How can they exert antagonistic effects? (After all, nerve impulses are nerve impulses—aren't they?)

They release different neurotransmitters, which bind to different receptors.

18. Name three structures that receive sympathetic but not parasympathetic innervation.

Adrenal glands, arrector pili muscles, and sweat glands.

19. A pelvic splanchnic nerve contains (circle one):

a. preganglionic sympathetic fibers.   (c. preganglionic parasympathetic fibers.)

b. postganglionic sympathetic fibers.   d. postganglionic parasympathetic fibers.

20. The following chart states a number of conditions. Use a check mark to show which division of the autonomic nervous system is involved in each.

Sympathetic division	Condition	Parasympathetic division
✓	Secretes norepinephrine; adrenergic fibers	
	Secretes acetylcholine; cholinergic fibers	✓
	Long preganglionic axon; short postganglionic axon	✓
✓	Short preganglionic axon; long postganglionic axon	
	Arises from cranial and sacral nerves	✓
✓	Arises from spinal nerves T_1 through L_3	
	Normally in control	✓
✓	"Fight or flight" system	
	Has more specific control (Look it up!)	✓

Galvanic Skin Response Using BIOPAC®

21. Describe exactly how, from a physiological standpoint, GSR can be correlated with activity of the autonomic nervous system.

    The autonomic nervous system controls sweat glands of the skin. Increased moisture on the skin decreases its electrical resistance, which

    can be recorded.

22. Based on this brief and unprofessional exposure to a polygraph, explain why this might not be an exact tool for testing the sincerity and honesty of a subject.

    It is not possible to state with certainty that every subject who lies will have an absolutely predictable autonomic nervous system re-

    sponse. For this reason, although GSR is useful as an investigative tool, it is not accepted as an exact measurement tool.

Human Reflex Physiology

The Reflex Arc

1. Define *reflex:* _Motor response to a stimulus which is mediated over a neural pathway called a reflex arc._

_____

2. Name five essential components of a reflex arc: _receptor_ _____, _sensory neuron_ _____,

integration center _____, _motor neuron_ _____, and _effector_ _____

3. In general, what is the importance of reflex testing in a routine physical examination? _Allows the condition of the nervous_

system to be assessed. Pathology is indicated by exaggeration, distortion, or absence of reflexes normally present.

_____

Somatic and Autonomic Reflexes

4. Use the key terms to complete the statements given below.

Key: a. abdominal reflex   d. corneal reflex   g. patellar reflex
       b. Achilles jerk   e. crossed extensor reflex h. plantar reflex
       c. ciliospinal reflex   f. gag reflex   i. pupillary light reflex

Reflexes classified as somatic reflexes include a _a_ , _b_ , _d_ , _e_ , _f_ , _g_ , and _h_ .

Of these, the simple stretch reflexes are _b_ and _g_ , and the superficial cord reflexes are _a_ and _h_ .

Reflexes classified as autonomic reflexes include _c_ and _i_ .

5. Name two cord-mediated reflexes: _Achilles reflex_ _____ and _patellar reflex (crossed extensor reflex is also_

cord-mediated)

Name two somatic reflexes in which the higher brain centers participate: _abdominal_ _____

and _plantar (also the corneal and gag reflexes)_

6. Can the stretch reflex be elicited in a pithed animal? _Yes, in a singly pithed frog in which the cord is intact._

Explain your answer. _It is a cord-mediated reflex (initiated and executed at the spinal cord level)._

_____

7. Trace the reflex arc, naming efferent and afferent nerves, receptors, effectors, and integration centers, for the following reflexes:

patellar reflex *Proprioceptors (stretch receptors) in the quadriceps muscle → afferent fibers of femoral nerve → spinal cord →*

efferent fibers of femoral nerve → quadriceps muscle.

Achilles reflex *Proprioceptors (stretch receptors) in the gastrocnemius muscle → afferent fibers of sciatic nerve → spinal cord →*

efferent fibers of sciatic nerve → gastrocnemius (triceps surae) muscle.

8. Three factors that influence the rapidity and effectiveness of reflex arcs were investigated in conjunction with patellar reflex testing—mental distraction, effect of simultaneous muscle activity in another body area, and fatigue.

Which of these factors increases the excitatory level of the spinal cord? *Simultaneous muscle activity*

Which factor decreases the excitatory level of the muscles? *Muscle fatigue (exercise)*

When the subject was concentrating on an arithmetic problem, did the change noted in the patellar reflex indicate that brain

activity is necessary for the patellar reflex or only that it may modify it? *Only that it may modify it. Will occur in any case.*

9. Name the division of the autonomic nervous system responsible for each of the following reflexes:

ciliospinal reflex *sympathetic*　　　　　　　　　salivary reflex *parasympathetic*

pupillary light reflex *parasympathetic*

10. The pupillary light reflex, the crossed extensor reflex, and the corneal reflex illustrate the purposeful nature of reflex activity. Describe the protective aspect of each:

pupillary light reflex *Protects the retina from excessive illumination, which is damaging to the photoreceptors.*

corneal reflex *Protects the eye from trauma.*

crossed extensor reflex *Withdraws the injured limb from the painful stimulus while simultaneously extending the opposite limb. If the*

upper limbs are involved, extension of the opposite limb acts to push the stimulus away. If the lower limbs are involved, extension of

the opposite limb prepares the limb to receive the body weight.

11. Was the pupillary consensual response contralateral or ipsilateral? *Contralateral*

Why would such a response be of significant value in this particular reflex? *If the light source was intense, both eyes would*

probably be illuminated.

12. Differentiate between the types of activities accomplished by somatic and autonomic reflexes. _Autonomic reflexes involve_

the activation of smooth or cardiac muscle and glands. Somatic reflexes involve the activation of skeletal muscles.

13. Several types of reflex activity were not investigated in this exercise. The most important of these are autonomic reflexes, which are difficult to illustrate in a laboratory situation. To rectify this omission, complete the following chart, using references as necessary.

Reflex	Organ involved	Receptors stimulated	Action
Micturition (urination)	*Bladder*	*Stretch receptors in the bladder wall*	*Impulse goes to cord (afferent fibers) and returns (efferent fibers), causing bladder contraction and relaxation of its internal sphincter.*
Hering-Breuer	*Lungs*	*Stretch receptors in the lungs*	*Upon excessive inspiration, afferent impulses are sent to the pons and medulla oblongata, which in turn send efferent impulses to terminate the inspiratory effort.*
Defecation	*Rectum*	*Stretch receptors in the rectal walls (colon terminus)*	*Afferent impulses to the sacral region of the cord followed by efferent impulses to the muscles of the rectum and the anal sphincters to initiate feces evacuation.*
Carotid sinus	*Carotid artery*	*Pressure receptors in the carotid sinus*	*When arterial pressure increases excessively, sensory impulses travel to the cardioinhibitory center in the medulla oblongata, which in turn sends efferent impulses via the vagus nerve to slow the heart, thus decreasing its rate and the blood pressure.*

Reaction Time of Basic and Learned or Acquired Reflexes

14. How do basic and learned or acquired reflexes differ? *Although there is no clear-cut distinction, in general basic reflexes are*

inborn and use a specific reflex arc. Learned or acquired reflexes are the result of practice and repetition, involving more neural path-

ways and higher intellectual activities.

15. Name at least three factors that may modify reaction time to a stimulus. *Receptor sensitivity, nerve conduction velocity, and the*

number of neurons and synapses involved.

16. In general, how did the response time for the unlearned activity performed in the laboratory compare to that for the simple

patellar reflex? *It was much longer.*

17. Did the response time without verbal stimuli decrease with practice? *Yes* Explain the reason for this.

The subject was anticipating the stimulus.

18. Explain, in detail, why response time increased when the subject had to react to a word stimulus.

Choice and decision making about the response involved and the large number of synapses involved increased the response time.

19. When measuring reaction time in the BIOPAC® activity, was there a difference in reaction time when the stimulus is predictable versus unpredictable? Explain your answer.

It is most likely that the reaction time will be shorter during the segments with predictable, evenly-spaced stimuli, than during the ran-

dom segments. The subject can more easily predict the onset of the stimulus, reducing reaction time.

General Sensation

Structure of General Sensory Receptors

1. Differentiate between interoceptors and exteroceptors relative to location and stimulus source:

interoceptor: _In viscera or deep in body tissues; internal stimuli_

exteroceptor: _At or close to the body surface; stimuli in external environment_

2. A number of activities and sensations are listed in the chart below. For each, check whether the receptors would be exteroceptors or interoceptors; and then name the specific receptor types. (Because visceral receptors were not described in detail in this exercise, you need only indicate that the receptor is a visceral receptor if it falls into that category.)

Activity or sensation	Exteroceptor	Interoceptor	Specific receptor type
Backing into a sun-heated iron railing	✓		_Pain receptors_
Someone steps on your foot	✓ ✓		_Pain receptors_ _Pacinian corpuscles_
Reading a book	✓		_Rods/cones of the eye (photoreceptors)_
Leaning on your elbows	✓	✓	_Pacinian corpuscles_ _Proprioceptors_
Doing sit-ups		✓	_Proprioceptors_
The "too full" sensation		✓	_Visceral receptors (stretch)_
Seasickness	✓		_Equilibrium apparatus of the inner ear_

Receptor Physiology

3. Explain how the sensory receptors act as transducers: _Convert other energy types, e.g. pressure (mechanical energy), to the electrochemical nerve impulse._

4. Define _stimulus_: _An irritant capable of producing a response._

5. What was demonstrated by the two-point discrimination test? _The relative density of touch receptors in various body areas (lips, fingertips, etc.)_

How well did your results correspond to your predictions? _____

_____

Correlate the accuracy of the subject's tactile localization with the results of the two-point discrimination test.

Areas with the most accurate touch localization were demonstrated to have the smallest two-point thresholds.

6. Define *punctate distribution*: _Having specific localization or found at certain descrete points._

7. Several questions regarding general sensation are posed below. Answer each by placing your response in the appropriately numbered blanks to the right.

    1.   Which cutaneous receptors are the most numerous?

    2–3. Which two body areas tested were most sensitive to touch?

    4–5. Which two body areas tested were least sensitive to touch?

    6.   Which appear to be more numerous—receptors that respond to cold or to heat?

    7–9. Where would referred pain appear if the following organs were receiving painful stimuli—(7) gallbladder, (8) kidneys, and (9) appendix? (Use your textbook if necessary.)

    10. Where was referred pain felt when the elbow was immersed in ice water during the laboratory experiment?

    11. What region of the cerebrum interprets the kind and intensity of stimuli that cause cutaneous sensations?

1. _pain receptors_

2. _lips_

3. _fingertips_

4. _back of calf_

5. _back of neck_

6. _cold_

7. _right inferior thorax_

8. _lumbar pain_

9. _right lower quadrant of abdominal surface_

10. _medial aspect of hand_

11. _somatosensory association area_

8. Define *adaptation of sensory receptors*: _Decline in receptor sensitivity and stimulation with prolonged unchanging stimuli._

9. Why is it advantageous to have pain receptors that are sensitive to all vigorous stimuli, whether heat, cold, or pressure?

Because all of these stimuli, if excessive, cause tissue damage.

Why is the nonadaptability of pain receptors important? _Pain is a warning of actual or potential tissue damage._

10. Imagine yourself without any cutaneous sense organs. Why might this be very dangerous? _Many external stimuli (heat, cold, pressure) which can threaten homeostasis might go undetected, and proper protective measures might not be taken._

11. Define *referred pain*: _An experience in which pain is perceived as coming from a site other than that receiving the painful stimulus._

What is the probable explanation for referred pain? (Consult your textbook or an appropriate reference if necessary.)

Both the site of referred pain and the visceral region receiving the actual painful stimulus are innervated by the same spinal nerve(s).

Special Senses: Vision

Anatomy of the Eye

1. Name five accessory eye structures that contribute to the formation of tears and/or aid in lubrication of the eyeball, and then name the major secretory product of each. Indicate which has antibacterial properties by circling the correct secretory product.

Accessory structures	Product
lacrimal glands	*saline solution;* (*lysozyme*)
conjunctiva	*mucus*
tarsal or meibomian glands	*oily secretion*
caruncle	*whitish. oily secretion*
ciliary glands	*sweat*

2. The eyeball is wrapped in adipose tissue within the orbit. What is the function of the adipose tissue?

To package, protect, and cushion the eyeball in the bony orbit.

What seven bones form the bony orbit? (Think! If you can't remember, check a skull or your text.)

sphenoid   *ethmoid*   *palatine*

zygomatic   *maxillary*

frontal   *lacrimal*

3. Why does one often have to blow one's nose after crying? *Because tears drain into the nasal cavities via the*

nasolacrimal ducts.

4. Identify the extrinsic eye muscle predominantly responsible for the actions described below.

lateral rectus   1. turns the eye laterally

medial rectus   2. turns the eye medially

inferior oblique   3. turns the eye up and laterally

inferior rectus   4. turns the eye inferiorly

superior rectus   5. turns the eye superiorly

superior oblique   6. turns the eye down and laterally

5. What is a sty? _Inflammation of a small oil or sweat gland associated with the eye exterior._

Conjunctivitis? _Inflammation of the conjunctiva._

6. Using the terms listed on the right, correctly identify all structures provided with leader lines in the diagram.

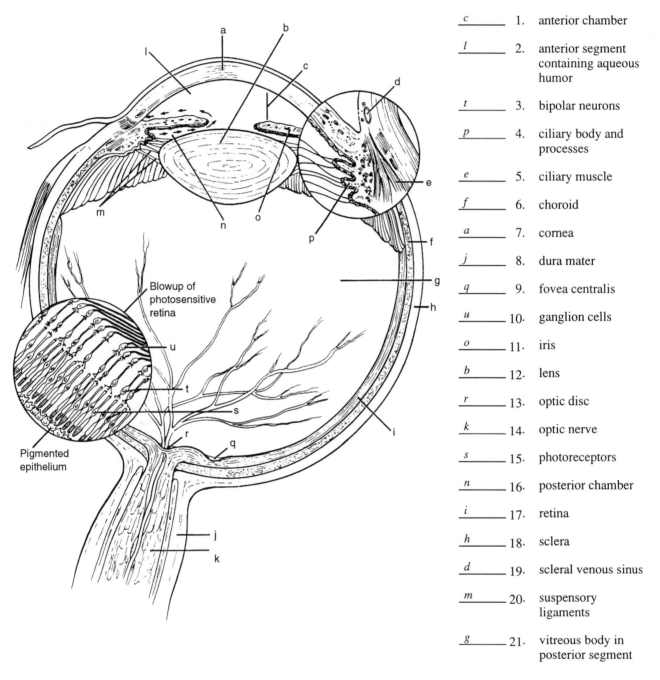

_c_	1.	anterior chamber
_l_	2.	anterior segment containing aqueous humor
_t_	3.	bipolar neurons
_p_	4.	ciliary body and processes
_e_	5.	ciliary muscle
_f_	6.	choroid
_a_	7.	cornea
_j_	8.	dura mater
_q_	9.	fovea centralis
_u_	10.	ganglion cells
_o_	11.	iris
_b_	12.	lens
_r_	13.	optic disc
_k_	14.	optic nerve
_s_	15.	photoreceptors
_n_	16.	posterior chamber
_i_	17.	retina
_h_	18.	sclera
_d_	19.	scleral venous sinus
_m_	20.	suspensory ligaments
_g_	21.	vitreous body in posterior segment

Notice the arrows drawn close to the left side of the iris in the diagram above. What do they indicate?

The flow of aqueous humor from the ciliary processes of the ciliary body to the scleral venous sinus (canal of Schlemm).

7. Match the key responses with the descriptive statements that follow.

Key: a. aqueous humor e. cornea j. retina
     b. choroid f. fovea centralis k. sclera
     c. ciliary body g. iris l. scleral venous sinus
     d. ciliary processes of h. lens m. suspensory ligament
        the ciliary body i. optic disc n. vitreous humor

m; suspensory ligament   1. attaches the lens to the ciliary body

a; aqueous humor   2. fluid filling the anterior segment of the eye

k; sclera   3. the "white" of the eye

i; optic disc   4. part of the retina that lacks photoreceptors

c; ciliary body   5. modification of the choroid that controls the shape of the crystalline lens

c; ciliary body   6. contains the ciliary muscle

l; scleral venous sinus   7. drains the aqueous humor from the eye

j; retina   8. tunic containing the rods and cones

n; vitreous humor   9. substance occupying the posterior segment of the eyeball

b; choroid   10. forms the bulk of the heavily pigmented vascular tunic

c; ciliary body , _g; iris_   11. smooth muscle structures

f; fovea centralis   12. area of critical focusing and discriminatory vision

d; ciliary processes of the ciliary body   13. form (by filtration) the aqueous humor

a; aqueous humor , _e; cornea_ , _h; lens_ ,

n; vitreous humor   14. light-bending media of the eye

e; cornea   15. anterior continuation of the sclera—your "window on the world"

k; sclera   16. composed of tough, white, opaque, fibrous connective tissue

8. The iris is composed primarily of two smooth muscle layers, one arranged radially and the other circularly.

Which of these dilates the pupil? _The radial layer_

9. You would expect the pupil to be dilated in which of the following circumstances? Circle the correct response(s).

  a. in brightly lit surroundings   c. during focusing for near vision

  (b. in dimly lit surroundings)   (d. in observing distant objects)

10. The intrinsic eye muscles are under the control of which of the following? (Circle the correct response.)

       (autonomic nervous system)   somatic nervous system

Microscopic Anatomy of the Retina

11. The two major layers of the retina are the epithelial and nervous layers. In the nervous layer, the neuron populations are arranged as follows from the epithelial layer to the vitreous humor. (Circle all proper responses.)

bipolar cells, ganglion cells, photoreceptors

photoreceptors, ganglion cells, bipolar cells

ganglion cells, bipolar cells, photoreceptors

(photoreceptors, bipolar cells, ganglion cells)

12. The axons of the _ganglion_ cells form the optic nerve, which exits from the eyeball.

13. Complete the following statements by writing either *rods* or *cones* on each blank:

The dim light receptors are the _rods_. Only _cones_ are found in the fovea centralis, whereas mostly _rods_ are found in the periphery of the retina.

Cones are the photoreceptors that operate best in bright light and allow for color vision.

Visual Pathways to the Brain

14. The visual pathway to the occipital lobe of the brain consists most simply of a chain of five neurons. Beginning with the photoreceptor cell of the retina, name them and note their location in the pathway.

(1) _photo receptor cell; retina_

(2) _bipolar cell; retina_

(3) _ganglion cell; retina_

(4) _neuron; lateral geniculate nucleus of the thalamus_

(5) _cortical neuron; occipital (visual) cortex of the_

cerebral hemisphere(s)

15. Visual field tests are done to reveal destruction along the visual pathway from the retina to the optic region of the brain. Note where the lesion is likely to be in the following cases:

Normal vision in left eye visual field; absence of vision in right eye visual field: _Right optic nerve_

Normal vision in both eyes for right half of the visual field; absence of vision in both eyes for left half of the visual

field: _Right optic tract (or right optic cortex)_

16. How is the right optic *tract* anatomically different from the right optic *nerve*? _The right optic nerve contains fibers from the right eye only. The right optic tract contains fibers from the lateral aspect of the right eye and the medial aspect of the left eye._

Dissection of the Cow (Sheep) Eye

17. What modification of the choroid that is not present in humans is found in the cow eye? _Tapetum lucidum_

What is its function? _To reflect light that enters the eye, thus increasing light stimulation of the retina under dim light conditions._

18. What does the retina look like? _Thin yellowish white membrane. (Often becomes crumpled during dissection of the eye.)_

At what point is it attached to the posterior aspect of the eyeball? _At the optic disc._

Visual Tests and Experiments

19. Match the terms in column B with the descriptions in column A:

Column A		Column B
g; refraction 1.	light bending	a. accommodation
a; accommodation 2.	ability to focus for close (under 20 ft) vision	b. astigmatism
d; emmetropia 3.	normal vision	c. convergence
e; hyperopia 4.	inability to focus well on close objects (farsightedness)	d. emmetropia
f; myopia 5.	nearsightedness	e. hyperopia
b; astigmatism 6.	blurred vision due to unequal curvatures of the lens or cornea	f. myopia
c; convergence 7.	medial movement of the eyes during focusing on close objects	g. refraction

20. Complete the following statements:

In farsightedness, the light is focused __1__ the retina. The lens required to treat myopia is a __2__ lens. The "near point" increases with age because the __3__ of the lens decreases as we get older. A convex lens, like that of the eye, produces an image that is upside down and reversed from left to right. Such an image is called a __4__ image.

1. _behind_
2. _concave_
3. _elasticity_
4. _real_

21. Use terms from the key to complete the statements concerning near and distance vision.

Key: a. contracted   b. decreased   c. increased   d. relaxed   e. taut

During distance vision: The ciliary muscle is _d_____, the suspensory ligament is _e_____, the convexity of the lens is _b_____, and light refraction is _b_____. During close vision: The ciliary muscle is _a_____, the suspensory ligament is _d_____, lens convexity is _c_____, and light refraction is _c_____.

22. Explain why vision is lost when light hits the blind spot. _This area lacks photoreceptors._

23. What is meant by the term *negative afterimage* and what does this phenomenon indicate? _Relative to retinal function, a negative afterimage is a dark image of a bright object (e.g. light bulb) that is "seen" when the eyes are closed after viewing the bright object. It indicates that the rhodopsin pigments have been bleached._

24. Record your Snellen eye test results below:

Left eye (without glasses) _____ (with glasses) _____

Right eye (without glasses) _____ (with glasses) _____

Is your visual acuity normal, less than normal, or better than normal? _____

Explain. _____

_____

Explain why each eye is tested separately when using the Snellen eye chart. *There is usually a slight difference in the visual*

acuity of the two eyes.

Explain 20/40 vision. *Poorer than normal vision. Able to read #40 letters at 20 feet. The normal eye reads these letters at 40 feet.*

_____

Explain 20/10 vision. *Better than normal vision. Can read #10 letters at 20 feet. The normal eye would have to be 10 feet away to*

read these letters.

25. Define *astigmatism:* *Blurred vision due to unequal curvatures of the lens or cornea.*

_____

How can it be corrected? *With specially ground (circularly ground) lenses.*

26. Record the distance of your near point of accommodation as tested in the laboratory:

right eye _____ left eye _____

Is your near point within the normal range for your age? _____

27. Define *presbyopia:* *"Old vision." A hyperopia resulting from decreasing lens elasticity with advancing age.*

_____

What causes it? *Decreased function of an increasingly inelastic lens.*

28. To which wavelengths of light do the three cone types of the retina respond maximally?

red _____, *blue* _____, and *green* _____

29. How can you explain the fact that we see a great range of colors even though only three cone types exist?

When more than one cone type is stimulated simultaneously, intermediate colors (of the visible spectrum) are seen.

_____

30. What is the usual cause of color blindness? *Malfunction or absence of one or more of the three cone types.*

_____

31. Explain the difference between binocular and panoramic vision. _Binocular—visual fields overlap considerably but not_ _completely; therefore, slightly different views are received by each eye. Panoramic—little or no overlap of visual fields; therefore,_ _each eye "sees" a different view._

What is the advantage of binocular vision? _Allows for depth perception._

What factor(s) are responsible for binocular vision? _The slight difference between the visual fields of the two eyes and the partial_ _crossover at the optic chiasma._

32. In the experiment on the convergence reflex, what happened to the position of the eyeballs as the object was moved closer to the subject's eyes? _Eyeballs turned medially._

What extrinsic eye muscles control the movement of the eyes during this reflex? _Medial recti_

What is the value of this reflex? _Allows the image to be precisely focused on the fovea of each eye._

What would be the visual result of an inability of these muscles to function? _Diplopia (double vision)_

33. In the experiment on the photopupillary reflex, what happened to the pupil of the eye exposed to light?

It constricted. What happened to the pupil of the nonilluminated eye? _It constricted._

Explanation? _Regulation of pupil constriction by the parasympathetic division of the autonomic nervous system is coordinate (i.e._ _consensual) and prevents overillumination of the delicate retinal cells._

34. Why is the ophthalmoscopic examination an important diagnostic tool? _Allows noninvasive examination of the retinal_ _condition and vasulature._

35. Many college students struggling through mountainous reading assignments are told that they need glasses for "eyestrain." Why is it more of a strain on the extrinsic and intrinsic eye muscles to look at close objects than at far objects?

No accommodation or convergence is required for distant vision.

Special Senses: Hearing and Equilibrium

Anatomy of the Ear

1. Select the terms from column B that apply to the column A descriptions. Some terms are used more than once.

Column A

_d_ , _i_ , _m_   1. structures composing the outer or external ear

_b_ , _k_ , _n_   2. structures composing the inner ear

_e_ , _f_ , _l_   3. collectively called the ossicles

_i_ , _k_   4. ear structures not involved with audition

_a_   5. involved in equalizing the pressure in the middle ear with atmospheric pressure

_m_   6. vibrates at the same frequency as sound waves hitting it; transmits the vibrations to the ossicles

_k_ , _n_   7. contain receptors for the sense of balance

_g_   8. transmits the vibratory motion of the stirrup to the fluid in the scala vestibuli of the inner ear

_j_   9. acts as a pressure relief valve for the increased fluid pressure in the scala tympani; bulges into the tympanic cavity

_a_   10. passage between the throat and the tympanic cavity

_c_   11. fluid contained within the membranous labyrinth

_h_   12. fluid contained within the osseous labyrinth and bathing the membranous labyrinth

Column B

a. auditory (pharyngotympanic) tube

b. cochlea

c. endolymph

d. external auditory canal

e. incus (anvil)

f. malleus (hammer)

g. oval window

h. perilymph

i. pinna

j. round window

k. semicircular canals

l. stapes (stirrup)

m. tympanic membrane

n. vestibule

2. Identify all indicated structures and ear regions in the following diagram.

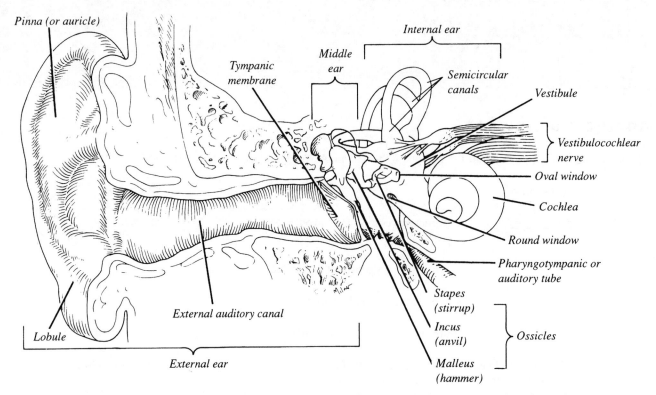

3. Match the membranous labyrinth structures listed in column B with the descriptive statements in column A:

Column A

<u>g</u> , <u>j</u>   1. sacs found within the vestibule

<u>c</u>   2. contains the organ of Corti

<u>g</u> , <u>j</u>   3. sites of the maculae

<u>h</u>   4. positioned in all spatial planes

<u>b</u>   5. hair cells of organ of Corti rest on this membrane

<u>i</u>   6. gelatinous membrane overlying the hair cells of the organ of Corti

<u>a</u>   7. contains the crista ampullaris

<u>f</u> , <u>g</u> , <u>j</u> , <u>k</u>   8. function in static equilibrium

<u>a</u> , <u>e</u> , <u>h</u> , <u>k</u>   9. function in dynamic equilibrium

<u>d</u>   10. carries auditory information to the brain

<u>e</u>   11. gelatinous cap overlying hair cells of the crista ampullaris

<u>f</u>   12. grains of calcium carbonate in the maculae

Column B

a. ampulla

b. basilar membrane

c. cochlear duct

d. cochlear nerve

e. cupula

f. otoliths

g. saccule

h. semicircular ducts

i. tectorial membrane

j. utricle

k. vestibular nerve

4. Sound waves hitting the eardrum initiate its vibratory motion. Trace the pathway through which vibrations and fluid currents are transmitted to finally stimulate the hair cells in the organ of Corti. (Name the appropriate ear structures in their correct sequence.) Eardrum → *malleus → incus → stapes → oval window → perilymph → cochlear duct → endolymph → basilar membrane with hair cells*

5. Describe how sounds of different frequency (pitch) are differentiated in the cochlea. *It is believed that high-frequency (high-pitched) sounds peak close to the oval window while low-frequency (low-pitched) sounds peak near the cochlear apex, disturbing hair cells there (the "Place Principle").*

6. Explain the role of the endolymph of the semicircular canals in activating the receptors during angular motion.

When angular motion occurs in one direction, the endolymph in a semicircular canal lags behind, pushing the cupula in a direction opposite to that of the angular motion. Depending on the ear, this depolarizes or hyperpolarizes the hair cells, resulting in enhanced or reduced impulses to the brain.

7. Explain the role of the otoliths in perception of static equilibrium (head position). *When the head position changes, the otoliths "roll" in gelatinous material (responding to gravitational pull). This triggers hyperpolarization or depolarization of the hair cells and modifies the rate of impulse transmission along the vestibular nerve.*

Laboratory Tests

8. Was the auditory acuity measurement made during the experiment on page 282 the same or different for both ears?

(student response) _____ What factors might account for a difference in the acuity of the two ears?

Ear wax, middle/outer ear infection, cochlear nerve damage, etc. Anything that affects sound conduction or nervous system structures associated with hearing.

9. During the sound localization experiment on page 282, in which position(s) was the sound least easily located?

When the sound was exactly in midline of the head and out of vision.

How can this phenomenon be explained? *The usual cues which allow sound to be localized (slight differences in loudness in the two ears and in the time the sound reaches each ear) are missing.*

10. In the frequency experiment on page 282, which tuning fork was the most difficult to hear? *(stu obs)* _____ Hz

What conclusion can you draw? *High-frequency sounds are heard less well at low intensity.*

11. When the tuning fork handle was pressed to your forehead during the Weber test, where did the sound seem to originate?

From the ears.

Where did it seem to originate when one ear was plugged with cotton? *From the plugged ear.*

How do sound waves reach the cochlea when conduction deafness is present? *By vibration through bones of the skull.*

12. Indicate whether the following conditions relate to conduction deafness (C) or sensorineural deafness (S):

c _____ 1. can result from the fusion of the ossicles

s _____ 2. can result from a lesion on the cochlear nerve

s _____ 3. sound heard in one ear but not in the other during bone and air conduction

c, s _____ 4. can result from otitis media

c _____ 5. can result from impacted cerumen or a perforated eardrum

s _____ 6. can result from a blood clot in the auditory cortex

13. The Rinne test evaluates an individual's ability to hear sounds conducted by air or bone. Which is more indicative of normal hearing? *Air-conducted sound*

14. Define *nystagmus*: *Involuntary rolling or trailing of the eyes in one direction and then rapid movement in the opposite direction.*

Define *vertigo*: *Sensation of dizziness and rotational movement when such movement is not occurring.*

15. The Barany test investigated the effect that rotatory acceleration had on the semicircular canals. Explain *why* the subject still had the sensation of rotation immediately after being stopped. *The fluids of the inner ear had not yet stopped moving.*

16. What is the usual reason for conducting the Romberg test? *To determine if proprioceptive impulses are being transmitted up the spinal cord to the brain properly.*

Was the degree of sway greater with the eyes open or closed? Why? *Closed. Visual cues (input) were lacking.*

17. Normal balance, or equilibrium, depends on input from a number of sensory receptors. Name them.

Proprioceptors of the muscles and tendons, vestibular apparatus of the ears, retina of the eye (photoreceptors).

18. What effect does alcohol consumption have on balance and equilibrium? Explain. *Alcohol depresses the nervous system and enhances inhibition of reflex and coordination centers, causing a loss of balance and equilibrium.*

Special Senses: Olfaction and Taste

Localization and Anatomy of Taste Buds

1. Name five sites where receptors for taste are found, and circle the predominant site:

(tongue papillae) _____ , epiglottis _____ , pharynx _____ ,

soft palate _____ , and cheek mucosa _____

2. Describe the cellular makeup and arrangement of a taste bud. (Use a diagram, if helpful.) _A structure consisting of centrally_

located gustatory (receptor) cells surrounded by supporting cells.

Localization and Anatomy of the Olfactory Receptors

3. Describe the cellular composition and the location of the olfactory epithelium. _1" square area on roof of nasal cavity on each_

side of nasal septum. Receptor cells (bipolar neurons) surrounded by supporting cells.

_____

4. How and why does sniffing improve your sense of smell? _Draws air superiorly into contact with the olfactory mucosa. (Most_

air entering the nasal passages passes inferior to the receptors.)

Laboratory Experiments

5. Taste and smell receptors are both classified as _chemoreceptors_ _____ , because they both

respond to _chemicals in aqueous solution._

6. Why is it impossible to taste substances with a dry tongue? _Substances must be in aqueous solution._

_____

7. State the most important sites of your taste-specific receptors, as determined during the plotting exercise in the laboratory:

salt _student data_ _____ sour _student data_ _____

bitter _student data_ _____ sweet _student data_ _____

8. The basic taste sensations are mediated by specific chemical substances or groups. Name them:

salt _influx of Na^+_ _____ sour _H^+ (hydrogen ions) and blockage of K^+ (or Na^+) channels_

bitter _G protein gustducin causing increased intracellular Ca^{2+}_ _____ sweet _G protein gustducin causing K^+ channels to close_

9. Name three factors that influence our appreciation of foods. Substantiate each choice with an example from the laboratory experience.

1. _smell_ _____ Substantiation _____

_____

_____

2. _texture_ _____ Substantiation _____

_____

_____

3. _temperature_ _____ Substantiation _____

_____

_____

Which of the factors chosen is most important? _Smell_ _____

Substantiate your choice with an example from everyday life. _____

_____

Expand on your explanation and choices by explaining why a cold, greasy hamburger is unappetizing to most people.

When hot, a hamburger is "juicy" and has an enticing aroma. When cold, the fat congeals, giving the hamburger a greasy taste and

texture.

10. Babies tend to favor bland foods, whereas adults tend to like highly seasoned foods. What is the basis for this phenomenon?

Taste buds (and olfactory receptors) are less acute and are replaced more slowly as we age. Thus, more highly seasoned foods are

necessary if the food is to be palatable (to most adults).

11. How palatable is food when you have a cold? _It's not._ _____

Explain. _Smell is half of taste. When you have clogged nasal passages, you lack this added sensory input._

_____

12. What is the mechanism of olfactory adaptation? _Receptors stop responding to a continuous unchanging stimulus. (However, if_

the stimulus or intensity is changed, the receptors will again begin to respond.)

_____

In your opinion, is olfactory adaptation desirable? _Yes._ _____ Explain your answer.

Continuous nonimportant (unchanging) olfactory stimuli would be distracting and (probably) irritating.

_____

Functional Anatomy of the Endocrine Glands

Gross Anatomy and Basic Function of the Endocrine Glands

1. Both the endocrine and nervous systems are major regulating systems of the body; however, the nervous system has been compared to an airmail delivery system and the endocrine system to the pony express. Briefly explain this comparison.

   The nervous system uses rapidly propagated electrical "messages," whereas endocrine system "messages" (hormones) are liberated

   into the blood to travel much more slowly to the target organs.

2. Define *hormone*: *A chemical substance liberated into the blood, which alters "target cell" metabolism in a specific*

   manner.

3. Chemically, hormones belong chiefly to two molecular groups, the *steroids*

   and the *amino acid-based molecules* .

4. What do all hormones have in common? *They are all chemical molecules that have specific target organs, which they reach via the*

   blood. Like enzymes, they are effective in minute quantities.

5. Define *target organ*: *Organ responding to a particular hormone in a specific way.*

6. If hormones travel in the bloodstream, why don't all tissues respond to all hormones? *The proper "hormone" receptors must*

   be present on the plasma membrane or within the cells for the tissue cells to respond.

7. Identify the endocrine organ described by the following statements:

   thyroid gland —— 1. located in the throat; bilobed gland connected by an isthmus

   adrenal gland —— 2. found close to the kidney

   pancreas —— 3. a mixed gland, located close to the stomach and small intestine

   testes —— 4. paired glands suspended in the scrotum

   parathyroids —— 5. ride "horseback" on the thyroid gland

   ovaries —— 6. found in the pelvic cavity of the female, concerned with ova and female hormone production

   thymus —— 7. found in the upper thorax overlying the heart; large during youth

   pineal body —— 8. found in the roof of the third ventricle

8. For each statement describing hormonal effects, identify the hormone(s) involved by choosing a number from key A, and note the hormone's site of production with a letter from key B. More than one hormone may be involved in some cases.

Key A:

1. ACTH
2. ADH
3. aldosterone
4. cortisone
5. epinephrine
6. estrogens
7. FSH
8. glucagon
9. GH
10. insulin
11. LH
12. melatonin
13. MSH
14. oxytocin
15. progesterone
16. prolactin
17. PTH
18. serotonin
19. T_4 / T_3
20. testosterone
21. thymosin
22. thyrocalcitonin/calcitonin
23. TSH

Key B:

a. adrenal cortex
b. adrenal medulla
c. anterior pituitary
d. hypothalamus
e. ovaries
f. pancreas
g. parathyroid glands
h. pineal gland
i. posterior pituitary
j. testes
k. thymus gland
l. thyroid gland

___19___, ___l___ 1. basal metabolism hormone

___21___, ___k___ 2. programming of T lymphocytes

___17___, ___g___ and ___22___, ___l___ 3. regulate blood calcium levels

___4___, ___a___ and ___5___, ___b___ 4. released in response to stressors

___6___, ___e___ and ___20___, ___j___ 5. drive development of secondary sexual characteristics

___1___, ___c___; ___7___, ___c___; ___11___, ___c___; and ___23___, ___c___ 6. regulate the function of another endocrine gland

___5___, ___b___ 7. mimics the sympathetic nervous system

___8___, ___f___ and ___10___, ___f___ 8. regulate blood glucose levels; produced by the same "mixed" gland

___6___, ___e___ and ___15___, ___e___ 9. directly responsible for regulation of the menstrual cycle

___7___, ___c___ and ___11___, ___c___ 10. regulate the ovarian cycle

___2___, ___d___ and ___3___, ___a___ 11. maintenance of salt and water balance in the ECF

___14___, ___d___ and ___16___, ___c___ 12. directly involved in milk production and ejection

___13___, ___c___ 13. questionable function; may stimulate the melanocytes of the skin

9. Although the pituitary gland is often referred to as the master gland of the body, the hypothalamus exerts some control over the pituitary gland. How does the hypothalamus control both anterior and posterior pituitary functioning?

Produces "releasing and inhibiting hormones," which control the production and release of anterior pituitary hormones; forms hor-

mones ADH and oxytocin, which are transported to the posterior pituitary and later released on nervous stimulation from the hypothal-

amus.

10. Indicate whether the release of the hormones listed below is stimulated by (A) another hormone; (B) the nervous system (neurotransmitters, or releasing factors); or (C) humoral factors (the concentration of specific nonhormonal substances in the blood or extracellular fluid):

_B_ 1. ADH   _C_ 4. insulin   _A_ 7. T_4 / T_3

_C_ 2. aldosterone   _B_ 5. norepinephrine   _A_ 8. testosterone

_A_ 3. estrogens   _C_ 6. parathyroid hormone   _B_ 9. TSH, FSH

11. Name the hormone(s) produced in *inadequate* amounts that directly result in the following conditions. (Use your textbook as necessary.)

estrogen (female) testosterone (male) — 1. sexual immaturity

PTH — 2. tetany

ADH — 3. excessive diuresis without high blood glucose levels

insulin — 4. polyurea, polyphagia, and polydipsia

growth hormone (GH) — 5. abnormally small stature, normal proportions

progesterone — 6. miscarriage

thyroxine (T_4)/triiodothyronine (T_3) (thyroid hormone) 7. lethargy, hair loss, low BMR, obesity

12. Name the hormone(s) produced in *excessive* amounts that directly result in the following conditions. (Use your textbook as necessary.)

growth hormone (GH) — 1. lantern jaw and large hands and feet in the adult

T_4/T_3 (thyroid hormone) — 2. bulging eyeballs, nervousness, increased pulse rate

PTH — 3. demineralization of bones, spontaneous fractures

Microscopic Anatomy of Selected Endocrine Glands (Optional)

13. Choose a response from the key below to name the hormone(s) produced by the cell types listed:

Key: a. insulin   d. calcitonin   g. glucagon
       b. GH, prolactin   e. TSH, ACTH, FSH, LH   h. PTH
       c. T_4 / T_3 f. mineralocorticoids   i. glucocorticoids

_a_ 1. parafollicular cells of the thyroid

_h_ 2. follicular epithelial cells of the thyroid

_e_ 3. beta cells of the pancreatic islets (islets of Langerhans)

_c_ 4. alpha cells of the pancreatic islets (islets of Langerhans)

_i_ 5. basophil cells of the anterior pituitary

_d_ 6. zona fasciculata cells

_f_ 7. zona glomerulosa cells

_g_ 8. chief cells

_b_ 9. acidophil cells of the anterior pituitary

14. Five diagrams of the microscopic structures of the endocrine glands are presented here. Identify each and name all indicated structures.

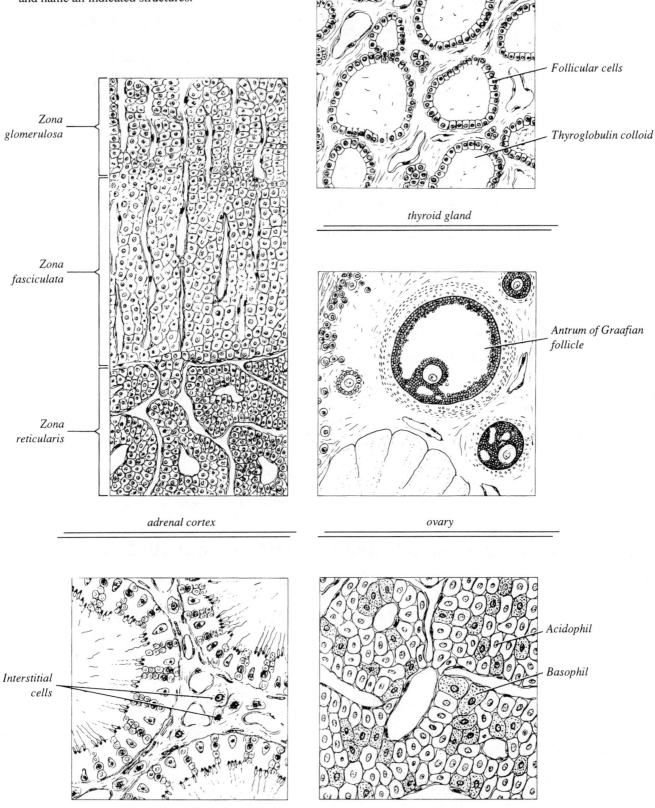

Follicular cells

Thyroglobulin colloid

thyroid gland

Zona glomerulosa

Zona fasciculata

Zona reticularis

Antrum of Graafian follicle

adrenal cortex

ovary

Interstitial cells

Acidophil

Basophil

testis

anterior pituitary

Hormonal Action: Wet Lab

Determining the Effect of Thyroid Hormone on Metabolic Rate

1. Considering the measurement of oxygen consumption in rats, which group had the highest metabolic rate?

   _Experimental group B_____ Which group had the lowest metabolic rate? _Experimental group A_____

   Correlate these observations with the pretreatment these animals received. _Group B received chow containing 2% dessicated_

   thyroid containing thyroid hormone, which increased the metabolic rate. Group A received normal chow and drinking water containing

   0.02% PTU. PTU inhibits T_4 and T_3 production.

   Which group of rats was hyperthyroid? _Group B_____

   Which euthyroid? _Control_____ Which hypothyroid? _Group A_____

2. Since oxygen used = carbon dioxide evolved, how were you able to measure the oxygen consumption in the experiments?

   _CO_2 evolved was absorbed by the soda lime; therefore, pressure changes indicated O_2 consumption._

3. What did changes in the fluid levels in the manometer arms indicate? _Changes in the fluid levels reflected pressure changes,_

   which in turn reflected O_2 consumption during the testing period.

4. The techniques used in this set of laboratory experiments probably allowed for several inaccuracies. One was the inability to control the activity of the rats. How would changes in their activity levels affect the results observed?

   Increased activity would lead to increased O_2 consumption/metabolic rate; whereas decreased activity would result in lower observed

   _O_2 consumption._

   Another possible source of error was the lack of control over the amount of food consumed by the rats in the 14-day period preceding the laboratory session. If each of the rats had been force-fed equivalent amounts of food in that 14-day period, which group (do you think) would have gained the most weight?

   _Group A_____ Which the least? _Group B_____ Explain your answers.

   Increasing the metabolic rate increases the rate at which food calories are oxidized by the tissue cells. The faster the rate, the less

   chance that food calories will be converted to fat, or result in weight gain.

5. TSH, produced by the anterior pituitary, prods the thyroid gland to release thyroid hormone to the blood. Which group of rats can be assumed to have the *highest* blood levels of TSH? _Group A_

   Which the lowest? _Group B_ Explain your reasoning. _Group A was producing no thyroid hormone because of PTU inhibition. Group B was receiving exogenous (excess) thyroxine, which would inhibit TSH release._

6. Use an appropriate reference to determine how each of the following factors modifies metabolic rate. Indicate increase by ↑ and decrease by ↓.

   increased exercise _↑_   aging _↓_   infection/fever _↑_

   small/slight stature _↑_   obesity _↓_   sex (♂ or ♀) _↑ in ♂_

Determining the Effect of Pituitary Hormones on the Ovary

7. In the experiment on the effects of pituitary hormones, two anterior pituitary hormones caused ovulation to occur in the experimental animal. Which of these actually triggered ovulation or egg expulsion?

   _LH_ The normal function of the second hormone involved, _FSH_,

   is to _stimulate follicle (and oocyte) maturation._

8. Why was a second frog injected with saline? _To provide a control._

Observing the Effects of Hyperinsulinism

9. Briefly explain what was happening within the fish's system when the fish was immersed in the insulin solution.

   Glucose was being swept out of the blood into the cells. This led to a hypoglycemic reaction, which affects nervous system functioning adversely.

10. What is the mechanism of the recovery process observed? _Glucose was added. Increased glucose levels in the blood reversed the effects noted above._

11. What would you do to help a friend who had inadvertently taken an overdose of insulin? _Give him/her a glass of orange juice or soda._ Why? _A sugar source will increase blood glucose levels as explained in #2._

12. What is a glucose tolerance test? (Use an appropriate reference, as necessary, to answer this question.)

    A test to determine a person's response to a specific amount of glucose. It is done to detect abnormalities of carbohydrate metabolism (i.e. diabetes mellitus). The person is given 100 grams of glucose and blood/urine samples are collected and assessed over a period of time.

13. How does diabetic coma differ from insulin shock? _Diabetic coma occurs when the person's blood glucose levels and ketone lev-_
els are very high and lead to severe acidosis. Insulin shock occurs as a result of excess insulin such that blood sugar levels are inade-
quate to maintain normal functioning; leads to unconsciousness.

Testing the Effect of Epinephrine on the Heart

14. Based on your observations, what is the effect of epinephrine on the force and rate of the heartbeat?

It increases both the force and rate of heartbeat.

15. What is the role of this effect in the "fight-or-flight" response?

Promotes faster delivery of blood throughout the body due to the increase in blood pressure.

Blood

Composition of Blood

1. What is the blood volume of an average-size adult male? _5–6_____ liters   An average adult female? _4–5_____ liters

2. What determines whether blood is bright red or a dull brick-red? _Its degree of oxygenation. The more oxygen it carries, the_

brighter red it is. _____

3. Use the key to identify the cell type(s) or blood elements that fit the following descriptive statements.

Key: a. red blood cell   d. basophil   g. lymphocyte
      b. megakaryocyte   e. monocyte   h. formed elements
      c. eosinophil   f. neutrophil   i. plasma

_f; neutrophil_____ 1. most numerous leukocyte

_c; eosinophil_____, _d; basophil_____, and

_f; neutrophil_____ 2. granulocytes

_a; red blood cell_____ 3. also called an erythrocyte; anucleate formed element

_e; monocyte_____, _f; neutrophil_____ 4. actively phagocytic leukocytes

_e; monocyte_____, _g; lymphocyte_____ 5. agranulocytes

_b; megakaryocyte_____ 6. ancestral cell of platelets

_h; formed elements_____ 7. (a) through (g) are all examples of these

_c; eosinophil_____ 8. number rises during parasite infections

_d; basophil_____ 9. releases histamine; promotes inflammation

_g; lymphocyte_____ 10. many formed in lymphoid tissue

_a; red blood cell_____ 11. transports oxygen

_i; plasma_____ 12. primarily water, noncellular; the fluid matrix of blood

_e; monocyte_____ 13. increases in number during prolonged infections

_c; eosinophil_____, _d; basophil_____, _e; monocyte_____,

_f; neutrophil_____, _g; lymphocyte_____ 14. also called white blood cells

4. List four classes of nutrients normally found in plasma: *sugar (e.g. glucose)* ,

amino acids , *lipids (fatty acids)* , and *vitamins*

Name two gases. *oxygen* and *carbon dioxide (nitrogen)*

Name three ions. *Na^+* , *Cl^-* , and *$Mg^{2+}(HCO_3^-)$*

5. Describe the consistency and color of the plasma you observed in the laboratory. *Viscous and sticky; straw-colored*

6. What is the average life span of a red blood cell? How does its anucleate condition affect this life span?

100–120 days. When the RBC's ATP reserves have been exhausted, the membrane begins to fragment. Without DNA to direct mRNA

(therefore protein) synthesis, needed enzymes cannot be made.

7. From memory, describe the structural characteristics of each of the following blood cell types as accurately as possible, and note the percentage of each in the total white blood cell population.

eosinophils: *Large, red-staining cytoplasmic granules; figure 8 or bilobed nucleus; 1–4% of WBC.*

neutrophils: *Pale pink cytoplasm with fine granules; nucleus is multilobed and stains deep purple; 40–70% of WBC.*

lymphocytes: *Small cell with sparse pale blue cytoplasm and dark purple-staining spherical nucleus; 20–45% of WBC.*

basophils: *Sparse dark blue cytoplasmic granules; large U-shaped nucleus which stains dark blue; 0.5% or less of WBC.*

monocytes: *Abundant gray-blue cytoplasm, dark blue-purple nucleus (often kidney-shaped); 4–8% of WBC.*

8. Correctly identify the blood pathologies described in column A by matching them with selections from column B:

Column A		Column B
b; leukocytosis _____ 1.	abnormal increase in the number of WBCs	a. anemia
d; polycythemia _____ 2.	abnormal increase in the number of RBCs	b. leukocytosis
a; anemia _____ 3.	condition of too few RBCs or of RBCs with hemoglobin deficiencies	c. leukopenia
c; leukopenia _____ 4.	abnormal decrease in the number of WBCs	d. polycythemia

Hematologic Tests

9. Broadly speaking, why are hematologic studies of blood so important in the diagnosis of disease?

   Specific changes from the normal numbers/types of formed elements and/or plasma constituents are characteristic of certain

   disease states.

10. In the chart below, record information from the blood tests you read about or conducted. Complete the chart by recording values for healthy male adults and indicating the significance of high or low values for each test.

Test	Student test results	Normal values (healthy male adults)	Significance — High values	Significance — Low values
Total WBC count	*No data*	$4000-11,000/mm^3$	*infectious process; leukemia*	*decreased body protection; may indicate chemical toxicity, agranulocytosis*
Total RBC count	*No data*	$5 \times 10^6/mm^3$	*polycythemia due to high altitude or pulmonary disease*	*anemia bone marrow cancer*
Hematocrit		*42–52 volume %*	*polycythemia hemoconcentration or abnormally large RBCs*	*anemia*
Hemoglobin determination		*13–18g/100 ml blood*	*polycythemia*	*anemia (particularly iron deficiency anemia)*
Bleeding time	*No data*	*2–7 min (Ivy) 0–5 min (Duke)*	*deficient or abnormal platelets*	*high platelet count*
Sedimentation rate		*0–6 mm/hr*	*nonspecific anemia, infection, tissue damage*	*abnormally shaped RBCs, polycythemia, and others*
Coagulation time		*3–6 min*	*hemophilia, leukemia, increased clotting time*	*thromboem- bolytic disorders*

11. Why is a differential WBC count more valuable than a total WBC count when trying to pin down the specific source of pathology? *A differential count determines the relative percent of each type of WBC. Increases or decreases in specific WBC populations are often indicative (diagnostic) of specific pathologies.*

12. What name is given to the process of RBC production? _Erythropoiesis_

What hormone acts as a stimulus for this process? _Erythropietin_

What organ provides this stimulus and under what conditions? _The kidneys produce erythropoietin under conditions of low_

oxygen tension in the blood.

13. Discuss the effect of each of the following factors on RBC count. Consult an appropriate reference as necessary, and explain your reasoning.

long-term effect of athletic training (for example, running 4 to 5 miles per day over a period of six to nine months)

Increases the RBC count. An athlete has relatively large muscle mass and needs an efficient oxygen delivery to the muscles when they

are working.

a permanent move from sea level to a high-altitude area _Increased RBC count. The air is thinner at high altitudes and contains_

less O_2. The body compensates by producing more RBCs so that the same relative amount of O_2 can be picked up and transported by

the blood.

14. Define _hematocrit:_ _Packed cell volume; volume percent of RBCs in 100 ml of blood._

15. If you had a high hematocrit, would you expect your hemoglobin determination to be high or low? _High_

Why? _Assuming the RBCs have a normal hemoglobin content, the higher the RBC volume, the higher the hemoglobin determination._

16. What is an anticoagulant? _A substance that inhibits blood clotting._

Name two anticoagulants used in conducting the hematologic tests. _Heparin (in capillary tubes)_

and _sodium citrate_

What is the body's natural anticoagulant? _Heparin_

17. If your blood clumped with both anti-A and anti-B sera, your ABO blood type would be _AB_

To what ABO blood groups could you give blood? _AB_

From which ABO donor types could you receive blood? _A, B, AB, O_

Which ABO blood type is most common? _O_   Least common? _AB_

18. What blood type is theoretically considered the universal donor? _O⁻_   Why? _These RBCs have no A, B or Rh antigens_

on the cell membrane, reducing the chance of a transfusion reaction.

19. Assume the blood of two patients has been typed for ABO blood type.

Typing results
Mr. Adams:

Blood drop and anti-A serum   **Blood drop and anti-B serum**

Typing results
Mr. Calhoon:

Blood drop and anti-A serum   **Blood drop and anti-B serum**

On the basis of these results, Mr. Adams has type ___O___ blood, and Mr. Calhoon has type ___A___ blood.

20. Explain why an Rh-negative person does not have a transfusion reaction on the first exposure to Rh-positive blood but *does*

have a reaction on the second exposure. *There are no preformed anti-Rh antibodies in his/her blood. Antibodies are formed after*

the first exposure to Rh⁺ blood.

What happens when an ABO blood type is mismatched for the first time? *A transfusion reaction occurs the first and every time.*

21. Record your observations of the five demonstration slides viewed.

a. Macrocytic hypochromic anemia: *RBCs are large and pale.*

b. Microcytic hypochromic anemia: *RBCs are small and pale.*

c. Sickle-cell anemia: *RBCs are crescent shaped.*

d. Lymphocytic leukemia (chronic): *Large number of small abnormal lymphocytes.*

e. Eosinophilia: *Increased number of eosinophils.*

Which of slides a through e above corresponds with the following conditions?

___b___ 1. iron-deficient diet

___d___ 2. a type of bone marrow cancer

___c___ 3. genetic defect that causes hemoglobin to become sharp/spiky

___a___ 4. lack of vitamin B$_{12}$

___e___ 5. a tapeworm infestation in the body

___b___ 6. a bleeding ulcer

22. Provide the normal, or at least "desirable," range for plasma cholesterol concentration:

_130–200_____ mg/100 ml

23. Describe the relationship between high blood cholesterol levels and cardiovascular diseases such as hypertension, heart attacks, and strokes.

High LDL levels favor cholesterol uptake and deposit in arteriosclerotic plaques, which, in turn: (1) narrow the vessel, reducing

blood flow to more distal tissues, and (2) increase the risk of thrombus formation. Narrowing of blood vessels is one cause of hyper-

tension. Attached thrombi or detached thrombi (emboli) are common causes of heart attack and stroke.

Anatomy of the Heart

Gross Anatomy of the Human Heart

1. An anterior view of the heart is shown here. Match each structure listed on the left with the correct key letter:

_g_ 1. right atrium

_j_ 2. right ventricle

_r_ 3. left atrium

_u_ 4. left ventricle

_b_ 5. superior vena cava

_k_ 6. inferior vena cava

_d_ 7. ascending aorta

_n_ 8. aortic arch

_a_ 9. brachiocephalic artery

_l_ 10. left common carotid artery

_m_ 11. left subclavian artery

_e_ 12. pulmonary trunk

_c_ 13. right pulmonary artery

_p_ 14. left pulmonary artery

_o_ 15. ligamentum arteriosum

_f_ 16. right pulmonary veins

_q_ 17. left pulmonary veins

_h_ 18. right coronary artery

_i_ 19. anterior cardiac vein

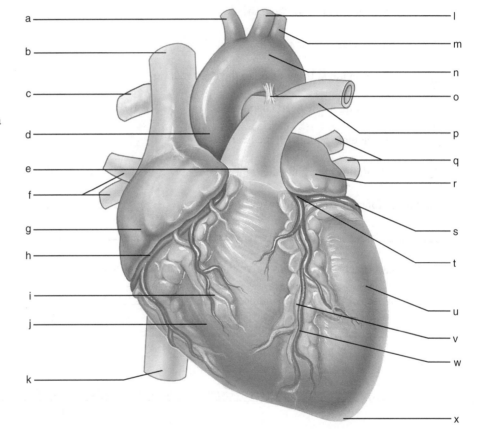

_t_ 20. left coronary artery

_s_ 21. circumflex artery

_w_ 22. anterior interventricular artery

_x_ 23. apex of heart

_v_ 24. great cardiac vein

2. What is the function of the fluid that fills the pericardial sac? _To reduce friction during heart activity._

3. Match the terms in the key to the descriptions provided below.

			Key:
_f_	1.	location of the heart in the thorax	a. atria
_a_	2.	superior heart chambers	b. coronary arteries
_h_	3.	inferior heart chambers	c. coronary sinus
_e_	4.	visceral pericardium	d. endocardium
_a_	5.	"anterooms" of the heart	e. epicardium
_g_	6.	equals cardiac muscle	f. mediastinum
_b_	7.	provide nutrient blood to the heart muscle	g. myocardium
_d_	8.	lining of the heart chambers	h. ventricles
_h_	9.	actual "pumps" of the heart	
_c_	10.	drains blood into the right atrium	

4. What is the function of the valves found in the heart? _They enforce a one-way flow of blood through the heart._

5. Can the heart function with leaky valves? (Think! Can a water pump function with leaky valves?) _Yes_

6. What is the role of the chordae tendineae? _They anchor the AV valve flaps during ventricular systole, thus preventing backflow of blood into the atria._

7. Define:

angina pectoris _Chest pain that occurs when the myocardium has insufficient oxygen._

pericarditis _Inflammation of the pericardium._

Pulmonary, Systemic, and Cardiac Circulations

8. A simple schematic of a so-called general circulation is shown below. What part of the circulation is missing from this diagram? *Pulmonary circulation is not distinct from systemic circulation.*

Add to the diagram as best you can to make it depict a complete systemic/pulmonary circulation and reidentify "general circulation" as the correct subcirculation.

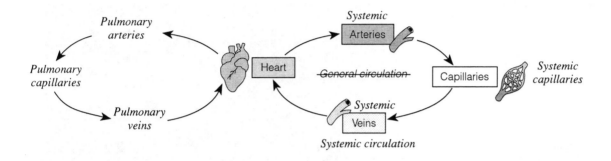

9. Differentiate clearly between the roles of the pulmonary and systemic circulations. *The pulmonary circuit provides for gas exchange only; the systemic circuit provides the functional supply of the body tissues.*

10. Complete the following scheme of circulation of a red blood cell in the human body:

Right atrium through the tricuspid valve to the *right ventricle* through the *pulmonary semilunar* valve to the pulmonary trunk to the *right and left pulmonary arteries* to the capillary beds of the lungs to the *pulmonary veins* to the *left atrium* of the heart through the *mitral/bicuspid* valve to the *left ventricle* through the *aortic semilunar* valve to the *aorta* to the systemic arteries to the *capillary beds* of the tissues to the systemic veins to the *inferior vena cava*, _____, and *superior vena cava* entering the right atrium of the heart.

11. If the mitral valve does not close properly, which circulation is affected? *Systemic*

12. Why might a thrombus (blood clot) in the anterior descending branch of the left coronary artery cause sudden death?
This artery supplies blood to the interventricular septum and the anterior walls of both ventricles. Ventricular damage, particularly to the left ventricle, is very serious.

Microscopic Anatomy of Cardiac Muscle

13. How would you distinguish the structure of cardiac muscle from the structure of skeletal muscle? _Both tissue types are stri-_

ated; thus, this is not a distinguishing feature. Skeletal muscle cells are long cylindrical cells with many nuclei per cell. Cardiac cells

have one (or two) centrally located nuclei per cell; their branched ends fit together at tight junctions called intercalated discs, which

are not seen in skeletal muscle.

14. Add the following terms to the photo of cardiac muscle at the right:

a. intercalated disc

b. nucleus of cardiac fiber

c. striations

d. cardiac muscle fiber

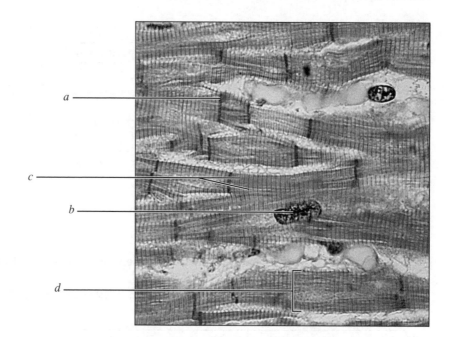

15. What role does the unique structure of cardiac muscle play in its function? (Note: Before attempting a response, *describe* the

unique anatomy.) _Cardiac muscle cells form a functional syncytium by virtue of their intercalated discs. This structural feature plus_

the special arrangement of cardiac muscle in the heart allows the pumping action of the heart to be carefully coordinated for maximal

efficiency.

Dissection of the Sheep Heart

16. During the sheep heart dissection, you were asked initially to identify the right and left ventricles without cutting into the heart. During this procedure, what differences did you observe between the two chambers?

The left ventricle was firmer, thicker, and less compressible; the right ventricle felt "flabby."

Knowing that structure and function are related, how would you say this structural difference reflects the relative functions of these two heart chambers? *The left ventricle pumps blood through the high-resistance systemic circulation; therefore, it has to be stronger than the right ventricle, which pumps blood through the short low-resistance pulmonary circuit.*

_____

_____

17. Semilunar valves prevent backflow into the _ventricles_____; AV valves prevent backflow into the _atria_____. Using your own observations, explain how the operation of the semilunar valves differs from that of the AV valves. *When the ventricle was compressed (as in systole), the AV valve flaps moved superiorly into the closed position. When water was poured (as when blood backflows) into the semilunar valves, the cusps filled and closed the valve.*

_____

_____

_____

18. Differentiate clearly between the location and appearance of pectinate muscle and trabeculae carneae. _____
Pectinate—comblike muscle ridges in the atria. Trabeculae carneae—pitted, ridged muscle bundles in the ventricular walls.

_____

19. Compare and contrast the structure of the right and left atrioventricular valves. *Both have thin flaps secured to papillary muscles by chordae tendinea. The right valve has three cusps, the left valve has two.*

_____

_____

_____

20. Two remnants of fetal structures are observable in the heart—the ligamentum arteriosum and the fossa ovalis. What were they called in the fetal heart, where was each located, and what common purpose did they serve as functioning fetal structures?

Ligamentum arteriosum—ductus arteriosus between the pulmonary trunk and the aorta. Fossa ovalis—foramen ovale, in the atrial septum. When they were open (and functional), they allowed blood to bypass the non-functional fetal lungs.

_____

_____

Conduction System of the Heart and Electrocardiography

The Intrinsic Conduction System

1. List the elements of the intrinsic conduction system in order starting from the SA node.

   SA node ⟶ _AV node_ ⟶ _AV bundle (bundle of His)_ ⟶

   left and right bundle branches ⟶ _Purkinje fibers_

   Which of those structures is replaced when an artificial pacemaker is installed? _SA node_

   At what structure in the transmission sequence is the impulse temporarily delayed? _AV node_

   Why? _Allows completion of atrial contraction before initiation of ventricular systole._

2. Even though cardiac muscle has an inherent ability to beat, the nodal system plays a critical role in heart physiology. What

   is that role? _Ensures that depolarization proceeds in an orderly manner from atria to ventricles; accelerates and coordinates heart_

   activity.

3. How does the "all-or-none" law apply to normal heart operation? _The myocardium (heart as a whole) beats as a unit as long_

   as the intrinsic conduction system is operative and the heart muscle is healthy.

Electrocardiography

4. Define *ECG*: _Recording of electrical changes occurring during heart activity._

5. Draw an ECG wave form representing one heartbeat. Label the P, QRS, and T waves; the P-R interval; the S-T segment, and the Q-T interval.

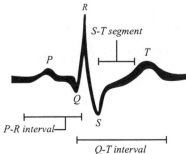

6. What is the normal length of the P-R interval? _(student data)_ _____ QRS interval? _(student data)_ _____

When the heart rate increases, which interval becomes shorter? _(student data)_ _____

7. What changes from *baseline* were noted in the ECG recorded during running? _None. The rate and strength of heart contrac-_ _tions is increased but the electrical current pattern height remains unchanged. ↑ rate; ↓ Q-T interval._

_____

Explain why these changes occurred. _Both increased body heat and muscular activity enforce a faster heart rate. During exercise,_ _cardiac output increases in almost linear proportion to the increased oxygen needs. This is mediated through sympathetic nerves._

_____

What changes in baseline were noted during breath holding? _See ↑ rate of heartbeat as above, but mechanism differs._

_____

Explain these changes. _Even though O_2 exchange is still occurring, CO_2 accumulation ↓ blood pH, causing cerebral vessel vasodila-_ _tion and exciting sympathetic centers, which in turn cause a reflex increase in heart rate and ↑ the respiratory drive._

_____

8. Describe what happens in the cardiac cycle in the following situations:

    1. during the P wave _depolarization of the atria_ _____

    2. immediately before the P wave _the heart is in relaxation (diastole)_ _____

    3. immediately after the P wave _contraction of the atria_ _____

    4. during the QRS wave _depolarization of the ventricles_ _____

    5. immediately after the QRS wave (S-T interval) _contraction of the ventricles_ _____

    6. during the T wave _repolarization of the ventricles_ _____

9. Define the following terms:

    1. tachycardia _Heart rate over 100 beats/min._ _____

    2. bradycardia _Heart rate below 60 beats/min._ _____

    3. flutter _Extremely rapid but coordinated heart activity, e.g. atrial flutter = 300 beats/min._ _____

    4. fibrillation _Very rapid uncoordinated myocardial activity._ _____

    5. myocardial infarction _Region of dead myocardium that does not depolarize._ _____

10. Which would be more serious, atrial or ventricular fibrillation? _Ventricular fibrillation_

Why? _The ventricles bear major responsibility for ejecting blood from the heart._

11. Abnormalities of heart valves can be detected more accurately by auscultation than by electrocardiography. Why is this so?

Most often serious valve problems can be detected (heard) with a stethoscope. However, since valves are not part of the depolarization pathway of the heart, their inefficiency would not be recorded on an ECG.

Anatomy of Blood Vessels

Microscopic Structure of the Blood Vessels

1. Use key choices to identify the blood vessel tunic described.

Key: a. tunica intima   b. tunica media   c. tunica externa

a; intima _____ 1. innermost tunic

b; media _____ 2. bulky middle tunic contains smooth muscle and elastin

a; intima _____ 3. its smooth surface decreases resistance to blood flow

a; intima _____ 4. tunic(s) of capillaries

a; intima _____, *b; media* _____, *c; externa* _____ 5. tunic(s) of arteries and veins

b; media _____ 6. is especially thick in elastic arteries

c; externa _____ 7. most superficial tunic

2. Servicing the capillaries is the essential function of the organs of the circulatory system. Explain this statement.

   Exchanges of nutrients, respiratory gases, and wastes can occur only through thin capillary walls. All other vessels serve simply to feed

   or drain capillary beds.

3. Cross-sectional views of an artery and of a vein are shown here. Identify each; and on the lines beneath, note the structural details that enabled you to make these identifications:

artery
(vessel type)

  open, circular lumen
(a)

  thick media
(b)

vein
(vessel type)

  somewhat collapsed lumen
(a)

  thinner media
(b)

4. Why are valves present in veins but not in arteries? *The high blood pressure in arteries propels the blood through them. The blood*

   pressure in veins is low and often the blood is flowing against gravity. Valves prevent backflow.

5. Name two events *occurring within the body* that aid in venous return:

   Skeletal muscle "milking action" _____ and *changes in thoracic cavity pressure during breathing.*

6. Why are the walls of arteries proportionately thicker than those of the corresponding veins? _Arteries must withstand high_

pressure and pressure fluctuations. Veins are low-pressure vessels.

Major Systemic Arteries and Veins of the Body

7. Use the key on the right to identify the arteries or veins described on the left.

		Key:	
_d_	1. the arterial system has one of these; the venous system has two	a.	anterior tibial
_i_	2. these arteries supply the myocardium	b.	basilic
_r_, _z_	3. two paired arteries serving the brain	c.	brachial
_o_	4. longest vein in the lower limb	d.	brachiocephalic
_k_	5. artery on the dorsum of the foot checked after leg surgery	e.	celiac trunk
_j_	6. serves the posterior thigh	f.	cephalic
_t_	7. supplies the diaphragm	g.	common carotid
_c_	8. formed by the union of the radial and ulnar veins	h.	common iliac
_b_, _f_	9. two superficial veins of the arm	i.	coronary
_w_	10. artery serving the kidney	j.	deep femoral
_p_	11. veins draining the liver	k.	dorsalis pedis
_q_	12. artery that supplies the distal half of the large intestine	l.	external carotid
_s_	13. drains the pelvic organs	m.	femoral
_m_	14. what the external iliac artery becomes on entry into the thigh	n.	fibular
_c_	15. major artery serving the arm	o.	greater saphenous
_y_	16. supplies most of the small intestine	p.	hepatic
_h_	17. join to form the inferior vena cava	q.	inferior mesenteric
_e_	18. an arterial trunk that has three major branches, which run to the liver, spleen, and stomach	r.	internal carotid
_l_	19. major artery serving the tissues external to the skull	s.	internal iliac
_a_, _n_, _u_	20. three veins serving the leg	t.	phrenic
_v_	21. artery generally used to take the pulse at the wrist	u.	posterior tibial
		v.	radial
		w.	renal
		x.	subclavian
		y.	superior mesenteric
		z.	vertebral

8. The human arterial and venous systems are diagrammed on the next two pages. Identify all indicated blood vessels.

Superficial temporal artery

Internal carotid artery

External carotid artery

Vertebral artery

Brachiocephalic trunk

Axillary artery

Anterior humeral circumflex artery

Ascending aorta

Brachial artery

Common hepatic artery

Abdominal aorta

Superior mesenteric artery

Gonadal artery

Inferior mesenteric artery

Common iliac artery

External iliac artery

Digital arteries

Lateral femoral circumflex artery

Femoral artery

Popliteal artery

Anterior tibial artery

Posterior tibial artery

Fibular artery

Dorsalis pedis artery

Arcuate artery

Metatarsal arteries

Facial artery

Common carotid arteries

Subclavian artery

Aortic arch

Descending thoracic aorta

Coronary artery

Celiac trunk

Splenic artery

Renal artery

Descending abdominal aorta

Radial artery

Ulnar artery

Internal iliac artery

Deep palmar artery

Superficial palmar arch

Deep femoral artery

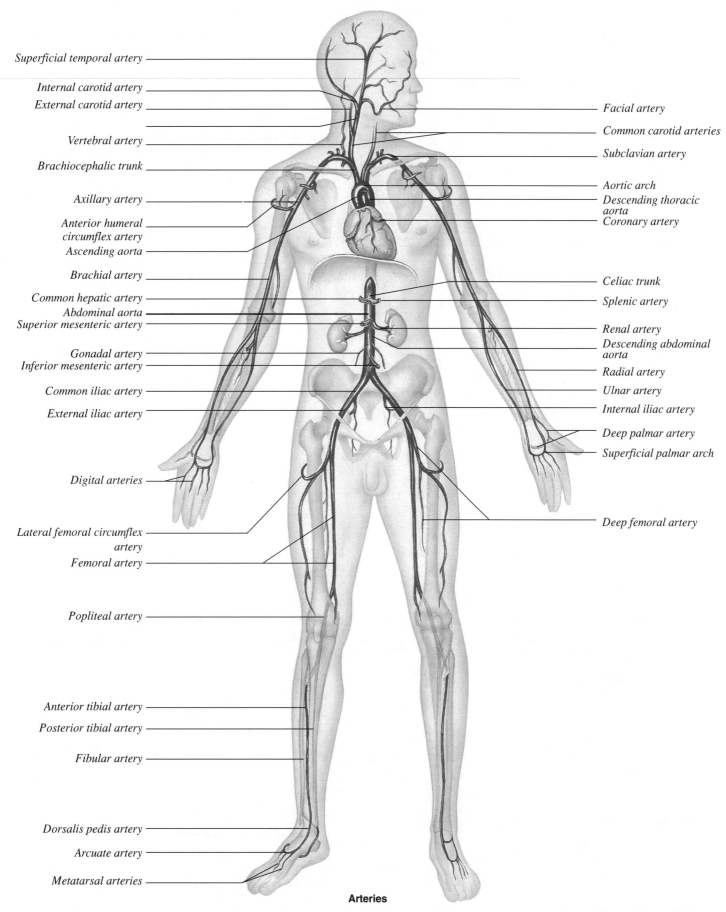

Arteries

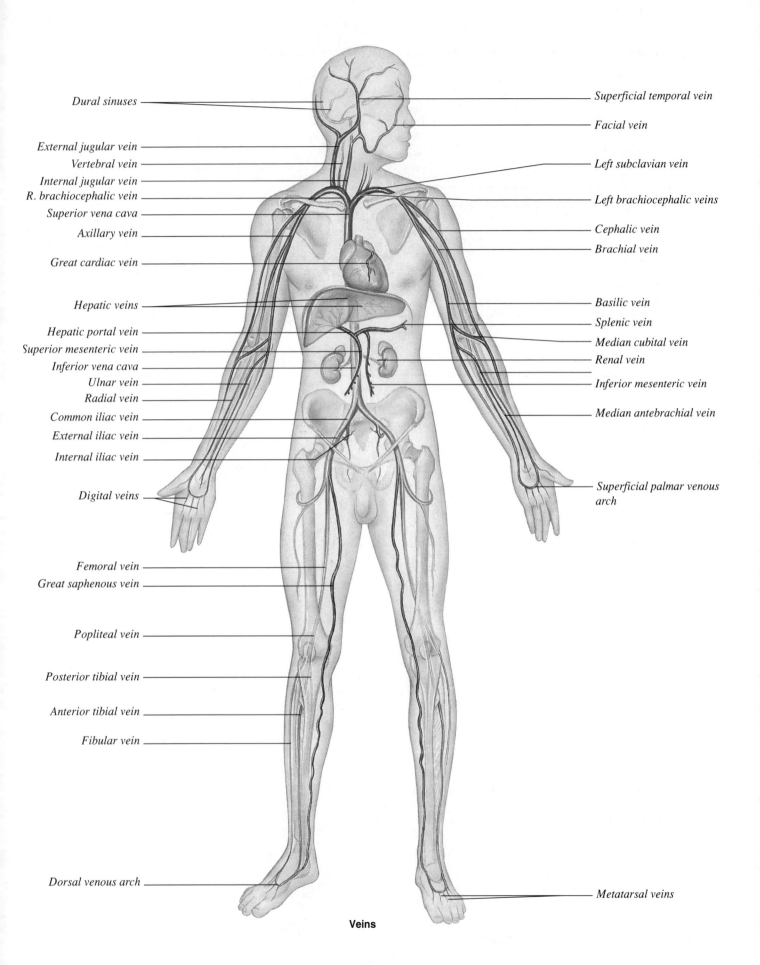

Dural sinuses

Superficial temporal vein

Facial vein

External jugular vein

Vertebral vein

Internal jugular vein

R. brachiocephalic vein

Superior vena cava

Axillary vein

Great cardiac vein

Hepatic veins

Hepatic portal vein

Superior mesenteric vein

Inferior vena cava

Ulnar vein

Radial vein

Common iliac vein

External iliac vein

Internal iliac vein

Digital veins

Left subclavian vein

Left brachiocephalic veins

Cephalic vein

Brachial vein

Basilic vein

Splenic vein

Median cubital vein

Renal vein

Inferior mesenteric vein

Median antebrachial vein

Superficial palmar venous arch

Femoral vein

Great saphenous vein

Popliteal vein

Posterior tibial vein

Anterior tibial vein

Fibular vein

Dorsal venous arch

Metatarsal veins

Veins

9. Trace the blood flow for the following situations:

a. from the capillary beds of the left thumb to the capillary beds of the right thumb *Digital vein, L radial vein, L brachial vein, L axillary vein, L subclavian vein, L brachiocephalic vein, superior vena cava, R atrium, R ventricle, pulmonary trunk, pulmonary artery, lobar artery, pulmonary capillaries of the lung, pulmonary veins, L atrium, L ventricle, aortic arch, brachiocephalic artery, R subclavian artery, R axillary artery, R brachial artery, R radial artery, digital artery.*

b. from the bicuspid valve to the tricuspid valve by way of the great toe *Through bicuspid valve into left ventricle, aorta, common iliac artery, external iliac artery, femoral artery, posterior tibial artery, lateral plantar artery, digital artery, capillary beds, digital vein, plantar arch, plantar vein, posterior tibial vein, external iliac vein, common iliac vein, inferior vena cava, right atrium, then through tricuspid valve.*

c. from the pulmonary vein to the pulmonary artery by way of the right side of the brain *Two pathways: (1) major pathway serves over 80% of cerebral tissue—pulmonary vein, L atrium, L ventricle, aortic arch, brachiocephalic trunk, R common carotid artery, R internal carotid artery, R middle cerebral and right anterior cerebral arteries, capillary beds, dural sinuses, internal jugular vein, brachiocephalic vein, superior vena cava, R atrium, R ventricle, pulmonary trunk, pulmonary artery; (2) pathway supplies occipital lobe and part of temporal lobe (follows pathway 1 until brachiocephalic artery), then R subclavian artery, R vertebral artery, basilar artery, R posterior cerebral artery, capillary beds (return route same as pathway 1).*

Special Circulations

Pulmonary Circulation

10. Trace the pathway of a carbon dioxide gas molecule in the blood from the inferior vena cava until it leaves the bloodstream. Name all structures (vessels, heart chambers, and others) passed through en route.

Inferior vena cava → right atrium → right ventricle → pulmonary trunk → right or left pulmonary artery → lobar artery → pulmonary capillary beds in lungs → air sacs (alveoli) of lungs.

11. Trace the pathway of oxygen gas molecules from an alveolus of the lung to the right atrium of the heart. Name all structures through which it passes. Circle the areas of gas exchange. _Alveolus → (alveolar/capillary walls) → pulmonary vein →_

left atrium → left ventricle → aorta → systemic arteries → (capillary beds of tissues) → systemic veins → superior or inferior

vena cava → right atrium.

12. Most arteries of the adult body carry oxygen-rich blood, and the veins carry oxygen-depleted, carbon dioxide–rich blood. How does this differ in the pulmonary arteries and veins? _The pulmonary arteries carry oxygen-poor blood to the lungs, whereas_

the pulmonary veins carry oxygen-rich blood from the lungs to the left heart.

13. How do the arteries of the pulmonary circulation differ structurally from the systemic arteries? What condition is indicated by this anatomical difference? _The pulmonary arteries are more like veins anatomically. They have relatively thin walls, reflecting_

the fact that the pulmonary circulation is a low pressure bed.

Hepatic Portal Circulation

14. What is the source of blood in the hepatic portal system? _Blood drained from the digestive viscera._

15. Why is this blood carried to the liver before it enters the systemic circulation? _This blood is rich in nutrients. The liver is the_

key body organ responsible for maintaining proper blood concentrations of glucose, proteins, etc. Its phagocytes also cleanse the blood

of debris.

16. The hepatic portal vein is formed by the union of the _splenic vein_ , which drains the

spleen , _pancreas_ , _greater curvature of the stomach,_ ,

and the _superior mesenteric_ , which drains the _small intestine_ and _ascending_

colon . The _gastric_ vein, which drains the lesser curvature of the

stomach, empties directly into the hepatic portal vein.

17. Trace the flow of a drop of blood from the small intestine to the right atrium of the heart, noting all structures encountered or passed through on the way. _Capillaries of small intestine → superior mesenteric vein → hepatic portal vein → liver sinu-_

soids → hepatic vein → inferior vena cava → right atrium of heart.

Arterial Supply of the Brain and the Circle of Willis

18. What two paired arteries enter the skull to supply the brain?

Internal carotids and _Vertebral_

19. Branches of the paired arteries just named cooperate to form a ring of blood vessels encircling the pituitary gland, at the base of the brain. What name is given to this communication network? _Circle of Willis_

What is its function? _Provides an alternate set of pathways for blood to reach brain tissue in case of impaired blood flow anywhere in the system._

20. What portion of the brain is served by the anterior and middle cerebral arteries? _The bulk of the cerebral hemispheres._

Both the anterior and middle cerebral arteries arise from the _internal carotid_ arteries.

21. Trace the pathway of a drop of blood from the aorta to the left occipital lobe of the brain, noting all structures through which it flows. _Aorta → subclavian artery → vertebral artery → basilar artery → posterior cerebral artery → occipital brain tissue._

Fetal Circulation

22. The failure of two of the fetal bypass structures to become obliterated after birth can cause congenital heart disease, in which the youngster would have improperly oxygenated blood. Which two structures are these?

ductus arteriosus and _foramen ovale_

23. For each of the following structures, first indicate its function in the fetus; and then note what happens to it or what it is converted to after birth. Circle the blood vessel that carries the most oxygen-rich blood.

Structure	Function in fetus	Fate
Umbilical artery	_Carries O$_2$-poor blood from the fetus to the placenta._	_Obliterated. Becomes the medial umbilical ligament._
(Umbilical vein)	_Carries O$_2$-rich blood from the placenta to the fetus._	_Obliterated. Becomes the round ligament of the liver (ligamentum teres)._
Ductus venosus	_Shunts blood through the fetal liver, bypassing the bulk of its tissue._	_Becomes the fibrous ligamentum venosus._
Ductus arteriosus	_Bypasses the fetal lungs by shunting blood from the pulmonary trunk to the aorta._	_Occludes. Becomes the ligamentum arteriosum._
Foramen ovale	_Bypasses the lungs by shunting blood from the right atrium to the left atrium._	_Closes. Becomes the fossa ovalis._

24. What organ serves as a respiratory/digestive/excretory organ for the fetus? _Placenta_

Human Cardiovascular Physiology: Blood Pressure and Pulse Determinations

Cardiac Cycle

1. Correctly identify valve closings and openings, chamber pressures, and volume lines, and the ECG and heart sound scan lines on the diagram below by matching the diagram labels with the terms to the right of the diagram.

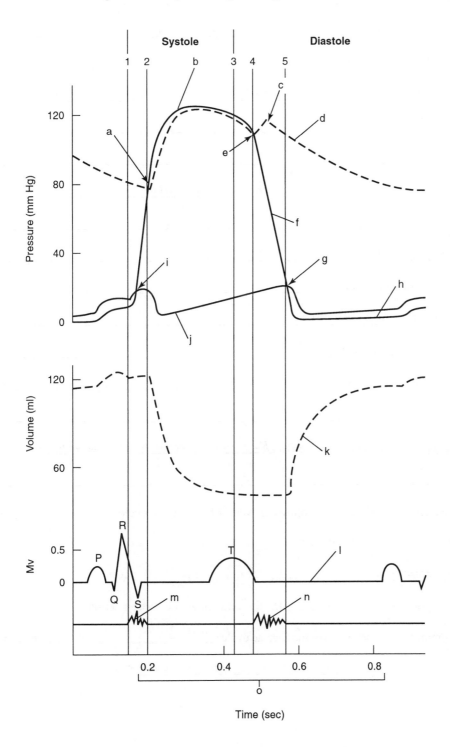

_f_	1. aortic and semilunar valves closed
_d_	2. aortic pressure
_e_	3. aortic valve closes
_a_	4. aortic valve opens
_j_	5. atrial pressure
_i_	6. AV valve closes
_g_	7. AV valve opens
_o_	8. cardiac cycle
_c_	9. dicrotic notch
_l_	10. ECG
_m_	11. first heart sound
_n_	12. second heart sound
_h_	13. ventricular diastole
_b_	14. peak of ventricular systole
_k_	15. ventricular volume

2. Define the following terms:

systole: *Contraction of the ventricles (general usage)*

diastole: *Ventricular relaxation (general usage)*

cardiac cycle: *One complete heartbeat including atrial and ventricular contraction*

3. Answer the following questions, which concern events of the cardiac cycle:

When are the AV valves closed? *During ventricular systole*

Open? *During atrial contraction and ventricular diastole*

What event within the heart causes the AV valves to open? *Ventricular pressure < atrial pressure*

What causes them to close? *Ventricular pressure > atrial pressure*

When are the semilunar valves closed? *During the period of relaxation of the heart as a whole and during atrial contraction.*

Open? *During ventricular systole*

What event causes the semilunar valves to open? *Ventricular pressure > pressure in great arteries*

To close? *Ventricular pressure < pressure in great arteries*

Are both sets of valves closed during any part of the cycle? *Yes*

If so, when? *Momentarily after atrial contraction and ventricular systole.*

Are both sets of valves open during any part of the cycle? *No*

At what point in the cardiac cycle is the pressure in the heart highest? *Ventricular systole*

Lowest? *Ventricular diastole*

What event results in the pressure deflection called the dicrotic notch? *The momentary increase in aortic pressure that occurs when its semilunar valves snap shut.*

4. Using the key below, indicate the time interval occupied by the following events of the cardiac cycle.

Key: a. 0.8 sec b. 0.4 sec c. 0.3 sec d. 0.1 sec

*a*_____ 1. the length of the normal cardiac cycle *b*_____ 3. the quiescent period, or pause

*d*_____ 2. the time interval of atrial systole *c*_____ 4. the ventricular contraction period

5. If an individual's heart rate is 80 beats/min, what is the length of the cardiac cycle? *0.75 sec* What portion of

the cardiac cycle is shortened by this more rapid heart rate? *Quiescent period (ventricular relaxation period).*

6. What two factors promote the movement of blood through the heart? *Alternate contraction and relaxation of the myocardium*

_____ and *opening and closing of the heart valves (which is responsive to*

pressure gradients). _____

Heart Sounds

7. Complete the following statements:

      The monosyllables describing the heart sounds are __1__ . The first heart sound is a result of closure of the __2__ valves, whereas the second is a result of closure of the __3__ valves. The heart chambers that have just been filled when you hear the first heart sound are the__4__, and the chambers that have just emptied are the__5__. Immediately after the second heart sound, the__6__ are filling with blood, and the__7__are empty.

1. *lub-dup* _____
2. *atrioventricular* _____
3. *semilunar* _____
4. *ventricles* _____
5. *atria* _____
6. *atria* _____
7. *ventricles* _____

8. As you listened to the heart sounds during the laboratory session, what differences in pitch, length, and amplitude (loudness)

of the two sounds did you observe? *First heart sound is longer, louder, and lower in pitch than the second heart sound, which is*

short, sharp, and high-pitched. _____

_____

9. Indicate where you would place your stethoscope to auscultate most accurately the following:

closure of the tricuspid valve: *Left or right sternal border of the 5th intercostal space.* _____

closure of the aortic semilunar valve: *Right sternal border of the 2nd intercostal space.* _____

apical heartbeat: *5th intercostal space in line with the middle of the left clavicle.* _____

Which valve is heard most clearly when the apical heartbeat is auscultated? *Bicuspid* _____

10. No one expects you to be a full-fledged physician on such short notice; but on the basis of what you have learned about heart sounds, how might abnormal sounds be used to diagnose heart problems?

Abnormal sounds such as swishing sounds after valvular closure or high-pitched sounds arising when blood is forced through

constricted (valve) openings might indicate valvular problems. _____

_____

The Pulse

11. Define *pulse*. *Pressure surges in an artery occurring during each contraction and relaxation of the left ventricle.* _____

_____

12. Describe the procedure used to take the pulse. _Place the first 2-3 fingertips of one hand over an arterial pressure point. Compress_

firmly and then release the pressure slightly to palpate the pulse.

13. Identify the artery palpated at each of the pressure points listed.

at the wrist: _Radial_   on the dorsum of the foot: _Dorsalis pedis_

in front of the ear: _Temporal_   at the side of the neck: _Carotid_

14. When you were palpating the various pulse or pressure points, which appeared to have the greatest amplitude or tension?

Carotid artery   Why do you think this was so? _The carotid artery(ies) is the major artery_

delivering blood to the brain (against gravity).

15. Assume someone has been injured in an auto accident and is hemorrhaging badly. What pressure point would you compress to help stop bleeding from each of the following areas?

the thigh: _Femoral artery_   the calf: _Popliteal artery_

the forearm: _Brachial artery_   the thumb: _Radial artery_

16. How could you tell by simple observation whether bleeding is arterial or venous? _If it spurts, it is arterial. It will flow evenly if_

it is venous blood.

17. You may sometimes observe a slight difference between the value obtained from an apical pulse (beats/min) and that from an arterial pulse taken elsewhere on the body. What is this difference called?

Pulse deficit

Blood Pressure Determinations

18. Define _blood pressure_. _Pressure exerted by blood against the walls of the blood vessels._

19. Identify the phase of the cardiac cycle to which each of the following apply.

systolic pressure: _Systole (ventricular contraction)_   diastolic pressure: _Diastole (relaxation)_

20. What is the name of the instrument used to compress the artery and record pressures in the auscultatory method of determining blood pressure? _Sphygmomanometer_

21. What are the sounds of Korotkoff? _Sounds that can be auscultated over a partially occluded artery._

What causes the systolic sound? _Sound of turbulent blood flow as it first begins to move through the constricted artery._

The disappearance of sound? _Blood is flowing freely; the artery is no longer constricted._

22. Interpret 145/85/82. *145=systolic pressure; 85=diastolic pressure reported as the point where the sound muffles; 82=diastolic pressure reported as the point at which sound disappears.*

23. Assume the following BP measurement was recorded for an elderly patient with severe arteriosclerosis:170/110/–. Explain the inability to obtain the third reading.

The patient's arteries are so narrowed by arteriosclerosis that blood flow is always partially occluded. Hence, the sound.

24. Define *pulse pressure*. *Systolic pressure minus diastolic pressure.*

Why is this measurement important? *It indicates the actual working pressure (actual amount of blood forced out of the heart during systole).*

25. How do venous pressures compare to arterial pressures? *Venous pressures are lower.*

Why? *Veins are far removed (in the circuit) from the pumping action of the heart.*

Observing the Effect of Various Factors on Blood Pressure and Heart Rate

26. What effect do the following have on blood pressure? (Indicate increase by I and decrease by D.)

D 1. increased diameter of the arterioles   *D* 4. hemorrhage

I 2. increased blood viscosity   *I* 5. arteriosclerosis

I 3. increased cardiac output   *I* 6. increased pulse rate

27. In which position (sitting, reclining, or standing) is the blood pressure normally the highest?

Standing _____ The lowest? *Reclining*

What immediate changes in blood pressure did you observe when the subject stood up after being in the sitting or reclining position? *It decreased initially and then increased.*

What changes in the blood vessels might account for the change? *Upon standing, gravitational pull caused blood pooling in the lower part of the body, but then vasoconstriction initiated by the vasomotor center caused blood pressure to rise.*

After the subject stood for 3 minutes, what changes in blood pressure were observed? *It decreased once again.*

How do you account for this change? *Decreased activity of the sympathetic nervous system.*

28. What was the effect of exercise on blood pressure? _It increased the blood pressure._

On pulse? _It increased the pulse._ Do you think these effects reflect changes in cardiac output *or* in

peripheral resistance? _Cardiac output (+ vasoconstriction of specific vascular beds, e.g., GI tract)._

Why are there normally no significant increases in diastolic pressure after exercise? _Since diastolic pressure reflects the heart_

in relaxation, it would not be expected to increase in healthy individuals.

29. What effects of the following did you observe on blood pressure in the laboratory?

nicotine _increased BP_ cold temperature _increased BP_

What do you think the effect of heat would be? _Decreased BP_

Why? _Vasodilation would occur._

30. Differentiate between a hypo- and a hyperreactor relative to the cold pressor test. _Hyperreactors exhibit a rise of 23 mm Hg or_

more in BP during the test. Hyporeactors exhibit a smaller increase or a decrease in BP.

Skin Color as an Indicator of Local Circulatory Dynamics

31. Describe normal skin color and the appearance of the veins in the subject's forearm before any testing was conducted.

Skin pink; veins flat and difficult to see.

32. What changes occurred when the subject emptied his forearm of blood (by raising his arm and making a fist) and the flow

was occluded with the cuff? _Skin becomes pale (cyanotic in some cases) and cool._

What changes occurred during venous congestion? _Skin becomes pink (red) and warm, and veins are congested and very visible._

33. What is the importance of collateral blood supplies? _Can maintain the blood supply to an organ (body part) in case the major_

nutrient artery is occluded.

34. Explain the mechanism by which mechanical stimulation of the skin produced a flare. _Local inflammatory response pro-_

duced by the chemical mediators released by injured tissue cells.

Frog Cardiovascular Physiology: Wet Lab

Special Electrical Properties of Cardiac Muscle: Automaticity and Rhythmicity

1. Define the following terms.

automaticity: _Ability to depolarize spontaneously in the absence of external stimulation._

rhythmicity: _Depolarization/repolarization events occur in a regular and continuous manner._

2. Discuss the anatomical differences you observed between frog and human hearts. _The frog heart has a single ventricle and_ _two atria. Dorsally there is an expanded area called the sinus venosus. The human heart has two atria and two ventricles. No sinus_ _venosus is present._

3. Which region of the dissected frog heart had the highest intrinsic rate of contraction? _Sinus venosus_

The greatest automaticity? _Sinus venosus_

The greatest regularity or rhythmicity? _Sinus venosus_ How do these properties correlate with the

duties of a pacemaker? _The human pacemaker (SA node) has automaticity, rhythmicity, and the highest depolarization rate in the_ _heart._

Is this region the pacemaker of the frog heart? _Yes_

Which region had the lowest intrinsic rate of contraction? _Ventricle_

Investigating the Refractory Period of Cardiac Muscle

4. Define *extrasystole:* _An extra beat occurring before the time a normal contraction would occur._

5. In responding to the following questions, refer to the recordings you made during this exercise:

What was the effect of stimulation of the heart during ventricular contraction? _No effect._

During ventricular relaxation (first portion)? _No effect._

During the pause interval? _No effect._

What does this indicate about the refractory period of cardiac muscle? _Much longer than that of skeletal muscle._

Can cardiac muscle be tetanized? _No_ Why or why not? _Because of its long refractory period._

Why is this important to the normal function of the heart? *Tetanus would interfere with the pumping activity of the heart.*

Assessing Physical and Chemical Modifiers of Heart Rate

6. Describe the effect of thermal factors on the frog heart.

cold: *Decreased heart rate*   heat: *increased heart rate*

7. What was the effect of vagal stimulation on heart rate? *Decreased heart rate*

Which of the following factors cause the same (or very similar) heart rate–reducing effects? Epinephrine, acetylcholine, atropine sulfate, pilocarpine, sympathetic nervous system activity, digitalis, potassium ions?

Acetylcholine, pilocarpine, digitalis, potassium ions.

Which of the factors listed above would reverse or antagonize vagal effects? *Epinephrine, atropine sulfate, sympathetic nervous system activity.*

8. What is vagal escape? *Return to a normal heart rate after a period of rate depression by the vagus nerve.*

Why is vagal escape valuable in maintaining homeostasis? *Continued vagal depression can completely stop the heart and lead to death.*

9. Once again refer to your recordings. Did the administration of the following produce any changes in force of contraction (shown by peaks of increasing or decreasing height)? If so, explain the mechanism.

epinephrine: *↑ rate and force of heartbeat. Acts on the SA and AV nodes and the myocardium to ↑ membrane permeability to Na^+ and Ca^{2+}.*

acetylcholine: *↓ rate and force of heartbeat. Acts on SA and AV nodes. Increases membrane permeability to K^+ which makes the tissue less excitable.*

calcium ions: *↑ strength of myocardial contraction. Effects as in skeletal muscle, i.e., Ca^{2+} is the "trigger" for sliding of myofilaments.*

10. Excessive amounts of each of the following ions would most likely interfere with normal heart activity. Note the type of changes caused in each case.

K^+ *heart block; cardiac arrest*

Ca^{2+} *↑ spasticity of cardiac activity*

Na^+ *↓ strength of contraction*

11. How does the Stannius ligature used in the laboratory produce heart block? _It physically blocks transmission of impulses from_

the atria to the ventricle.

12. Define *partial heart block,* and describe how it was recognized in the laboratory. _When the 1:1 ratio of atrial to ventricular_

contractions was replaced by different whole number ratios, e.g. 2:1, 3:1, the heart was in partial heart block.

13. Define *total heart block,* and describe how it was recognized in the laboratory. _No synchrony between depolarization waves_

of atria and ventricle. Impulses not being transmitted from atria to the ventricle; no whole number relationship between atrial and ven-

tricular contractions was demonstrated.

14. What do your heart block experiment results indicate about the spread of impulses from the atria to the ventricles?

In normal heart activity, the ventricles are depolarized by the depolarization wave spreading from the atria.

Observing the Microcirculation Under Various Conditions

15. In what way are the red blood cells of the frog different from those of the human? _Frog RBCs are nucleated; human RBCs are_

anucleate.

On the basis of this one factor, would you expect their life spans to be longer or shorter? _Longer_

16. The following statements refer to your observation of one or more of the vessel types observed in the microcirculation in the frog's web. Characterize each statement by choosing one or more responses from the key.

Key: a.   arteriole   b.   venule   c.   capillary

_c_____ 1. smallest vessels observed

_a_____ 2. vessel within which the blood flow is rapid, pulsating

_c_____ 3. vessel in which blood flow is least rapid

_c_____ 4. red blood cells pass through these vessels in single file

_b_____ 5. blood flow smooth and steady

_c_____ 6. most numerous vessels

_a_____ 7. vessels that deliver blood to the capillary bed

_c_____ 8. vessels that serve the needs of the tissues via exchanges

_b_____ 9. vessels that drain the capillary beds

17. Which of the vessel diameters changed most? *Arterioles*

What division of the nervous system controls the vessels? *Autonomic nervous system, sympathetic division.*

18. Discuss the effects of the following on blood vessel diameter (state specifically the blood vessels involved) and rate of blood flow. Then explain the importance of the reaction observed to the general well-being of the body.

local application of cold: *Vasoconstriction of arterioles. Bypasses the skin capillaries and withdraws blood to deeper body tissues*

to prevent heat loss to the external environment.

local application of heat: *Vasodilation of arterioles and flushing of capillary bed with blood. Increases the local blood supply and*

allows heat radiation from the skin surface.

inflammation (or application of HCl): *Vasodilation locally bringing in WBCs, and more nutrients to help fight the inflammatory*

stimulus.

histamine: *As with inflammation.*

The Lymphatic System and Immune Response

The Lymphatic System

1. Match the terms below with the correct letters on the diagram.

_k_ _____ 1. axillary lymph nodes

_i_ _____ 2. bone marrow

_b_ _____ 3. cervical lymph nodes

_j_ _____ 4. cisterna chyli

_g_ _____ 5. inguinal lymph nodes

_h_ _____ 6. lymphatic vessels

_f_ _____ 7. Peyer's patches (in intestine)

_l_ _____ 8. right lymphatic duct

_e_ _____ 9. spleen

_c_ _____ 10. thoracic duct

_d_ _____ 11. thymus gland

_a_ _____ 12. tonsils

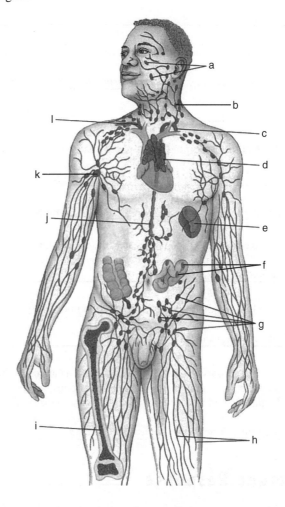

2. Explain why the lymphatic system is a one-way system, whereas the blood vascular system is a two-way system.

Blood vessels form a complete circuit from and to the heart. The lymphatic system lacks arteries and begins with blind-ended lymph

capillaries. Thus, it is a "return" system only.

3. How do lymphatic vessels resemble veins? _They are thin walled and have valves._

How do lymphatic capillaries differ from blood capillaries? *Lymph capillaries are more permeable and are blind ended; they have no "feeder" arterioles.*

4. What is the function of the lymphatic vessels? *To pick up and return excess tissue fluid (and leaked proteins) to the blood vascular system.*

5. What is lymph? *Leaked plasma (but contains fewer proteins).*

6. What factors are involved in the flow of lymphatic fluid? *"Milking" action of skeletal muscles; pressure changes in the thorax.*

7. What name is given to the terminal duct draining most of the body? *Thoracic duct.*

8. What is the cisterna chyli? *Enlarged terminus of the thoracic duct, which receives lymph from the digestive viscera.*

How does the composition of lymph in the cisterna chyli differ from that in the general lymphatic stream?
Same, except that the lymph in the cisterna chyli is very fat-rich.

9. Which portion of the body is drained by the right lymphatic duct? *Right half of upper torso and head; right arm.*

10. Note three areas where lymph nodes are densely clustered: *axillary region* , *cervical region* , and *groin*

11. What are the two major functions of the lymph nodes? *To remove debris from the lymph and to provide a site for cloning and multiplication of lymphocytes.*

12. The radical mastectomy is an operation in which a cancerous breast, surrounding tissues, and the underlying muscles of the anterior thoracic wall, plus the axillary lymph nodes, are removed. After such an operation, the arm usually swells, or becomes edematous, and is very uncomfortable—sometimes for months. Why?

The lymphatic fluid is not being drained from the area.

The Immune Response

13. What is the function of B cells in the immune response? *Upon antigen challenge, they clone to produce daughter cells, most of which are plasma cells that release antibodies to the blood. (Humoral response.)*

14. What is the role of T cells? *Mount cell-mediated immunity. Attack virus-infected cells, tumor cells, bacteria, etc. Also activate B cells and enhance the migration of other WBCs into the area to help destroy antigens.*

15. Define the following terms related to the operation of the immune system.

immunological memory: _Response that recognizes and mounts an attack on antigens previously encountered_

specificity: _Ability to distinguish between closely related antigens._

recognition of self from nonself: _Ability to recognize proteins on own tissue cells as "self" and not attack them._

autoimmune disease: _An inability of the immune system to recognize self, resulting in attack of self cells by the immune system._

Studying the Microscopic Anatomy of a Lymph Node, the Spleen and a Tonsil

16. In the space below, make a rough drawing of the structure of a lymph node. Identify the cortex area, germinal centers, and medulla. For each identified area, note the cell type (T cell, B cell, or macrophage) most likely to be found there.

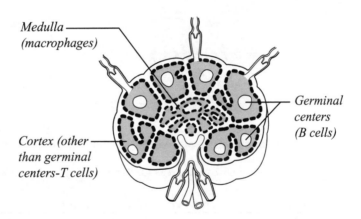

Medulla (macrophages)

Germinal centers (B cells)

Cortex (other than germinal centers-T cells)

17. What structural characteristic ensures a *slow* flow of lymph through a lymph node? _There are more afferent than efferent_ _vessels._

Why is this desirable? _Allows time for the macrophages in the node to remove antigens and other debris, and for activation of im-_ _mune cells._

18. What similarities in structure and function are found in the lymph nodes, spleen, and tonsils? _All are lymphoid tissue_ _containing macrophages and lymphocytes. They are all areas where exposure to antigen causes lymphocytes to proliferate and form_ _clones._

Antibodies and Tests for Their Presence

19. Distinguish between antigen and antibody. *An antigen is a molecule capable of provoking an immune response. An antibody is a*

protein produced by plasma cells that interacts with a particular antigen to form a complex.

20. Describe the structure of the immunoglobulin monomer, and label the diagram with the choices given in the key. *Four*

polypeptide chains, two "heavy" and two "light," held together by disulfide bonds to form a Y-shaped molecule. Each chain has con-

stant (c) and variable (v) regions.

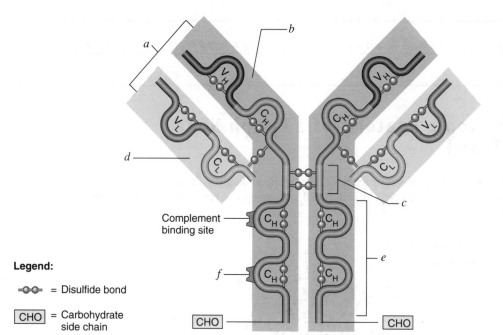

Key:

a. antigen binding site

b. heavy chain

c. hinge region

d. light chain

e. stem region

f. macrophage binding site

Complement binding site

Legend:

=●●= = Disulfide bond

CHO = Carbohydrate side chain

21. Are the genes coding for one antibody entirely different from those coding for a different antibody? *No*

Explain. *Only a few genes exist for coding antibody-constant regions; therefore many antibodies have identical c regions. The vari-*

able (antigen-binding) regions differ for each antibody responding to a different antigen.

22. In the Ouchterlony test, what happened when the antibody to horse serum albumin mixed with horse serum albumin?

A white precipitate formed (between wells 1 and 2).

23. If the unknown antigen contained bovine and swine serum albumin, what would you expect to happen in the Ouchterlony

test and why? *Antigen-antibody complexes would form a white precipitate between bovine serum albumin and the antibody to bovine*

serum albumin (between wells 1 and 3), and between swine serum albumin and antibody to swine serum albumin (between wells 1

and 4).

Anatomy of the Respiratory System

Upper and Lower Respiratory System Structures

1. Complete the labeling of the diagram of the upper respiratory structures (sagittal section).

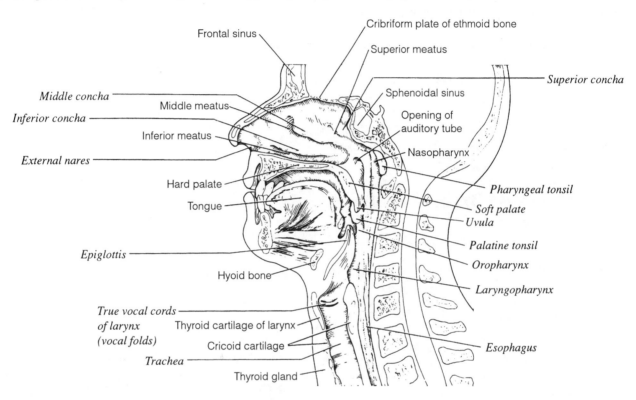

2. Two pairs of vocal folds are found in the larynx. Which pair are the true vocal cords (superior or inferior)?

   Inferior _____

3. Name the specific cartilages in the larynx that correspond to the following descriptions:

   forms the Adam's apple: _thyroid_ _____   shaped like a signet ring: _cricoid_ _____

   a "lid" for the larynx: _epiglottis_ _____   vocal cord attachment: _arytenoid_ _____

4. What is the significance of the fact that the human trachea is reinforced with cartilage rings?

   Prevents its collapse during pressure changes occurring during breathing. _____

   Of the fact that the rings are incomplete posteriorly? _Allows a food bolus traveling down the posterior esophagus to bulge anteri-_

   orly.

5. What is the function of the pleural membranes? _Produce a serous fluid that reduces friction during breathing movements and helps_

to hold the lungs tightly to the thorax wall.

6. Name two functions of the nasal cavity mucosa: _Warms and moistens incoming air._

7. The following questions refer to the primary bronchi.

Which is longer? _Left_   Larger in diameter? _Right_   More horizontal? _Left_

The more common site for lodging of a foreign object that has entered the respiratory passageways? _Right_

8. Appropriately label all structures provided with leader lines on the diagrams below.

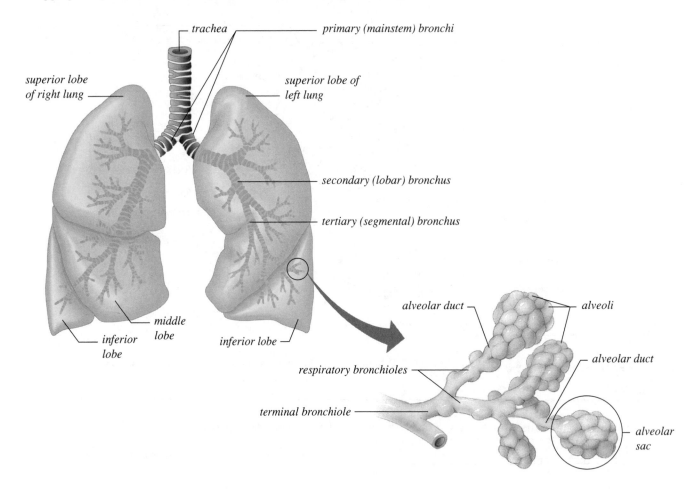

9. Trace a molecule of oxygen from the external nares to the pulmonary capillaries of the lungs: External nares →

nasal cavity → *pharynx* → *larynx* → *trachea* → *primary bronchus* → *secondary/tertiary bronchi (etc.)* → *bronchiole* → *respiratory bronchiole* → *alveolar duct* → *alveolar sac* → *across alveolar/capillary walls* → *pulmonary blood*

10. Match the terms in column B to the descriptions in column A.

Column A	Column B
_n_ 1. connects the larynx to the primary bronchi	a. alveolus
_k_ 2. site of tonsils	b. bronchiole
_e_ 3. food passageway posterior to the trachea	c. concha
_d_ 4. covers the glottis during swallowing of food	d. epiglottis
_g_ 5. contains the vocal cords	e. esophagus
_l_ 6. nerve that activates the diaphragm during inspiration	f. glottis
_j_ 7. pleural layer lining the walls of the thorax	g. larynx
_a_ 8. site from which oxygen enters the pulmonary blood	h. opening of auditory tube
_h_ 9. connects the middle ear to the nasopharynx	i. palate
_f_ 10. opening between the vocal folds	j. parietal pleura
_c_ 11. increases air turbulence in the nasal cavity	k. pharynx
_i_ 12. separates the oral cavity from the nasal cavity	l. phrenic nerve
	m. primary bronchi
	n. trachea
	o. vagus nerve
	p. visceral pleura

11. What portions of the respiratory system are referred to as anatomical dead space? *All but the respiratory zone structures (respiratory bronchioles, alveolar ducts and sacs, and alveoli).*

Why? *Because no gas exchange occurs except in the respiratory zone, particularly in the alveoli.*

12. Define the following terms.

external respiration: *Exchange of gases across the respiratory membrane in the lungs.*

internal respiration: *Exchange of respiratory gases between the blood of the systemic capillaries and the tissue cells of the body.*

cellular respiration: *Oxygen-using cellular processes.*

13. On the diagram below identify alveolar epithelium, capillary endothelium, alveoli, and red blood cells. Bracket the respiratory membrane.

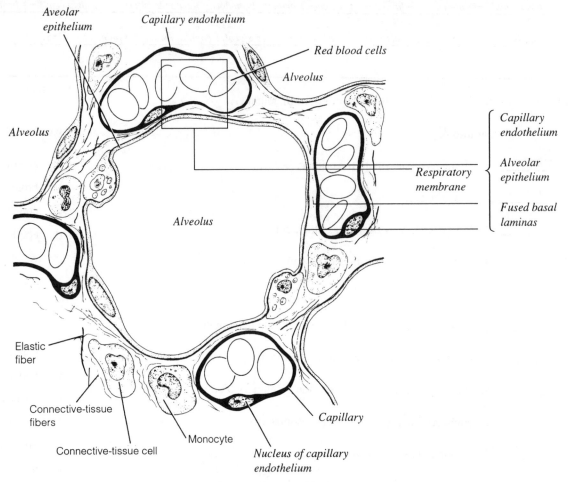

Demonstrating Lung Inflation in a Sheep Pluck

14. Does the lung inflate part by part or as a whole, like a balloon? *Part by part.*

15. What happened when the pressure was released? *The lung deflated.*

16. What type of tissue ensures this phenomenon? *Elastic connective tissue.*

Examining Prepared Slides of Lung and Tracheal Tissue

17. The tracheal epithelium is ciliated and has goblet cells. What is the function of each of these modifications?

Cilia? *Sweep (debris-laden) mucus superiorly away from lungs.*

Goblet cells? *Produce mucus.*

18. The tracheal epithelium is said to be pseudostratified. Why? *It looks stratified because the cells extend different distances from the basement membrane; however, it is a simple columnar epithelium.*

19. What structural characteristics of the alveoli make them an ideal site for the diffusion of gases?

Thin walls, extremely large surface area.

Why does oxygen move from the alveoli into the pulmonary capillary blood? *Because the partial pressure of oxygen is greater*

in the alveoli; therefore, it moves according to the laws of diffusion into the pulmonary blood.

20. If you observed pathological lung sections, what were the responsible conditions and how did the tissue differ from normal lung tissue?

Slide type	Observations
Student data.	*Student data.*

Respiratory System Physiology

Mechanics of Respiration

1. For each of the following cases, check the column appropriate to your observations on the operation of the model lung.

Change	Diaphragm pushed up		Diaphragm pulled down	
	Increased	Decreased	Increased	Decreased
In internal volume of the bell jar (thoracic cage)		✓	✓	
In internal pressure	✓			✓
In the size of the balloons (lungs)		✓	✓	
In direction of air flow	Into lungs	Out of lungs ✓	Into lungs ✓	Out of lungs

2. Base your answers to the following on your observations in question 1.

Under what internal conditions does air tend to flow into the lungs? _↑ thoracic volume, and ↓ pressure._

Under what internal conditions does air tend to flow out of the lungs? Explain why this is so. _↓ thoracic volume, ↑ pressure._

Gases move in the direction that tends to equalize pressure inside and outside the "container."

3. Activation of the diaphragm and the external intercostal muscles begins the inspiratory process. What effect does contraction of these muscles have on thoracic volume, and how is this accomplished? _↑ thoracic volume. The diaphragm moves inferiorly, increasing the superior-inferior dimension; the ribs swing up and out, increasing the lateral and anterior/posterior dimensions._

4. What was the approximate increase in diameter of chest circumference during a quiet inspiration?

(student data) _____ inches   During forced inspiration? _(student data)_ _____ inches

What temporary physiological advantage is created by the substantial increase in chest circumference during forced inspiration?

Increases the thoracic volume more; therefore, creates a greater negative internal pressure, causing the gases to rush in quickly. Also,

more "fresh" air reaches the alveoli.

5. The presence of a partial vacuum between the pleural membranes is integral to normal breathing movements. What would happen if an opening were made into the chest cavity, as with a puncture wound?

Destroys the partial vacuum in the pleural space and the lung on the affected side collapses.

How is this condition treated medically? *Air is withdrawn (chest tube) and the chest is closed.*

Respiratory Sounds

6. Which of the respiratory sounds is heard during both inspiration and expiration? *Bronchial*

Which is heard primarily during inspiration? *Vesicular*

7. Where did you best hear the vesicular respiratory sounds? *Heard over most of the lung area.*

Respiratory Volumes and Capacities—Spirometry

8. Write the respiratory volume term and the normal value that is described by the following statements.

Volume of air present in the lungs after a forceful expiration: *residual volume (~1100 ml)*

Volume of air that can be expired forcibly after a normal expiration: *expiratory reserve (~1200 ml)*

Volume of air that is breathed in and out during a normal respiration: *tidal volume (~500 ml)*

Volume of air that can be inspired forcibly after a normal inspiration: *inspiratory reserve (~2700–2800 ml)*

Volume of air corresponding to TV + IRV + ERV: *vital capacity (~4800 ml)*

9. Record experimental respiratory volumes as determined in the laboratory. (Corrected values are for the recording spirometer only.)

Average TV: *(student data)* ml

Corrected value for TV: *(student data)* ml

Average IRV: *(student data)* ml

Corrected value for IRV: *(student data)* ml

MRV: *(student data)* ml/min

Average ERV: *(student data)* ml

Corrected value for ERV: *(student data)* ml

Average VC: *(student data)* ml

Corrected value for VC: *(student data)* ml

% predicted VC: *(student data)* %

FEV_1: *(student data)* % FVC

10. Would your vital-capacity measurement differ if you performed the test while standing? _Yes_ While lying down?

Yes Explain. _When lying down or sitting, the abdominal organs press against the diaphragm, making it more difficult for the_

diaphragm to move inferiorly.

11. Which respiratory ailments can respiratory volume tests be used to detect?

Chronic bronchitis and emphysema (often associated). Chronic bronchitis ↓ the volume of air that can be inhaled due to excessive

mucus production; emphysema ↓ the amount of air that can be exhaled (check-valve effect).

12. Using an appropriate reference, complete the chart below:

		O_2	CO_2	N_2
% of composition of air	Inspired	~21%	~0.04%	~78%
	Expired	~16%	~4%	~74%

Use of the Pneumograph to Determine Factors Influencing Rate and Depth of Respiration

13. Where are the neural control centers of respiratory rhythm? _medulla oblongata_ and _pons_

14. Based on pneumograph reading of respiratory variation, what was the rate of quiet breathing?

Initial testing _(student data)_ breaths/min

Record observations of how the initial pneumograph or respiratory belt transducer recording was modified during the various testing procedures described below. Indicate the respiratory rate, and include comments on the relative depth of the respiratory peaks observed.

Test performed	Observations
Talking	_Respiratory rate becomes irregular during talking._
Yawning	_Yawning is reflected by extremely deep prolonged inspiration._
Laughing	_Respiratory rate becomes irregular. Respiratory depth may be ↑ or ↓ depending on the nature of the laugh._
Standing	_Regular rhythm and rate._
Concentrating	_Respiratory rate is regular unless punctuated by intervals of apnea in individuals who hold their breath when concentrating._
Swallowing water	_Respiration ceases during the period of swallowing._
Coughing	_Respiration rate becomes irregular and marked by expirations during coughing._
Lying down	_Regular rhythm and regular (or slightly depressed) rate. Depth decreases._
Running in place	_Increased rate and depth of breathing._

15. Student data:

Breath-holding interval after a deep inhalation _____ sec   length of recovery period _____ sec

Breath-holding interval after a forceful expiration _____ sec   length of recovery period _____ sec

After breathing quietly and taking a deep breath (which you held), was your urge to inspire or expire? *expire* _____

After exhaling and then holding one's breath, was the desire for inspiration or expiration? *inspiration* _____

Explain these results. (*Hint:* what reflex is involved here?) *Hering-Breuer reflex. Both extreme deflation and inflation of the*

lungs excites receptors there. Impulses are transmitted to the medulla oblongata, which then initiates inspiration or expiration (respec-

tively).

16. Observations after hyperventilation: *(student data)* _____

_____

17. Length of breath holding after hyperventilation: *(s.d.)* _____ sec

Why does hyperventilation produce apnea or a reduced respiratory rate? *Hyperventilation washes CO_2 out of the blood. Since*

CO_2 is the major chemical stimulus for inspiration, the desire or drive to breathe is decreased.

_____

18. Observations for rebreathing breathed air: *(student data)* _____

_____

Why does rebreathing breathed air produce an increased respiratory rate? *CO_2 (exhaled) accumulates in the bag; this stimu-*

lates increased force/rate of respiration.

19. What was the effect of running in place (exercise) on the duration of breath holding? *↓ the duration.* _____

Explain this effect. *The body's need for oxygen and to get rid of CO_2 is increased by exercise.*

_____

20. Relative to the test illustrating the effect of respiration on circulation. *(student data)*

Radial pulse before beginning test: _____ /min   Radial pulse after testing: _____ /min

Relative pulse force before beginning test: _____   Relative force of radial pulse after testing: _____

Condition of neck and facial veins after testing: _____

Explain these data. *Forced expiration increases intrathoracic pressure, reducing blood flow back to the heart, resulting in dilation of*

the neck and facial veins. Decreased cardiac output results in increased cardiac rate (seen here as increased pulse rate).

21. Do the following factors generally increase (indicate with I) or decrease (indicate with D) the respiratory rate and depth?

   1. increase in blood CO_2 _I_____   3. increase in blood pH _D_____

   2. decrease in blood O_2 _I_____   4. decrease in blood pH _I_____

   Did it appear that CO_2 or O_2 had a more marked effect on modifying the respiratory rate? _CO_2_____

22. Where are sensory receptors sensitive to changes in blood pressure located? _Aortic arch and carotid sinus._____

23. Where are sensory receptors sensitive to changes in O_2 levels in the blood located? _Aortic bodies in the aortic arch and_____

   carotid bodies at the bifurcation of the common carotid artery_____

24. What is the primary factor that initiates breathing in a newborn infant? _$\uparrow$ levels of CO_2 in the blood._____

25. Blood CO_2 levels and blood pH are related. When blood CO_2 levels increase, does the pH increase or decrease?

   _Decrease_____ Explain why. _CO_2 combines with water (H_2O) to produce carbonic acid (H_2CO_3), which dissoci-_

   ates and liberates a hydrogen ion (H^+)._____

Role of the Respiratory System in Acid-Base Balance of Blood

26. Define *buffer*. _A molecule or molecular system that acts to resist changes in pH._____

27. How successful was the laboratory buffer (pH 7) in resisting changes in pH when the acid was added? _____

   _(student data) (Anticipated response: very successful.)_____

   When the base was added? _(student data) (Anticipated response: very successful.)_____

   How successful was the buffer in resisting changes in pH when the additional aliquots (3 more drops) of the acid and base

   were added to the original samples? _Successful; only slight pH changes are seen._____

28. What buffer system operates in blood plasma? _Carbonic acid–bicarbonate system._____

   Which of its species resists a *drop* in pH? _HCO_3^-_____

   Which resists a *rise* in pH? _H_2CO_3_____

29. Explain how the carbonic acid–bicarbonate buffer system of the blood operates. _H_2CO_3, a weak acid, remains undissociated at physiologic pH or acid pH. However, if the pH starts to rise, H_2CO_3 dissociates and liberates H^+, which acts to ↓ the pH. HCO_3^- (bicarbonate ion) is the "alkaline reserve"; it acts to tie up excess H^+ into H_2CO_3 when the environment becomes too acidic. Since it is a weak base, it does not function under physiologic or alkaline conditions._

30. What happened when the carbon dioxide in exhaled air mixed with water? _Phenol red turned yellow as CO_2 mixed with water to form carbonic acid._

What role does exhalation of carbon dioxide play in maintaining relatively constant blood pH? _CO_2 leaves the blood during exhalation. This prevents an accumulation of carbonic acid._

Measuring Respiratory Volumes Using BIOPAC®

31. Which, if any, of the measurable volumes would likely be exaggerated in a person who is cardiovascularly fit, such as a runner or a swimmer?

It is common to observe abnormally large vital capacities in athletes who have trained aerobically for considerable periods of time in their life.

Which, if any, of the measurable volumes would likely be exaggerated in a person who has smoked a lot for over twenty years?

Increases in TLC, FRC, and RV may occur as a result of hyperinflation of the lungs in <u>obstructive diseases</u>, whereas VC, TLC, FRC, and RV are reduced in restrictive diseases, which limit lung expansion.

Anatomy of the Digestive System

General Histological Plan of the Alimentary Canal

1. The general anatomical features of the digestive tube are listed below. Fill in the table to complete the information.

Wall layer	Subdivisions of the layer (if applicable)	Major functions
mucosa	1) epithelium 2) lamina propria 3) muscularis mucosa	absorption secretion
submucosa	(not applicable)	vascular supply for mucosa; protection
muscularis externa	1) circular layer 2) longitudinal layer	churning; mixing; propulsion of food along the tract
serosa or adventitia	(not applicable)	protection

Organs of the Alimentary Canal

2. The tubelike digestive system canal that extends from the mouth to the anus is the _alimentary_ canal.

3. How is the muscularis externa of the stomach modified? _It has a third (obliquely oriented) muscle layer._

How does this modification relate to the function of the stomach? _Vigorous churning activity occurs here._

4. What transition in epithelium type exists at the gastroesophageal junction? _Changes from stratified squamous (esophagus) to_ _simple columnar (stomach)_

How do the epithelia of these two organs relate to their specific functions? _The esophagus is subjected to constant abrasion_ _(stratified squamous is well adapted for this). The stomach has secretory (and some absorptive) functions._

5. Differentiate between the colon and the large intestine. _The large intestine includes the colon, but also includes the cecum, ver-_ _miform appendix, rectum, and anal canal._

6. Match the items in column B with the descriptive statements in column A.

Column A

_l_ 1. structure that suspends the small intestine from the posterior body wall

_y_ 2. fingerlike extensions of the intestinal mucosa that increase the surface area for absorption

_p_ 3. large collections of lymphoid tissue found in the submucosa of the small intestine

_c_ 4. deep folds of the mucosa and submucosa that extend completely or partially around the circumference of the small intestine

_n_, _v_ 5. regions that break down foodstuffs mechanically

_w_ 6. mobile organ that manipulates food in the mouth and initiates swallowing

_q_ 7. conduit for both air and food

_f_, _k_, _l_ 8. three structures continuous with and representing modifications of the peritoneum

_d_ 9. the "gullet"; no digestive/absorptive function

_s_ 10. folds of the gastric mucosa

_h_ 11. sacculations of the large intestine

_m_ 12. projections of the plasma membrane of a mucosal epithelial cell

_i_ 13. valve at the junction of the small and large intestines

_t_ 14. primary region of food and water absorption

_e_ 15. membrane securing the tongue to the floor of the mouth

_j_ 16. absorbs water and forms feces

_x_ 17. area between the teeth and lips/cheeks

_b_ 18. wormlike sac that outpockets from the cecum

_v_ 19. initiates protein digestion

_k_ 20. structure attached to the lesser curvature of the stomach

_t_ 21. organ distal to the stomach

_r_ 22. valve controlling food movement from the stomach into the duodenum

_u_ 23. posterosuperior boundary of the oral cavity

_t_ 24. location of the hepatopancreatic sphincter through which pancreatic secretions and bile pass

_o_ 25. serous lining of the abdominal cavity wall

_j_ 26. principal site for the synthesis of vitamin K by microorganisms

_a_ 27. region containing two sphincters through which feces are expelled

_g_ 28. bone-supported anterosuperior boundary of the oral cavity

Column B

a. anus

b. appendix

c. circular folds

d. esophagus

e. frenulum

f. greater omentum

g. hard palate

h. haustra

i. ileocecal valve

j. large intestine

k. lesser omentum

l. mesentery

m. microvilli

n. oral cavity

o. parietal peritoneum

p. Peyer's patches

q. pharynx

r. pyloric valve

s. rugae

t. small intestine

u. soft palate

v. stomach

w. tongue

x. vestibule

y. villi

z. visceral peritoneum

7. Correctly identify all organs depicted in the diagram below.

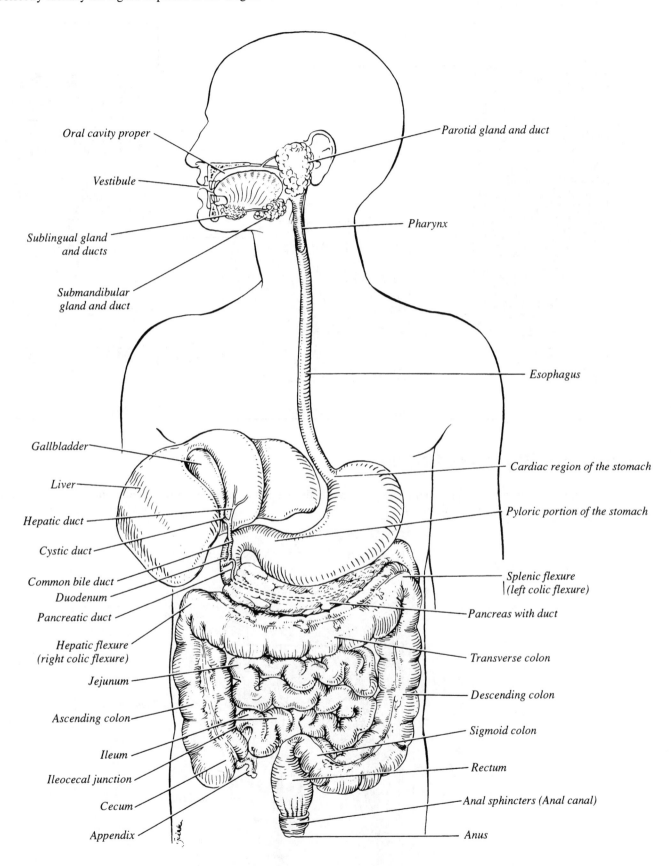

Oral cavity proper

Vestibule

Sublingual gland and ducts

Submandibular gland and duct

Parotid gland and duct

Pharynx

Esophagus

Gallbladder

Liver

Hepatic duct

Cystic duct

Common bile duct

Duodenum

Pancreatic duct

Hepatic flexure (right colic flexure)

Jejunum

Ascending colon

Ileum

Ileocecal junction

Cecum

Appendix

Cardiac region of the stomach

Pyloric portion of the stomach

Splenic flexure (left colic flexure)

Pancreas with duct

Transverse colon

Descending colon

Sigmoid colon

Rectum

Anal sphincters (Anal canal)

Anus

8. You have studied the histological structure of a number of organs in this laboratory. Three of these are diagrammed below. Identify and correctly label each.

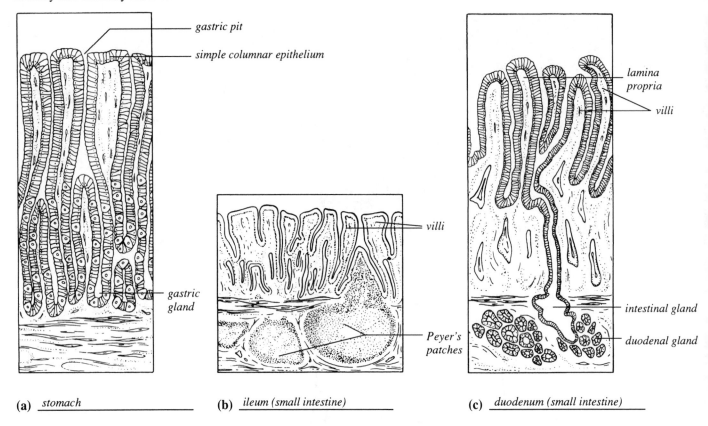

gastric pit

simple columnar epithelium

gastric gland

villi

Peyer's patches

lamina propria

villi

intestinal gland

duodenal gland

(a) <u>stomach</u>   (b) <u>ileum (small intestine)</u>   (c) <u>duodenum (small intestine)</u>

Accessory Digestive Organs

9. Correctly label all structures provided with leader lines in the diagram of a molar below. (Note: Some of the terms in the key for item 10 may be helpful in this task.)

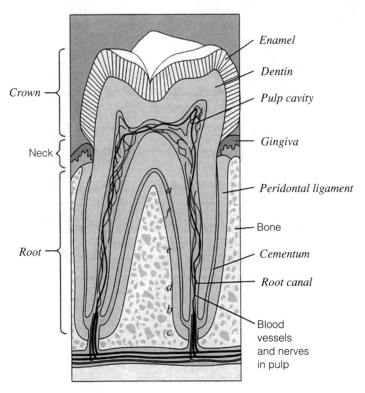

Crown

Neck

Root

Enamel

Dentin

Pulp cavity

Gingiva

Peridontal ligament

Bone

Cementum

Root canal

Blood vessels and nerves in pulp

10. Use the key to identify each tooth area described below.

Key:
a. anatomical crown
b. cementum
c. clinical crown
d. dentin
e. enamel
f. gingiva
g. odontoblast
h. periodontal ligament
i. pulp
j. root

_c_ 1. visible portion of the tooth *in situ*

_b_ 2. material covering the tooth root

_e_ 3. hardest substance in the body

_h_ 4. attaches the tooth to bone and surrounding alveolar structures

_j_ 5. portion of the tooth embedded in bone

_d_ 6. forms the major portion of tooth structure; similar to bone

_g_ 7. produces the dentin

_i_ 8. site of blood vessels, nerves, and lymphatics

_a_ 9. entire portion of the tooth covered with enamel

11. In the human, the number of deciduous teeth is _20_; the number of permanent teeth is _32_.

12. The dental formula for permanent teeth is $\frac{2,1,2,3}{2,1,2,3} \times 2 = 32$

Explain what this means. _There are 2 incisors, 1 canine, 2 premolars, and 3 molars in each jaw (upper and lower) from the median line posteriorly._

What is the dental formula for the deciduous teeth? $\frac{2,1,0,2}{2,1,0,2} \times 2$ *or* $\frac{2I,1C,2M}{2I,1C,2M} \times 2$ *(no premolars)*

13. What teeth are the "wisdom teeth"? _The number 3 (most posterior) molars._

14. Various types of glands form a part of the alimentary tube wall or duct their secretions into it. Match the glands listed in column B with the function/locations described in column A.

Column A

_a_ 1. produce(s) mucus; found in the submucosa of the small intestine

_f_ 2. produce(s) a product containing amylase that begins starch breakdown in the mouth

_e_ 3. produce(s) a whole spectrum of enzymes and an alkaline fluid that is secreted into the duodenum

_d_ 4. produce(s) bile that it secretes into the duodenum via the bile duct

_b_ 5. produce(s) HCl and pepsinogen

_c_ 6. found in the mucosa of the small intestine; produce(s) intestinal juice

Column B

a. duodenal glands
b. gastric glands
c. intestinal crypts
d. liver
e. pancreas
f. salivary glands

15. Which of the salivary glands produces a secretion that is mainly serous? _Parotid._

16. What is the role of the gallbladder? _To store and concentrate bile made by the liver._

17. Name three structures always found in the portal triad regions of the liver. _Branch of the bile duct_, _branch of hepatic artery_ and _branch of hepatic portal vein_.

18. Where would you expect to find the Kupffer cells of the liver? _Lining the sinusoids._

What is their function? _Phagocytosis of debris._

19. Why is the liver so dark red in the living animal? _Because it is a blood reservoir._

20. The pancreas has two major populations of secretory cells—those in the islets and the acinar cells. Which population serves

the digestive process? _Acinar cells._

Chemical and Physical Processes of Digestion: Wet Lab

Chemical Digestion of Foodstuffs: Enzymatic Action

1. Match the following definitions with the proper choices from the key.

Key: a. catalyst   b. control   c. enzyme   d. substrate

a; catalyst _____ 1. increases the rate of a chemical reaction without becoming part of the product

b; control _____ 2. provides a standard of comparison for test results

c; enzyme _____ 3. biologic catalyst; protein in nature

d; substrate _____ 4. substance on which a catalyst works

2. List the three characteristics of enzymes. *Specificity (act on one or a small number of substrates); temperature specific; pH specific.*

_____

_____

3. The enzymes of the digestive system are classified as hydrolases. What does this mean?

Hydrolases break down organic food molecules by adding water to the molecular bonds, thus cleaving the bonds between the subunits

or monomers.

4. Fill in the following chart about the various digestive system enzymes encountered in this exercise.

Enzyme	Organ producing it	Site of action	Substrate(s)	Optimal pH
Salivary amylase	*salivary glands*	*oral cavity*	*starch*	*6.7–7.0*
Trypsin	*pancreas*	*small intestine*	*proteins*	*8.0*
Lipase (pancreatic)	*pancreas*	*small intestine*	*starch, fats, proteins, etc.*	*7.4–8.0*

5. Name the end products of digestion for the following types of foods.

proteins: *amino acids* _____   carbohydrates: *simple sugars* _____

fats: *fatty acids* _____   and *glycerol (monoglycerides)* _____

6. You used several indicators or tests in the laboratory to determine the presence or absence of certain substances. Choose the correct test or indicator from the key to correspond to the condition described below.

Key: a.   IKI (Lugol's iodine)   b.   Benedict's solution   c.   litmus   d.   BAPNA

_d_____ 1.   used to test for protein hydrolysis, which was indicated by a yellow color

_a_____ 2.   used to test for the presence of starch, which was indicated by blue-black color

_c_____ 3.   used to test for the presence of fatty acids, which was evidenced by a color change from blue to pink

_b_____ 4.   used to test for the presence of reducing sugars (maltose, sucrose, glucose) as indicated by a blue to green color change

7. What conclusions can you draw when an experimental sample gives both a positive starch test and a positive maltose test

after incubation? _Starch digestion is partial (incomplete)._____

Why was 37°C the optimal incubation temperature? _It is body temperature._____

Why did very little, if any, starch digestion occur in test tube 4A? _The enzyme was destroyed by boiling._____

_____

If starch was incubated with amylase at 0°C, would you expect to see any starch digestion? _no_____

                                    Amylase has an optimal temperature closer to that of the human body. At 0°C, the rate of enzyme activity and diffu-
Why or why not? _sion of enzymes and substrate has slowed to near zero._____

Assume you have made the statement to a group of your peers that amylase is capable of starch hydrolysis to maltose. If you

had not done control tube 1A, what objection to your statement could be raised? _A positive maltose test could also result from_

_maltose contamination of the starting amylase solution._____

What if you had not done tube 2A? _#2A proves that we started with starch, and it was not contaminated with maltose._____

8. In the exercise concerning trypsin function, why was an enzyme assay like Benedict's or Lugol's IKI (which test for the pres-
                                    The enzyme assay is "built in" to the substrate BAPNA. Peptide bond cleavage results
ence of a reaction product) not necessary? _in a yellow color._____

Why was tube 1T necessary? _Tube 1T was a control to prove that trypsin did not turn yellow by itself._____

Why was tube 2T necessary? _Tube 2T proved that BAPNA did not turn yellow by itself._____

Trypsin is a protease similar to pepsin, the protein-digesting enzyme in the stomach. Would trypsin work well in the

stomach? _No_____ Why? _The pH optimum for trypsin is slightly basic; the pH optimum for pepsin is acidic (stomach is acidic)._

9. In the procedure concerning pancreatic lipase digestion of fats and the action of bile salts, how did the appearance of tubes

1E and 2E differ? _1E—2 layers; oil over water. 2E—fat droplets dispersed._____

_____

Can you explain the difference? _Bile, present in tube 2E, acted to emulsify the fat._____

_____

Why did the litmus indicator change from blue to pink during fat hydrolysis? *Fatty acids decreased the pH. Litmus cream is an*

indicator that changes from blue to red as the pH changes from alkaline to basic conditions.

Why is bile not considered an enzyme? *Bile only physically separates the fat droplets. It does not break the molecular bonds as do the digestive enzymes.*

How did the tubes containing bile compare with those not containing bile? *The tubes containing bile showed more hydrolysis than those not containing bile.*

What role does bile play in fat digestion? *Emulsification of fat by bile increases the surface area for lipase activity.*

10. The three-dimensional structure of a functional protein is altered by intense heat or nonphysiological pH even though peptide bonds may not break. Such inactivation is called denaturation, and denatured enzymes are nonfunctional. Explain why.

   Their three-dimensional structures and active sites are necessary for their activity. If their structures are changed, they are

   inactivated.

   What specific experimental conditions resulted in denatured enzymes? *Boiling the enzyme solution in all experiments dena-*

   tured the enzymes.

11. Pancreatic and intestinal enzymes operate optimally at a pH that is slightly alkaline, yet the chyme entering the duodenum from the stomach is very acid. How is the proper pH for the functioning of the pancreatic-intestinal enzymes ensured?

   The pancreas delivers its enzymes to the small intestine in an alkaline-rich (HCO_3^-) fluid.

12. Assume you have been chewing a piece of bread for 5 or 6 minutes. How would you expect its taste to change during this

   interval? *The bread would begin to taste sweet.*

   Why? *Starch is broken down to glucose by amylase.*

13. Note the mechanism of absorption (passive or active transport) of the following food breakdown products, and indicate by a check mark (✓) whether the absorption would result in their movement into the blood capillaries or the lymph capillaries (lacteals).

Substance	Mechanism of absorption	Blood	Lymph
Monosaccharides	*Most by active transport*	✓	
Fatty acids and glycerol	*Diffusion*	*Some*	*Most*
Amino acids	*Active transport*	✓	
Water	*Osmosis (diffusion)*	✓	
Na^+, Cl^-, Ca^{2+}	*Na^+, Ca^{2+} active transport; Cl^- diffusion*	✓	

14. People on a strict diet to lose weight begin to metabolize stored fats at an accelerated rate. How does this condition affect

   blood pH? *It would become acidic (decreased pH).*

15. Using a flow chart, trace the pathway of a ham sandwich (ham = protein and fat; bread = starch) from the mouth to the site of absorption of its breakdown products, noting where digestion occurs and what specific enzymes are involved.

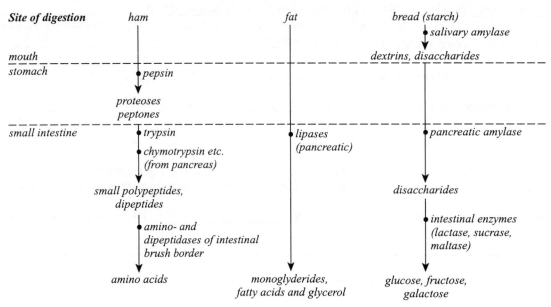

16. Some of the digestive organs have groups of secretory cells that liberate hormones (parahormones) into the blood. These exert an effect on the digestive process by acting on other cells or structures and causing them to release digestive enzymes, expel bile, or increase the mobility of the digestive tract. For each hormone below, note the organ producing the hormone and its effects on the digestive process. Include the target organs affected.

Hormone	Produced by	Target organ(s) and effects
Secretin	*intestinal mucosa*	*It stimulates (1) the pancreas to release bicarbonate-rich fluid, and (2) the liver to secrete bile.*
Gastrin	*stomach cells*	*Gastrin acts on the stomach glands to increase their secretory activity (particularly of HCl).*
Cholecystokinin	*intestinal cells*	*It stimulates release of enzymes from the pancreas, causes gall bladder contraction, and inhibits gastric secretion.*

Physical Processes: Mechanisms of Food Propulsion and Mixing

17. Complete the following statements.

Swallowing, or __1__, occurs in two phases—the __2__ and __3__. One of these phases, the __4__ phase, is voluntary. During the voluntary phase, the __5__ is used to push the food into the back of the throat. During swallowing, the __6__ rises to ensure that its passageway is covered by the epiglottis so that the ingested substances don't enter the respiratory passageways. It is possible to swallow water while standing on your head because the water is carried along the esophagus involuntarily by the process of __7__. The pressure exerted by the foodstuffs on the __8__ sphincter causes it to open, allowing the foodstuffs to enter the stomach.

The two major types of propulsive movements that occur in the small intestine are __9__ and __10__. One of these movements, the __11__, acts to continually mix the foods and to increase the absorption rate by moving different parts of the chyme mass over the intestinal mucosa, but has less of a role in moving foods along the digestive tract.

1. *deglutition*

2. *buccal*

3. *pharyngeal-esophageal*

4. *buccal*

5. *tongue*

6. *larynx*

7. *peristalsis*

8. *gastroesophageal*

9. *peristaltic*

10. *segmental*

11. *segmental*

Anatomy of the Urinary System

Gross Anatomy of the Human Urinary System

1. Complete the following statements:

The kidney is referred to as an excretory organ because it excretes __1__ wastes. It is also a major homeostatic organ because it maintains the electrolyte, __2__ , and __3__ balance of the blood.

Urine is continuously formed by the __4__ and is routed down the __5__ by the mechanism of __6__ to a storage organ called the __7__ . Eventually, the urine is conducted to the body __8__ by the urethra. In the male, the urethra is __9__ centimeters long and transports both urine and __10__ . The female urethra is __11__ centimeters long and transports only urine.

Voiding or emptying the bladder is called __12__ . Voiding has both voluntary and involuntary components. The voluntary sphincter is the __13__ sphincter. An inability to control this sphincter is referred to as __14__ .

1. _nitrogenous_ _____

2. _water_ _____

3. _acid-base_ _____

4. _kidneys_ _____

5. _ureters_ _____

6. _peristalsis_ _____

7. _urinary bladder_ _____

8. _exterior_ _____

9. _8_ _____

10. _semen_ _____

11. _1.5_ _____

12. _micturition_ _____

13. _external urethral_ _____

14. _incontinence_ _____

2. What is the function of the fat cushion that surrounds the kidneys in life? _Helps to anchor the kidneys to the dorsal body wall._

_____

3. Define *ptosis:* _Dropping of the kidney(s) to a more inferior position in the abdominal cavity._

_____

4. Why is incontinence a normal phenomenon in the child under 1½ to 2 years old? _Muscular control over the voluntary sphinc-_

ter has not yet been achieved.

What events may lead to its occurrence in the adult? _Emotional problems; bladder irritability (as in infection); increased pres-_

sure on the bladder (as in pregnancy); nerve or spinal cord injury; and others.

_____

5. Complete the labeling of the diagram to correctly identify the urinary system organs.

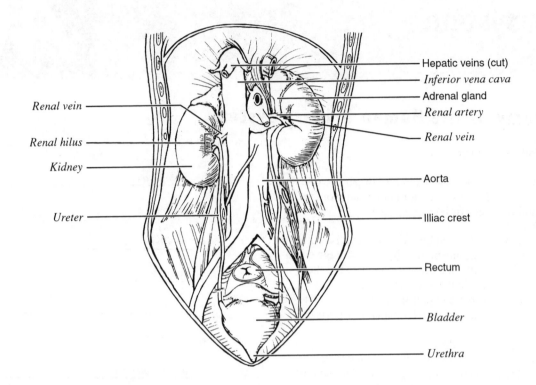

Gross Internal Anatomy of the Pig or Sheep Kidney

6. Match the appropriate structure in column B to its description in column A.

Column A

_d_ _____ 1. smooth membrane, tightly adherent to the kidney surface

_b_ _____ 2. portion of the kidney containing mostly collecting ducts

_a_ _____ 3. portion of the kidney containing the bulk of the nephron structures

_a_ _____ 4. superficial region of kidney tissue

_f_ _____ 5. basinlike area of the kidney, continuous with the ureter

_c_ _____ 6. a cup-shaped extension of the pelvis that encircles the apex of a pyramid

_e_ _____ 7. area of cortical tissue running between the medullary pyramids

Column B

a. cortex

b. medulla

c. minor calyx

d. renal capsule

e. renal column

f. renal pelvis

Functional Microscopic Anatomy of the Kidney and Bladder

7. Use the key letters to identify the diagram of the nephron (and associated renal blood supply) on the left.

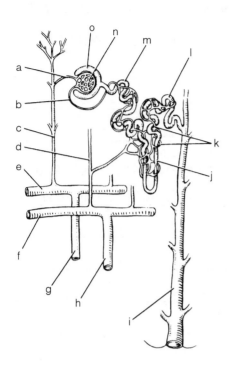

<u>*e*</u>   1. arcuate artery

<u>*f*</u>   2. arcuate vein

<u>*a*</u>   3. afferent arteriole

<u>*i*</u>   4. collecting duct

<u>*l*</u>   5. distal convoluted tubule

<u>*b*</u>   6. efferent arteriole

<u>*o*</u>   7. glomerular capsule

<u>*n*</u>   8. glomerulus

<u>*g*</u>   9. interlobar artery

<u>*d*</u>   10. interlobar vein

<u>*c*</u>   11. interlobular artery

<u>*d*</u>   12. interlobular vein

<u>*j*</u>   13. loop of Henle

<u>*k*</u>   14. peritubular capillaries

<u>*m*</u>   15. proximal convoluted tubule

8. Using the terms provided in item 7, identify the following:

<u>glomerulus (n)</u>   1. site of filtrate formation

<u>proximal convoluted tubule (m)</u>   2. primary site of tubular reabsorption

<u>distal convoluted tubule (l)</u>   3. secondarily important site of tubular reabsorption

<u>collecting duct (i)</u>   4. structure that conveys the processed filtrate (urine) to the renal pelvis

<u>peritubular capillaries (k)</u>   5. blood supply that directly receives substances from the tubular cells

<u>glomerular capsule (o)</u>   6. its inner (visceral) membrane forms part of the filtration membrane

9. Explain *why* the glomerulus is such a high-pressure capillary bed. *It is both fed and drained by arterioles (which are high-pressure vessels compared to venules), and the afferent arteriole has a larger diameter than the efferent arteriole.*

How does its high-pressure condition aid its function of filtrate formation? *The higher the capillary pressure, the more filtrate will be formed.*

10. What structural modification of certain tubule cells enhances their ability to reabsorb substances from the filtrate?

Their possession of dense microvilli (especially the PCT cells).

11. Explain the mechanism of tubular secretion and explain its importance in the urine formation process. *Tubular secretion is the process of moving substances from the tubule cells or from the peritubular capillary blood into the tubule filtrate. It is important for adjusting pH and eliminating substances not already in the filtrate.*

12. Compare and contrast the composition of blood plasma and glomerular filtrate. *Glomerular filtrate = blood plasma without most of the blood proteins.*

13. Trace a drop of blood from the time it enters the kidney in the renal artery until it leaves the kidney through the renal vein.

Renal artery → *segmental A. → lobar A. → interlobar A. → arcuate A. → interlobular A. → afferent arteriole glomerulus → efferent arteriole → peritubular capillary bed → interlobular V. → arcuate V. → interlobar V.*

→ renal vein

14. Define *juxtaglomerular apparatus*: *Macula densa cells of the DCT and granular juxtaglomerular cells of the afferent arteriole that play a role in regulating the rate of filtrate formation and systemic blood pressure.*

15. Label the figure using the key letters of the correct terms.

Key: a. *juxtaglomerular cells*
b. *cuboidal epithelium*
c. *macula densa*
d. *glomerular capsule (parietal layer)*
e. *distal convoluted tubule*

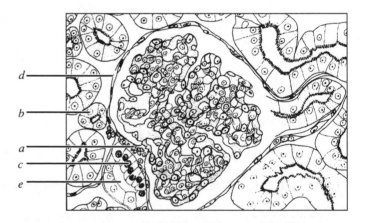

16. Trace the anatomical pathway of a molecule of creatinine (metabolic waste) from the glomerular capsule to the urethra. Note each microscopic and/or gross structure it passes through in its travels. Name the subdivisions of the renal tubule.

Glomerular capsule → *proximal convoluted tubule → loop of Henle → distal convoluted tubule → collecting tubule → papillary duct → minor calyx → major calyx → renal pelvis → ureter → bladder*

→ urethra

17. What is important functionally about the specialized epithelium (transitional epithelium) in the bladder?

The cells have the ability to move over one another as the bladder fills, thus decreasing the bladder wall thickness and increasing the internal bladder volume.

Urinalysis

Characteristics of Urine

1. What is the normal volume of urine excreted in a 24-hour period? _c_____

   a. 0.1–0.5 liters   b. 0.5–1.2 liters   c. 1.0–1.8 liters

2. Assuming normal conditions, note whether each of the following substances would be (a) in greater relative concentration in the urine than in the glomerular filtrate, (b) in lesser concentration in the urine than in the glomerular filtrate, or (c) absent in both the urine and the glomerular filtrate.

   _b___ 1. water   _b___ 6. amino acids   _a___ 11. uric acid

   _a___ 2. phosphate ions   _b___ 7. glucose   _a___ 12. creatinine

   _a___ 3. sulfate ions   _c___ 8. albumin   _c___ 13. pus (WBC)

   _a___ 4. potassium ions   _c___ 9. red blood cells   _c___ 14. nitrites

   _b___ 5. sodium ions   _a___ 10. urea

3. Explain why urinalysis is a routine part of any good physical examination. _Finding "abnormal" constituents in the urine may_

   indicate pathology. _____

4. What substance is responsible for the normal yellow color of urine? _Urochrome_____

5. Which has a greater specific gravity: 1 ml of urine or 1 ml of distilled water? _1 ml of urine_____

   Explain. _Urine contains dissolved solutes, which are not found in distilled water and add to the density of the sample._

   _____

6. Explain the relationship between the color, specific gravity, and volume of urine. _Generally, the smaller the volume, the greater_

   the specific gravity (more solutes/volume) and the deeper the color. _____

Abnormal Urinary Constituents

7. A microscopic examination of urine may reveal the presence of certain abnormal urinary constituents.

   Name three constituents that might be present if a urinary tract infection exists. _WBCs (pus)_____ ,

   _RBCs_____ , and _casts_____

8. How does a urinary tract infection influence urine pH? _Becomes alkaline_____

   How does starvation influence urine pH? _Becomes acidic_____

9. Several specific terms have been used to indicate the presence of abnormal urine constituents. Identify each of the abnormalities described below by inserting a term from the list at the right that names the condition.

c; hematuria   1.   presence of erythrocytes in the urine

d; hemoglobinuria   2.   presence of hemoglobin in the urine

b; glycosuria   3.   presence of glucose in the urine

a; albuminuria   4.   presence of albumin in the urine

e; ketonuria   5.   presence of ketone bodies (acetone and others) in the urine

f; pyuria   6.   presence of pus (white blood cells) in the urine

Key:

a.   albuminuria
b.   glycosuria
c.   hematuria
d.   hemoglobinuria
e.   ketonuria
f.   pyuria

10. What are renal calculi and what conditions favor their formation? _Kidney stones; urinary retention, urinary tract infection, alkaline urine._

11. All urine specimens become alkaline and cloudy on standing at room temperature. Explain why. _This is a result of bacterial metabolism or urinary components._

12. Glucose and albumin are both normally absent in the urine, but the reason for their exclusion differs. Explain the reason for the absence of glucose. _It is completely reabsorbed (unless present in the blood in excessive levels)._

Explain the reason for the absence of albumin. _It is too large to pass through the filtration membrane._

13. Several conditions (both pathological and nonpathological) are named below. Using the key provided, characterize the probable abnormal constituents or conditions of the urinary product of each. More than one choice is necessary to fully characterize the condition in most cases.

_a, d_   1.   glomerulonephritis   _h_   7.   starvation

_e, g, h_   2.   diabetes mellitus   _i_   8.   diabetes insipidus

_a_   3.   pregnancy, exertion   _c_   9.   kidney stones

_b_   4.   hepatitis, cirrhosis of the liver   _e_   10.   eating a 5-lb box of candy at one sitting

_d, g, j_   5.   pyelonephritis   _f_   11.   hemolytic anemias

_g, j_   6.   gonorrhea   _h, j_   12.   cystitis (inflammation of the bladder)

Key:

a.   albumin
b.   bilirubin
c.   blood cells
d.   casts
e.   glucose
f.   hemoglobin
g.   high specific gravity
h.   ketone bodies
i.   low specific gravity
j.   pus

14. Name the three major nitrogenous wastes found in the urine. _Urea_ , _uric acid_ , and _creatinine_

15. Explain the difference between organized and unorganized sediments. _Organized sediments (such as certain salts and uric acid) crystallize or precipitate out of solution, whereas unorganized sediments contain cellular elements (WBCs, epithelial cells, etc.)._

Anatomy of the Reproductive System

Gross Anatomy of the Human Male Reproductive System

1. List the two principal functions of the testis. *Sperm production, testosterone production* _____

2. Identify all indicated structures or portions of structures on the diagrammatic view of the male reproductive system below.

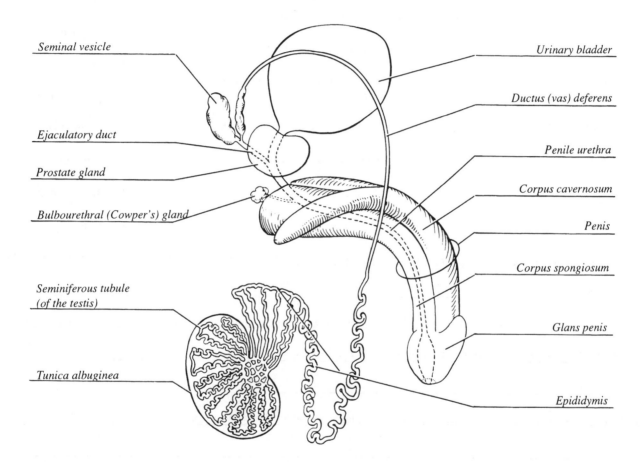

3. A common part of any physical examination of the male is palpation of the prostate gland. How is this accomplished?

(Think!) *Through the anterior wall of the rectum.* _____

4. How might enlargement of the prostate gland interfere with urination or the reproductive ability of the male?

Constriction of the urethra at that point may lead to nonpassage of urine or semen. _____

5. Match the terms in column B to the descriptive statements in column A.

Column A

f; penis _____ 1. copulatory organ/penetrating device

m; testes _____ 2. site of sperm/androgen production

b; ductus deferens _____ 3. muscular passageway conveying sperm to the ejaculatory duct; in the spermatic cord

l; spongy urethra _____ 4. transports both sperm and urine

c; epididymis _____ 5. sperm maturation site

k; scrotum _____ 6. location of the testis in adult males

g; prepuce _____ 7. loose fold of skin encircling the glans penis

e; membranous urethra _____ 8. portion of the urethra between the prostate gland and the penis

h; prostate gland _____ 9. empties a secretion into the prostatic urethra

a; bulbourethral glands _____ 10. empties a secretion into the membranous urethra

Column B

a. bulbourethral glands

b. ductus deferens

c. epididymis

d. glans penis

e. membranous urethra

f. penis

g. prepuce

h. prostate gland

i. prostatic urethra

j. seminal vesicles

k. scrotum

l. spongy urethra

m. testes

6. Why are the testes located in the scrotum? *Viable sperm production requires a temperature slightly lower (94–95°F) than body tem-* *perature.*

7. Describe the composition of semen and name all structures contributing to its formation. *Sperm and the alkaline secretions of* *the prostate, seminal vesicles (also containing fructose), and the bulbourethral glands.*

8. Of what importance is the fact that seminal fluid is alkaline? *Buffers the sperm against the acid environment of the female repro-* *ductive tract.*

9. What structures compose the spermatic cord? *Connective tissue sheath (extension of abdominal fascia), ductus deferens, blood ves-* *sels.*

Where is it located? *Passes from the scrotal sac through the inguinal canal into the abdominal cavity.*

10. Using the following terms, trace the pathway of sperm from the testes to the urethra: rete testis, epididymis, seminiferous tubule, ductus deferens.

seminiferous tubule → *rete testis* → *epididymis* → *ductus deferens*

11. Using an appropriate reference, define *cryptorchidism* and discuss its significance.

Failure of the testes to descend into the scrotum from the abdominal cavity, resulting in sterility if uncorrected.

Gross Anatomy of the Human Female Reproductive System

12. On the diagram below of a frontal section of a portion of the female reproductive system, identify all indicated structures.

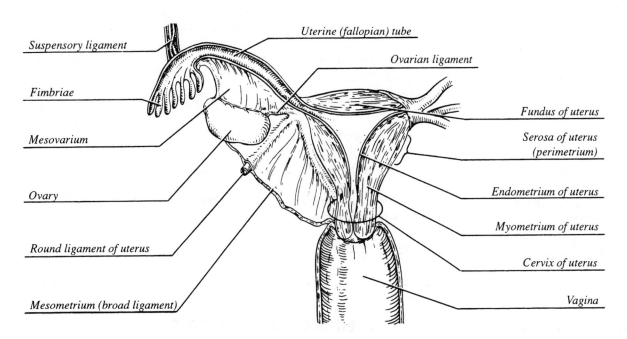

Suspensory ligament

Uterine (fallopian) tube

Fimbriae

Ovarian ligament

Mesovarium

Fundus of uterus

Serosa of uterus (perimetrium)

Ovary

Endometrium of uterus

Myometrium of uterus

Round ligament of uterus

Cervix of uterus

Mesometrium (broad ligament)

Vagina

13. Identify the female reproductive system structures described below:

uterus	1.	site of fetal development
vagina	2.	copulatory canal
uterine tube	3.	"fertilized egg" typically formed here
clitoris	4.	becomes erectile during sexual excitement
uterine tube	5.	duct extending superolaterally from the uterus
hymen	6.	partially closes the vaginal canal; a membrane
ovary	7.	produces oocytes, estrogens, and progesterone
fimbriae	8.	fingerlike ends of the fallopian tube

14. Do any sperm enter the pelvic cavity of the female? Why or why not? *Yes. There is no anatomic continuity between the ovary and the first part of the duct system (i.e. uterine tube).*

15. What is an ectopic pregnancy, and how can it happen? *Implantation of the embryo in a site other than the uterus. May occur when*

    the uterine tubes are blocked (prevents passage) or when the egg is "lost" in the peritoneal cavity and fertilization occurs there.

16. Name the structures composing the external genitalia, or vulva, of the female. *Mons pubis, labia majora and minora, clitoris,*

    vaginal and urethral openings, hymen, and greater vestibular glands.

17. Put the following vestibular-perineal structures in their proper order from the anterior to the posterior aspect: vaginal orifice, anus, urethral opening, and clitoris.

    Anterior limit: *clitoris* → *urethral opening* → *vaginal orifice* → *anus*

18. Name the male structure that is homologous to the female structures named below.

    labia majora *scrotum*   clitoris *penis*

19. Assume a couple has just consummated the sex act and the male's sperm have been deposited in the woman's vagina. Trace the pathway of the sperm through the female reproductive tract.

    vagina → cervix → uterus → uterine tube → peritoneal cavity

20. Define *ovulation:* *Ejection of an egg (actually an oocyte) from the ovary.*

Microscopic Anatomy of Selected Male and Female Reproductive Organs

21. The testis is divided into a number of lobes by connective tissue. Each of these lobes contains one to four *seminiferous*

    tubules, which converge on a tubular region at the testis hilus called the *rete*

    testis.

22. What is the function of the cavernous bodies seen in the male penis? *This tissue can become engorged with blood, thus making*

    the penis stiff and more effective as a penetrating device.

23. Name the three layers of the uterine wall from the inside out.

    endometrium, *myometrium*, *serosa (perimetrium)*

    Which of these is sloughed during menses? *Endometrium*

    Which contracts during childbirth? *Myometrium*

24. What is the function of the stereocilia exhibited by the epithelial cells of the mucosa of the epididymis? _Absorb excess fluid_

and provide nutrients to the maturing sperm.

25. On the diagram showing the sagittal section of the human testis, correctly identify all structures provided with leader lines.

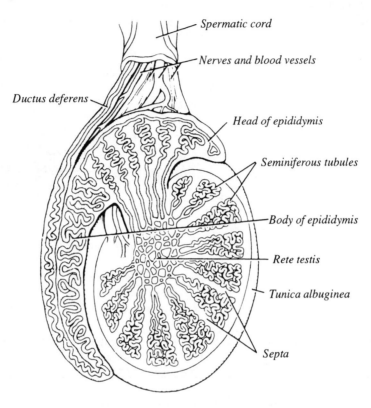

The Mammary Glands

26. Match the term with the correct description.

a; alveoli _____ glands that produce milk during lactation   a.   alveoli

e; lobule _____ subdivisions of mammary lobes that contain alveoli   b.   areola

d; lactiferous sinus __ enlarged storage chambers for milk   c.   lactiferous duct

c; lactiferous duct __ ducts connecting alveoli to the lactiferous sinus   d.   lactiferous sinus

b; areola _____ pigmented area surrounding the nipple   e.   lobule

f; nipple _____ releases milk to the outside   f.   nipple

27. Using the key terms, correctly identify breast structures.

Key: a. adipose tissue
       b. lobule containing alveoli
       c. areola
       d. lactiferous duct
       e. lactiferous sinus
       f. nipple

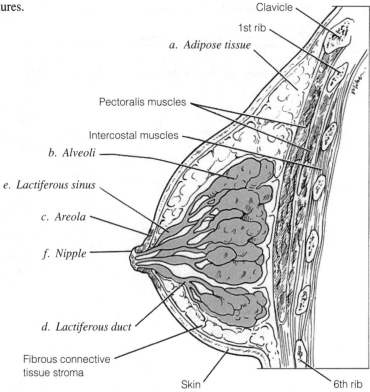

Clavicle

1st rib

a. Adipose tissue

Pectoralis muscles

Intercostal muscles

b. Alveoli

e. Lactiferous sinus

c. Areola

f. Nipple

d. Lactiferous duct

Fibrous connective tissue stroma

Skin

6th rib

28. Describe the procedure for self-examination of the breasts. (Men are not exempt from breast cancer, you know!)

1. Stand in front of a mirror, arms relaxed at sides; examine breasts for changes in size, shape, dimpling, etc. 2. Lie in supine position,

pillow under one shoulder, arm raised. Examine the breast on that raised side by pressing the breast tissue with flattened fingers in small

circular motions, moving from the periphery of the breast toward the nipple. Continue 360 degrees around the breast. Repeat for oppo-

site side.

Physiology of Reproduction: Gametogenesis and the Female Cycles

Meiosis

1. The following statements refer to events occurring during mitosis and/or meiosis. For each statement, decide if the event occurs in (a) mitosis only, (b) meiosis only, or (c) both mitosis and meiosis.

   _c_   1. dyads are visible

   _b_   2. tetrads are visible

   _a_   3. product is two diploid daughter cells

   _b_   4. product is four haploid daughter cells

   _c_   5. involves the phases prophase, metaphase, anaphase, and telophase

   _a_   6. occurs throughout the body

   _b_   7. occurs only in the ovaries and testes

   _a_   8. provides cells for growth and repair

   _b_   9. homologues synapse and chiasmata are seen

   _b_   10. daughter cells are quantitatively and qualitatively different from the mother cell

   _a_   11. daughter cells are genetically identical to the mother cell

   _c_   12. chromosomes are replicated before the division process begins

   _b_   13. provides cells for replication of the species

   _b_   14. consists of two consecutive nuclear divisions, without chromosomal replication occurring before the second division

2. Describe the process of synapsis. _The homologous chromosomes become closely aligned along their entire length._

3. How does crossover introduce variability in the daughter cells? _Where crossovers occur, chromosome breakage occurs and parts are exchanged. This results in chromosomes with different parental contributions._

4. Define *homologous chromosomes*. _Chromosomes that carry genes for the same traits. (One = paternal chromosome, the other = maternal chromosome.)_

Spermatogenesis

5. The cell types seen in the seminiferous tubules are listed in the key. Match the correct cell type(s) with the descriptions given below.

Key: a. primary spermatocyte   c. spermatogonium   e. spermatid
      b. secondary spermatocyte   d. sustentacular cell   f. sperm

_c_ _____ 1. primitive stem cell

_b, e, f_ _____ 2. haploid

_d_ _____ 3. provides nutrients to developing sperm

_e_ _____ 4. products of meiosis II

_f_ _____ 5. product of spermiogenesis

_b_ _____ 6. product of meiosis I

6. Why are spermatids not considered functional gametes? _Too much superfluous cytoplasm; nonmotile._

7. Differentiate between *spermatogenesis* and *spermiogenesis*. _Formation of haploid gametes by the male._

Sloughing off excessive spermatid cytoplasm to form a motile functional sperm.

8. Draw a sperm below and identify the *acrosome, head, midpiece,* and *tail.* Then beside each label, note the composition and function of each of these sperm structures.

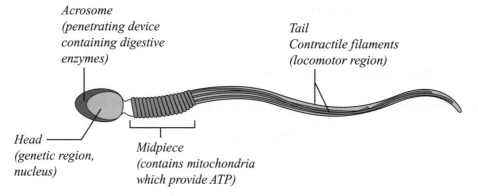

Acrosome
(penetrating device
containing digestive
enzymes)

Tail
Contractile filaments
(locomotor region)

Head
(genetic region,
nucleus)

Midpiece
(contains mitochondria
which provide ATP)

9. The life span of a sperm is very short. What anatomical characteristics might lead you to suspect this even if you didn't know its life span? _No cytoplasm (to speak of) in which to store nutrients._

Oogenesis, the Ovarian Cycle, and the Menstrual Cycle

10. The sequence of events leading to germ cell formation in the female begins during fetal development. By the time the child is born, all viable oogonia have been converted to _primary oocytes_ .

In view of this fact, how does the total germ cell potential of the female compare to that of the male?

Much smaller, and the total number is predetermined.

11. The female gametes develop in structures called *follicles*. What is a follicle? _A structure consisting of a capsule of follicle (or_

granulosa) cells that encloses a developing gamete (oocyte).

How are primary and vesicular follicles anatomically different? _The primary follicle has one or a small number of layers of_

follicle cells surrounding the oocyte; the vesicular follicle has a large antrum containing fluid produced by the granulosa cells, and the

developing oocyte, surrounded by several layers of granulosa cells, is pushed to one side.

What is a corpus luteum? _Glandular ovarian structure that produces progesterone. The ruptured vesicular follicle is converted to a_

corpus luteum.

12. What is the major hormone produced by the vesicular follicle? _Estrogen_

By the corpus luteum? _Progesterone (and some estrogen)_

13. Use the key to identify the cell type you would expect to find in the following structures.

Key: a. oogonium   b. primary oocyte   c. secondary oocyte   d. ovum

_b_ ___ 1. forming part of the primary follicle in the   _c_ ___ 3.   in the mature vesicular follicle of the ovary
ovary

_c_ ___ 2. in the uterine tube before fertilization   _d_ ___ 4.   in the uterine tube shortly after sperm penetra-
tion

14. The cellular product of spermatogenesis is four _spermatids_ ___; the final product of oogenesis is one

ovum ___ and three _polar bodies_ ___. What is the function of this unequal cytoplasmic

division seen during oogenesis in the female? _To provide the ovum or functional gamete with adequate nutritional reserves so that_

it can survive during its journey to the uterus.

What is the fate of the three tiny cells produced during oogenesis? _They deteriorate._

Why? _They lack sustaining cytoplasm with nutrient reserves._

15. The following statements deal with anterior pituitary, ovarian hormones, and hormonal interrelationships. Name the hor-
mone(s) described in each statement.

FSH (follicle-stimulating ___ 1. produced by primary follicles in the ovary
hormone)

LH (luteinizing hormone) ___ 2. ovulation occurs after its burstlike release

estrogen ___ and _progesterone_ ___ 3. exert negative feedback on the anterior pituitary
relative to FSH secretion

estrogen ___ 4. stimulates LH release by the anterior pituitary

_LH_ ___ 5. stimulates the corpus luteum to produce progesterone and estrogen

_LH_ ___ 6. maintains the hormonal production of the corpus luteum in a nonpregnant woman

16. Why does the corpus luteum deteriorate toward the end of the ovarian cycle? _Because blood levels of the anterior pituitary_

hormone LH are extremely low.

17. For each statement below dealing with hormonal blood levels during the female ovarian and menstrual cycles, decide whether the condition in column A is usually (a) greater than, (b) less than, or (c) essentially equal to the condition in column B.

	Column A	Column B
_b_ 1.	amount of estrogen in the blood during menses	amount of estrogen in the blood at ovulation
_b_ 2.	amount of progesterone in the blood on day 14	amount of progesterone in the blood on day 23
_b_ 3.	amount of LH in the blood during menses	amount of LH in the blood at ovulation
_a_ 4.	amount of FSH in the blood on day 6 of the cycle	amount of FSH in the blood on day 20 of the cycle
_a_ 5.	amount of estrogen in the blood on day 10	amount of progesterone in the blood on day 10

18. Ovulation and menstruation usually cease by the age of _55–60_.

19. What uterine tissue undergoes dramatic changes during the menstrual cycle? _Endometrium_

20. When during the female menstrual cycle would fertilization be unlikely? Explain why. _Any time but the three-day interval_

(days 14–16) around ovulation. (Twenty-eight day cycle is assumed.)

21. Assume that a woman could be an "on demand" ovulator like the rabbit, in which copulation stimulates the hypothalamic-anterior pituitary axis and causes LH release, and an oocyte was ovulated and fertilized on day 26 of her 28-day cycle. Why would a successful pregnancy be unlikely at this time? _The hormonal production of the ovary has ceased; the_

endometrium is beyond the receptive stage and is ready to slough off in menses.

22. The menstrual cycle depends on events within the female ovary. The stages of the menstrual cycle are listed below. For each, note its approximate time span and the related events in the uterus; and then to the right, record the ovarian events occurring simultaneously. Pay particular attention to hormonal events.

Menstrual cycle stage	Uterine events	Ovarian events
Menstruation	_Days 1–5. Endometrium is sloughing off._	_Primary follicle begins to grow._
Proliferative	_Days 6–14. Endometrium repaired, glands and blood vessels proliferate. Endometrium thickens._	_Follicular growth continues and vesicular follicle(s) produced. Estrogen secreted and peaks at day 14. Ovulation occurs on the 14th day._
Secretory	_Days 15–28. Vascular supply increases and glands begin secretory activity._	_Ruptured follicle is converted to a corpus luteum, which begins to produce progesterone (and some estrogen). Peaks at day 23 and then begins to decline._

Survey of Embryonic Development

Developmental Stages of Sea Urchins and Humans

1. Define zygote. *Fertilized egg.* _____

2. Describe how you were able to tell by observation when a sea urchin egg was fertilized. *A fertilization membrane is present*

beneath the outer jelly coat. _____

3. Use the key choices to identify the embryonic stage or process described below.

Key: a. cleavage   c. zygote   e. blastula
        b. morula   d. fertilization   f. gastrulation

_*d*_____ 1.   fusion of male and female pronuclei

_*b*_____ 2.   solid ball of embryonic cells

_*a*_____ 3.   process of rapid mitotic cell division without intervening growth periods

_*c*_____ 4.   combination of egg and sperm

_*f*_____ 5.   process involving cell rearrangements to form the three primary germ layers

_*e*_____ 6.   embryonic stage in which the embryo consists of a hollow ball of cells

4. What is the importance of cleavage in embryonic development? *It provides a large number of smaller cells for morphogenesis.*

_____

How is cleavage different from mitotic cell division, which occurs later in life? *During cleavage there are no intervening growth*

periods between the successive divisions. Therefore the cells get smaller and smaller, but the embryonic mass remains essentially the same

size. _____

5. The cells of the human blastula (blastocyst) have various fates. Which blastocyst structures have the following fates?

_*inner cell mass*_____ 1.   produces the embryonic body

_*trophoblast*_____ 2.   becomes the chorion and cooperates with uterine tissues to form the placenta

_*inner cell mass*_____ 3.   produces the amnion, yolk sac, and allantois

_*yolk sac*_____ 4.   produces the primordial germ cells (an embryonic membrane)

_*allantois*_____ 5.   an embryonic membrane that provides the structural basis for the body stalk or umbilical cord

6. Using the letters on the diagram, correctly identify each of the following maternal or embryonic structures.

_j_ amnion   _g_ chorion   _b_ decidua basalis   _f_ endoderm

_i_ body stalk   _h_ chorionic villi   _a_ decidua capsularis   _e_ mesoderm

          _d_ ectoderm   _c_ uterine cavity

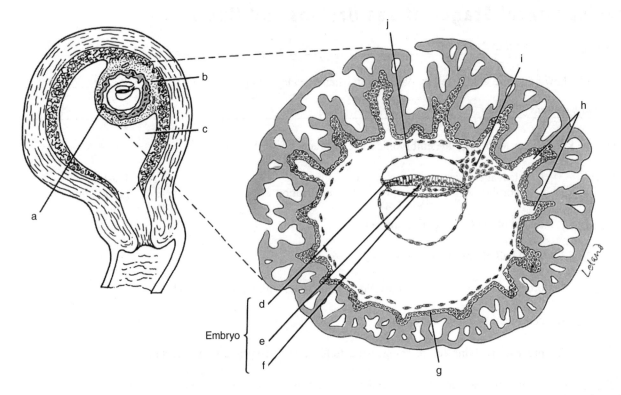

7. Explain the importance of gastrulation. _It involves the migration, movement, and rearrangement of embryonic cells, so that a three-_ _layer embryo (three primary germ layers) is formed._

8. What is the function of the amnion and the amniotic fluid? _The amnion is a protective, fluid-filled sac that surrounds the embryo._ _The fluid "buffer" protects the embryo from physical trauma and prevents adhesion formation._

9. Describe the process of implantation, noting the role of the trophoblast cells. _The trophoblast cells overlying the inner cell mass_ _adhere to the endometrium. The trophoblast cells then secrete enzymes that erode the endometrial lining to reach the vascular supply be-_ _neath it._

10. How many days after fertilization is implantation generally completed? _7_ What event in the female menstrual cycle ordinarily occurs just about this time if implantation does not occur? _Menses, because this is usually the 14th day after ovula-_ _tion._

11. What name is given to the part of the uterine wall directly under the implanting embryo? _Decidua basalis_

That surrounding the rest of the embryonic structure? _Decidua capsularis_

12. Using an appropriate reference, find out what *decidua* means and state the definition. _That which "falls off" or is subject to periodic shedding._

How is this terminology applicable to the deciduas of pregnancy? _After birth they slough off and are flushed out of the uterus._

13. Referring to the illustrations and text of *A Colour Atlas of Life Before Birth: Normal Fetal Development,* answer the following:

Which two organ systems are extensively developed in the *very young* embryo?

nervous system and _circulatory system_

Describe the direction of development by circling the correct descriptions below:

(proximal-distal)   distal-proximal   caudal-rostral   (rostral-caudal)

Does bodily control during infancy develop in the same directions? Think! Can an infant pick up a common pin (pincer grasp) or wave his arms earlier? Is arm-hand or leg-foot control achieved earlier?

Yes. Arm-hand control occurs before leg-foot control is achieved.

14. Note whether each of the following organs or organ systems develops from the (a) ectoderm, (b) endoderm, or (c) mesoderm. Use an appropriate reference as necessary.

_c_ 1. skeletal muscle   _b_ 4. respiratory mucosa   _a_ 7. nervous system

_c_ 2. skeleton   _c_ 5. circulatory system   _c_ 8. serosa membrane

_b_ 3. lining of gut   _a_ 6. epidermis of skin   _b_ 9. liver, pancreas

In Utero Development

15. Make the following comparisons between a human and the pregnant dissected animal structures.

Comparison object	Human	Dissected animal
Shape of the placenta	*Disc-shaped*	*(depends on animal)*
Shape of the uterus	*Pear-shaped*	*Y-shaped*

16. Where in the human uterus do implantation and placentation ordinarily occur? _High in the uterus._

17. Describe the function(s) of the placenta. _Provides nutrients and oxygen to the fetus, removes fetal wastes, and produces the hormones of pregnancy._

What embryonic membranes has the placenta more or less "put out of business"? *Yolk sac and allantois.*

18. When does the human embryo come to be called a fetus? *Ninth week of development.*

19. What is the usual and most desirable fetal position in utero? *Head down.*

    Why is this the most desirable position? *The largest fetal dimension is the skull. Therefore, if the skull is used as a wedge, the rest of the body is delivered easily. Also, if difficulties are encountered, the baby can be suctioned and given oxygen even before delivery is completed.*

Gross and Microscopic Anatomy of the Placenta

20. Describe fully the gross structure of the human placenta as observed in the laboratory. *Smooth on the side from which the umbilical cord issues. Torn, rough, and bloody on the side that was united with maternal tissues. Blood-rich.*

21. What is the tissue origin of the placenta: fetal, maternal, or both? *Both*

22. What are the placental barriers that must be crossed to exchange materials? *The membranes of the villi and capillary walls of the fetal vascular supply.*

Principles of Heredity

Introduction to the Language of Genetics

1. Match the key choices with the definitions given below.

Key: a. alleles d. genotype g. phenotype
  b. autosomes e. heterozygous h. recessive
  c. dominant f. homozygous i. sex chromosomes

d; genotype _____ 1. actual genetic makeup

i; sex chromosomes _____ 2. chromosomes determining maleness/femaleness

f; homozygous _____ 3. situation in which an individual has identical alleles for a particular trait

h; recessive _____ 4. genes not expressed unless they are present in homozygous condition

g; phenotype _____ 5. expression of a genetic trait

e; heterozygous _____ 6. situation in which an individual has different alleles making up his genotype for a particular trait

a; alleles _____ 7. genes for the same trait that may have different expressions

b; autosomes _____ 8. chromosomes regulating most body characteristics

c; dominant _____ 9. the more-potent gene allele; masks the expression of the less-potent allele

Dominant-Recessive Inheritance

2. In humans, farsightedness is inherited by possession of a dominant gene. If a man who is homozygous for normal vision (*aa*) marries a woman who is heterozygous for farsightedness, what proportion of their children would be expected to be

farsighted? _50_ %

3. A metabolic disorder called PKU is due to an abnormal recessive gene (*p*). Only homozygous recessive individuals exhibit

this disorder. What percentage of the offspring will be anticipated to have PKU if the parents are *Pp* and *pp*? _50_ %

4. A man obtained 32 spotted and 10 solid-color rabbits from a mating of two spotted rabbits.

Which trait is dominant? _spotted_____ Recessive? _solid-color_____

What is the probable genotype of the rabbit parents? _Ss_____ × _Ss_____

5. Assume that the allele controlling brown eyes (*B*) is dominant over that controlling blue eyes (*b*) in human beings. (In actuality, eye color in humans is an example of multigene inheritance, which is much more complex than this.) A blue-eyed man marries a brown-eyed woman; and they have six children, all brown-eyed. What is the most likely genotype of the father?

    bb Of the mother? *BB* If the seventh child had *blue* eyes, what could you conclude about the parents' genotypes?

    Female is Bb; male is bb.

Incomplete Dominance

6. Tail length on a bobcat is controlled by incomplete dominance. The alleles are *T* for normal tail length and *t* for tail-less.

   What name could/would you give to the tails of heterozygous (*Tt*) cats? *Bobtail*

   How would their tail length compare with that of *TT* or *tt* bobcats? *Intermediate in length*

7. If curly-haired individuals are genotypically *CC,* straight-haired individuals are *cc,* and wavy-haired individuals are heterozygotes (*Cc*), what percentage of the various phenotypes would be anticipated from a cross between a *CC* woman and a *cc* man?

    0 % curly   *100* % wavy   *0* % straight

Sex-Linked Inheritance

8. What does it mean when someone says a particular characteristic is sex-linked? *It is carried on the female X (sex) chromosome.*

9. You are a male, and you have been told that hemophilia "runs in your genes." Whose ancestors, your mother's or your father's, should you investigate? *Mother's* Why? *Males can only receive the X chromosome from their mothers; the father's contribution is always Y.*

10. An $X^C X^c$ female marries an $X^C Y$ man. Do a Punnett square for this match.

    What is the probability of producing a color-blind son? *25%*

    A color-blind daughter? *0%*

    A daughter that is a carrier for the color-blind gene? *25%*

	X^C	X^c
X^C	$X^C X^C$	$X^C X^c$
Y	$X^C Y$	$X^c Y$

11. Why are consanguineous marriages (marriages between blood relatives) prohibited in most cultures?

    Blood relatives have similar gene pools. Thus, the likelihood of receiving a double dose of recessive genes (many of which are detrimental) is dramatically increased.

Probability

12. What is the probability of having three daughters in a row? <u>$(\frac{1}{2} \times \frac{1}{2} \times \frac{1}{2}) = \frac{1}{8}$ or 12.5%</u>

13. A man and a woman, each of seemingly normal intellect, marry. Although neither is aware of the fact, each is a heterozygote for the allele for feeblemindedness. Is the allele for feeblemindedness dominant or recessive? <u>*Recessive*</u>

What are the chances of their having one feebleminded child? <u>*25% ($\frac{1}{4}$)*</u>

What are the chances that all of their children (they plan a family of four) will be feebleminded? <u>$(\frac{1}{4} \times \frac{1}{4} \times \frac{1}{4} \times \frac{1}{4}) = \frac{1}{256}$ or 0.39%</u>

Genetic Determination of Selected Human Characteristics

14. Look back at your data to complete this section. For each of the situations described here, determine if an offspring with the characteristics noted is possible with the parental genotypes listed. Check (✓) the appropriate column.

Parental genotypes	Phenotype of child	Possibility	
		Yes	**No**
$Jj \times jj$	Double-jointed thumbs	✓	
$FF \times Ff$	Straight little finger		✓
$EE \times ee$	Detached ear lobes	✓	
$HH \times Hh$	Middigital hair	✓	
$I^A i \times I^B i$	Type O blood	✓	
$I^A I^B \times ii$	Type B blood	✓	

15. You have dimples, and you would like to know if you are homozygous or heterozygous for this trait. You have six brothers and sisters. By observing your siblings, how could you tell, with some degree of certainty, that you are a heterozygote?

<u>*Absence of dimples indicates the homozygous recessive condition. If one or more of your siblings does not have dimples, there was a 50%*</u>

<u>*chance at your conception that you would be heterozygous for this trait.*</u>

Identifying Hemoglobin Phenotypes Using Agar Gel Electrophoresis

16. Draw the banding patterns you obtained on the figure below. Indicate the genotype of each band.

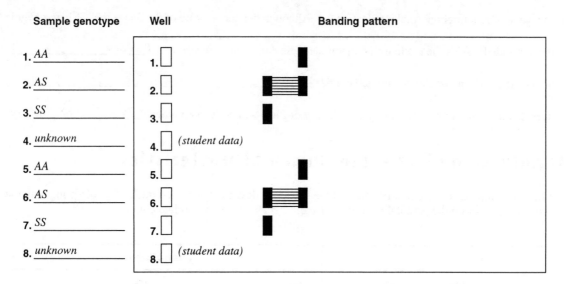

Sample genotype	Well
1. *AA*	1.
2. *AS*	2.
3. *SS*	3.
4. *unknown*	4. *(student data)*
5. *AA*	5.
6. *AS*	6.
7. *SS*	7.
8. *unknown*	8. *(student data)*

17. What is the genotype of sickle cell anemia? *SS*_____ Sickle cell trait? *AS*_____

18. Why does sickle-cell hemoglobin behave differently from normal hemoglobin during agarose gel electrophoresis?

HbS has fewer negative charges than HbA, due to the base substitution of valine for glutamic acid in HbS.

Surface Anatomy Roundup

_c_ _____ **1.** A blow to the cheek is most likely to break what superficial bone or bone part? (a) superciliary arches, (b) the philtrum, (c) zygomatic arch, (d) the tragus.

_a_ _____ **2.** Rebound tenderness (a) occurs in appendicitis, (b) is whiplash of the neck, (c) is a sore foot from playing basketball, (d) occurs when the larynx falls back into place after swallowing.

_b_ _____ **3.** The anatomical snuff box (a) is in the nose, (b) contains the styloid process of the radius, (c) is defined by tendons of the flexor carpi radialis and palmaris longus, (d) cannot really hold snuff.

_d_ _____ **4.** Some landmarks on the body surface can be seen or felt, but others are abstractions that you must construct by drawing imaginary lines. Which of the following pairs of structures is abstract and invisible? (a) umbilicus and costal margin, (b) anterior superior iliac spine and natal cleft, (c) linea alba and linea semilunaris, (d) McBurney's point and midaxillary line, (e) philtrum and sternocleidomastoid.

_c_ _____ **5.** Many pelvic organs can be palpated by placing a finger in the rectum or the vagina, but only one pelvic organ is readily palpated through the skin. This is the (a) nonpregnant uterus, (b) prostate gland, (c) full bladder, (d) ovaries, (e) rectum.

_b_ _____ **6.** A muscle that contributes to the posterior axillary fold is the (a) pectoralis major, (b) latissimus dorsi, (c) trapezius, (d) infraspinatus, (e) pectoralis minor, (f) a and e.

_c_ _____ **7.** Which of the following is not a pulse point? (a) anatomical snuff box, (b) inferior margin of mandible anterior to masseter muscle, (c) center of distal forearm at palmaris longus tendon, (d) medial bicipital furrow on arm, (e) dorsum of foot between the first two metatarsals.

_b_ _____ **8.** Which pair of ribs inserts on the sternum at the sternal angle? (a) first, (b) second, (c) third, (d) fourth, (e) fifth.

_b_ _____ **9.** The inferior angle of the scapula is at the same level as the spinous process of which vertebra? (a) C_5, (b) C_7, (c) T_3, (d) T_7, (e) L_4.

_a_ _____**10.** An important bony landmark that can be recognized by a distinct dimple in the skin is the (a) posterior superior iliac spine, (b) styloid process of the ulna, (c) shaft of the radius, (d) acromion.

_a_ _____**11.** A nurse missed a patient's median cubital vein while trying to withdraw blood and then inserted the needle far too deeply into the cubital fossa. This error could cause any of the following problems, except this one: (a) paralysis of the ulnar nerve, (b) paralysis of the median nerve, (c) bruising the insertion tendon of the biceps brachii muscle, (d) blood spurting from the brachial artery.

_c_ _____**12.** Which of these organs is almost impossible to study with surface anatomy techniques? (a) heart, (b) lungs, (c) brain, (d) nose.

_c_ _____**13.** A preferred site for inserting an intravenous medication line into a blood vessel is the (a) medial bicipital furrow on arm, (b) external carotid artery, (c) dorsal venous arch of hand, (d) popliteal fossa.

_a_ _____**14.** One listens for bowel sounds with a stethoscope placed (a) on the four quadrants of the abdominal wall; (b) in the triangle of auscultation; (c) in the right and left midaxillary line, just superior to the iliac crests; (d) inside the patient's bowels (intestines), on the tip of an endoscope.

Dissection and Identification of Cat Muscles

Time Allotment: Skin removal; 1 hour. Muscle dissection; 4–6 hours+ (depending on detail required).

Multimedia Resources: See Appendix F for a list of multimedia offerings.

The Anatomy of the Cat (CBS, 85 minutes, VHS)
Cat Dissection (WNS, 39 minutes, VHS)

Cat WORKS (ED, CD-ROM)

Solution:
Carboglycerine solution
30 grams fungicide (Benomyl, Sigma)
250 milliliters glycerine
1 liter water
Mix together and store in a closed container.

Advance Preparation

1. Order cats well in advance, as they may be in short supply.

2. Make arrangements for appropriate storage, disposal, and cleanup of dissection materials. Check with the Department of Health or the Department of Environmental Protection, or their counterparts, for state regulations. Designate a disposal container for organic debris, set up a dishwashing area with hot soapy water and sponges, and provide lab disinfectant such as Wavicide-01 (Carolina) for washing down the lab benches.

3. Set out disposable gloves, safety glasses, dissecting kits, dissection tray, plastic storage bags, paper towels, and name tags.

4. Set out dissection animals (one per group of two to four students).

5. Set out *carboglycerine solution* or small plastic bags to hold embalming fluid.

Comments and Pitfalls

1. Be sure that students understand that the skin is to be removed in one piece.

2. Emphasize the use of the blunt probe as a dissecting instrument, rather than the scalpel. Cut only when everyone in the group agrees that a cut should be made!

3. Cat fur tends to clog the sink drains. Emphasize correct disposal of organic debris.

4. Students often "invent" muscles by tearing tissue apart. Emphasize that they should be separating muscles by breaking through the surrounding connective tissue.

5. Sometimes the dissection animal is in very poor condition, in which case the student should exchange it for a different specimen.

Answers to Questions

Activity 2: Dissecting Neck and Trunk Muscles; Muscles of the Abdominal Wall (p. 745)

2. The external oblique muscles run medially and downward, while the internal oblique muscle fibers run upward and medially. They are not quite perpendicular to each other.

Superficial Muscles of the Shoulder and Dorsal Trunk and Neck (p. 747)

1. The clavotrapezius appears to originate on the occipital bone. This is similar to a part of the origin of the trapezius muscle in humans. The three cat muscles seem to have the same functions as the human trapezius muscle.

2. In humans the levator scapulae elevates the scapula and bends the neck laterally if the scapula is fixed.

3. The clavodeltoid inserts on the proximal end of the ulna. This muscle is used to flex the lower limb in walking.

Activity 3: Dissecting Forelimb Muscles; Muscles of the Lateral Surface (p. 750)

1. The triceps muscle has a similar function in cats and humans.

Muscles of the Medial Surface (p. 751)

1. The biceps brachii has only one head in the cat.

Activity 4: Dissecting Hindlimb Muscles; Posterolateral Hindlimb Muscles (pp. 751–756)

5. In humans the semimembranosus is also medial to and partially obscured by the semi-tendinosus. The human semimembranosus inserts on the tibia, but not on the femur.

Anteromedial Hindlimb Muscles (pp. 755–756)

2. The origin of the rectus femoris in humans is the anterior inferior iliac spine and just above the acetabulum.

3. The human gracilis muscle has a very similar origin and insertion.

Dissection Review

Many human muscles are modified from those of the cat (or any quadruped) as a result of the requirements of an upright posture. The following questions refer to these differences.

1. How does the human trapezius muscle differ from the cat's?

   Cat's trapezius is triparite (clavo-, acromio-, and spino- portions); the human trapezius is a single muscle.

2. How does the deltoid differ?

   Cat has three deltoid muscles, the clavodeltoid, acromiodeltoid, and spinodeltoid. The human has a single deltoid

   muscle.

3. How does the extent and orientation of the human sartorious muscle differ from its relative position in the cat?

   In humans, the satorius is a thin straplike muscle running obliquely across the anterior thigh. In the cat it is broad

   and flat and covers most of the anterolateral thigh.

4. Explain the differences in terms of differences in function.

   The sartorius adducts and rotates the thigh in both the human and the cat. In the cat (but not the human) it is also an

   important knee extensor.

5. The human rectus abdominis is definitely divided by four transverse tendons (tendinous intersections). These tendons are absent or difficult to identify in the cat. How do these tendons affect the human upright posture?

   These tendons support the abdominal muscular wall so that the viscera are not allowed to become pendulous in the

   upright posture of humans.

6. Match the terms in Column B to the descriptions in Column A.

	Column A	Column B
_a_	1. to separate muscles	a. dissect
_c_	2. to fold back a muscle	b. embalm
_d_	3. to cut through a muscle	c. reflect
_b_	4. to preserve tissue	d. transect

Dissection of Cat Spinal Nerves

dissection exercise

2

 Time Allotment: 1¹/₂ hours.

 Multimedia Resources: See Appendix F for a list of multimedia offerings.

The Anatomy of the Cat (CBS, 85 minutes, VHS)
Cat Dissection (WNS, 39 minutes, VHS)

Cat WORKS (ED, CD-ROM)

Advance Preparation

1. See Dissection Exercise 1 for setup instructions.

2. If cats were not skinned previously, see instructions in Dissection Exercise 1. Allow extra time for skinning.

Dissection Review

1. From anterior to posterior, put the nerves issuing from the brachial plexus in their proper order (i.e., the median, musculocutaneous, radial, and ulnar nerves).

    musculocutaneous, radial, median, ulnar
    _____

    _____

2. Which of the nerves named above serves the cat's forearm extensor muscles?
    the median nerve _____ Which serves the forearm flexors? *the radial nerve* _____

3. Just superior to the gastrocnemius muscle the sciatic nerve divides into its two main branches, the *tibial* _____ and *common fibular* _____ nerves.

4. What name is given to the cutaneous nerve of the cat's thigh? *the saphenous nerve* _____

Identification of Selected Endocrine Organs of the Cat

Time Allotment: 1 hour.

Multimedia Resources: See Appendix F for a list of multimedia offerings.

The Anatomy of the Cat (CBS, 85 minutes, VHS)
Cat Dissection (WNS, 39 minutes, VHS)

Cat WORKS (ED, CD-ROM)

Advance Preparation

1. See Dissection Exercise 1 for setup instructions.

2. If cats were not skinned previously, see instructions in Dissection Exercise 1. Allow extra time for skinning. (Note: It is not absolutely necessary to skin the cats to do dissection of internal structures.)

Comments and Pitfalls

1. It is possible to leave identification of glands in the dissection animal until later dissections.

Dissection Review

1. How do the location of the endocrine organs in the cat compare with those in the human?

   They are similar but in the cat the pancreas is more diffuse, and the adrenal glands are medial rather than superior to

   the kidneys.

2. Name the two endocrine organs located in the throat region: *thyroid gland*
   and *thymus gland*

3. Name three endocrine organs located in the abdominal cavity.

   pancreas, adrenal glands, ovaries in female

4. Given the assumption (not necessarily true) that human beings have more stress than cats, which endocrine organs would you expect to be relatively larger?

the adrenal glands

5. Cats are smaller animals than humans. Which would you expect to have a (relatively speaking) more active thyroid gland—cats or humans? *cats* Why? (We know we are asking a lot with this one, but give it a whirl.)

It is a general rule of thumb that basal metabolic rate increases as body size decreases. The effect of an increased

surface to volume relationship in maintaining internal temperature may be one of several factors explaining this

phenomenon.

Dissection of the Blood Vessels of the Cat

 Time Allotment: 1½–2 hours (depending on detail required in dissection).

 Multimedia Resources: See Appendix F for a list of multimedia offerings.

The Anatomy of the Cat (CBS, 85 minutes, VHS)
Cat Dissection (WNS, 39 minutes, VHS)

Cat WORKS (ED, CD-ROM)

Advance Preparation

1. See Dissection Exercise 1 for setup instructions.

2. If cats were not skinned previously, see instructions in Dissection Exercise 1. Allow extra time for skinning. (Note: It is not absolutely necessary to skin the cats to do dissection of internal structures.)

Comments and Pitfalls

1. As students dissect out the arteries and veins, caution them to avoid damaging other organs that will be studied in later exercises. Especially caution them against cutting away the greater omentum.

2. Students may want to forge ahead and do the entire dissection once the ventral body cavity has been opened. Remind them that the individual systems will be studied in detail at a later date.

3. If time is limited, the circulatory system may be studied in conjunction with the study of individual systems rather than as a separate exercise.

4. If desired by the instructor, a previously dissected animal may be put on demonstration.

Dissection Review

1. What differences did you observe between the origins of the left common carotid arteries in the cat and in the human?

   In the cat, both the R and L carotid arteries branch off the R brachiocephalic artery. In humans, the L common

   carotid branches directly off the aortic arch; only the R common carotid branches off the brachiocephalic artery.

   Between the origin of the internal and external iliac arteries?

   In the cat, the aorta ends by dividing into the two external iliac arteries and a single median internal iliac artery

   (which then divides into the R and L internal iliac arteries). In humans, the external and internal iliac arteries arise

   by branching off the common iliac arteries (which do not exist in the cat).

2. How do the relative sizes of the external and internal jugular veins differ in the human and the cat?

   In the cat, the external jugular vein is larger. In humans, the internal jugular vein is larger.

3. In the cat the inferior vena cava is called the _postcava_, and the superior vena cava is referred to as the _precava_.

4. Define:

   Ascending aorta:

   The aorta as it emerges from the heart and travels to the head.

   Aortic arch:

   The aorta as it bends to head caudally.

   Descending thoracic aorta:

   The aorta as it passes through the thoracic cavity.

   Descending abdominal aorta:

   The aorta as it passes through the abdominal cavity.

The Main Lymphatic Ducts of the Cat

**dissection
exercise

5**

 Time Allotment: 1/2 hour (may be easily included with Dissection Exercise 4).

 Multimedia Resources: See Appendix F for a list of multimedia offerings.

The Anatomy of the Cat (CBS, 85 minutes, VHS)
Cat Dissection (WNS, 39 minutes, VHS)

Cat WORKS (ED, CD-ROM)

Advance Preparation

1. See Dissection Exercise 1 for setup instructions.

2. If cats were not skinned previously, see instructions in Dissection Exercise 1. Allow extra time for skinning. (Note: It is not absolutely necessary to skin the cats to do dissection of internal structures.)

Comments and Pitfalls

1. If the student cats are double injected, it might be of value to order one triple-injected cat for demonstration of the lymphatic system.

Dissection Review

1. How does the cat's lymphatic drainage pattern compare to that of humans?

    basically the same

2. What is the role of:
    a. the thoracic duct? *It returns lymph from the lower body and upper left quadrant to the left subclavian vein.*

    b. the right lymphatic duct? *It returns lymph to the right subclavian vein from the upper right quadrant.*

Dissection of the Respiratory System of the Cat

Time Allotment: 1 1/2 hours.

Multimedia Resources: See Appendix F for a list of multimedia offerings.

The Anatomy of the Cat (CBS, 85 minutes, VHS)
Cat Dissection (WNS, 39 minutes, VHS)

Cat WORKS (ED, CD-ROM)

Advance Preparation

1. See Dissection Exercise 1 for setup instructions.

2. If cats were not skinned previously, see instructions in Dissection Exercise 1. Allow extra time for skinning. (Note: It is not absolutely necessary to skin the cats to do dissection of internal structures.)

3. Set out dissecting microscopes.

Dissection Review

1. Are the cartilaginous rings in the cat trachea complete or incomplete? *incomplete*

2. How does the number of lung lobes in the cat compare with the number in humans?

   5 in humans; 7 in the cat

3. Describe the appearance of the bronchial tree in the cat lung.

   The bronchial tree is a series of branching tubing. The primary bronchi are large, subsequent branches are

   smaller and smaller in diameter.

4. Describe the appearance of lung tissue under the dissection microscope.

   Spongy-looking with small, irregular openings

Dissection of the Digestive System of the Cat

Time Allotment: 2 hours.

Multimedia Resources: See Appendix F for a list of multimedia offerings.

The Anatomy of the Cat (CBS, 85 minutes, VHS)
Cat Dissection (WNS, 39 minutes, VHS)

Cat WORKS (ED, CD-ROM)

Advance Preparation

1. See Dissection Exercise 1 for setup instructions.

2. Set out bone cutters, water bottles for flushing the intestines, and hand lenses.

Comments and Pitfalls

1. Warn students that they will probably encounter roundworms in the cat's stomach and intestines.

Answers to Questions

Activity 1: Identifying Alimentary Canal Organs (pp. 782–784)

2. The cat liver has five lobes, the human liver has four lobes.

4. The stomach is a curved sac. Blood vessels, lymphatics, and nerves are present in the mesenteries.

6. The mesenteries provide a route for blood and lymphatic vessels and nerves to travel to and from the small intestine. There are no major differences in external anatomy along the length of the small intestine. The inner surface of the ileum feels like velvet. The villi in the duodenum are more elongated than those in the ileum.

7. The cat does not have an appendix.

Activity 2: Exposing and Viewing the Salivary Glands and Oral Cavity Structures (pp. 784–785)

2. Rugae are not as well developed in humans. Cats do not have a uvula. The numerous filiform papillae are used by the cat for grooming and for removing flesh from bones. Cats are carnivores and their teeth are adapted for hunting prey and tearing food. Thus they retain three incisors on each side of the upper jaw for biting. The canine teeth, used for tearing, are relatively large. The number of molars, used for grinding food, is reduced. The last premolar of the upper jaw and the lower molar form a complex shearing structure. Human dentition is more adapted to softer foods, which require some grinding.

Dissection Review

1. Compare the appearance of tongue papillae in cats and humans.

   The cat has numerous sharp, bristly filiform papillae. Human filiform papillae are less numerous, blunted, and

   softer.

2. Compare the number of lobes of the liver in cats and humans.

   The cat liver has five lobes; the human liver has four.

3. Does the cat have a uvula? _no_ An appendix? _no_

4. Give an explanation for the different adult dental formulas in cats and humans.

   Cats are carnivores and need extra incisors for biting. They have a reduced need for grinding and thus have

   fewer molars.

5. How do the villi differ in the duodenum and the ileum? Explain.

   The villi in the duodenum are more elongated than those in the ileum.

Dissection of the Urinary System of the Cat

 Time Allotment: 1 hour.

 Multimedia Resources: See Appendix F for a list of multimedia offerings.

The Anatomy of the Cat (CBS, 85 minutes, VHS)
Cat Dissection (WNS, 39 minutes, VHS)

Cat WORKS (ED, CD-ROM)

Advance Preparation:

1. See Dissection Exercise 1 for setup instructions.

Comments and Pitfalls

1. Emphasize the importance of clearing away the peritoneum and fat tissue. Once the kidneys have been isolated there should be no difficulty identifying the ureters.

2. Remind the students that they are responsible for both the male and the female urinary systems.

3. This dissection fits nicely with the dissection of the reproductive system.

Answers to Questions

Activity 1: Identifying Organs of the Urinary System (p. 786)

4. The ureters enter the bladder on the right and left lateral surfaces toward the posterior (caudal) end.

Dissection Review

1. a. How does the position of the kidneys in the cat differ from their position in humans?

   In humans, the left kidney is more superior. In the cat, the kidneys are located at the same level or the

   right kidney is more anterior.

   b. In what way is the position similar? *Both are retroperitoneal.*

2. Distinguish between a ureter and the urethra.

The ureter carries urine from the kidney to the urinary bladder. The urethra carries urine from the urinary

bladder to the exterior.

3. How does the site of urethral emptying in the female cat differ from its termination point in the human female?

Human: empties to the body exterior. Cat: empties into the urogenital sinus along with the vagina.

4. What is a urogenital sinus?

It is a common chamber into which the urethra and vagina enter.

5. What gland encircles the neck of the bladder in the male? *prostate*_____ Is this part of the urinary system? *no*_____ What is its function?

Part of the male reproductive system. Produces a secretion, which contributes to seminal fluid.

6. Compare the location of the adrenal glands in the cat to the location in humans.

In humans the adrenal glands sit atop the kidneys. In the cat they are superior and medial to the kidneys,

close to the inferior vena cava.

Dissection of the Reproductive System of the Cat

dissection
exercise

9

 Time Allotment: 1 1/2–2 hours.

 Multimedia Resources: See Appendix F for a list of multimedia offerings.

The Anatomy of the Cat (CBS, 85 minutes, VHS)
Cat Dissection (WNS, 39 minutes, VHS)

Cat WORKS (ED, CD-ROM)

Advance Preparation

1. See Dissection Exercise 1 for setup instructions.
2. Set out metric rulers and bone clippers.

Comments and Pitfalls

1. Students usually encounter some difficulty dissecting out the penis. It takes time as the overlying skin is tightly attached in some places.
2. Caution students with male dissection animals to be careful when dissecting out the spermatic cord to avoid breaking it.
3. Remind students that they are responsible for both male and female dissections.
4. It is interesting to have at least one pregnant cat for dissection.
5. Students must use bone clippers to cut through the pubic region of the pelvis to complete the dissection. It is easiest if the cut is through the pubic symphysis.

Answers to Questions

Activity 2: Identifying Organs of the Female Reproductive System (p. 792)

4. The human female has separate openings for the vagina and the urethra.

6. The vagina is two to three centimeters long (will vary).

Dissection Review

1. The female cat has a _bipartite_ uterus; that of the human female is _simplex_. Explain the difference in structure of these two uterine types.

   Cat: Y-shaped central inferior chamber (body) from which two horns (cornua) extend. Human: undivided single

   pear-shaped chamber.

2. What reproductive advantage is conferred by the feline uterine type?

   Can produce multiple offspring (litters).

3. Cite the differences between the cat and the human relative to the following structures:

   Uterine tubes or oviducts *Cat's are much reduced in size and length*

   Site of entry of ductus deferens into the urethra *More distal to the bladder in the cat*

   Location of the prostate gland *Smaller and more distal to the bladder in the cat*

   Seminal vesicles *Not present in cat*

   Urethral and vaginal openings in the female *Open into a common chamber (urogenital sinus) in the*

   cat. In humans, each organ opens independently to the body exterior.

Dissection and Identification of Fetal Pig Muscles

 Time Allotment: Muscle dissection; 4 hours.

 Multimedia Resources: See Appendix F for a list of multimedia offerings.

The Anatomy of the Fetal Pig (CBS, 62 minutes, VHS)

Fetal Pig (DryLab Plus) (ED, CD-ROM)
The Fetal Pig: A Technological Dissection (ED, CD-ROM)

 Solution:
Carboglycerine solution
30 grams fungicide (Benomyl, Sigma)
250 milliliters glycerine
1 liter water
Mix together and store in a closed container.

Advance Preparation

1. Make arrangements for appropriate storage, disposal, and cleanup of dissection materials. Check with the Department of Health or the Department of Environmental Protection, or their counterparts, for state regulations. Designate a disposal container for organic debris, set up a dishwashing area with hot soapy water and sponges, and provide lab disinfectant such as Wavicide-01 (Carolina) for washing down the lab benches.

2. Set out disposable gloves, safety glasses, dissecting kits, dissection tray, plastic storage bags, twine, metric rulers, paper towels, and name tags.

3. Set out dissection animals (one per group of two to four students).

4. Set out *carboglycerine solution* or small plastic bags to hold embalming fluid.

Comments and Pitfalls

1. Emphasize the use of the blunt probe as a dissecting instrument, rather than the scalpel. Cut only when everyone in the group agrees that a cut should be made!

2. Muscle development may be poor in some fetal pig specimens if they are very young.

3. Students often "invent" muscles by tearing tissue apart. Emphasize that they should be separating muscles by breaking through the surrounding connective tissue.

4. Sometimes the dissection animal is in very poor condition, in which case the student should exchange it for a different specimen.

Answers to Questions

Activity 3: Superficial Muscles of the Posterior Trunk and Neck (p. 749)

2. The acromiotrapezius and spinotrapezius muscles appear to have the same functions in the pig as in humans.

Activity 4: Dissecting Forelimb Muscles; Upper Forelimb Muscles (p. 751)

1. The triceps brachii has a similar function in pigs and humans.

3. The biceps brachii has only one head in the pig.

Activity 5: Dissecting Hindlimb Muscles; Muscles of the Posterolateral Hindlimb (pp. 751–753)

3. In humans the semimembranosus is also medial to and partially obscured by the semi-tendinosus. The human semimembranosus inserts on the tibia, but not on the femur.

Muscles of the Anteromedial Hindlimb (pp. 753–755)

2. The origin of the rectus femoris in humans is the anterior inferior iliac spine and just above the acetabulum.

3. The human gracilis muscle has a very similar origin and insertion.

Dissection Review

Many human muscles are modified from those of the pig (or any quadruped) as a result of the requirements of an upright posture. The following questions refer to these differences.

1. How does the human trapezius muscle differ from the pig's?

   The pig's trapezius is triparite (clavo-, acromio-, and spino- portions); the human trapezius is a single muscle.

2. How does the deltoid differ?

   The pig's deltoid is a tripartite muscle; the human deltoid is a single muscle.

3. How does the extent and orientation of the human sartorious muscle differ from its relative position in the pig?

   In humans, the satorius is a thin straplike muscle running obliquely across the anterior thigh. In the pig it is broad

   and flat and covers most of the anterolateral thigh. Its course is oblique, but appears less so because it is much larger.

4. Explain the differences in terms of differences in function.

In humans the sartorius adducts and rotates the thigh. In addition to these functions, it also extends the knee in the

pig.

5. The human rectus abdominis is definitely divided by four transverse tendons (tendinous intersections). These tendons are absent or difficult to identify in the pig. How do these tendons affect the human upright posture?

These tendons support the muscular abdominal wall so that the viscera are not allowed to become pendulous in the

upright posture of humans.

Dissection of Fetal Pig Spinal Nerves

 Time Allotment: 1½ hours.

 Multimedia Resources: See Appendix F for a list of multimedia offerings.

The Anatomy of the Fetal Pig (CBS, 62 minutes, VHS)

Fetal Pig (DryLab Plus) (ED, CD-ROM)
The Fetal Pig: A Technological Dissection (ED, CD-ROM)

Advance Preparation

1. See Dissection Exercise 1 for setup instructions.
2. Set out bone cutters.

Dissection Review

1. In what region (cervical, thoracic, lumbar, or sacral) of the spinal cord would you find the following special features?

   Enlargements: *cervical and lumbar*

   Cauda equina: *sacral*

2. As you trace a spinal nerve laterally, it divides into dorsal and ventral *rami* (rami/roots).

3. Describe the appearance of the sympathetic trunk as seen in your dissection animal.

   a white cord with periodic enlargements

4. From anterior to posterior, put the nerves issuing from the brachial plexus of the pig in proper order (i.e., the median, radial, and ulnar nerves). *radial, median, ulnar*

5. Just superior to the fetal pig's gastrocnemius muscle, the sciatic nerve divides into two main branches, the *internal popliteal* and the *external popliteal* nerves.

Identification of Selected Endocrine Organs of the Fetal Pig

 Time Allotment: 1 hour.

 Multimedia Resources: See Appendix F for a list of multimedia offerings.

The Anatomy of the Fetal Pig (CBS, 62 minutes, VHS)

Fetal Pig (DryLab Plus) (ED, CD-ROM)
The Fetal Pig: A Technological Dissection (ED, CD-ROM)

Advance Preparation

1. See Dissection Exercise 1 for setup instructions.

Comments and Pitfalls

1. It is also possible to leave identification of glands in the dissection animal until later dissections.

Dissection Review

1. How do the location of the endocrine organs in the fetal pig compare with those in the human?

   They are similar but in the pig the pancreas is more diffuse, and the adrenal glands are medial rather than superior

   to the kidneys.

2. Name the two endocrine organs located in the throat region: *thyroid gland*
   and *thymus gland*

3. Name three endocrine organs located in the abdominal cavity.

   pancreas, adrenal glands, ovaries in female

4. Given the assumption (not necessarily true) that human beings have more stress than adult pigs, which endocrine organs would you expect to be relatively larger in humans?

   the adrenal glands

5. Explain why the thymus in the fetal pig is so large, relatively speaking.

During fetal development, T cells are rapidly dividing and maturing in the thymus gland.

Dissection of the Blood Vessels of the Fetal Pig

 Time Allotment: 1¹/₂–2 hours (depending on detail required in dissection).

 Multimedia Resources: See Appendix F for a list of multimedia offerings.

The Anatomy of the Fetal Pig (CBS, 62 minutes, VHS)

Fetal Pig (DryLab Plus) (ED, CD-ROM)
The Fetal Pig: A Technological Dissection (ED, CD-ROM)

Advance Preparation

1. See Dissection Exercise 1 for setup instructions.

Comments and Pitfalls

1. As students dissect out the arteries and veins, caution them to avoid damaging other organs that will be studied in later exercises. Especially caution them against cutting away the greater omentum.

2. Students may want to forge ahead and do the entire dissection once the ventral body cavity has been opened. Remind them that the individual systems will be studied in detail at a later date.

3. If time is limited, the circulatory system may be studied in conjunction with the study of individual systems rather than as a separate exercise.

4. If desired by the instructor, a previously dissected animal may be put on demonstration.

Dissection Review

1. What differences did you observe between the origin of the common carotid arteries in the pig and in the human?

In the pig, the common carotid arteries arise from the bicarotid trunk (a branch off the brachiocephalic trunk). In

humans, the right common carotid artery arises from the brachiocephalic artery; the left common carotid artery

arises directly from the aortic arch.

2. How do the relative sizes of the external and internal jugular veins differ in the human and the pig?

In the pig, the external jugular vein is larger. In humans, the internal jugular vein is larger.

3. How do the brachial veins of the pig differ from those of humans?

In the pig, there are two brachial veins in each forelimb, which anastomose frequently along their course.

In humans, the brachial vein is singular.

4. What difference was noted between the origin of the hepatic portal vein in the pig and in humans?

Pig: from the union of the gastrosplenic and mesenteric veins.

Humans: from the union of the splenic and superior mesenteric veins.

Between the origin of the internal and external iliac arteries?

Pig: external iliac arteries issue directly from the aorta. The internal iliac arteries are branches of the umbilical

arteries at the aorta terminus. Humans: the external and internal iliac arteries arise from the division of the common

iliac arteries, which are the final aorta branches.

5. In the pig the inferior vena cava is called the *posterior vena cava*, and the superior vena cava is referred to as the *anterior vena cava*.

6. Define:

Ascending aorta:

The aorta as it emerges from the heart and travels to the head.

Aortic arch:

The aorta as it bends to head caudally.

Descending thoracic aorta:

The aorta as it passes through the thoracic cavity.

Descending abdominal aorta:

The aorta as it passes through the abdominal cavity.

Dissection of the Main Lymphatic Ducts of the Fetal Pig

 Time Allotment: 1/2 hour (may be easily included with Dissection Exercise 4).

 Multimedia Resources: See Appendix F for a list of multimedia offerings.

The Anatomy of the Fetal Pig (CBS, 62 minutes, VHS)

Fetal Pig (DryLab Plus) (ED, CD-ROM)
The Fetal Pig: A Technological Dissection (ED, CD-ROM)

Advance Preparation

1. See Dissection Exercise 1 for setup instructions.

Dissection Review

1. Is the pig's lymphatic drainage pattern basically similar or dissimilar to that of humans?

   basically similar

2. What is the role of:

   a. the thoracic duct? *It returns lymph from the lower body and upper left quadrant to the left subclavian vein.*

   b. the right lymphatic duct? *It returns lymph from the upper right quadrant to the right subclavian vein.*

Dissection of the Respiratory System of the Fetal Pig

 Time Allotment: 1¹/2 hours.

 Multimedia Resources: See Appendix F for a list of multimedia offerings.

The Anatomy of the Fetal Pig (CBS, 62 minutes, VHS)

Fetal Pig (DryLab Plus) (ED, CD-ROM)
The Fetal Pig: A Technological Dissection (ED, CD-ROM)

Advance Preparation

1. See Dissection Exercise 1 for setup instructions.
2. Set out dissecting microscopes and small beakers.

Answers to Questions

Activity 1: Identifying Respiratory Organs of the Fetal Pig (pp. 774–777)

3. The mucosa helps to warm and moisten the air entering the nasal cavity.

8. The segment of fetal lung tissue will sink to the bottom of the beaker of water. Fetal lungs have not yet inflated and the tissue is still dense.

Dissection Review

1. Are the cartilagenous rings in the pig trachea complete or incomplete? *incomplete*

2. How does the number of lung lobes in the pig compare with the number in humans?

   5 in humans; 7 in the pig.

3. Describe the appearance of lung tissue under the dissection microscope.

   Dense but spongy-looking.

4. Why did the segment of lung tissue, cut from the fetal pig's lung, *sink* when placed in water?

   The lungs have never been inflated; therefore the tissue contains essentially no air and is dense. Lungs that have

   been inflated contain trapped air and will float.

Dissection of the Digestive System of the Fetal Pig

 Time Allotment: 2 hours.

 Multimedia Resources: See Appendix F for a list of multimedia offerings.

The Anatomy of the Fetal Pig (CBS, 62 minutes, VHS)

Fetal Pig (DryLab Plus) (ED, CD-ROM)
The Fetal Pig: A Technological Dissection (ED, CD-ROM)

Advance Preparation

1. See Dissection Exercise 1 for setup instructions.

2. Set out bone cutters, water bottles, and hand lenses.

Comments and Pitfalls

1. In the pig the large intestine will have a very different arrangement from that of the human.

Answers to Questions

Activity 2: Identifying Digestive Organs in the Abdominal Cavity (pp. 781–782)

3. The stomach is a curved sac.

5. Blood vessels, lymphatics, and nerves are present in the mesenteries. The mesenteries provide a route for vessels and nerves to travel to and from the small intestine. The inner surface of the ileum feels like velvet. The villi in the duodenum are more elongated than those in the ileum.

6. The ileocecal valve prevents regurgitation of material from the cecum into the ileum. The pig does not have an appendix.

Dissection Review

Several differences between pig and human digestive anatomy should have become apparent during the dissection. State the pertinent differences between the human and the pig relative to the following structures:

Structure	Pig	Human
Number of liver lobes	*Five*	*Four*
Appendix	*Absent cecum present*	*Present*
Appearance and distribution of colon	*Ascends and then forms a tight coil before descending*	*Basically an inverted U with ascending, transverse, and descending portions*
Presence of round ligament	*Absent. Umbilical vein is still present. It later becomes the round ligament.*	*Present*

Dissection of the Urinary System of the Fetal Pig

 Time Allotment: 1 hour.

 Multimedia Resources: See Appendix F for a list of multimedia offerings.

The Anatomy of the Fetal Pig (CBS, 62 minutes, VHS)

Fetal Pig (DryLab Plus) (ED, CD-ROM)
The Fetal Pig: A Technological Dissection (ED, CD-ROM)

Advance Preparation:

1. See Dissection Exercise 1 for setup instructions.

Comments and Pitfalls

1. Emphasize the importance of clearing away the peritoneum and fat tissue. Once the kidneys have been isolated there should be no difficulty identifying the ureters.

2. Remind the students that they are responsible for both the male and the female urinary systems.

3. This dissection fits nicely with the dissection of the reproductive system.

Dissection Review

1. How does the structure and distribution of the allantoic bladder of the fetal pig differ from the urinary bladder of the human (or that of the adult pig, for that matter)?

   The allantoic bladder is very elongated and continues into the umbilical cord as the allantoic stalk. After birth, it is

   transformed into the bladder, which empties into the urethra.

2. What differences in fetal elimination of nitrogenous wastes account for the structural differences described above?

   Fetal elimination of nitrogenous waste occurs through the placenta. (The extraembryonic portion of the allantois

   forms a part of the placenta.)

3. How does the site of urethral emptying in the female pig differ from its termination point in the human female?

The pig's urethra and vagina empty into a common chamber, the urogenital sinus. The human female's urethra and

vagina terminate independently at the body surface.

Dissection of the Reproductive System of the Fetal Pig

 Time Allotment: 1½–2 hours.

 Multimedia Resources: See Appendix F for a list of multimedia offerings.

The Anatomy of the Fetal Pig (CBS, 62 minutes, VHS)

Fetal Pig (DryLab Plus) (ED, CD-ROM)
The Fetal Pig: A Technological Dissection (ED, CD-ROM)

Advance Preparation

1. See Dissection Exercise 1 for setup instructions.
2. Set out metric rulers, water bottles, and bone cutters.

Comments and Pitfalls

1. Caution students with male dissection animals to be careful when dissecting out the spermatic cord to avoid breaking it.
2. Remind students that they are responsible for both male and female dissections.
3. Students must use bone clippers to cut through the pubic region of the pelvis to complete the dissection. It is easiest if the cut is through the pubic symphysis.

Answers to Questions

Activity 2: Identifying Organs of the Female Reproductive System (p. 791)

4. The human female has separate openings for the vagina and the urethra.
6. The vagina is two to three centimeters long (will vary).

Dissection Review

1. The female pig has a <u>*bipartite*</u> uterus; that of the human female is <u>*simplex*</u>. Explain the difference in structure of these two uterine types.

   Pig: Y-shaped central chamber (body) from which two horns (cornua) extend. Human: undivided pear-shaped

   chamber.

2. What reproductive advantage is conferred by the pig's uterine type?

Can produce litters.

3. Cite the differences between the pig and the human relative to the following structures:

uterine tubes or oviducts *They are very tiny and relatively much shorter in the pig.*

urethral and vaginal openings in the female *In the pig, both open into a common chamber, the*

urogenital sinus. In humans, both structures empty independently to the body exterior.

The Cell: Transport Mechanisms and Permeability— Computer Simulation

 Time Allotment: 2 hours minimum, 3 hours preferred.

The following minimum computer hardware is recommended for PhysioEx™ 5.0:

Windows® 98, NT, 2000, ME; Pentium® I processor/ 266 mHz
Mac®: 9.2 or higher
64 MB RAM (128 MB recommended)
800 x 600 screen resolution; millions of colors
Netscape Navigator® 7.0+ or Internet Explorer® 5.0+ (Netscape® installer is included on CD)
Macromedia Flash 6® plug-in (installer is included on CD)
4x CD-ROM drive
Printer

Advance Preparation, Comments, and Pitfalls

1. *If you are using PhysioEx™ in a computer lab:* Because PhysioEx™ 5.0 requires a browser (such as Netscape® or Internet Explorer®) and the Flash 6® plug-in to run, it is recommended that you make sure these items are already installed on student computers before beginning this lab. Installers for both Netscape® and Flash 6® are provided on the CD (instructions are included on the liner notes accompanying the CD).

2. After installing Netscape® or Flash 6®, the computer may attempt to connect to the web. If you do not have a live Internet connection, you may see a dialogue box appear, alerting you of an inability to connect to the web. Simply ignore the message and close the box. **You do not need to have a live Internet connection to run the CD.**

3. *If you are using the web version of PhysioEx™:* Have your students go to http://www.physioex.com and follow the registration instructions found in the very front of their lab manual.

4. It is helpful to instruct students in the proper operation of the mouse and menu system as part of the lab introduction.

5. When considering an upgrade for computer systems, memory (RAM) offers the largest performance increase for the least cost.

6. Having students work in pairs results in the most successful lab experience. If students must work in larger groups, have them each get keyboard and mouse experience with the program.

7. Occasionally, data in the Cell Transport Mechanisms and Permeability module will appear with "#" symbols next to numbers. In the Simple Diffusion, Facilitated Diffusion, and Osmosis experiments, the "#" symbol after "rate" data indicates that equilibrium was not reached for that solute. In the Active Transport experiment, the symbol after "rate" data indicates 1) for glucose data, that equilibrium was not reached for glucose; 2) for NaCl and KCl, that transport was interrupted for that solute. In the Osmosis experiment, the symbol after "pressure" data means that osmotic equilibrium was not reached.

Answers to Questions

Activity 1: Simulating Dialysis (Simple Diffusion) (p. P-4)

All solutes except albumin are able to diffuse into the right beaker.

Using distilled water in the right beaker and either the 100 MWCO or 200 MWCO membrane and will remove urea from the left beaker and leave albumin

If the left beaker contains NaCl, urea, and albumin, you can selectively remove urea by dispensing a concentration of NaCl into the right beaker equivalent to that in the left beaker and by using the 100 or 200 MWCO membrane. Albumin is too large to diffuse and there will be no net diffusion of NaCl. However, urea will move down its concentration gradient into the right beaker.

Activity 2: Simulating Facilitated Diffusion (p. P-6)

Carrier proteins facilitate the movement of solute molecules across semipermeable membranes, so increasing their number will increase the rate of diffusion.

Because facilitated diffusion requires a concentration gradient, making the concentration on both sides of the membrane equal stops net diffusion.

NaCl does not have an effect on glucose diffusion.

Activity 3: Simulating Osmosis Pressure (p. P-8)

Using the 20 MWCO membrane results in an osmotic pressure increase using any of the solutes. The 50 and 100 MWCO membranes caused osmotic increase with albumin and glucose. Only albumin caused osmotic increase using the 200 MWCO membrane.

NaCl appeared in the right beaker with all membranes except the 20 MWCO membrane.

Increasing the number of non-diffusible particles increases osmotic pressure.

If solutes are able to diffuse, then equilibrium will be established and osmotic pressure will not be generated.

Osmotic pressure would be zero if albumin concentration was the same on both sides of the membrane.

If you increased the concentration of albumin, osmotic pressure will also increase.

Glucose is freely diffusible using the 200 MWCO membrane and therefore has no effect on osmotic pressure.

The 100 MWCO membrane does not allow glucose to pass and therefore glucose will generate an osmotic influence. Because albumin concentration in the left beaker is 9.00 mM and glucose concentration in the right beaker is 10.00 mM, (1.00 mM higher than the left), the small gradient dictates that an osmotic pressure increase will appear in the right beaker.

Activity 4: Simulating Filtration (p. P-10)

Smaller MWCO numbers translate to smaller pore sizes, which correlate with lower filtration rate.

Powdered charcoal did not appear in the filtrate using any membrane.

Increasing the force driving filtration increases filtration rate.

Increasing the pressure gradient effectively increases the filtration rate.

By examining the filtration results, we can predict that the molecular weight of glucose must be greater than NaCl but less than powdered charcoal.

Activity 5: Simulating Active Transport (p. P-12)

Solute transport stops before the completion of transport because of a lack of ATP.

Sodium and potassium transport will not occur if ATP is not available.

Yes, transport has changed because more ATP is available. This fact supports the earlier supposition that ATP is required for active transport.

The rate of active transport will decrease if fewer solute pumps are available, but will still go to completion given enough ATP and time.

You can show that this is an active process by making the sodium concentration in the right beaker greater than the sodium concentration in the left beaker. Transport will occur against the concentration gradient in active transport but not in diffusion.

Sodium transport is not affected by putting NaCl into the right beaker.

Increasing the number of pump proteins will increase solute transport.

Glucose presence does not affect active transport.

Skeletal Muscle Physiology: Computer Simulation

 Time Allotment: 2–2.5 hours minimum if students are well-prepared, 3 hours preferred.

The following minimum computer hardware is recommended for PhysioEx™ 5.0:

Windows® 98, NT, 2000, ME; Pentium® I processor/ 266 mHz
Mac®: 9.2 or higher
64 MB RAM (128 MB recommended)
800 x 600 screen resolution; millions of colors
Netscape Navigator® 7.0+ or Internet Explorer® 5.0+ (Netscape® installer is included on CD)
Macromedia Flash 6® plug-in (installer is included on CD)
4x CD-ROM drive
Printer

Advance Preparation, Comments, and Pitfalls

1. *If you are using PhysioEx™ in a computer lab:* Because PhysioEx™ 5.0 requires a browser (such as Netscape® or Internet Explorer®) and the Flash 6® plug-in to run, it is recommended that you make sure these items are already installed on student computers before beginning this lab. Installers for both Netscape® and Flash 6® are provided on the CD (instructions are included on the liner notes accompanying the CD).

2. After installing Netscape® or Flash 6®, the computer may attempt to connect to the web. If you do not have a live Internet connection, you may see a dialogue box appear, alerting you of an inability to connect to the web. Simply ignore the message and close the box. **You do not need to have a live Internet connection to run the CD.**

3. *If you are using the web version of PhysioEx™:* Have your students go to http://www.physioex.com and follow the registration instructions found in the very front of their lab manual.

4. It is helpful to instruct students in the proper operation of the mouse and menu system as part of the lab introduction.

5. When considering an upgrade for computer systems, memory (RAM) offers the largest performance increase for the least cost.

6. Having students work in pairs results in the most successful lab experience. If students must work in larger groups, have them each get keyboard and mouse experience with the program.

7. Prior to the lab, suggest to the students that they become familiar with the exercise before coming to class. If students have a home computer, or access to a computer on campus, they can become familiar with the general operation of the simulations before coming to class.

8. You might do a short introductory presentation with the following elements:

   a. Describe the basics of muscle contraction at the cellular level, focusing on the sarcomere. This explanation is especially important for the isometric part of the simulation.

   b. Students often have problems distinguishing between *in vivo* stimulation via the nervous system versus the electrical stimulation we apply to whole skeletal muscle in an experiment. Mention that increasing the intensity of an electrical stimulus to the surface of whole muscle is not the same as stimulation via the nervous system, but that the outcome of increased force production is similar in both methods.

   c. Encourage students to try to apply the concepts from the simulation to human skeletal muscles as they work through the program.

   d. If a demonstration computer screen is available, briefly show students the basic equipment parts.

9. Keep in mind that many students in an introductory science course are deficient in their graphing skills. Review the principles of plotting before the class begins may prove helpful.

10. Be prepared to help the students answer the more difficult "What if..." questions.

Answers to Questions

Electrical Stimulation

Activity 2: Determining the Latent Period (p. P-19)

The latent period should be approximately 2.78 msec.

The muscle cell is biochemically preparing for contraction, including events such as the release of calcium from the sarcoplasmic reticulum, and the movement of the chemicals of contraction within the cell.

Activity 3: Investigating Graded Muscle Response to Increased Stimulus Intensity (p. P-20)

The minimal stimulus is about 0.8 volts.

The maximal stimulus can be estimated at approximately 8.0 volts. However, if you look carefully at the force measurements recorded in the data grid, you will see that force increases until 8.2 volts is achieved.

As more voltage is delivered to the whole muscle, more muscle fibers are activated and total force produced by muscle is increased.

This is called multiple motor unit summation.

Multiple Stimulus

Activity 4: Investigating Treppe (p. P-20)

As long as stimuli are delivered relatively close together, the active force produced by subsequent stimuli slightly increases for the first few stimuli.

Activity 5: Investigating Wave Summation (p. P-20)

The peak force produced in the second contraction is greater than that produced by the first stimulus.

The total force production even greater when stimuli are delivered more rapidly.

It is not possible to produce smooth force at 2 gms; the twitch tracing rises and falls.

Although you still cannot produce smooth force at 3 gms, the tracing is smoother than trying to produce smooth force at 2 gms.

If you could click even faster, the tracing would be smoother and the force production higher.

If the voltage is lowered, the force produced will be lower.

Human skeletal muscles can manipulate stimulus frequency and the number of motor units activated to produce the desired level of force.

Activity 6: Investigating Fusion Frequency (p. P-22)

The force rises and falls at 30 stimuli/sec.

As the stimulation rate is increased, the active force produced by the muscle also increases. Additionally, the force tracing becomes smoother (smaller peaks).

The stimulus rate above which there appears to be no significant increase in force is at approximately 120 stimuli/sec.

Smooth, sustained force at 2 gms can be produced at approximately 1.2 volts and 120 stimuli/sec.

Smooth, sustained force at 3 gms can be produced at approximately 1.6 volts and 120 stimuli/sec.

Increasing the stimulation rate causes smoother force production. Lowering the voltage decreases the total force produced. Manipulating both allows the muscle to produce smooth force at any desired level. For example, increasing the stimulus rate while decreasing the voltage allowed the muscle to produce smooth force at a level of 2 gms.

Activity 7: Investigating Muscle Fatigue (p. P-23)

The muscle force falls because the muscle is consuming ATP faster than it is producing it.

When the stimulator is turned off the muscle is able to "catch up" a little with ATP production.

The second tracing shows faster fatigue than the tracing in which the stimulator was turned on and off.

Isometric Contraction

Activity 8: Investigating Isometric Contraction (p. P-24)

As the muscle length is increased from 50 mm to 100 mm, the passive force is initially zero and then begins to sharply rise.

As the muscle length is increased from 50 mm to 100 mm, the active force increases steadily until a muscle length of 75 mm and then begins to fall with increasing muscle length.

As the muscle length is increased from 50 mm to 100 mm, the total force initially rises, then begins to fall, and finally rises again, producing a dip in the curve.

Because the total force curve is the result of the numerical sum of the active and passive force data points, we see a rise on the left side of the total force due to the rise in the active force. Note that the passive force has no influence in the rise on the left side. The total force curve begins to fall because the active force falls. However, the total force does not fall as fast as the active force because the passive force is simultaneously rising. Finally, the sharp increase at the right side of the total force curve is almost entirely due to the passive force.

Isotonic Contraction

Activity 9: Investigating the Effect of Load on Skeletal Muscle (p. P-25)

During the flat part of the tracing, the muscle rises from the surface of the platform and then descends again.

The force production does not change during the flat part of the tracing (the tracing is flat!).

As the muscle moves the weight up, the muscle is in isotonic contraction. As the muscle lengthens, it is in isotonic relaxation.

The force rises during the first part of the muscle tracing and is due to isometric contraction while the fall in force on the right side of the tracing corresponds to isometric relaxation.

The lighter weight results in the highest initial velocity of shortening.

As the resistance increases, the initial velocity of shortening decreases.

As the starting length of the muscle is increased from 60 mm to 90 mm, the initial velocity of shortening first increases (to a muscle length of 75 mm) and then decreases.

These results support the results obtained in the isometric exercise.

Although we can set up a contraction that is completely isometric by using a large weight, it is not possible to produce an entirely isotonic contraction.

An isotonic contraction is one that maintains constant force production. Because the muscle starts at zero force which increases during contraction, there will never be a condition where we will see a completely isotonic contraction.

Neurophysiology of Nerve Impulses: Computer Simulation

 Time Allotment: 2 hours.

The following minimum computer hardware is recommended for PhysioEx™ 5.0:

Windows® 98, NT, 2000, ME; Pentium® I processor/ 266 mHz
Mac®: 9.2 or higher
64 MB RAM (128 MB recommended)
800 x 600 screen resolution; millions of colors
Netscape Navigator® 7.0+ or Internet Explorer® 5.0+ (Netscape® installer is included on CD)
Macromedia Flash 6® plug-in (installer is included on CD)
4x CD-ROM drive
Printer

Advance Preparation, Comments, and Pitfalls

1. *If you are using PhysioEx™ in a computer lab:* Because PhysioEx™ 5.0 requires a browser (such as Netscape® or Internet Explorer®) and the Flash 6® plug-in to run, it is recommended that you make sure these items are already installed on student computers before beginning this lab. Installers for both Netscape® and Flash 6® are provided on the CD (instructions are included on the liner notes accompanying the CD).

2. After installing Netscape® or Flash 6®, the computer may attempt to connect to the web. If you do not have a live Internet connection, you may see a dialogue box appear, alerting you of an inability to connect to the web. Simply ignore the message and close the box. **You do not need to have a live Internet connection to run the CD.**

3. *If you are using the web version of PhysioEx™:* Have your students go to http://www.physioex.com and follow the registration instructions found in the very front of their lab manual.

4. It is helpful to instruct students in the proper operation of the mouse and menu system as part of the lab introduction.

5. When considering an upgrade for computer systems, memory (RAM) offers the largest performance increase for the least cost.

6. Having students work in pairs results in the most successful lab experience. If students must work in larger groups, have them each get keyboard and mouse experience with the program.

Eliciting a Nerve Impulse

Activity 1: Electrical Stimulation (p. P-30)

At 1.0 V, there is no response—the screen displays a flat line.

The threshold voltage is at 3.0 V.

The slight increase in voltage results in a slight increase in the height of the action potential peak.

At threshold voltage, the smaller fibers in a nerve are stimulated and an action potential is seen. Increasing the voltage will cause most, if not all of the neural fibers to undergo depolarization. A given nerve is made up of literally thousands of neuron processes (axons) so this slight increase is noted when all fibers in the nerve fire.

The maximal voltage is 4.0 V.

Activity 2: Mechanical Stimulation (p. P-31)

An action potential is generated when you touch the rod to the nerve.

The tracing is identical to the tracing generated at the threshold voltage.

Activity 3: Thermal Stimulation (p. P-32)

An action potential is generated when you touch the heated rod to the nerve.

The tracing shows the action potential peaking slightly higher than the peak generated by the unheated rod.

Thermal stimulation can also elicit a nerve response.

Activity 4: Chemical Stimulation (p. P-32)

Yes, dropping sodium chloride on the nerve generates an action potential.

No, the tracing does not differ from the original threshold stimulus tracing.

Yes, dropping hydrochloric acid on the nerve generates an action potential.

No, the tracing does not differ from the original threshold stimulus tracing.

Electrical, mechnical, thermal, and chemical stimulation are all capable of generating an action potential in a nerve.

Inhibiting a Nerve Response

Activity 5: Testing the Effects of Ether (p. P-32)

The screen displays a flat line, indicating no nerve response.

The nerve has been anesthesized by the ether.

The nerve begins to respond to electrical stimuli again after about 5 minutes.

Activity 6: Testing the Effects of Curare (p. P-33)

There is no change to the action potential tracing.

Nerve propogation is unaffected because curare works on the synaptic ends of the nerve.

Curare would ultimately kill the organism by blocking nerve transmission.

Activity 7: Testing the Effects of Lidocaine (p. P-34)

No.

At threshold voltage, the screen still displays a flat line.

Lidocaine is a sodium ion channel antagonist which will block sodium channels from opening, thus inhibiting any action potential from being generated.

Nerve Conduction Velocity

Activity 8: Measuring Nerve Conduction Velocity (p. P-35)

The chart should look like this:

Nerve	Earthworm	Frog	Rat Nerve 1	Rat Nerve 2
Threshold voltage	5.0 V	3.0 V	2.5 V	3.0 V
Elapsed time from stimulation to action potential	about 4.86 msec	about 1.56 msec	about 2.5 msec	about 0.92 msec
Conduction velocity	about 8.85 m/sec	about 27.56 m/sec	about 17.2 m/sec	about 46.74 m/sec

The earthworm has the slowest conduction velocity.

The speed of the earthworm nerve was about 8.85 m/sec.

Rat nerve 2 had the fastest conduction velocity.

The speed of rat nerve 2 was about 46.74 m/sec.

The larger the nerve, the faster the conduction velocity.

Conduction velocity is faster if the nerve is myelinated than if it is not.

In myelinated nerves, conduction velocity is faster as the action potential jumps from node of Ranvier (internode) to node of Ranvier and does not travel along the cell membrane.

Endocrine System Physiology: Computer Simulation

 Time Allotment: 3.0 hours.

The following minimum computer hardware is recommended for PhysioEx™ 5.0:

Windows® 98, NT, 2000, ME; Pentium® I processor/ 266 mHz
Mac®: 9.2 or higher
64 MB RAM (128 MB recommended)
800 x 600 screen resolution; millions of colors
Netscape Navigator® 7.0+ or Internet Explorer® 5.0+ (Netscape® installer is included on CD)
Macromedia Flash 6® plug-in (installer is included on CD)
4x CD-ROM drive
Printer

Advance Preparation, Comments, and Pitfalls

1. *If you are using PhysioEx™ in a computer lab:* Because PhysioEx™ 5.0 requires a browser (such as Netscape® or Internet Explorer®) and the Flash 6® plug-in to run, it is recommended that you make sure these items are already installed on student computers before beginning this lab. Installers for both Netscape® and Flash 6® are provided on the CD (instructions are included on the liner notes accompanying the CD).

2. After installing Netscape® or Flash 6®, the computer may attempt to connect to the web. If you do not have a live Internet connection, you may see a dialogue box appear, alerting you of an inability to connect to the web. Simply ignore the message and close the box. **You do not need to have a live Internet connection to run the CD.**

3. *If you are using the web version of PhysioEx™:* Have your students go to http://www.physioex.com and follow the registration instructions found in the very front of their lab manual.

4. It is helpful to instruct students in the proper operation of the mouse and menu system as part of the lab introduction.

5. When considering an upgrade for computer systems, memory (RAM) offers the largest performance increase for the least cost.

6. Having students work in pairs results in the most successful lab experience. If students must work in larger groups, have them each get keyboard and mouse experience with the program.

Metabolism

Upon completion of all activities, the chart should look like this:

	Normal Rat	Thyroidectomized Rat	Hypophysectomized Rat
Baseline			
Weight	249–251 grams	244–246 grams	244–246 grams
ml O_2 used in 1 minute	7.1 ml	6.3 ml	6.3 ml
ml O_2 used per hour	426 ml	378 ml	378 ml
Metabolic rate	1704 ml O_2/Kg./Hr.	1542 ml O_2/Kg./Hr.	1542 ml O_2/Kg./Hr.
With Thyroxine			
Weight	249–251 grams	244–246 grams	244–246 grams
ml O_2 used in 1 minute	7.6 ml	7.1 ml	7.1 ml
ml O_2 used per hour	456 ml	426 ml	426 ml
Metabolic rate	1824 ml O_2/Kg./Hr.	1738 ml O_2/Kg./Hr.	1738 ml O_2/Kg./Hr.
With TSH			
Weight	249–251 grams	244–246 grams	244–246 grams
ml O_2 used in 1 minute	7.6 ml	6.3 ml	7.1 ml
ml O_2 used per hour	456 ml	378 ml	426 ml
Metabolic rate	1824 ml O_2/Kg./Hr.	1542 ml O_2/Kg./Hr.	1738 ml O_2/Kg./Hr.
With Propylthiouracil			
Weight	249–251 grams	244–246 grams	244–246 grams
ml O_2 used in 1 minute	6.3 ml	6.3 ml	6.3 ml
ml O_2 used per hour	378 ml	378 ml	378 ml
Metabolic rate	1512 ml O_2/Kg./Hr.	1542 ml O_2/Kg./Hr.	1542 O_2/Kg./Hr.

Activity 1: Determining Baseline Metabolic Rates (p. P-39)

The normal rat's metabolic rate is faster than the metabolic rates of the thyroidectomized and hypophysectomized rats.

The thyroidectomized rat lacks a thyroid, thus produced no thyroxine. The hypophysectomized rat lacks a pituitary gland, thus produced no thyroid stimulating hormone to stimulate thyroxine production. Because the normal rat produced thyroxine normally, its metabolic rate was faster than the other rats.

Activity 2: Determining the Effect of Thyroxine on Metabolic Rate (p. P-40)

On the normal rat, the metabolic rate after thyroxine injection is **faster** than the baseline metabolic rate.

The action of thyroxine is to increase the metabolic rate of all cells.

On the thyroidectomized rat, the metabolic rate after thyroxine injection is **faster** than the baseline metabolic rate.

The injected thyroxine compensated for the thyroxine lost when the thyroid was removed.

On the hypophysectomized rat, the metabolic rate after thyroxine injection is **faster** than the baseline metabolic rate.

The injected thyroxine compensated for the thyroxine lost when the pituitary gland was removed.

Activity 3: Determining the Effect of TSH on Metabolic Rate (p. P-41)

On the normal rat, the metabolic rate after TSH injection is **faster** than the baseline metabolic rate.

The TSH increased production of thyroxine.

On the thyroidectomized rat, the metabolic rate after TSH injection **the same as** the baseline metabolic rate.

Since there is no thyroid gland in the thyroidectomized rat, the injected TSH had nothing to act upon. There was no organ to receive the pituitary TSH and produce thyroxine,

On the hypophysectomized rat, the metabolic rate after TSH injection is **faster** than the baseline metabolic rate.

The injected TSH compensated for the TSH lost when the pituitary gland was removed, and spurs production of thyroxine.

Activity 4: Determining the Effect of Propylthiouracil on Metabolic Rate (p. P-41)

On the normal rat, the metabolic rate after propylthiouracil injection is **slower** than the baseline metabolic rate.

Propylthiouracil is antagonistic to thyroxine and will tend to decrease the effects of thyroxine.

On the thyroidectomized rat, the metabolic rate after propylthiouracil injection is **the same as** the baseline metabolic rate.

Since the thyroidectomized rat cannot make any thyroxine, the propylthiouracil has nothing to be antagonistic to and therefore has no effect.

On the hypophysectomized rat, the metabolic rate after propylthiouracil injection is **the same as** the baseline metabolic rate.

Since the hypophysectomized rat does not have a functional thyroid gland, no thyroxine is being made and there is nothing for the propylthiouracil to be antagonistic to.

Hormone Replacement Therapy

Activity 5: Hormone Replacement Therapy (p. P-42)

The uterus weight of the control rat should be about 0.1000 g.

The uterus weight of the experimental rat should be about 0.6600 g.

The uterus of the experimental rat is noticeably heavier than that of the control rat.

The administration of estrogen injections to the experimental rat caused the uterine tissue to grow.

If testosterone had been administered instead, nothing would have happened to the uterine tissue. There are very specific hormone receptors which can bind to estrogen and not to testosterone, leading to growth with the former and no effect with the latter.

Insulin and Diabetes

Activity 7: Comparing Glucose Levels Before and After Insulin Injection (p. P-45)

Glucose readings should be approximately:
Tube #1: ~86 mg glucose
Tube #2: ~129 mg glucose
Tube #3: ~86 mg glucose
Tube #4: ~96 mg glucose

The glucose level in tube 1 is lower than the glucose level in tube 2.

The glucose level in tube 2 is higher than in tube 1 because the sample in tube 2 is from the rat that received alloxan, which prevented the rat from producing the insulin necessary to remove sugar from the bloodstream.

Alloxan has caused diabetes mellitus in the experimental rat.

The glucose levels in tubes 3 and tube 1 are nearly identical.

Tubes 1 and 3 are both blood samples from the control rat. The injection of insulin had no effect on this rat because the additional insulin injected only lowered the blood sugar by so much; the rat's body then released glucagon to restore the blood sugar to normal levels.

The glucose level in tube 4 is lower than the glucose level in tube 2.

The injection of insulin into the diabetic rat allowed the rat to remove glucose from its bloodstream for use by body cells.

Administering insulin to the control animal had no effect.

Administering insulin to the experimental (diabetic) animal had the positive effect of lowering blood sugar levels in the animal.

Blood Analysis: Computer Simulation

29B

 Time Allotment: 2 hours

The following minimum computer hardware is recommended for PhysioEx™ 5.0:

> Windows® 98, NT, 2000, ME; Pentium® I processor/ 266 mHz
> Mac®: OS 9.2 or higher
> 64 MB RAM (128 MB recommended)
> 800 x 600 screen resolution; millions of colors
> Netscape Navigator® 7.0+ or Internet Explorer® 5.0+ (Netscape® installer is included on CD)
> Macromedia Flash 6® plug-in (installer is included on CD)
> 4x CD-ROM drive
> Printer

Advance Preparation, Comments, and Pitfalls

1. *If you are using PhysioEx™ in a computer lab:* Because PhysioEx™ 5.0 requires a browser (such as Netscape® or Internet Explorer®) and the Flash 6® plug-in to run, it is recommended that you make sure these items are already installed on student computers before beginning this lab. Installers for both Netscape® and Flash 6® are provided on the CD (instructions are included on the liner notes accompanying the CD).

2. After installing Netscape® or Flash 6®, the computer may attempt to connect to the web. If you do not have a live Internet connection, you may see a dialogue box appear, alerting you of an inability to connect to the web. Simply ignore the message and close the box. **You do not need to have a live Internet connection to run the CD.**

3. *If you are using the web version of PhysioEx™:* Have your students go to http://www.physioex.com and follow the registration instructions found in the very front of their lab manual.

4. It is helpful to instruct students in the proper operation of the mouse and menu system as part of the lab introduction.

5. When considering an upgrade for computer systems, memory (RAM) offers the largest performance increase for the least cost.

6. Having students work in pairs results in the most successful lab experience. If students must work in larger groups, have them each get keyboard and mouse experience with the program.

Answers to Questions

Activity 1: Hematocrit Determination (p. P-49)

The hematocrit value of the healthy male living at sea level in Boston is 48.

The hematocrit level of the healthy male living at one mile elevation in Denver is 55.

No, the air in Denver is "thinner" than it is in Boston.

When the blood flowing through the kidneys is hypoxic (low oxygen level), the kidneys respond by producing a hormone, *erythropoietin,* which targets the bone marrow to produce more red blood cells.

If your bone marrow is producing an elevated number of red blood cells, your hematocrit is elevated.

The hematocrit value of the male with aplastic anemia is 19.

The red blood cell count for an individual with aplastic anemia would be *lower* than the red blood cell count of a healthy individual.

The hematocrit value of the healthy female living in Boston is 44.

The female with iron-deficiency anemia does not have as many normal sized red blood cells as the healthy female living in Boston, so her hematocrit (packed cell volume) is lower. She is not able to make adequate hemoglobin molecules to fill her red blood cells.

Activity 2: Erythrocyte Sedimentation Rate (p. P-52)

The blood has settled 5 millimeters.

The beige colored portion of the tube is blood plasma.

No, the person with sickle-cell anemia did not show an elevated ESR.

The ESR for the person with iron-deficiency anemia was *higher* than the ESR for the healthy individual.

The menstruating female is suffering from iron-deficiency anemia, causing her red blood cells to settle.

The ESR is elevated in the patient suffering from myocardial infarction (heart attack), but is normal in angina pectoris.

Activity 3: Hemoglobin (Hb) Determination (p. P-54)

The normal hematocrit value for a healthy male is 48.

The normal hematocrit value for a healthy female is 44.

The ratio of PCV to Hb for the female with iron-deficiency anemia tells you that she may have a normal number of red blood cells, but they do not contain adequate hemoglobin molecules.

Yes, the male with polycythemia has a normal ratio of PCV to Hb (a ratio of 3:1).

Yes, the red blood cells of the male with polycythemia contain adequate molecules of hemoglobin.

Yes, the female Olympic athlete has a normal ratio of PCV to Hb (a ratio of 3:1).

Yes, the red blood cells of the female Olympic athlete contain adequate molecules of hemoglobin.

Activity 4: Blood Typing (p. P-56)

If the anti-A antibody causes the blood to coagulate, antigen (agglutinogen) A would be present on the blood cells.

If a person has type AB blood, antigen (agglutinogens) A & B are present on their red blood cells.

In a person with type AB blood, neither A nor B antibodies (agglutinins) are present.

A person with type O blood has neither A nor B antigens (agglutinogens).

Activity 5: Blood Cholesterol (p. P-57)

Patient #2 has elevated cholesterol, which has been associated with increased risk of cardio-vascular disease.

Patient #4 has borderline elevated cholesterol. He should be advised to decrease his dietary intake of meats and saturated fats. He should also be encouraged to exercise more.

Cardiovascular Dynamics: Computer Simulation

exercise

33B

 Time Allotment: 2 hours minimum if students are well-prepared, 3 hours preferred.

The following minimum computer hardware is recommended for PhysioEx™ 5.0:

Windows® 98, NT, 2000, ME; Pentium® I processor/ 266 mHz

Mac®: 9.2 or higher

64 MB RAM (128 MB recommended)

800 x 600 screen resolution; millions of colors

Netscape Navigator® 7.0+ or Internet Explorer® 5.0+ (Netscape® installer is included on CD)

Macromedia Flash 6® plug-in (installer is included on CD)

4x CD-ROM drive

Printer

Advance Preparation, Comments, and Pitfalls

1. *If you are using PhysioEx™ in a computer lab:* Because PhysioEx™ 5.0 requires a browser (such as Netscape® or Internet Explorer®) and the Flash 6® plug-in to run, it is recommended that you make sure these items are already installed on student computers before beginning this lab. Installers for both Netscape® and Flash 6® are provided on the CD (instructions are included on the liner notes accompanying the CD).

2. After installing Netscape® or Flash 6®, the computer may attempt to connect to the web. If you do not have a live Internet connection, you may see a dialogue box appear, alerting you of an inability to connect to the web. Simply ignore the message and close the box. **You do not need to have a live Internet connection to run the CD.**

3. *If you are using the web version of PhysioEx™:* Have your students go to http://www.physioex.com and follow the registration instructions found in the very front of their lab manual.

4. It is helpful to instruct students in the proper operation of the mouse and menu system as part of the lab introduction.

5. When considering an upgrade for computer systems, memory (RAM) offers the largest performance increase for the least cost.

6. Having students work in pairs results in the most successful lab experience. If students must work in larger groups, have them each get keyboard and mouse experience with the program.

7. Consider doing a short introductory presentation with the following elements:

   a. Describe the basics of peripheral resistance.

   b. Encourage students to try to apply the concepts from the simulation to the human as they work through the program.

   c. If a demonstration computer screen is available, show students both main screens of the simulation and describe the basic equipment parts.

   d. Explain how the simulated pump is similar to the left ventricle (or the right ventricle) of the heart.

   e. Point out the fact that the pump operates much like a syringe, with adjustable starting and ending volumes.

   f. It is often helpful to explain the basics of end diastolic and end systolic volumes and their relationship to the simulated pump.

   g. Indicate the analogies between the parts of the simulation and the parts of the human heart.

Answers to Questions

Vessel Resistance

Activity 1: Studying the Effect of Flow Tube Radius on Fluid Flow (p. P-61)

Fluid flow increases as the radius of the flow tube is increased.

Because fluid flow is proportional to the fourth power of the radius, small changes in tube radius cause large changes in fluid flow.

The relationship between fluid flow and flow tube radius is exponential.

We alter blood flow in the human body by increasing or decreasing the diameter of blood vessels.

After a heavy meal when we are relatively inactive, we might expect blood vessels in the skeletal muscles to be somewhat constricted while blood vessels in the digestive organs are probably dilated

Activity 2: Studying the Effect of Viscosity on Fluid Flow (p. P-63)

Fluid flow decreases as viscosity is increased.

Fluid flow versus viscosity is an inverse relationship.

The effect of viscosity does not effect fluid flow as much as vessel radius.

Anemia would result in fewer red cells than normal, which would decrease the viscosity of the blood. Consequently, blood flow rate would be increased.

If you increased the numbers of red blood cells, blood flow rate would decrease.

Changing viscosity would not be a reasonable means of blood pressure control because the body would not have control of blow to specific organs, and viscosity changes would be too slow.

Blood viscosity would increase in conditions of dehydration, resulting in decreased blood flow.

Activity 3: Studying the Effect of Flow Tube Length on Fluid Flow (p. P-64)

Increasing flow tube length will decrease fluid flow rate.

The body would not be able to change blood vessel length fast enough to change flow rate, and the changes would be too small to notice.

Activity 4: Studying the Effect of Pressure on Fluid Flow (p. P-64)

Increasing the pressure increases fluid flow.

The length versus flow rate plot is linear.

Changing pressure would not be a reasonable method of flow control because large changes in pressure is needed to significantly change flow rate

Pump Mechanics

Activity 5: Studying the Effect of Radius on Pump Activity (p. P-66)

The radius plot in this experiment appears different from the radius plot in the vessel resistance experiment because only the outflow of the pump was changed. Since the inflow remained constant during the course of the experiment, an entirely different flow pattern is established.

As the right flow tube radius is increased, fluid flow rate (<u>increases</u>, decreases). This is analogous to (<u>dilation</u>, constriction) of blood vessels in the human body.

Even though the pump pressure remains constant, the pump rate (<u>increases</u>, decreases) as the radius of the right flow tube is increased. This happens because the resistance to fluid flow is (increased, <u>decreased</u>).

The heart must contract (<u>more</u>, less) forcefully to maintain cardiac output if the resistance to blood flow in the vessels exiting the heart is increased.

Increasing the resistance (e.g., a constriction) of the blood vessels entering the heart would (<u>increase</u>, decrease) the time needed to fill the heart chambers.

If the left flow tube radius is changed, flow rate into the pump is increased, which increases the pump rate.

Activity 6: Studying the Effect of Stroke Volume on Pump Activity (p. P-67)

As the stroke volume is increased, it takes longer to fill the pump and the pump rate slows.

To maintain adequate blood flow to tissues, the stroke volume must be greater in an athlete if their heart rate is slower.

If we keep the rate constant, increasing the stroke volume, cardiac output will increase.

When heart rate is increased, the time of ventricular filling is (increased, <u>decreased</u>), which in turn (increases, <u>decreases</u>) the stroke volume

If the valve in the right flow tube became leaky, back pressure from the right beaker would increase the pressure in the pump.

If the aortic valve became leaky, pressure in the left heart would increase, in turn, increasing pressure in the pulmonary circuit.

If the aortic valve became constricted, the heart would need to contract with greater force to deliver the same amount of blood per minute.

Activity 7: Studying Combined Effects (p. P-68)

When the right flow tube radius is kept constant and the left flow tube radius is changed, the pump filling time is changed which in turn changes the pump's rate.

Although decreasing the radius of the left flow tube increases the time required to fill the pump, it does not affect the ability of the pump to empty.

Manipulating the pump's starting volume has the same effect as changing the pump's ending volume. The pump rate will increase as stroke volume is decreased to maintain the same flow rate.

Increasing the pressure in the left beaker increases fluid delivery to the pump from the left beaker.

Decreasing the pressure in the left beaker to 10 mm Hg greatly increases the time required to fill the pump.

The pump's rate increases if the filling time is decreased.

If the pressure in the right beaker equals the pump pressure, fluid can not flow.

Activity 8: Studying Compensation (p. P-69)

If the right flow tube radius is decreased to 2.5 mm, the flow rate decreases.

The increased peripheral resistance can be overcome by: (1) increasing the pump's pressure, (2) decreasing the pressure in the right beaker, and (3) increasing the radius of the left flow tube to decrease the pump's filling time.

Decreasing the right flow tube radius is similar to a partial (leakage, blockage) of the aortic valve or (increased, decreased) resistance in the arterial system.

The human heart could compensate for this condition by increasing it's force of contraction to overcome the increased resistance.

To control blood flow to specific organs, it is necessary to adjust the radius of the blood vessels feeding them. It would not be reasonable to adjust the hart rate because that would affect all organs equally.

If we decreased overall peripheral resistance in the human body, (e.g., an athlete) the heart would need to generate (more, less) pressure to deliver an adequate amount of blood flow and arterial pressure would be (higher, lower).

If the diameter if the arteries of the body were partly filled with fatty deposits, the heart would need to generate (more, less) force to maintain blood flow, and pressure in the arterial system would be (higher, lower) than normal.

Frog Cardiovascular Physiology: Computer Simulation

Time Allotment: 1.5–2 hours.

The following minimum computer hardware is recommended for PhysioEx™ 5.0:

Windows® 98, NT, 2000, ME; Pentium® I processor/ 266 mHz
Mac®: 9.2 or higher
64 MB RAM (128 MB recommended)
800 x 600 screen resolution; millions of colors
Netscape Navigator® 7.0+ or Internet Explorer® 5.0+ (Netscape® installer is included on CD)
Macromedia Flash 6® plug-in (installer is included on CD)
4x CD-ROM drive
Printer

Advance Preparation, Comments, and Pitfalls

1. *If you are using PhysioEx™ in a computer lab:* Because PhysioEx™ 5.0 requires a browser (such as Netscape® or Internet Explorer®) and the Flash 6® plug-in to run, it is recommended that you make sure these items are already installed on student computers before beginning this lab. Installers for both Netscape® and Flash 6® are provided on the CD (instructions are included on the liner notes accompanying the CD).

2. After installing Netscape® or Flash 6®, the computer may attempt to connect to the web. If you do not have a live Internet connection, you may see a dialogue box appear, alerting you of an inability to connect to the web. Simply ignore the message and close the box. **You do not need to have a live Internet connection to run the CD.**

3. *If you are using the web version of PhysioEx™:* Have your students go to http://www.physioex.com and follow the registration instructions found in the very front of their lab manual.

4. It is helpful to instruct students in the proper operation of the mouse and menu system as part of the lab introduction.

5. When considering an upgrade for computer systems, memory (RAM) offers the largest performance increase for the least cost.

6. Having students work in pairs results in the most successful lab experience. If students must work in larger groups, have them each get keyboard and mouse experience with the program.

7. If students will be using an older computer and are having difficulty with the tracings, have them adjust the tracing to suit them. To make the tracings faster, click the **Tools** menu, choose **Modify Tracing** and then click **Increase Speed**. On the other hand, if they want to see a higher-quality tracing, choose **Improve Tracing**.

8. Suggest to the students that they become familiar with the exercise before coming to lab. If students have a home computer, or access to a computer on campus, they can become familiar with the general operation of the simulations.

9. A short introductory presentation with the following elements is often helpful:

   a. Review the basics of heart anatomy and physiology, particularly the sequence of atrial to ventricular contraction.

   b. Reinforce the concept of the electrical system of the heart, including the basics of electrical function at the cellular level.

   c. Mention the sympathetic and parasympathetic connections to the heart, including the neurotransmitters and their functions.

   d. Compare how this procedure is accomplished in a traditional wet lab to what they expect to see in the simulation.

Answers to Questions

Activity 2: Investigating the Refractory Period of Cardiac Muscle (p. P-73)

It is possible to induce an extrasystole in the relaxation part of the cardiac cycle.

The heart can not be tetanized by multiple stimuli.

Tetanization would make the heart ineffective as a pump.

Activity 3: Examining the Effect of Vagus Nerve Stimulation (p. P-74)

5. Vagal stimulation initially decreased heart rate and force of contraction, but returns to a relatively normal contraction state after vagal escape initiates.

Activity 4: Assessing the Effect of Temperature (p. P-74)

2. Cold Ringer's solution decreased heart rate.

5. Warm Ringer's solution increased heart rate.

   Increasing the temperature causes an increase in heart rate.

Activity 5: Assessing the Effect of Pilocarpine (p. P-75)

5. Pilocarpine mimics vagal stimulation and slows the heart.

Activity 6: Assessing the Effect of Atropine (p. P-76)

4. The heart rate should increase. Atropine is antagonistic to pilocarpine.

   Atropine and pilocarpine are antagonistic in their action.

Activity 7: Assessing the Effect of Epinephrine (p. P-76)

Epinephrine increases the heart rate and force of contraction

Epinephrine mimics the effects of the sympathetic nervous system.

Activity 8: Assessing the Effect of Digitalis (p. P-76)

4. Digitalis slows and steadies the heart.

Activity 9: Assessing the Effect of Various Ions (p. P-76)

6. Calcium increases the strength of contraction; probably induces spasticity.

   - The heart rate does not stabilize until 23°C Ringers solution is applied.
   - The heartbeat is irregular, speeding up at times, slowing down at others.

Sodium decreases the strength and rate of contraction.

   - The heart rate does not stabilize until 23°C Ringers solution is applied.
   - The heartbeat is irregular, speeding up at times, slowing down at others.

Potassium weakens cardiac contractions.

   - The heart rate does not stabilize until 23°C Ringers solution is applied.
   - The heartbeat decreases considerable at first, then becomse erratic—alternately speeding up and slowing down.

Yes, all three ions may induce arrythmias.

Respiratory System Mechanics: Computer Simulation

 Time Allotment: 1.5–2.0 hours.

The following minimum computer hardware is recommended for PhysioEx™ 5.0:

Windows® 98, NT, 2000, ME; Pentium® I processor/ 266 mHz
Mac®: 9.2 or higher
64 MB RAM (128 MB recommended)
800 x 600 screen resolution; millions of colors
Netscape Navigator® 7.0+ or Internet Explorer® 5.0+ (Netscape® installer is included on CD)
Macromedia Flash 6® plug-in (installer is included on CD)
4x CD-ROM drive
Printer

Advance Preparation, Comments, and Pitfalls

1. *If you are using PhysioEx™ in a computer lab:* Because PhysioEx™ 5.0 requires a browser (such as Netscape® or Internet Explorer®) and the Flash 6® plug-in to run, it is recommended that you make sure these items are already installed on student computers before beginning this lab. Installers for both Netscape® and Flash 6® are provided on the CD (instructions are included on the liner notes accompanying the CD).

2. After installing Netscape® or Flash 6®, the computer may attempt to connect to the web. If you do not have a live Internet connection, you may see a dialogue box appear, alerting you of an inability to connect to the web. Simply ignore the message and close the box. **You do not need to have a live Internet connection to run the CD.**

3. *If you are using the web version of PhysioEx™:* Have your students go to http://www.physioex.com and follow the registration instructions found in the very front of their lab manual.

4. It is helpful to instruct students in the proper operation of the mouse and menu system as part of the lab introduction.

5. When considering an upgrade for computer systems, memory (RAM) offers the largest performance increase for the least cost.

6. Having students work in pairs results in the most successful lab experience. If students must work in larger groups, have them each get keyboard and mouse experience with the program.

7. Demonstrate the mechanics of the lungs during respiration if a bell jar and balloon lungs are available.

8. Prior to the lab, suggest to the students that they become familiar with the exercise before coming to class. If students have a home computer, or access to a computer on campus, they can become familiar with the general operation of the simulations before coming to class. In particular, they should understand the lung volumes.

9. A short introductory presentation with the following elements is often helpful:

   a. Review the basics of respiratory anatomy, particularly the inspiratory and expiratory sequence.

   b. Reinforce the fact that there are no fibrous or muscular connections between the lungs and the thoracic wall when doing the bell jar demonstration. Students often remember this demonstration more than most others.

   c. Mention that inspiration requires muscle action but that expiration is passive.

   d. If a demonstration computer and bell jar lungs are available, compare the operation of the on-screen lungs with the balloon lungs in the bell jar.

   e. A pair of microscope slides with a thin film of water between makes an excellent demonstration of the concept of water tension.

   f. Briefly explain the idea of carbon dioxide retention in the blood during hypoventilation and its removal from the blood by hyperventilation.

Answers to Questions

Activity 1: Measuring Respiratory Volumes (p. P-80)

Expiratory reserve volume (ERV) does not include tidal volume

Expiratory reserve volume is the amount of air that can be expelled after a normal tidal exhalation. This means that tidal volume is not included in the ERV measurement.

Activity 2: Examining the Effect of Changing Airway Resistance on Respiratory Volumes (p. P-80)

FEV_1 (%) will decrease as the airway radius is decreased.

FEV_1 (%) is the amount of air that can be expelled from the lungs in one second during forced expiration. If the airway becomes smaller then the resistance to air flow will increase and FEV_1 (%) will become lower.

Activity 3: Examining the Effect of Surfactant (p. P-81)

Airflow increases when surfactant is applied because the resistance to lung inflation has been reduced.

Surfactant is not produced in premature infants. Because surfactant is necessary for the lungs to inflate, it is not normally needed until birth.

Activity 4: Investigating Intrapleural Pressure (p. P-82)

The lung in the left side of the bell jar deflated.

The pressure in the left lung was zero and the pressure in the right lung changed constantly.

Because there was an opening to the atmosphere in the left side of the bell jar, air moved into the intrapleural space through the opening, which is the path of least resistance.

The total air flow was reduced by one half.

Both lungs would collapse when the thoracic wall was punctured if the two lungs were in a single cavity instead of individual cavities.

The lungs did not reinflate when the valve was closed.

In additon to closing off the opening to the atmosphere, the excess air in the intrapleural space must be removed before the lungs will reinflate.

After clicking Reset and running the experiment again, the function of the simulated lungs returned to normal. This happened because the air was removed from the intrapleural space, allowing the lungs to reinflate.

Activity 5: Exploring Various Breathing Patterns (p. P-83)

PCO_2 decreased during hyperventilation because more CO_2 was removed from the blood than normal. Each breath expels a certain amount of CO_2. If the breathing rate increases, then more CO_2 is expelled.

PCO_2 increases during rebreathing because the CO_2 gradient is being reduced.

The depth and rate of respirations increased during rebreathing. This is due in part to the increased CO_2 in the blood causing stimulating of the respiratory centers in the brain stem.

PCO_2 increased dramatically during breath holding.

Chemical and Physical Processes of Digestion: Computer Simulation

39B

 Time Allotment: 2 hours minimum if students are well-prepared. 3 hours preferred for the full exercise. 2 hours minimum if only the simulation is used.

The following minimum computer hardware is recommended for PhysioEx™ 5.0:

Windows® 98, NT, 2000, ME; Pentium® I processor/ 266 mHz
Mac®: 9.2 or higher
64 MB RAM (128 MB recommended)
800 x 600 screen resolution; millions of colors
Netscape Navigator® 7.0+ or Internet Explorer® 5.0+ (Netscape® installer is included on CD)
Macromedia Flash 6® plug-in (installer is included on CD)
4x CD-ROM drive
Printer

Advance Preparation, Comments, and Pitfalls

1. *If you are using PhysioEx™ in a computer lab:* Because PhysioEx™ 5.0 requires a browser (such as Netscape® or Internet Explorer®) and the Flash 6® plug-in to run, it is recommended that you make sure these items are already installed on student computers before beginning this lab. Installers for both Netscape® and Flash 6® are provided on the CD (instructions are included on the liner notes accompanying the CD).

2. After installing Netscape® or Flash 6®, the computer may attempt to connect to the web. If you do not have a live Internet connection, you may see a dialogue box appear, alerting you of an inability to connect to the web. Simply ignore the message and close the box. **You do not need to have a live Internet connection to run the CD.**

3. *If you are using the web version of PhysioEx™:* Have your students go to http://www.physioex.com and follow the registration instructions found in the very front of their lab manual.

4. It is helpful to instruct students in the proper operation of the mouse and menu system as part of the lab introduction.

5. When considering an upgrade for computer systems, memory (RAM) offers the largest performance increase for the least cost.

6. Having students work in pairs results in the most successful lab experience. If students must work in larger groups, have them each get keyboard and mouse experience with the program.

7. Suggest to the students that they become familiar with the exercise before coming to class. If students have a home computer or access to a computer on campus they can become familiar with the general operation of the simulations before coming to class.

8. A short introductory presentation with the following elements is often helpful:

   a. Describe the basics of enzymatic hydrolysis, mentioning how the enzyme-substrate interaction puts stress on the chemical bonds within the substrate to aid in the hydrolytic action.

   b. Students need to clearly understand why the different control tubes are necessary. Explain this concept with plenty of examples.

   c. Because enzymes work as well in vitro as they do in vivo, encourage students to apply what they see in the simulation to what must occur in the lumen of the digestive system.

   d. If a demonstration computer screen is available, briefly show students the basic equipment parts.

9. As the lab progresses, ask students question directing them to think about the logic of the experiment. For example, if a group of students makes the statement: "Amylase digests starch to maltose," try asking some of the following questions as the opportunity arises:

   • How do you know that the amylase preparation was not contaminated with maltose?

   • How do you know that the buffer was not contaminated with maltose?

   • How do you know that the water was not contaminated with maltose?

   • How do you know that you even started with starch, and that the starch was not contaminated with maltose?

10. Be prepared to help the students answer the more difficult "What if …" questions.

Answers to Questions

Activity 1: Assessing Starch Digestion by Salivary Amylase (p. P-88)

Tubes 2, 6, and 7 showed the effect of pH on amylase activity. The results of this experiment indicate that the activity maximum of amylase is at pH 7.0, whereas pH 2.0 and pH 9.0 demonstrated very little activity.

In this experiment, pH 7.0 showed the highest level of amylase activity.

Tube 3 showed that amylase did not contain maltose contamination.

Tubes 3, 4, and 5 showed that water had no starch or maltose contamination. Tube 3 directly showed that water did not have maltose or starch contamination. Tube 4 was a starch control (with the same water) that showed no maltose, and tube 5 was a maltose control (also with water) that showed no starch.

If control tubes 3, 4, or 5 were not done, then what is perceived as digestion might really be starch or maltose contamination.

Saliva would not be active in the stomach because the stomach pH is too low.

Boiling inactivates, or denatures, enzymes.

Activity 2: Assessing Cellulose Digestion (p. P-89)

Tubes #4, 5, and 6 showed positive tests for the IKI reageant.

Tubes #1, 2, 3, and 7 showed positive tests for the Benedict's reageant.

Freezing had no effect.

Freezing does not restrict enzyme activity, unlike boiling.

Amylase had no effect on the glucose in tube #3.

Glucose is the smallest a carbohydrate can get. Amylase does not have any effect on glucose.

Amylase had no effect on the cellulose in tube #4.

Bonding between the glucose molecules in cellulose is different, and amylase cannot break this bond for digestion.

Cellulose isn't digested by salivary amylase. However, it is digestible by bacteria.

Peptidase had no effect on animal starch. Peptidase does not work on carbohydrate substrates so has no effect on digestion of these molecules.

Activity 3: Assessing Protein Digestion by Pepsin (p. P-92)

pH 2.0 allowed the highest pepsin activity.

Pepsin would not be active in the mouth. The pH optimum of pepsin is pH 2.0 and the pH in the mouth is relatively neutral.

Boiling tube 1 inactivated pepsin.

Because there was no activity in tube 1, its optical density was 0.0. In contrast, there was relatively high activity in tube 2.

Tube 2 showed a yellow color indicating BAPNA digestion, and tube 3 showed that yellow color did not appear in pepsin without BAPNA.

If the incubation time were decreased to 30 minutes, less BAPNA would be digested, and the optical density reading would be lower.

Because digestive enzymes work best at body temperature, incubating at a cooler temperature would decrease the amount of BAPNA digested.

Activity 4: Assessing Fat Digestion by Pancreatic Lipase and the Action of Bile (p. P-93)

Tube 1 investigated the action of bile on enzyme activity and tube 2 examines lipase activity without bile. Bile enhances fat digestion by lipase.

Yes, you can determine if activity occurred in tube 6 because the pH would drop below pH 9.0.

The optimim pH for lipase activity was pH 7.0.

Using a pH method to assay for activity at pH 2.0 does not work because the buffer is already quite acid. There could have been activity at pH 2.0 that was not detectable by this method.

In theory, lipase would be active in the mouth because its pH optimum is relatively neutral. However, it would not be active in the stomach because of the acid pH condition.

We could expect to find amylase in areas of neutral pH, for example, the mouth and the small intestine. Although the optimal pH for lipase is near neutral, lipase would be found in the small intestine not in the mouth. Pepsin would only be found in the stomach.

Renal Physiology— The Function of the Nephron: Computer Simulation

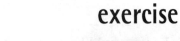

exercise

41B

 Time Allotment: 2 hours.

The following minimum computer hardware is recommended for PhysioEx™ 5.0:

Windows® 98, NT, 2000, ME; Pentium® I processor/ 266 mHz
Mac®: 9.2 or higher
64 MB RAM (128 MB recommended)
800 x 600 screen resolution; millions of colors
Netscape Navigator® 7.0+ or Internet Explorer® 5.0+ (Netscape® installer is included on CD)
Macromedia Flash 6® plug-in (installer is included on CD)
4x CD-ROM drive
Printer

Advance Preparation, Comments, and Pitfalls

1. *If you are using PhysioEx™ in a computer lab:* Because PhysioEx™ 5.0 requires a browser (such as Netscape® or Internet Explorer®) and the Flash 6® plug-in to run, it is recommended that you make sure these items are already installed on student computers before beginning this lab. Installers for both Netscape® and Flash 6® are provided on the CD (instructions are included on the liner notes accompanying the CD).

2. After installing Netscape® or Flash 6®, the computer may attempt to connect to the web. If you do not have a live Internet connection, you may see a dialogue box appear, alerting you of an inability to connect to the web. Simply ignore the message and close the box. **You do not need to have a live Internet connection to run the CD.**

3. *If you are using the web version of PhysioEx™:* Have your students go to http://www.physioex.com and follow the registration instructions found in the very front of their lab manual.

4. It is helpful to instruct students in the proper operation of the mouse and menu system as part of the lab introduction.

5. When considering an upgrade for computer systems, memory (RAM) offers the largest performance increase for the least cost.

6. Having students work in pairs results in the most successful lab experience. If students must work in larger groups, have them each get keyboard and mouse experience with the program.

7. Prior to the lab, suggest to the students that they become familiar with the exercise before coming to class. If students have a home computer, or access to a computer on campus, they can become familiar with the general operation of the simulations before coming to class. In particular, they should examine the structrure of the nephron in the textbook.

8. A good working knowledge of diffusion and osmosis is important in understanding renal function. Suggest to the students that they review those concepts before coming to class.

9. A short introductory presentation with the following elements is often helpful:

   a. Review the basics of nephron anatomy and basic renal physiology, focusing on the major concepts such as glomerular filtration and the movement of substances due to passive and active forces.

   b. Reinforce the idea of how changing the arteriole diameter influences the filtration pressure in the glomerulus.

   c. Use the analogy of a coffee filter when describing the filtration that takes place in the glomerulus.

   d. If the students have not been exposed to the concept of carrier transport maximum, a short introduction using glucose as an example might be helpful.

   e. Encourage students to make the transition from what they see in the simulation to what they see under microscopic examination.

   f. Remind students that they are manipulating a single nephron that represents the function of the entire kidney, but that the living kidney contains many nephrons.

10. Be prepared to help the students answer the more difficult "What if …" questions.

Answers to Questions

Activity 1: Investigation the Effect of Flow Tube Radius on Glomerular Filtration (p. P-99)

Glomerular filtration rate increases as afferent arteriole diameter increases due to the increased blood flow into the glomerulus.

If the diameter of the efferent arteriole was increased, filtration pressure in the glomerulus would decrease thereby decreasing glomerular filtration rate. If the radius of the efferent arteriole was decreased, upstream pressure would increase and glomerular filtration would also increase.

Activity 2: Studying the Effect of Pressure on Glomerular Filtration (p. P-99)

Glomerular filtration rate increased.

GFR increased because the net filtration pressure was increased. Net filtration pressure relies on glomerular hydrostatic pressure, which rises when the pressure in the beaker is increased.

Activity 3: Assessing Combined Effects on Glomerular Filtration (p. P-100)

When the valve is closed, urine output is zero because the glomerular filtration rate is zero. GFR is zero because the capsular hydrostatic pressure is high enough to prevent filtrate movement.

If all collecting tubules in a kidney were blocked, the urine output of that kidney would be zero. The kidney would not function.

Kidney function would not be noticeably affected if a single nephron was blocked beacuse all other million nephrons would still be functioning.

The kidney would not function if glomerular filtration rate was zero because no filtrate would be moving through the nephron.

The body could dilate the afferent arteriole or constrict the efferent arteriole to increase glomerular filtration rate.

If the beaker pressure was increased, then the afferent arteriole could be constricted to maintain GFR at a constant rate.

Activity 4: Exploring the Role of the Solute Gradient on Maximum Urine Concentration Achievable (p. P-102)

When ADH is present, urine concentration increases as the interstitial gradient increases.

The osmolarity of the interstitial gradient determines the maximum possible urine concentration.

Osmotic forces draw water out of the collecting tubule. Therefore, increasing the concentration of solutes outside the tubule will increase the maximum possible urine concentration. The maximum possible urine concentration will therefore not be greater than the interstitial solute concentration.

Activity 5: Studying the Effect of Glucose Carrier Proteins on Glucose Reabsorption (p. P-102)

The amount of glucose in the urine decreased as the number of glucose carriers was increased.

If there was more glucose than could be transported by the number of available glucose carriers, then glucose would be present in the urine.

We would expect to find glucose in the urine of a diabetic person because there is too much glucose in the filtrate to be reabsorbed.

Activity 6: Testing the Effect of Hormones on Urine Formation (p. P-103)

When aldosterone is present, urine volume is decreased.

Aldosterone causes sodium reabsorption in the distal tubule at the expense of potassium, which will be transported to the lumen of the tubule and into the urine.

When ADH is present, urine volume is greatly reduced.

There is no difference in the amount of potassium in the urine. Although the concentration is higher when ADH is present and the volume of urine has been reduced, the total amount of potassium has not changed.

The effects of aldosterone and ADH are similar.

The amount of aldosterone would need to be increased while the amount of ADH would need to decrease.

If ADH was not present then water would not move from the lumen of the tubule and a dilute urine would be produced.

Acid-Base Balance: Computer Simulation

exercise

47B

Time Allotment: 2 hours.

The following minimum computer hardware is recommended for PhysioEx™ 5.0:

Windows® 98, NT, 2000, ME; Pentium® I processor/ 266 mHz
Mac®: 9.2 or higher
64 MB RAM (128 MB recommended)
800 x 600 screen resolution; millions of colors
Netscape Navigator® 7.0+ or Internet Explorer® 5.0+ (Netscape® installer is included on CD)
Macromedia Flash 6® plug-in (installer is included on CD)
4x CD-ROM drive
Printer

Advance Preparation, Comments, and Pitfalls

1. *If you are using PhysioEx™ in a computer lab:* Because PhysioEx™ 5.0 requires a browser (such as Netscape® or Internet Explorer®) and the Flash 6® plug-in to run, it is recommended that you make sure these items are already installed on student computers before beginning this lab. Installers for both Netscape® and Flash 6® are provided on the CD (instructions are included on the liner notes accompanying the CD).
2. After installing Netscape® or Flash 6®, the computer may attempt to connect to the web. If you do not have a live Internet connection, you may see a dialogue box appear, alerting you of an inability to connect to the web. Simply ignore the message and close the box. **You do not need to have a live Internet connection to run the CD.**
3. *If you are using the web version of PhysioEx™:* Have your students go to http://www.physioex.com and follow the registration instructions found in the very front of their lab manual.
4. It is helpful to instruct students in the proper operation of the mouse and menu system as part of the lab introduction.
5. When considering an upgrade for computer systems, memory (RAM) offers the largest performance increase for the least cost.

Answers to Questions

Activity 1: Normal Breathing (p. P-106)

Answers will vary from run to run, but always remain constant within an individual run. The pH will always be between 7.38 and 7.42.

No, the pH level of the blood did not change during normal breathing.

Yes, the pH level remained within the normal range for the human body.

No, the P_{CO2} level did not change during the course of normal breathing.

Activity 2a: Hyperventilation: Run #1 (p. P-107)

at 20 seconds, pH= about 7.45
at 40 seconds, pH= about 7.54
at 60 seconds, pH= about 7.67

Yes, the pH level of the blood increased over time.

No, the pH level was not always within the normal range.

The pH value began to exceed the normal range between 10 and 20 seconds—as soon as it rose above 7.45. This indicated the condition of alkalosis.

Yes, the P_{CO2} level decreased over time.

You would expect the renal system to compensate for alkalosis by retaining [H+] and ex creting bicarbonate in order to lower the blood pH levels back to within the normal range.

The hyperventilation trace had higher peaks and valleys than the normal breathing trace. The tidal volumes were also larger in the hyperventilation trace.

Causes of hyperventilation include fever or anxiety.

Activity 2b: Hyperventilation: Run #2 (p. P-108)

After the 20 second mark, when hyperventilation was stopped, the trace flat-lined, indicating that breathing was suspended. Breathing did not return to normal immediately. The body temporarily stopped breathing in order to restore P_{CO2} levels to normal values.

Activity 3: Rebreathing (p. P-108)

at 20 seconds, pH= about 7.35
at 40 seconds, pH= about 7.3
at 60 seconds, pH= about 7.25

Yes, the pH level of the blood decreased over time.

No, the pH level was not always within the normal range.

The pH value began to dip below the normal range between 20 and 30 seconds—as soon as it was below 7.35. This indicated the condition of acidosis.

Yes, the P_{CO2} level increased over time.

You would expect the renal system to compensate for acidosis by excreting [H$^+$] and retaining bicarbonate in order to raise the blood pH levels back to within normal range.

The rebreathing trace had slightly higher peaks and valleys than the normal breathing trace. The tidal volumes were also larger in the rebreathing trace.

Respiratory problems that would result in lowered pH values and higher P_{CO2} levels include lung disease and airway obstruction—anything that impairs breathing.

Activity 4: Renal Response to Normal Acid-Base Balance (p. P-109)

At normal P_{CO2} and pH levels, a normal level of H$^+$ was present in the urine.

A normal level of [HCO$_3^-$] was present in the urine.

The blood pH value changes as P_{CO2} changes because P_{CO2} levels directly affect blood pH levels. As P_{CO2} increases, pH values decrease. As P_{CO2} levels decrease, pH values increase.

Activity 5: Renal Response to Respiratory Alkalosis (p. P-109)

At $P_{CO2} = 35$, a normal level of H+ was present in the urine. At $P_{CO2} = 30$ and 20, a decreased level of H+ was present in the urine.

At $P_{CO2} = 35$, a normal level of [HCO$_3^-$] was present in the urine. At $P_{CO2} = 30$ and 20, an elevated level of [HCO$_3^-$] was present in the urine

You would expect P_{CO2} levels to eventually increase.

You would expect pH levels to eventually decrease.

Reduced P_{CO2} levels most closely resemble the P_{CO2} levels we observed during hyperventilation.

Hyperventilation resulted in alkalosis because more carbon dioxide is being expelled by the body during this kind of breathing. The reduction of carbon dioxide inside the blood results in less [H$^+$] being generated, which can cause pH levels to rise to the point of alkalosis.

Activity 6: Renal Response to Respiratory Acidosis (p. P-111)

At $P_{CO2} = 60$, 75, and 90, an elevated level of [H$^+$] was present in the urine.

At $P_{CO2} = 60$, 75, and 90, decreased levels of [HCO$_3^-$] were present in the urine.

You would expect P_{CO2} levels to eventually decrease.

You would expect pH levels to eventually increase.

Elevated P_{CO2} levels most closely resemble the P_{CO2} levels we observed during rebreathing.

Rebreathing resulted in acidosis because carbon dioxide is being retained by the body during this kind of breathing. The increase in carbon dioxide inside the blood results in more [H$^+$] being generated, which can cause pH levels to dip to point of acidosis.

Activity 7: Respiratory Response to Normal Metabolism (p. P-112)

The respiratory rate is 15 breaths per minute.

Yes, the blood pH and P_{CO2} values are within normal ranges.

Activity 8: Respiratory Response to Increased Metabolism

As the body's metabolic rate increased:

respiration increased
blood pH decreased
P_{CO2} values increased
[H⁺] increased
[HCO₃⁻] decreased

As the body's metabolic rate increased, more carbon dioxide was formed as a metabolic waste product. This caused an increase in [H⁺] generation, which lowered the plasma pH, causing respiration to increase in order to expel the elevated levels of carbon dioxide and restore pH to a normal value.

Metabolic rates of 70 and 80 resulted in acidosis.

At metabolic rate = 70, the pH value was about 7.27. At metabolic rate = 80, the pH value was about 7.25. Acidosis occurs at pH levels below 7.35. (The pH values will vary slightly from run to run.)

By the time the respiratory system fully compensated for acidosis, you would expect pH levels to rise to normal values.

Activity 9: Respiratory Response to Decreased Metabolism

As the body's metabolic rate decreased:

respiration decreased
blood pH increased
P_{CO2} values decreased
[H⁺] decreased
[HCO₃⁻] increased

As the body's metabolic rate decreased, less carbon dioxide was formed as a metabolic waste product. This caused a decrease in [H+] generation, which increased the plasma pH, causing respiration to decrease in order to retain more carbon dioxide in the blood and restore pH to a normal value.

Metabolic rates of 30 and 20 resulted in alkalosis.

At metabolic rate = 30, the pH value was about 7.47. At metabolic rate = 20, the pH value was about 7.51. Alkalosis occurs at pH values above 7.45. (The pH values will vary slightly from run to run.)

By the time the respiratory system fully compensated for alkalosis, you would expect pH levels to decrease to normal values.

Cell Transport Mechanisms and Permeability: Computer Simulation

Choose all answers that apply to items 1 and 2, and place their letters on the response blanks to the right.

1. Differential permeability: _a, b_____

   a. is also called selective permeability
   b. refers to the ability of the plasma membrane to select what passes through it
   c. implies that all substances pass through membranes without hindrance
   d. keeps wastes inside the cell and nutrients outside the cell

2. Passive transport includes: _a, b, e_____

   a. osmosis   b. simple diffusion   c. bulk-phase endocytosis   d. pinocytosis   e. facilitated diffusion

3. The following refer to the dialysis simulation.

   Did the 20 MWCO membrane exclude any solute(s)? _It excluded all solutes._____

   Which solute(s) passed through the 100 MWCO membrane? _Na^+ and urea_____

   Which solute exhibited the highest diffusion rate through the 100 MWCO membrane? _Na^+_____

   Explain why this is so: _Smaller particles exhibit a higher diffusion rate._____

4. The following refer to the facilitated diffusion simulation.

   Are substances able to travel against their concentration gradient? _No_____

   Name two ways to increase the rate of glucose transport. _Increase glucose concentration, increase the number of glucose carriers_

   Did NaCl affect glucose transport? _No_____

   Does NaCl require a transport protein for diffusion? _No, diffusion occurs through the membrane pores._____

5. The following refer to the osmosis simulation.

   Does osmosis require energy? _No, it is a passive process._____

   Is water excluded by any of the dialysis membranes? _No, water is small enough to pass through all the MWCO membranes._

   Is osmotic pressure generated if solutes freely diffuse? _No_____

   Explain how solute concentration affects osmotic pressure. _Increasing solute concentration increases osmotic pressure._

   _____

6. The following refer to the filtration simulation.

What does the simulated filtration membrane represent in a living organism? _The filtration membrane of the renal corpuscle_

What characteristic of a solute determines whether or not it passes through a filtration membrane?

Size

Would filtration occur if we equalized the pressure on both sides of a filtration membrane? _No_

7. The following questions refer to the active transport simulation.

Does the presence of glucose carrier proteins affect Na^+ transport? _No_

Can Na^+ be transported against its concentration gradient? _Yes_

Are Na^+ and K^+ transported in the same direction? _No_

The ratio of Na^+ to K^+ transport is _3_ Na^+ transported out of the cell for every _2_ K^+ transported into the cell.

8. What single characteristic of the semipermeable membranes used in the simple diffusion and filtration experiments determines which substances pass through them? _Molecular weight_

In addition to this characteristic, what other factors influence the passage of substances through living membranes?

Solubility in lipids, charge, presence of carrier molecules

9. Assume the left beaker contains 4 mM NaCl, 9 mM glucose, and 10 mM albumin. The right beaker contains 10 mM NaCl, 10 mM glucose, and 40 mM albumin. Furthermore, the dialysis membrane is permeable to all substances except albumin. State whether the substance will move (a) to the right beaker, (b) to the left beaker, or (c) not move.

Glucose _(b)_   Albumin _(c)_

Water _(a)_   NaCl _(b)_

10. Assume you are conducting the experiment illustrated below. Both hydrochloric acid (HCl) with a molecular weight of about 36.5 and ammonium hydroxide (NH_4OH) with a molecular weight of 35 are volatile and easily enter the gaseous state. When they meet, the following reaction will occur:

$$HCl + NH_4OH \rightarrow H_2O + NH_4Cl$$

Ammonium chloride (NH_4Cl) will be deposited on the glass tubing as a smoky precipitate where the two gases meet. Predict which gas will diffuse more quickly and indicate to which end of the tube the smoky precipitate will be closer.

a.   The faster diffusing gas is _NH_4OH_.

b.   The precipitate forms closer to the _HCl_ end.

11. When food is pickled for human consumption, as much water as possible is removed from the food. What method is used to achieve this dehydrating effect? *Osmosis. Cells (in food) are placed in a solution with a high salt concentration. Water moves out of the cells.*

12. What determines whether a transport process is active or passive? *Whether or not the cell must provide ATP for the process; if the cells provide ATP, then the process is active.*

13. Characterize passive and active transport as fully as possible by choosing all the phrases that apply and inserting their letters on the answer blanks.

Passive transport *a, c, e*   Active transport *b, d, f*

   a.   accounts for the movement of fats and respiratory gases through the plasma membrane
   b.   explains solute pumping, bulk-phase endocytosis, and pinocytosis
   c.   includes osmosis, simple diffusion, and filtration
   d.   may occur against concentration and/or electrical gradients
   e.   uses hydrostatic pressure or molecular energy as the driving force
   f.   moves ions, amino acids, and some sugars across the plasma membrane

14. Define the following:

diffusion: *Movement of molecules from a region of their higher concentration to a region of their lower concentration*

osmosis: *Diffusion of water through a semipermeable or differentially permeable membrane*

simple diffusion: *Diffusion of a substance (through a semipermeable membrane) from where it is in higher concentration to an area where it is in lower concentration*

filtration: *Passage of substances across a membrane from an area of higher hydrostatic pressure to an area of lower hydrostatic pressure*

active transport: *A transport system that requires ATP—one such system is the solute pump*

bulk-phase endocytosis: *Engulfment of extracellular particles by pseudopod formation—"cell eating"*

pinocytosis: *Intake of extracellular fluids by vesicle formation—"cell drinking"*

facilitated diffusion: *Diffusion of a solute through a semipermeable membrane in which a carrier protein is required*

Skeletal Muscle Physiology: Computer Simulation

Electrical Stimulation

1. Complete the following statements by filling in your answer on the lines provided below.

A motor unit consists of a __a__ and all the __b__ it innervates. Whole muscle contraction is a(n) __c__ response. In order for muscles to work in a practical sense, __d__ is the method used to produce a slow, steady increase in muscle force.

When we see the slightest evidence of force production on a tracing, the stimulus applied must have reached __e__.

The weakest stimulation that will elicit the strongest contraction that a muscle is capable of is called the __f__. That level of contraction is called the __g__.

When the __h__ of stimulation is so high that the muscle tracing shows fused peaks, __i__ has been achieved.

a. _motor neuron_____   f. _maximal stimulus_____

b. _muscle cells_____   g. _maximal response_____

c. _graded_____   h. _rate_____

d. _summation_____   i. _tetanus_____

e. _threshold_____

2. Name each phase of a typical muscle twitch and describe what is happening in each phase.

a. _latent period_____

_The muscle cells are biochemically preparing to contract. Contraction has not started, force is zero._____

b. _contraction phase_____

_Sarcomeres are shortening, causing the muscle cells to contract in turn, which causes a force increase._____

c. _relaxation phase_____

_Sarcomeres are lengthening due to relaxation; force is falling._____

3. Explain how the PhysioEx experimental muscle stimulation differs from the *in vivo* stimulation via the nervous system. (Note that the graded muscle response following both stimulation methods is similar.)

Causes the electrical shock to spread throughout the muscle. Increased voltage causes more cells to be stimulated. In contrast, the

_nervous system stimulates each cell individually via a motor unit._____

_____

4. What are the two *experimental* ways in which mode of stimulation can affect the muscle force?

_stimulus rate_____ and _stimulus intensity_____

Explain your answer.

Increasing either the stimulus rate or the stimulus intensity will increase force production. Increasing stimulus intensity increases the

total number of cells contracting whereas increasing the stimulus rate will increase force by wave summation.

Isometric Contraction

5. Identify the following conditions by choosing one of the key terms listed on the right.

_b_____ is generated by muscle tissue when it is being stretched

_c_____ requires the input of energy

_a_____ is measured by recording instrumentation during contraction

Key:

a.   Total force

b.   Resting force

c.   Active force

6. Circle the correct response in the parentheses for each statement.

An increase in resting length results in a(n) (increase/decrease) in passive force.

The active force initially (increased/decreased) and then (increased/decreased) as the resting length was increased from minimum to maximum.

As the total force increased, the active force (increased/decreased).

7. Explain what happens to muscle force production at extremes of length (too short or too long). Hint: think about sarcomere structure.

Muscle too short: _If sarcomeres are shortened to the point where they are not capable of shortening further, force cannot be generated._

Muscle too long: _If sarcomeres are lengthened (e.g., stretching) beyond the point where the actin and myosin overlap, there will be no_

interaction between the myofilaments; hence, force production will not occur.

Isotonic Contraction

8. Assuming a fixed starting length, describe the effect resistance has on the initial velocity of shortening, and explain why it has this effect.

Increasing the resistance causes a decrease in the initial velocity of shortening. This occurs because of the increased force required to

move the larger weights. More work is used just to move the weight with the higher loads.

9. A muscle has just been stimulated under conditions that will allow both isometric and isotonic contractions. Describe what is happening in terms of length and force.

Isometric: *Contraction: force builds until it equals the resistance. Relaxation: force falls until it reaches zero. In both cases, the length*

of the muscle is not changing.

Isotonic: *Contraction: force is not changing because the resistance (weight) is moving up. Relaxation: force is not changing because the*

resistance is moving down. At the point where the resistance touches the platform, the force becomes isometric again.

Terms

10. Select the condition from column B that most correctly identifies the term in column A.

Column A	Column B
_c_ 1. muscle twitch	a. response is all-or-none
_e_ 2. wave summation	b. affects the force a muscle can generate
_d_ 3. multiple motor unit summation	c. a single contraction of intact muscle
_b_ 4. resting length	d. recruitment
_h_ 5. resistance	e. increasing force produced by increasing stimulus frequency
_j_ 6. initial velocity of shortening	f. muscle length changing due to relaxation
_k_ 7. isotonic shortening	g. caused by application of maximal stimulus
_f_ 8. isotonic lengthening	h. weight
_a_ 9. motor unit	i. exhibits graded response
_i_ 10. whole muscle	j. high values with low resistance values
_l_ 11. tetanus	k. changing muscle length due to active forces
_g_ 12. maximal response	l. recording shows no evidence of muscle relaxation

Neurophysiology of Nerve Impulses: Computer Simulation

The Nerve Impulse

1. Match each of the terms in column B with the appropriate definition in column A.

Column A

   d   1. term used to denote that a membrane potential is sitting at about −70 mV

   f   2. reversal of membrane potential due to influx of sodium ions

   b   3. major cation found outside the cell

   a   4. minimal stimulus needed to elicit an action potential

   e   5. period when cell membrane is totally insensitive to additional stimuli, regardless of the stimulus force used

   c   6. major cation found inside the cell

Column B

a. threshold

b. sodium

c. potassium

d. resting membrane potential

e. absolute refractory period

f. depolarization

2. Fill in the blanks with the correct words or terms.

Neurons, as with other excitable cells of the body, have two major physiological properties: *irritability* and

conductivity. A neuron has a positive charge on the outer surface of the cell membrane due in part to the

action of an active transport system called the *sodium-potassium pump*. This system moves

sodium out of the cell and *potassium* into the cell. The inside of the cell membrane will

be negative, not only due to the active transport system but also because of *protein ions*, which remain
negative due to intracellular pH and keep the inside of the cell membrane negative.

3. Why don't the terms *depolarization* and *action potential* mean the same thing?

Depolarization (reduction of the negative membrane potential) may only be a short-lived event if the change in the membrane is sub-

threshold. When an action potential occurs, there is a large reversal of the membrane polarity that occurs when the membrane depolar-

izes to threshold.

4. What is the difference between membrane irritability and membrane conductivity?

Irritability is the ability to respond to stimuli and convert these stimuli into neural impulses or action potentials. Conductivity is the abil-

ity to take this action potential and pass it along the cell membrane until the synapse (a gap between neural cells) is reached.

Eliciting a Nerve Impulse

5. Why does the nerve action potential increase slightly when you add 1.0 V to the threshold voltage and stimulate the nerve?

Nerves are made up of literally thousands of processes from neurons (called axons) that are of various sizes. The threshold voltage will stimulate the smaller nerve fibers to achieve an action potential. A higher voltage will stimulate even more nerve fibers to achieve an action potential.

6. If you were to spend a lot of time studying nerve physiology in the laboratory, what type of stimulus would you use and why?

Although many different stimuli work, electrical stimulators are convenient because the voltage duration, and frequency of the shock can be very precisely set for use.

7. Why does the addition of sodium chloride elicit an action potential? *While the sodium-potassium pump is pumping sodium out of the cell and potassium into the cell, these ions are leaking back where they came from by diffusion. By adding sodium chloride, a more-than-normal amount of sodium will diffuse into the nerve, causing the resting membrane potential to reach the threshold value, bringing about a membrane depolarization.*

Inhibiting a Nerve Impulse

8. What was the effect of ether on eliciting an action potential? *The ether narcotizes the nerve fiber in between the stimulating and recording electrodes, thus blocking any action potential from being generated.*

9. Does the addition of ether to the nerve cause any permanent alteration in neural response?

No, the ether has no lasting effect.

10. What was the effect of curare on eliciting an action potential?

Curare had no effect—an action potential was still generated when the nerve was stimulated at threshold voltage.

11. Explain the reason for your answer to question 3 above.

Curare works by blocking synaptic transmissions so that neural impulses do not travel from neuron to neuron. The detached nerve which we are experimenting with does not have any synapses to be blocked. In a living animal, however, curare will kill, as neural impulses cannot jump synapses to allow the heart to work or the animal to breathe.

12. What was the effect of lidocaine on eliciting an action potential?

Lidocaine is a sodium channel antagonist and will block sodium ion channels from working, preventing the generation of an action potential.

Nerve Conduction Velocity

13. What is the relationship between size of the nerve and conduction velocity? *The larger the size of the nerve, the faster the*

conduction velocity.

14. Keeping your answer to question 1 in mind, how might you draw an analogy between the nerves in the human body and electrical wires? *The larger the size of the elecrical wire, the faster the speed of electrons within it. Smaller wires have a high resistance to*

electron flow.

15. Hypothesize what types of animals would have the fastest conduction velocities.

Mammals, because they tend to be larger.

16. How does myelination affect nerve conduction velocity? Explain. *Myelination will speed the nerve conduction velocity consid-*

erably. Myelin is found in Schwann cells which encircle a given axon. It acts mainly as an insulator so that depolarization in one cell

does not set off depolarizations in adjoining cells. When a neural membrane is depolarized, local currents are set up between positive

and negative ions causing membrane conduction. In myelinated fibers, the local currents go from one internode (or Node of Ranvier) in

between two Schwann cells to the next internode. Thus we have "salutatory conduction" where a neural impulse actually jumps from one

internode to the next without being conducted down the entire cell membrane.

17. If any of the nerves used were reversed in their placement on the stimulating and recording electrodes, would any differences be seen in conduction velocity? Explain. *No. Once a neural membrane is depolarized and the impulse is being conducted along the*

neural membrane, which direction is which does not matter. We state that a neural impulse is set up in the neuron's trigger zone (mainly

due to the large number of sodium channels there) but once the depolarization is set up, it not only travels down the axon but also around

the soma of the cell.

Endocrine System Physiology: Computer Simulation

1. In the following columns, match the hormone on the left with its source on the right.

    _b_ thyroxine

    _a_ estrogen

    _d_ thyroid-stimulating hormone (TSH)

    _c_ insulin

    a. ovary

    b. thyroid gland

    c. pancreas

    d. pituitary gland

2. Each hormone is known to have a specific target tissue. For each hormone listed, what is its target tissue and what is its specific action?

    thyroxine _All body cells; action is to increase metabolic rate_

    estrogen _Female tissue, especially uterus and breast; action is to cause the growth of the endometrium of the uterus and ductal growth_

    in the breast

    thyroid-stimulating hormone (TSH) _Thyroid; action is to stimulate production of thyroxine_

    insulin _All body cells, especially the liver; action is to cause the uptake of glucose into the cell to be stored as animal starch (glycogen)_

    follicle-stimulating hormone (FSH) _Ovary (follicle); action is to cause maturation of the developing follicle_

Metabolism

3. In the metabolism experiment, what was the effect of thyroxine on the overall metabolic rate of the animals?

    Thyroxine increased the metabolic rates of the animals.

4. Using the respirometer-manometer, you observed the amount of oxygen being used by animals in a closed chamber. What

    happened to the carbon dioxide the animals produced while in the chamber? _It was absorbed by the soda lime on the bottom of_

    the chamber.

5. If the experimental animals in the chamber were engaged in physical activity (such as running in a wheel), how do you think this would change the results of the metabolism experiment? *Metabolic rates can be expected to increase with physical activity.* What changes would you expect to see in fluid levels of the manometer? *The fluid level would rise even higher on the left side of the manometer, demonstrating that more oxygen had been used up by the rat when it was engaged in physical activity.*

6. Why didn't the administration of thyroid-stimulating hormone (TSH) have any effect on the metabolic rate of the thyroidectomized rat? *Because the thyroidectomized rat lacked a thyroid, the TSH had nothing to act on.*

7. Why didn't the administration of propylthiouracil have any effect on the metabolic rate of either the thyroidectomized rat or the hypophysectomized rat? *Propylthiouracil inhibits the production of thyroxine. Since the thyroidectomized and hypophysectomized rats are already not producing thyroxine, the propylthiouracil has nothing to act on.*

Hormone Replacement Therapy

8. In the experiment with hormone replacement therapy, what was the effect of removing the ovaries from the animals? *The animals could no longer produce estrogen.*

9. Specifically, what hormone did the ovariectomies effectively remove from the animals, and what purpose does this hormone serve? *Estradiol. The major action of this hormone is to promote uterine growth.*

10. If a hormone such as testosterone were used in place of estrogen, would any effect be seen? Explain your answer. *No, because different hormones have different receptors within the cell and have different modes of action.*

11. In the experiment, you administered 7 injections of estrogen to the experimental rat over the course of 7 days. What do you think would happen if you administered one injection of estrogen per day for an additional week? *Tissue only grows so large. The weight of the uterus may increase to 0.8 or 0.9 grams, but not much more than that.*

12. What do you think would happen if you administered 7 injections of estrogen to the experimental rat all in one day?

Not much. Most of the "excess" estrogen will be urinated away by the rat.

13. In a wet lab, why would you need to wait several weeks after the animals received their ovariectomies before you could perform this experiment on them? *To ensure that no residual hormones remain in the animals' systems.*

Insulin and Diabetes

14. In the insulin and diabetes experiment, what was the effect of administering alloxan to the experimental animal?

Alloxan caused the rat to become diabetic.

15. When insulin travels to the cells of the body, the concentration of what compound will elevate within the cells?

Glucose

What is the specific action of this compound, within the cells? *Glucose molecules are joined together to form animal starch*

or glycogen

16. Name the diseases described below:

a. the condition when insulin is not produced by the pancreas: *diabetes mellitus Type I*

b. the condition when insulin is produced by the pancreas, but the body fails to respond to the insulin:

diabetes mellitus Type II

17. What was the effect of administering insulin to the diabetic rat? *Insulin lowered the amount of glucose present in the blood of*

the diabetic rat.

18. What is a *glucose standard curve*, and why did you need to obtain one for this experiment? *A glucose standard curve is a point*

of reference obtained by taking known amounts of glucose in samples and placing the samples in a light spectrophotometer in order to

correlate optical density values with glucose levels. Without a glucose standard curve, you would have no way of knowing how to trans-

late optical density values into glucose levels.

19. Would altering the light wavelength of the spectrophotometer have any bearing on the results obtained? Explain your

answer. *Yes. The spectrophotometer is preset at a wavelength selected for optimal absorption. Another wavelength might tend to give*

misleading results.

20. What would you do to help a friend who had inadvertently taken an overdose of insulin? Why? *Give them something to eat,*

in order to raise the level of glucose in their bloodstream.

Blood Analysis: Computer Simulation

Hematocrit Determination

1. Hematocrit values are usually ((higher) lower) in healthy males, compared to healthy females.

   Give one possible explanation for this. *Females of reproductive age lose blood each month during their menstrual periods.*

   _____

2. Living at high elevations will cause a person's hematocrit to ((increase) decrease).

   Explain your answer. *There is less oxygen in the air at higher elevations. The kidneys respond to hypoxia by secreting the hormone*

   erythropoietin, which stimulates red blood cell production.

3. Long-term athletic training will cause a person's hematocrit to ((increase) decrease).

4. What is anemia? *A condition in which inadequate oxygen is delivered to the body's cells.*

5. Anemia will cause a person's hematocrit to (increase (decrease)).

6. Pernicious anemia is due to a lack of vitamin *B_{12}* _____

7. How does deficiency of intrinsic factor lead to pernicious anemia? *Intrinsic factor, made in the stomach, is necessary for the ab-*

   sorption of vitamin B_{12} from the diet.

8. Why would a diet deficient in iron lead to anemia? *Iron is an important element in hemoglobin. Without adequate iron, the body*

   cannot manufacture enough hemoglobin to fill red blood cells.

9. Which hormone, secreted by the kidney, is responsible for increased production of red blood cells?

   Erythropoietin

Erythrocyte Sedimentation Rate (ESR)

10. Sickled red blood cells have an abnormal shape and do not tend to form stacks of cells (rouleaux formation). This would (increase (decrease)) the sedimentation rate.

11. Is the ESR test a specific test used to diagnose a disease? *No* _____

12. The blood of a cancer patient undergoing chemotherapy is given an ESR test. The results show a slower ESR from the previous month. What might this indicate about the patient's disease?

   The decrease in the ESR may indicate an improvement in the patient's cancer.

13. How can the ESR be useful in the evaluation of a patient complaining of chest pains?

   The ESR is not elevated in cases of angina pectoris, but is elevated in established myocardial infarctions.

14. How can the ESR be useful in the evaluation of a female patient suffering from severe abdominal pains?
   The ESR is not elevated in the early stages of acute appendicitis, but is elevated in the early stage of acute pelvic inflammatory disease, or in cases of ruptured ectopic pregnancy.

Hemoglobin Determination

15. What is the value, in terms of grams of hemoglobin per 100 milliliters of blood, for the following:

   a. healthy male: *16 grams per 100 ml of blood*

   b. healthy female: *14 grams per 100 ml of blood*

   c. male with polycythemia: *20 grams per 100 ml of blood*

   d. female with iron deficiency anemia: *8 grams per 100 ml of blood*

16. Explain your answer to (c) above. *In polycythemia, there are above-normal numbers of red blood cells. Hemoglobin molecules fill red blood cells. So, more red blood cells results in more hemoglobin.*

17. Explain your answer to (d) above. *In iron-deficiency anemia, there are not enough atoms of iron for the body to use in manufacturing hemoglobin.*

18. Complete the following questions to describe hemoglobin.

   How many polypeptide chains form the globin portion of the molecule? *4*

   Each heme group contains an atom of the element *Iron*.

   How many heme groups are contained in one molecule of hemoglobin? *4*

   Each hemoglobin molecule can transport *4* molecules of oxygen.

   What color is oxyhemoglobin? *Bright red*

19. Hemoglobin values rise in COPD (chronic obstructive pulmonary disease). Give a possible explanation for this.

   In COPD, there is inadequate oxygen in the blood. The kidneys respond to this condition of hypoxia by releasing a hormone called erythropoietin. Erythropoietin stimulates the production of red blood cells, which contain hemoglobin.

20. Hemoglobin values decrease in renal disease. Give a possible explanation for this.

   The kidneys respond to hypoxia by secreting the hormone erythropoietin, which stimulates red blood cell production. If the kidneys are damaged in renal disease, they may not be able to secrete sufficient erythropoietin.

Blood Typing

21. Define the following terms.

agglutinogen: _A protein antigen found on the surface of red blood cells_

agglutinin: _An antibody to agglutinogens, found pre-formed in the blood plasma_

gene allele: _Directions on a chromosome for the manufacture of a particular polypeptide or protein_

22. What is the most common ABO blood type in the United States? _Type O_

23. What is the least common ABO blood type in the United States? _Type AB_

24. Most Americans are Rh (positive / negative).

25. *Erythroblastosis fetalis* is an uncommon condition in newborn infants. In this condition, the baby is Rh (positive / negative) and the mother is Rh (positive / negative).

26. If your blood agglutinates with both anti-A and anti-B sera, your blood type is _AB_.

27. If you have type O blood, which antigens are present on your red blood cells?

Neither A nor B

Which antibodies are present in your plasma? _Both anti-A and anti-B_

28. Blood type O is considered to be the universal donor type. However, if type O blood is transfused into a person with blood type B, which of the following is important to remember?

   a.   Use the entire pint of type O blood for the transfusion

   b.   Separate the type O blood into packed cells and plasma, and use only the packed cells for the transfusion

   c.   Separate the type O blood into packed cells and plasma, and use only the plasma for the transfusion

Total Blood Cholesterol Determination

29. Cholesterol is an essential factor in homeostasis. Name four uses that the human body has for cholesterol.

   a. _Forming cell membranes_

   b. _Manufacture of bile salts_

   c. _Manufacture of steroid hormones_

   d. _Manufacture of vitamin D_

30. Most of the cholesterol that your body needs is made by what organ? _Liver_

31. High blood cholesterol levels are above _200_ mg/100 ml of blood.

32. What is atherosclerosis? _The accumulation of lipid deposits on the walls of large arteries_

33. What is the connection between high blood cholesterol levels and atherosclerosis?

High blood cholesterol levels can indicate atherosclerosis.

34. What are lipoproteins? *Small lipid protein complexes that transport triglycerides and cholesterol in the watery blood.*

35. Low density lipoproteins (LDLs) transport cholesterol to *the peripheral tissues of the body, making it available for membrane or hormone synthesis.*

36. High density lipoproteins (HDLs) transport cholesterol from the *peripheral tissues* to the *liver*, where it is broken down and becomes part of bile.

37. Cigarette smoking, stress, and coffee drinking increase levels of *low density lipoproteins (LDL)*, or "bad cholesterol."

38. Regular aerobic exercise increases levels of *high density lipoproteins (HDL)*, or "good cholesterol."

Cardiovascular Dynamics: Computer Simulation

For numbers 1 and 2 below, choose all answers that apply and place their letters on the response blanks to the right of the statement.

1. The circulation of blood through the vascular system is influenced by _a, b, c, d_____.

   a. blood viscosity
   b. the length of blood vessels
   c. the driving pressure behind the blood
   d. the radius or diameter of blood vessels

2. Peripheral resistance depends on _a, c, d_____.

   a. blood viscosity
   b. blood pressure
   c. vessel length
   d. vessel radius

3. Complete the following statements.

   The volume of blood remaining in the heart after ventricular contraction is called the _end systolic volume_____.

   Cardiac output is defined as _the amount of blood pumped by the heart in one minute_____.

   The amount of blood pumped by the heart in a single beat is called the _stroke_____ volume.

   The human heart is actually two individual pumps working in _series_____.

   Stroke volume is calculated by _subtracting end systolic volume from end diastolic volume_____.

   If stroke volume decreased, heart rate would _increase_____ in order to maintain blood flow.

4. How could the heart compensate to maintain proper blood flow for the following conditions?

   High peripheral resistance: _Increased force of contraction_____

   A leaky atrioventricular valve: _Pump harder and faster_____

   A constricted semilunar valve: _Pump harder and faster_____

5. How does the size of the heart change under conditions of chronic high peripheral resistance?

   _The cells of the heart will increase in size, increasing overall size of the heart._____

6. The following questions refer to the Vessel Resistance experiment.

   How was the flow rate affected when the radius of the flow tube was increased? _Fluid flow greatly increased_____

   Which of the adjustable parameters had the greatest effect on fluid flow? _Adjusting the radius_____

   How does vessel length affect fluid flow? _Increasing the length decreases the flow rate_____

If you increased fluid viscosity, what parameter(s) could you adjust to keep fluid flow constant?

Increase pressure, increase radius, decrease length

Explain your answer. *Increasing the driving pressure pushes fluid through at a higher rate; increasing the radius and decreasing*

the length will decrease the peripheral resistance.

If the driving pressure in the left beaker was 100 mm Hg, how could you adjust the conditions of the experiment to completely stop fluid flow? *Decrease the pressure to zero and flow would stop.*

7. The following questions refer to the Pump Mechanics experiment.

What would happen if the right side of the heart pumped faster than the left side of the heart?

Because the heart is two pumps in series, pumping faster in the right side would cause an increase in pressure in the lungs.

When you change the radius of the right flow tube in Pump Mechanics, the resulting plot looks different than the radius plot in the Vessel Resistance experiment. How would the plot look if you changed the radius of both flow tubes in Pump Mechanics instead of just the right flow tube?

The plot would look exactly like the plot in Vessel Resistance.

Why are valves needed in the Pump Mechanics equipment? *To keep blood moving in one direction*

What happens to blood flow if peripheral resistance equals pump pressure? *Fluid flow would stop*

Theoretically, what would happen to the pumping ability of the heart if the end systolic volume was equal to the end diastolic volume? *It would mean that the heart is not delivering any volume during its contraction.*

8. Match the part in the simulation equipment to the analogous cardiac structure or physiological term listed in the key below.

Simulation equipment:

_e_ 1. valve leading to the right beaker

_b_ 2. valve leading to the pump

_a_ 3. left flow tube

_g_ 4. right flow tube

_h_ 5. pump end volume

_f_ 6. pump starting volume

_d_ 7. pressure in the right beaker

_c_ 8. pressure in the left beaker

_i_ 9. pump pressure

Key:

a. pulmonary veins

b. bicuspid valve

c. ventricular filling pressure

d. peripheral resistance

e. aortic valve

f. end diastolic volume

g. aorta

h. end systolic volume

i. systolic pressure

9. Define the following terms:

blood flow: _The amount of blood moving through a body area or the entire cardiovascular system in a given amount of time_

peripheral resistance: _The opposition to blood flow_

viscosity: _A measure of the "thickness" of the blood_

radius: _One-half of the diameter_

end diastolic volume: _The volume in the ventricles at the end of diastole_

systole: _Contraction of the heart_

diastole: _Relaxation of the heart_

Frog Cardiovascular Physiology: Computer Simulation

Special Electrical Properties of Cardiac Muscle: Automaticity and Rhythmicity

1. Define the following terms:

Automaticity _The ability to depolarize spontaneously in the absence of external stimulation._

Rhythmicity _Depolarization/repolarization events occur in a regular and continuous manner._

2. Explain the anatomical differences between frog and human hearts.

The frog heart has one ventricle and two atria. Dorsally there is an expanded area called the sinus venosus. The human heart has two

atria and two ventricles and no sinus venosus.

Baseline Frog Heart Activity

3. Define the following terms:

Intrinsic heart control _Control from within the heart._

Extrinsic heart control _Control from an external source, the nervous system._

4. Why is it necessary to keep the frog heart moistened with Ringer's solution? _Cellular drying would lead to a change in the_

electrical responsiveness of the cardiac cells. The heart would not contract normally.

Refractory Period of Cardiac Muscle

5. Define *extrasystole* _An extra beat occuring before the time a normal contraction would occur._

6. Refer to the exercise to answer the following questions.

What was the effect of stimulating the heart during ventricular contraction? _No effect._

During ventricular relaxation _May cause an extrasystole._

During the pause interval _No effect._

What does this information indicate about the refractory period of cardiac muscle?

It is much longer than skeletal muscle.

Can cardiac muscle be tetanized? _No_ Why or why not? _Because of the long refractory period._

The Effect of Vagus Nerve Stimulation

7. What was the effect of vagal stimulation on heart rate? *Decreased, then stopped the heart.*

8. What is vagal escape? *Heart rate increased even with continuous vagal stimulation.*

9. Why is the vagal escape valuable in maintaining homeostasis? *If vagal escape did not occur, death would result.*

Physical and Chemical Modifiers of Heart Rate

10. Describe the effect of thermal factors on the frog heart.

Cold *Decreases heart rate.*   Heat *Increases heart rate.*

11. Which of the following factors caused the same, or very similar, heart rate-reducing effects: epinephrine, atropine, pilocarpine, digitalis, potassium ions.

Pilocarpine, digitalis and potassium ions

Which of the factors listed above would reverse or antagonize vagal effects? *Epinephrine and atropine*

12. Did administering any of the following produce any changes in force of contraction (shown by peaks of increasing or decreasing height)? If so, explain the mechanism.

Epinephrine *Increased rate and force of contraction. Acts on the SA and AV nodes and myocardium. Increases membrane permeability*

to sodium and calcium.

Calcium ions *Increases strength of myocardial contraction. Calcium is the "trigger" for the sliding filaments.*

13. Excessive amounts of each of the following ions would most likely interfere with normal heart activity. Explain the type of changes caused in each case.

K^+ *Cardiac arrest, heart block*

Ca^{2+} *Increased spasticity of the heart*

Na^+ *Decreased strength of contraction*

14. Define the following:

Parasympathomimetic *"Mimicking" parasympathetic activity*

Ectopic pacemaker *A site in the myocardium (other than the true pacemaker) acting as a pacemaker.*

15. Explain how digitalis works. *Inhibits the Na^+/K^+ pump and enhances calcium entry into cardiac cells.*

Respiratory System Mechanics: Computer Simulation

Define the following terms:

1. Ventilation: *Another term for breathing*

2. Inspiration: *The act of taking air into the lungs*

3. Expiration: *The act of moving air out of the lungs*

Measuring Respiratory Volumes

4. Write the respiratory volume term and the normal value that is described by the following statements:

   Volume of air present in the lungs after a forceful expiration *residual volume*

   Volume of air that can be expired forcefully after a normal expiration *expiratory reserve volume*

   Volume of air that is breathed in and out during a normal respiration *tidal volume*

   Volume of air that can be inspired forcefully after a normal inspiration *inspiratory reserve volume*

   Volume of air corresponding to TV + IRV + ERV *vital capacity*

5. Fill in the formula for minute respiratory volume:

   tidal volume × breaths per minute

Examining the Effect of Changing Airway Resistance on Respiratory Volumes

6. Even though pulmonary function tests are not diagnostic, they can help determine the difference between

   obstructive and *restrictive* disorders.

7. Chronic bronchitis and asthma are examples of *obstructive* disorders.

8. Describe FEV_1: *The amount of air that can be expelled when the subject takes the deepest possible breath and exhales as completely and rapidly as possible*

9. Explain the difference between FVC and FEV_1: *FEV_1 is a measure of the amount of FVC that is exhaled in 1 second*

10. What effect would increasing airway resistance have on FEV_1? *FEV_1 would be reduced*

Examining the Effect of Surfactant

11. Explain the term *surface tension*. *The molecules of a liquid are attracted more strongly to each other than they are to the air molecu-*

les at any gas-liquid boundary. This unequal attraction produces surface tension at the liquid surface.

12. Surfactant is a detergent-like *lipoprotein* .

13. How does surfactant work? *It decreases the attraction of water molecules to each other.*

14. What might happen to ventilation if the watery film lining the alveoli did not contain surfactant?

The lungs would probably not be able to inflate.

Investigating Intrapleural Pressure

15. Complete the following statements.

The pressure within the pleural cavity, __1__ , is __2__ than the pressure within the alveoli. This __3__ pressure condition is caused by two forces, the tendency of the lung to recoil due to its __4__ properties and the __5__ of the alveolar fluid. These two forces act to pull the lungs away from the thoracic wall, creating a partial __6__ in the pleural cavity. Because the pressure in the __7__ space is lower than __8__ , any opening created in the thoracic wall equalizes the intrapleural pressure with the atmospheric pressure, allowing air to enter the pleural cavity, a condition called __9__ . Pneumothorax allows __10__ , a condition called __11__ .

1. *intrapleural pressure*

2. *less*

3. *negative*

4. *elastic*

5. *surface tension*

6. *vacuum*

7. *intrapleural*

8. *atmospheric pressure*

9. *pneumothorax*

10. *lung collapse*

11. *atelectasis*

16. Why is the intrapleural pressure negative rather than positive? *The elastic properties of lung tends to pull the lungs away*

from the parietal pleura.

17. Would intrapleural pressure be positive or negative when blowing up a balloon? Explain your answer.

It would be positive—because you are exhaling against a resistance (the elasticity of the balloon), positive pressure is required; the tho-

racic wall would be pressuring against the lungs.

Exploring Various Breathing Patterns

18. Match the term listed in column B with the descriptive phrase in column A. (There may be more than one correct answer.)

Column A

*b*___1. causes a drop in carbon dioxide concentration in the blood

*a, c*___2. results in lower blood pH

*a, c*___3. stimulates an increased respiratory rate

*b*___4. results in a lower respiratory rate

*c*___5. can be considered an extreme form of rebreathing

*a, c*___6. causes a rise in blood carbon dioxide

Column B

a. rebreathing

b. hyperventilation

c. breath holding

19. Because carbon dioxide is the main stimulus for respirations, what would happen to respiratory drive if you held your breath? *Respiratory drive increases when carbon dioxide level in the blood rises.*

Chemical and Physical Processes of Digestion: Computer Simulation

Chemical Digestion of Foodstuffs: Enzymatic Action

1. Match the following definitions with the proper choices from the key.

Key: a.   catalyst   b.   control   c.   enzyme   d.   substrate

a, c _____ 1.   increases the rate of a chemical reaction without becoming part of the product

b _____ 2.   provides a standard of comparison for test results

c _____ 3.   biological catalyst: protein in nature

d _____ 4.   substance on which an enzyme works

2. Name three characteristics of enzymes. *(1) protein, (2) biological catalyst, (3) increase the rate of chemical reactions without* _____

becoming part of the product _____

3. Explain the following statement: The enzymes of the digestive system are classified as hydrolases.

Hydrolases are enzymes that break down molecules by adding water to the chemical bond. _____

_____

4. Fill in the chart below with what you have learned about the various digestive system enzymes encountered in this exercise.

Enzyme	Organ producing it	Site of action	Substrate(s)	Optimal pH
Salivary amylase	*salivary glands*	*oral cavity*	*starch*	*neutral*
Pepsin	*gastric gland*	*stomach*	*proteins*	*acid*
Lipase (pancreatic)	*pancreas*	*small intestine*	*fats*	*neutral*

5. Name the end products of digestion for the following types of foods.

Proteins: *amino acids* _____ Carbohydrates: *monosaccharides* _____

Fats: *monoglycerides* _____ and *fatty acids* _____

6. You used several different indicators or tests in the laboratory to determine the presence or absence of certain substances. Choose the correct test or indicator from the key to correspond to the condition described below.

Key: a. IKI b. Benedict's solution c. pH meter d. BAPNA

d 1. used to test for protein hydrolysis, which was indicated by a yellow color

a 2. used to test for the presence of starch, which was indicated by a blue-black color

c 3. used to test for the presence of fatty acids

b 4. used to test for the presence of maltose, which was indicated by a blue to green (or to rust) color change

7. The three-dimensional structure of a functional protein is altered by intense heat or nonphysiological pH even though peptide bonds may not break. Such a change in protein structure is called denaturation, and denatured enzymes are not functional. Explain why.

   Denaturation can change the way a protein folds, which may directly impact the active site on the enzyme which catalyzes its enzyme-specific reaction.

8. What experimental conditions in the simulation resulted in denatured enzymes? *Boiling clearly denatured the enzymes as evidenced by a lack of hydrolysis.*

9. Complete the mechanism of absorption section in the chart below for each of the substances listed. Use a check mark to indicate whether the absorption would result in the movement of a substance into the blood capillaries or the lymph capillaries (lacteals).

Substance	Mechanism of absorption	Blood	Lymph
Monosaccharides	*active transport*	✓	
Fatty acids and glycerol	*passive transport*		✓
Amino acids	*active transport*	✓	

10. Imagine that you have been chewing a piece of bread for 5 to 6 minutes. How would you expect its taste to change during this time? *The bread should become sweet as the starch is digested to maltose.*

11. People on a strict diet to lose weight begin to metabolize stored fats at an accelerated rate. How could this condition affect blood pH? *Increasing amounts of fatty acids will decrease the pH of a fluid.*

Starch Digestion by Salivary Amylase

12. What conclusions can you draw when an experimental sample gives both a positive starch test and a positive maltose test?

Enzymatic hydrolysis was not complete. Only part of the starch was digested to maltose.

13. Why was 37°C the optimal incubation temperature? *It is safe to assume that enzymes "designed" for the body will operate at*

body temperature.

14. Why did very little, if any, starch digestion occur in tube 1? *The enzyme was denatured by boiling.*

15. Why did very little starch digestion occur in tubes 6 and 7? *pH 2.0 and pH 9.0 are outside the normal pH of amylase.*

16. Imagine that you have told a group of your peers that amylase is capable of digesting starch to maltose. If you had not run the experiment in control tubes 3, 4, and 5, what objections to your statement could be raised?

The objections could be regarding the purity of the substances used in the experiment. For example, "How do you know the starch was

not contaminated with maltose?" or "How do you know the amylase solution was not contaminated with maltose?"

Assessing Cellulose Digestion

17. What is the effect of freezing on enzyme activity?

Freezing has no effect on enzyme activity.

18. What can you conclude about the ability of salivary amylase to digest cellulose?

Salivary amylase does not digest cellulose.

19. What can you conclude about the ability of bacteria to digest cellulose?

Bacteria is capable of digesting cellulose.

Protein Digestion by Pepsin

20. Why is an indicator reagent such as IKI or Benedict's solution not necessary when using a substrate like BAPNA?

The yellow indicator is designed as part of the synethetic substrate, BAPNA.

21. Trypsin is a pancreatic hydrolase present in the small intestine during digestion. Would trypsin work well in the stomach? Explain your answer.

The pH optimum of trypsin is approximately neutral. The pH in the stomach is very acid.

22. How does the optical density of a solution containing BAPNA relate to enzyme activity?

Increasing color in a solution means that the dye has been clipped off the BAPNA, which results in a higher optical density.

23. What happens to pepsin activity as it reaches the small intestine? *Pepsin activity decreases because of the neutral pH.*

Fat Digestion by Pancreatic Lipase and the Action of Bile

24. Why does the pH of a fatty solution decrease as enzymatic hydrolysis increases? _Triglycerides are at a neutral pH. Lipase_

    hydrolyzes triglyceride to monoglyceride and fatty acids, which decrease the pH of a solution.

25. How does bile affect fat digestion? _Bile emulsifies fat (increases surface area) to increase the efficiency of hydrolysis._

26. Why is it not possible to determine the activity of lipase in the pH 2.0 buffer using the pH meter assay method?

    Since the pH is already very acidic, the addition of the fatty acids does not appreciably alter the pH of the solution.

27. Why is bile not considered an enzyme? _Bile is not a catalyst. It merely is a way to transport fat in a watery solution._

Physical Processes: Mechanisms of Food Propulsion and Mixing

28. Complete the following statements. Write your answers in the numbered spaces below.

    Swallowing, or __1__, occurs in two phases—the __2__ and __3__. One of these phases, the __4__ phase, is voluntary. During the voluntary phase, the __5__ is used to push the food into the back of the throat. During swallowing, the __6__ rises to ensure that its passageway is covered by the epiglottis so that the ingested substances do not enter the respiratory passageways. It is possible to swallow water while standing on your head because the water is carried along the esophagus involuntarily by the process of __7__. The pressure exerted by the foodstuffs on the __8__ sphincter causes it to open, allowing the food to enter the stomach.

    The two major types of propulsive movements that occur in the small intestine are __9__ and __10__. One of these movements, __11__, acts to continually mix the foods and to increase the absorption rate by moving different parts of the chyme mass over the intestinal mucosa, but it has less of a role in moving foods along the digestive tract.

1. _food_

2. _buccal_

3. _pharyngeal-esophageal_

4. _buccal_

5. _tongue_

6. _larynx_

7. _peristalsis_

8. _gastroesophageal_

9. _segmentation_

10. _peristalsis_

11. _segmentation_

Renal Physiology—The Function of the Nephron: Computer Simulation

Define the following terms:

1. Glomerulus _is a tangled capillary knot that filters fluid from the blood into the lumen of the renal tubule_

2. Renal tubule _a filtrate-processing tubule_

3. Glomerular capsule _an enlarged structure at the beginning of the renal tubule_

4. Renal corpuscle _the glomerulus plus the glomerular capsule_

5. Afferent arteriole _arteriole supplying the glomerulus_

6. Efferent arteriole _arteriole draining the glomerulus_

Investigating the Effect of Flow Tube Radius on Glomerular Filtration

7. In terms of the blood supply to and from the glomerulus, explain why the glomerular capillary bed is unusual.

   Normally, a venule drains a capillary bed. In the kidney, an efferent arteriole drains the glomerular capillary bed.

   _____

8. How would pressure in the glomerulus be affected by constricting the afferent arteriole? Explain your answer.

   By restricting the outflow of the glomerulus, pressure in the glomerulus is increased.

   _____

9. How would pressure in the glomerulus be affected by constricting the efferent arteriole? Explain your answer.

   Constricting the afferent arteriole will reduce the amount of blood flowing into the glomerulus thereby reducing glomerular pressure.

   _____

Assessing Combined Effects on Glomerular Filtration

10. If systemic blood pressure started to rise, what could the arterioles of the glomerulus do to keep glomerular filtration rate

    constant? _the afferent arterioles could constrict_

    _____

11. One of the experiments you performed in the simulation was to close the valve at the end of the collecting duct. Is closing that valve more like constricting an afferent arteriole or more like a kidney stone? Explain your answer.

    It is like having a kidney stone—glomerular filtration rate is zero when a stone is present (or when the valve was closed),

    Constricting the arteriole would reduce but not eliminate glomerular filtration.

12. Constricting the efferent arteriole would have the same effect on glomerular filtration as (constricting/dilating) the afferent arteriole.

It is the same as dilating the afferent arteriole.

Exploring the Role of the Solute Gradient on Maximum Urine Concentration Achievable

13. Complete the following statements.

In the process of urine formation, solutes and water move from the __1__ of the nephron into the __2__ spaces. The passive movement of solutes and water from the lumen of the renal tubule into the interstitial spaces relies in part on the __3__ surrounding the nephron. When the nephron is permeable to solutes or water, and __4__ will be reached between the interstitial fluid and the contents of the nephron. __5__ is a hormone that increases the water permeability of the __6__ and the collecting duct, allowing water to flow to areas of higher solute concentration, usually from the lumen of the nephron into the surrounding interstitial area. __7__ is hormone that causes __8__ reabsorption at the expense of __9__ loss into the lumen of the tubule.

1. *lumen*

2. *interstitial*

3. *total solute gradient*

4. *equilibrium*

5. *ADH*

6. *DCT*

7. *aldosterone*

8. *sodium*

9. *potassium*

14. Would the passive movement of substances occur if the interstitial solute concentration was the same as the filtrate solute concentration? Explain your answer.

There would be no net movement of substances because passive movements depend on a gradient.

Studying the Effect of Glucose Carrier Proteins on Glucose Reabsorption

15. In terms of the function of the nephron, explain why one might find glucose in the urine exiting the collecting duct.

If there was more glucose than could be transported by the number of available glucose carrier proteins, the remaining glucose will stay

in the tubule lumen.

16. Imagine this scenario: a person has the normal number of glucose carriers in the nephrons yet has glucose in the urine. What could be the cause of this condition? (Hint: think about filtration rate.)

If the glomerular filtration rate is too high then there might not be enough time to reabsorb the glucose in the renal tubule.

Testing the Effect of Hormones on Urine Formation

17. Complete the following statements.

The concentration of the __1__ excreted by our kidneys changes depending on our immediate needs. For example, if a person consumes a large quantity of water, the excess water will be eliminated, producing __2__ urine. On the other hand, under conditions of dehydration, there is a clear benefit to being able to produce urine as __3__ as possible, thereby retaining precious water. Although the medullary gradient makes it possible to excrete concentrated urine, urine dilution or concentration is ultimately under __4__ control. In this experiment, you will investigate the effects of two different hormones on renal function, aldosterone produced by the __5__ and ADH manufactured by the __6__ and stored in the __7__. Aldosterone works to reabsorb __8__ (and thereby water) at the expense of losing __9__. Its site of action is the __10__. ADH makes the distal tubule and collecting duct more permeable to __11__, thereby allowing the body to reabsorb more water from the filtrate when it is present.

1. _urine_
2. _dilute_
3. _concentrated_
4. _hormonal_
5. _adrenal gland_
6. _hypothalamus_
7. _pituitary_
8. _sodium_
9. _potassium_
10. _distal convoluted tubule_
11. _water_

18. Match the term listed in column B with the descriptive phrase in column A. (There may be more than one correct answer.)

Column A

_c_ 1. causes production of dilute urine

_d_ 2. results in increased sodium loss

_d_ 3. causes the body to retain more potassium

_b_ 4. will cause water retention due to sodium movement

_a, b_ 5. causes water reabsorption due to increased membrane permeability

_b_ 6. increases sodium reabsorption

Column B

a. increased ADH

b. increased aldosterone

c. decreased ADH

d. decreased aldosterone

Acid-Base Balance

1. Match each of the terms in column A with the appropriate description in column B.

Column A		Column B	
_f_	1. pH	a.	condition in which the human body's pH levels fall below 7.35
_e_	2. acid	b.	condition in which the human body's pH levels rise above 7.45
_d_	3. base	c.	mixes with water in the blood to form carbonic acid
_a_	4. acidosis	d.	substance that binds to H^+ in solution
_b_	5. alkalosis	e.	substance that releases H^+ in solution
_c_	6. carbon dioxide	f.	term used to denote hydrogen ion concentration in body fluids

2. What is the normal range of pH levels of blood and tissue fluids in the human body?

7.35 to 7.45

3. What is the difference between a *strong acid* and a *weak acid*?

A strong acid dissociates completely in solution, releasing all of its hydrogen ions. A weak acid dissociates incompletely and does not release all of its hydrogen ions.

4. What is the difference between a *strong base* and a *weak base*?

A strong base has a tendency to bind to H^+; a weak base binds less of the H^+.

5. What is the difference between respiratory acidosis/alkalosis and metabolic acidosis/alkalosis?

Respiratory acidosis/alkalosis result from the respiratory system accumulating too much or too little CO_2 in the blood. Metabolic

acidosis/alkalosis refer to all other conditions of acidosis or alkalosis.

6. What are the body's two major physiological buffer systems for compensating for acid-base imbalances?

The renal system and the respiratory system

Respiratory Acidosis and Alkalosis

7. What are some of the causes of respiratory acidosis?

Airway obstruction, depression of the respiratory center in the brain stem, lung disease, drug overdose, or any result in impaired respiration or "hypoventilation"

8. What are some of the causes of respiratory alkalosis?

Travelling to a high altitude, hyperventilation (which may be brought on by high fever or anxiety

9. What happens to blood pH levels during hyperventilation? Why?

They rise because more CO_2 is being expelled from the blood, resulting in less H^+ generation and thus higher pH levels.

10. What happens to blood pH levels during rebreathing? Why?

They fall because more CO_2 is being retained in the blood, resulting in more H^+ generation and thus lower pH levels.

11. Circle the correct bolfaced terms:

As respiration increases, P_{CO_2} levels **increase** / **decrease** and pH levels **rise** / **fall.**

As respiration decreases, P_{CO_2} levels **increase** / **decrease** and pH levels **rise** / **fall.**

Renal Compensation

12. How does the renal system compensate for conditions of respiratory acidosis?

By excreting more H^+ in urine and retaining more HCO_3^-

13. How does the renal system compensate for conditions of respiratory alkalosis?

By retaining more H^+ and excreting more HCO_3^- in urine

Metabolic Acidosis and Alkalosis

14. What are some of the causes of metabolic acidosis?

Diabetes mellitus (which can result in ketoacidosis), salicyate poisoning, too much alcohol, diarrhea, strenuous exercise

15. What are some of the causes of metabolic alkalosis?

Alkali ingestion, vomiting, constipation

16. Explain how the respiratory system compensates for metabolic acidosis and alkalosis.

The respiratory system compensates for metabolic acidosis by expelling CO_2 at a faster rate (breathing rate increases). The respiratory system compensates for metabolic alkalosis by expelling CO_2 at a slower rate (breathing rate decreases). By regulating CO_2, the respiratory system regulates the amount of H^+ in blood and helps maintain a normal pH level.

17. Explain how the renal system compensates for metabolic acidosis and alkalosis.

The renal system compensates for metabolic acidosis by expelling more H^+ in urine and retaining more bicarbonate. The renal system compensates for metabolic alkalosis by expelling more bicarbonate in the urine and retaining more H^+.

18. Circle the correct bolfaced terms:

As metabolic rate increases, respiration **increases** / **decreases,** P_{CO_2} levels **increase** / **decrease,** and pH levels **rise** / **fall.**

As metabolic rate decreases, respiration **increases** / **decreases,** P_{CO_2} levels **increase** / **decrease** and pH levels **rise** / **fall.**

Histology Review Supplement

Answers to Questions

Skeletal Muscle Tissue Review (p. P-157)

What is the functional unit of contraction in skeletal muscle?

Sarcomere

What are the two principal contractile proteins that compose the functional unit of contraction?

Actin and myosin

What is the specific relationship of the functional unit of contraction to the striated appearance of a skeletal muscle fiber?

The sarcomere is comprised of an overlapping arrangement of myofilaments, primarily actin and myosin. The repeating pattern of sarcomeres lying end to end along the length of the cell creates the striped appearance seen in longitudinal section.

Would you characterize skeletal muscle as voluntary or involuntary?

Voluntary

Name the site of close juxtaposition of an axon terminal with the muscle cell plasmalemma.

Neuromuscular junction (myoneural junction)

What is the name of the loose areolar connective tissue covering of an individual muscle fiber?

Endomysium

The perimysium is a collagenous connective tissue layer that groups several muscle fibers together into bundles called:

Fascicles

Which connective tissue layer surrounds the entire muscle and merges with connective tissue of tendons and aponeuroses?

Epimysium

Nervous Tissue Review (p. P-159)

What is the primary unit of function in nervous tissue?

Nerve cell or neuron

Name the pale-staining region of the cell body from which the axon arises.

Axon hillock

What is the general name for all support cells within the CNS?

Neuroglia or glia

Name the specific myelinating cell of the CNS.

Oligodendroglia or oligodendrocyte

What is the relationship of the endoneurium to the myelin sheath?

The endoneurium is a very delicate connective tissue layer that lies outside of the myelin sheath.

Endocrine Tissue Review (p. P-161)

Thyroid Gland

Why is the thyroid gland considered to be an endocrine organ?

Thyroid gland follicular cells secrete T_3 and T_4 directly into the blood vasculature.

What hormone secreted by the pituitary gland controls the synthesis and secretion of T_3 and T_4 (thyroxine)?

Thyroid stimulating hormone (TSH)

What is the function of calcitonin?

Calcitonin decreases plasma calcium concentrations.

Ovary

Which cells of the ovarian follicle secrete estrogen?

Granulosa cells

Uterus

Which layer of the endometrium is shed during the menstrual phase of the menstrual cycle?

Functional layer (stratum functionalis)

What is the function of the deep basal layer (stratum basalis) of the endometrium?

It is the reserve layer from which new endometrial tissue and glands are regenerated.

What comprises a serosa?

A serosa is a simple squamous epithelium (mesothelium) and a small amount of subjacent loose connective tissue.

How does the serosa of the uterus, where present, differ from visceral peritoneum?

It is the same as visceral peritoneum.

Pancreas

Do the islets of Langerhans cells secrete their hormones into the same duct system used by the exocrine secretory cells?

No. Islets of Langerhans cells secrete their hormones directly into the blood vasculature.

Cardiovascular Tissue Review (p. P-163)

Heart

Which component of the intercalated disk is a strong intercellular junction that functions to keep cells from being pulled apart during contraction?

Desmosome (macula adherens)

What is a functional syncytium?

A true syncytium is a large multinucleated cell formed by the fusion of many cells. A functional syncytium is a number of individual cells that function together as if they were a single cell.

Which component of the intercalated disk is a junction that provides the intercellular communication required for the myocardium to perform as a functional syncytium?

Gap junction

Blood Vessels

The tunica media of the aorta would have a much greater proportion of what type of tissue than a small artery?

Elastic tissue

In general, which vessel would have a larger lumen, an artery or its corresponding vein?

Vein

Why would the tunica media and tunica adventitia not be present in a capillary?

The thickness of a tunica media and tunica adventitia would be too great to permit exchange to take place.

Respiratory Tissue Review (p. P-165)

What are the primary functions of the respiratory epithelium?

Respiratory epithelium functions to add humidity to inspired air, provide mucus to entrap bacteria and particulate matter, and provide synchronized ciliary movements to move the mucus toward the pharynx where it can be swallowed.

Why doesn't gas exchange occur in bronchi?

The walls of bronchi are composed of layers of connective tissue, smooth muscle, and cartilage that make them too thick to permit gas exchange to occur.

What is the primary functional unit of the lung?

Alveolus

The alveolar wall is very delicate and subject to collapse. Why is there no smooth muscle present in its wall for support?

Efficient gas exchange could not occur through a layer of smooth muscle.

What are the three basic components of the air-blood barrier?

The three components of the air-blood barrier are the simple squamous epithelial cell of the alveolus, the simple squamous endothelial cell of the capillary, and their thin, fused basal laminae between them.

Digestive Tissue Review (p. P-167)

Salivary Gland

Are salivary glands endocrine or exocrine glands?

Exocrine glands

Which salivary secretions, mucus or serous, is more thin and watery in consistency?

Serous secretion

Esophagus

Briefly explain the difference between an adventitia and a serosa.

An adventitia is a connective tissue layer that blends with surrounding connective tissue. A serosa is a simple squamous epithelium (mesothelium) subtended by a small amount of loose connective tissue that covers an organ on the side that projects into a body cavity.

Stomach

What is the function of the mucus secreted by surface mucous cells?

To protect the surface epithelium from the highly acid environment in the stomach lumen

Small Intestine

Why is it important for the duodenum to add large quantities of mucus (from Brunner's glands) to the partially digested food entering it from the stomach?

To protect the lining of the duodenum from the high pH of the food passing into it from the stomach

Colon

Why is it important to have an abundance of mucous goblet cells in the colon?

To lubricate the lining of the colon so that the dehydrated bolus can be passed out of the body

Liver

What general type of cell is the phagocytic Kupffer cell?

Macrophage

Blood in the portal vein flows directly from what organs?

Abdominal viscera

What is the function of bile in the digestive process?

Emulsification of fats

Renal Tissue Review (p. P-169)

In which segment of the renal tubule does roughly 75–80% of reabsorption occur?

Proximal convoluted tubule

How are proximal convoluted tubule (PCT) cells similar to enterocytes of the small intestine?

They both are equipped with microvilli to increase their surface area for absorption.

What are the three layers through which the filtrate must pass starting from inside the glomerular capillary through to the urinary space?

Glomerular capillary endothelium, basal laminae of endothelium and podocyte, and filtration slits between podocyte foot processes

Under normal circumstances in a healthy individual, would red blood cells or any other cells be present in the renal filtrate?

No

In addition to providing nutrients to the kidney tubules, what is one other function of the capillaries in the peritubular capillary bed?

Conduct water and electrolytes that have been reabsorbed back into the general circulation

Intelitool® Computerized Exercises

This appendix contains four lab exercises that use Intelitool® equipment and students as subjects. These exercises can be used in place of the lab manual's traditional exercises on the same topics. For example, reflex physiology is presented as both a traditional lab exercise (Exercise 22) and an Intelitool® exercise (Exercise 22i in this appendix). While each Intelitool exercise is numbered to correspond with the traditional exercise on the same topic, the Intelitool® exercise numbers all end in *i*. The following table lists the four lab topics that appear as both traditional and Intelitool® exercises.

For Intelitool® Exercises 16i, 22i, 31i, and 37i, use the review sheets that correspond with traditional lab Exercises 16A, 22, 31, and 37.

The Intelitool® exercises are written for Windows® computers. Please consult the Intelitool® documentation for specific procedures if you are using the Macintosh® version of Intelitool®. The students should be familiar with the use of the computer and with Intelitool software before beginning the exercises. For Intellitool® (Phipps & Bird) technical support, call (800) 955-7621.

Exercise topic	Traditional lab exercise	Intelitool® lab exercise
Muscle Physiology	Ex. 16A, p. 167	Ex. 16i, p. 450
Human Reflex Physiology	Ex. 22, p. 247	Ex. 22i, p. 454
Conduction System of the Heart and Electrocardiography	Ex. 31, p. 332	Ex. 31i, p. 463
Respiratory System Physiology	Ex. 37, p. 399	Ex. 37i, p. 469

Muscle Physiology

OBJECTIVES

1. To define:

agonist	*antagonist*
muscle tension	*load*
muscle tone	*isotonic contraction*
isometric contraction	*electromyogram*

2. To distinguish between muscle tone and muscle contractions that cause movement.

3. To demonstrate the difference between isometric and isotonic muscle contraction.

4. To realize that the electrical activity of internal organs can be measured at the surface of the body.

5. To recognize that whole muscle contraction is a result of electrical activity of many muscle cells.

6. To realize the difference between intracellular electrical recordings and those using surface electrodes.

7. To demonstrate that variations in recorded electrical activity are a result of changing muscle activity.

8. To understand the relationship between agonists and antagonists.

9. To explain results obtained in terms of muscle structure.

MATERIALS

5-lb exercise weights (a large book provides a good substitute)

Cot (if available)

Tape measures

Hand dynamometer

Alcohol swabs

Windows computer with Cardiocomp7™ software installed

McADDAM II™ interface with power module and serial port cable

Cardiocomp™ junction box

Cardiocomp™ manual

Cardiocomp™ electrode cables

Four flat plate electrodes and attachment straps or disposable electrodes

---

MUSCLE ACTIVITY

Because muscles are capable only of shortening in length (they always pull and never push), muscle shortening (contraction) is required to move a body part. A muscle that causes a desired movement is called a **prime mover** or **agonist.** For example, the biceps brachii is a muscle that flexes (bends) the forearm, and is called the agonist of forearm flexion. Muscles that oppose or reverse the action of the agonist are called **antagonists.** Because the triceps brachii causes extension (straightening) of the forearm, it is the antagonist in forearm flexion. On the other hand, when the desired action is forearm **extension,** the triceps is the agonist and the biceps is the antagonist.

Muscle Tone

Although skeletal muscles are called voluntary muscles, many of their responses are controlled reflexively. For example, even relaxed muscles are in a slight state of contraction called *muscle tone* (a state of slight but sustained contraction), due to spinal reflexes which activate different groups of muscle cells in sequence. Muscle tone helps keep muscle cells healthy and ready to respond quickly. Skeletal muscle tone also helps maintain body posture; indeed, we would collapse without the continuous, even if slight, muscle contractions.

Activity 1: Examining Muscle Tone

1. Obtain a 5-lb exercise weight from the supply area.

2. As you perform the activities listed below, your partner is to record the activity of your right biceps brachii and triceps brachii by placing a check mark in the appropriate column of Chart 1 when the muscle contracts (hardens or bulges).

- Stand comfortably with arms relaxed at the sides.
- Stand comfortably while holding the weight at the right side of the body.
- Sit comfortably with forearm relaxed on the lab bench, and in a supinated position (palm facing up).
- Sit comfortably with forearm relaxed on the lab bench, and in a pronated position (palm facing down).
- Sit comfortably while lifting and holding the weight a few inches above the lab bench.

CHART 1

Activity	Muscle(s) contracted	
	Biceps brachii	Triceps brachii
Standing, arms at sides		
Standing, holding weight at side		
Sitting, forearm supinated		
Sitting, forearm pronated		
Sitting, lifting the weight		

Which activity produced the greatest contraction (evidenced by hardness of the muscle)? _____

3. Again working with your lab partner, carry out a similar evaluation on each gastrocnemius (calf) muscle under the following conditions and record results in Chart 2.

*   Standing comfortably, but with legs relaxed
*   Standing on your toes, reaching overhead toward the ceiling
*   Standing erect with knees locked
*   Sitting comfortably on the edge of the lab bench, with legs relaxed and not touching the floor
*   Sitting comfortably on a chair with both feet on the floor
*   Lying prone (face down) on a cot if available, or on the bench top

CHART 2

Activity	Gastrocnemius contracted	
	Right leg	Left leg
Standing, with legs relaxed		
Standing, reaching toward the ceiling		
Standing, knees locked		
Sitting on lab bench		
Sitting on chair, feet touching floor		
Lying prone		

During which activities was muscle tone exhibited?

_____

_____ ■

Isometric and Isotonic Contractions

The force exerted by the muscle during contraction is referred to as *muscle tension,* and the weight (resistance to movement) exerted by the object being moved is called the *load.* However, muscles do not always shorten during contraction even though they are producing force. For example, when an object is too heavy to lift, the muscle exerts maximum force, but nothing moves. The condition in which a muscle develops tension but does not shorten is called *isometric* (*iso* = same; *metric* = measure) contraction. More typically, we are able to move most of the objects we attempt to lift, a form of muscle shortening called *isotonic* (*tonic* = tension) contraction.

Activity 2: Studying Isometric and Isotonic Contractions

1. Obtain two tape measures from the supply area and use the same weight from the previous exercise on muscle tone.

2. Measure the circumference of the subject's arm around the largest part of the muscle bulge while he or she carries out each of the following muscle activities. Record the results in Chart 3.

*   Extend both arms directly in front of the body.
*   With forearms supinated, flex both forearms five times and then remeasure.
*   Extend the right arm while holding the weight.
*   Extend the left arm while holding the weight.
*   Flex and then extend the right forearm five times while holding the weight and then remeasure.
*   Flex and then extend the left forearm five times while holding the weight and then remeasure.

CHART 3

Activity	Measurements (cm)	
	Right arm	Left arm
Upper limbs extended		
Forearms flexed, supinated		
Right arm extended, holding weight		
Left arm extended, holding weight		
Right arm flexed, holding weight		
Left arm flexed, holding weight		

If there was any difference in the measurements between right and left arms, explain why. _____

_____

_____

3. Evaluate gastrocnemius muscle activity under the following conditions and record results in Chart 4:

- Stand erect, comfortably relaxed.
- Stand on your toes, reaching toward the ceiling.
- Stand on your toes with arms at your sides.
- Sit on the lab bench with legs dangling and relaxed.
- While you sit on the lab bench, your lab partner holds your legs in place while you try to move your feet forward and upward.
- Lie prone on a cot or lab bench with the gastrocnemius relaxed.
- Still lying prone, contract the gastrocnemius.

CHART 4

| Activity | Measurements (cm) | |
	Right leg	Left leg
Standing erect		
Standing on toes, reaching toward ceiling		
Standing on toes, arms at sides		
Sitting with legs relaxed		
Sitting, legs restrained		
Lying prone, gastrocnemius relaxed		
Lying prone, gastrocnemius contracted		

If there was any difference in the measurements between right and left gastrocnemius, explain why. _____

_____

_____ ■

The Electromyogram

An electromyogram (EMG) is the graphing of the gross electrical signal created by the action potentials of many muscle fibers as a muscle is contracting. These action potentials are due to transmembrane electrical potential excursions very similar to the transmembrane excursions of cardiac muscle cells as described in section 2.1 of the Cardiocomp™ Electrocardiography Primer. The main difference being that, unlike cardiac muscle cells, skeletal muscle fibers are stable and require a direct stimulus for an action potential to occur. In the preceding sections electrocardiography is discussed. The electrocardiogram is actually an electromyogram of a specific muscle, the heart. Because the heart is a syncytium, and because of the sweeping, spreading nature of the cardiac muscle cells' action potential, the cardiac electromyogram has very distinct features. An electromyogram of skeletal muscles is very different because the activity of skeletal muscles involves the rapid switching of independent motor units under neurological control.

Skeletal muscles are made up of functional units called motor units. Each motor unit consists of a nerve which supplies one or more muscle fibers. When a motor unit is active, its muscular component will contract. In a given muscle there are many motor units and these units vary in their level of irritability. That is, some will respond to a weak stimulus, while others may require a much stronger stimulus. Often the smaller units are less irritable than the larger units, therefore we often have better control when the task requires only slight strength, and we have poorer control when greater strength is needed. The overall strength of a contraction of a muscle is the summation of the pull of the motor units operating at any one time.

Because of the rapid motor unit switching in a skeletal muscle, the electrical signal that is observed at the surface of the body usually looks like rapidly fluctuating random noise. The magnitude of the noise tells us something about the number and size of motor units that are in use at any one time. If the muscle is inactive, no signal will be observed from that muscle.

Muscles cannot push, they can only contract (pull). For this reason muscles are usually arranged in antagonistic systems. One of the easiest to understand of these antagonistic systems is the system involving the biceps brachii, which causes flexion (bending) of the arm, and the triceps brachii which causes extension (straightening) of the arm. This antagonist system involves a reflex arc, which is found in nearly all antagonistic muscle systems, where the contracting muscle's antagonist is inhibited from contracting. Because of this reflex arc, when the biceps brachii is contracting, the triceps brachii is inhibited, and when the triceps brachii is contracting, the biceps brachii is inhibited.

Activity 3: Investigating Electromyography

Work in groups of 2 to 4 students. Group members should strive to gain computer operating experience. Each group is expected to explain all operations to the experimental subject.

PROCEDURE

1. Set up the Cardiocomp™ junction box, cables and McADDAM II™ as described in the User Manual.

2. Start the Cardiocomp7™ program.

3. Select **New** from the **File** menu, make sure the setup is correct then click **OK** on the setup window.

4. Uncheck all the LEADs except for LEAD II.

5. Check (click on) the **Continuous** checkbox. To apply electrodes, firmly scrub the electrode sites with alcohol. For disposable electrodes, the female connector should be snapped firmly onto the male connector. For flat plate electrodes, apply a liberal amount of electrode gel between each electrode and the skin. Strap the electrode to the appendage and be sure the strap is snug but not too tight. The female snap connector should be snapped firmly onto the bolt of the flat plate electrode.

6. Apply two electrodes to the anterior surface of one of the upper arms, one over the distal end of the biceps brachii and one over the proximal end of the biceps brachii. Connect one of these electrodes to the electrode cable coming from the negative jack (RA for LEAD II) and connect the other electrode to the positive electrode (LA for LEAD II).

7. Apply an electrode anywhere on the wrist of the same arm as the biceps brachii on which you have placed the other two electrodes. Connect this electrode to the electrode jack which is labeled RA.

8. Have the subject sit at a table, so that the forearm is resting comfortably on the table top with the palm up, and the elbow bent at 90°. During the following procedure be very careful not to jiggle or move the wires. Try to drape the wires so that they will be stable and out of the way.

9. Record an EMG while the muscle is at rest. This is **spontaneous activity.** Click on the **New Note** button and label "muscle at rest." Describe the EMG of a resting muscle.

———————————————

———————————————

10. Place objects of varying weight in the hand of the subject, having the subject lift these objects slightly off the table. Notice the changes in electrical activity with the changes in work being done by the subject's biceps brachii. Have the subject try to lift an impossibly heavy object, like another person. Notice the degree of electrical activity due to this maximal workload.

Click on **New Note** button to label each event. How does the electrical activity recorded change with each increase in weight.

———————————————

———————————————

Explain in terms of motor units.

———————————————

———————————————

11. Have the subject push down hard on the table top with the back of the hand. Notice the relatively diminished amount of electrical activity in the biceps brachii. Make a note and describe what you observe.

———————————————

———————————————

12. Rotate the two electrodes 180° to the posterior surface of the upper arm so that one is over the distal end of the triceps brachii and one is over the proximal end of the triceps brachii.

13. Have the subject push down hard on the table with the back of their hand. Notice this time that the signal is much stronger than when the subject was pushing down on the table top and the biceps brachii were being monitored. How does this electrical activity compare with that seen during the biceps activity previously recorded?

———————————————

———————————————

14. If you did not understand what you saw, or if you can think of some other experiments you would like to try, you can now easily switch the wires from biceps brachii to triceps brachii. In particular observe the differences in each muscle's signal as the arm is both extended and flexed. You might like to try experiments with other muscles. You can also demonstrate muscle fatigue by asking the subject to repeatedly lift a heavy object until he or she is really fatigued. Use **New Note** to label data. Describe your observations.

———————————————

———————————————

15. "Lock" the file (under the **Analysis** menu) and save to an appropriate file.

Human Reflex Physiology

THE REFLEX ARC

Reflexes are rapid, predictable, involuntary motor responses to stimuli; they are mediated over neural pathways called **reflex arcs.** All reflex arcs have five essential parts (Figure 22i.1a):

1. The *receptor,* which reacts to a stimulus
2. The *sensory neuron,* which conducts the afferent impulses to the CNS
3. The *integration center,* consisting of one or more synapses in the CNS
4. The *motor neuron,* which conducts the efferent impulses from the integration center to the effector
5. The *effector,* the muscle fibers or glands that respond to the efferent impulses by contracting or secreting a product, respectively

The simple patellar or knee-jerk reflex shown in Figure 22i.1b is an example of a simple, two-neuron, *monosynaptic* (literally, "one synapse") reflex arc. It will be demonstrated in the laboratory. However, most reflexes are more complex and *polysynaptic,* involving the participation of one or more association neurons in the reflex arc pathway. A three-neuron reflex arc (flexor reflex) is diagrammed in Figure 22i.1c. Since delay or

inhibition of the reflex may occur at the synapses, the more synapses encountered in a reflex pathway, the more time is required to effect the reflex.

Reflexes of many types may be considered programmed into the neural anatomy. For example, many *spinal reflexes* (reflexes that are initiated and completed at the spinal cord level, such as the flexor reflex) occur without the involvement of higher brain centers. These reflexes work equally well in decerebrate animals (those in which the brain has been destroyed), as long as the spinal cord is functional. Conversely, other reflexes require the involvement of functional brain tissue, since many different types of inputs must be evaluated before the appropriate reflex is determined. Superficial cord reflexes and pupillary responses to light are in this category. In addition, although many spinal cord reflexes do not require the involvement of higher centers, the brain is "advised" of spinal cord reflex activity and may alter it by facilitating or inhibiting the reflexes.

H Reflex testing is an important diagnostic tool for assessing the condition of the nervous system. Distorted, exaggerated, or absent responses may indicate degeneration or pathology of portions of the nervous system, often before other signs are apparent. ●

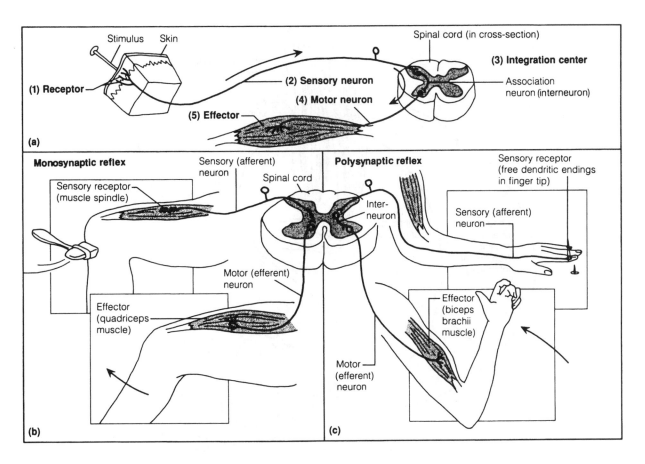

F22i.1

Simple reflex arcs. **(a)** Components of all human reflex arcs: receptor, sensory neuron, integration center (one or more synapses in the CNS), motor neuron, and effector. **(b)** Monosynaptic reflex arc. **(c)** Polysynaptic reflex arc. The integration center is in the spinal cord, and in each example the receptor and effector are in the same limb.

If the spinal cord is damaged, the easily performed reflex tests can help pinpoint the area (level) of spinal cord injury. Motor nerves above the injured area may be unaffected, whereas those at or below the lesion site may be unable to participate in normal reflex activity. ■

Reflexes can be categorized into one of two large groups: somatic reflexes and autonomic reflexes. **Autonomic** (or visceral) **reflexes** are mediated through the autonomic nervous system and are not subject to conscious control. These reflexes activate smooth muscles, cardiac muscle, and the glands of the body, and they regulate body functions such as digestion, elimination, blood pressure, salivation, and sweating. **Somatic reflexes** include all those reflexes that involve stimulation of skeletal muscles by the somatic division of the nervous system. An example of such a reflex is the rapid withdrawal of the hand from a hot object.

SOMATIC REFLEXES

There are several types of somatic reflexes, including several that you will be eliciting during this laboratory session—the stretch, crossed extensor, superficial cord,

corneal, and gag reflexes. Some require only spinal cord activity; others require brain involvement as well.

Spinal Reflexes

STRETCH REFLEXES **Stretch reflexes** are important postural reflexes, normally acting to maintain posture, balance, and locomotion. Stretch reflexes are initiated by tapping a tendon, which stretches the muscle the tendon is attached to. This stimulates the muscle spindles and causes reflex contraction of the stretched muscle or muscles, which resists further stretching. Even as the primary stretch reflex is occurring, impulses are being sent to other destinations as well. For example, branches of the afferent fibers (from the muscle spindles) also synapse with interneurons (association neurons) controlling the antagonistic muscles (Figure 22i.2). The inhibition of the antagonistic muscles that follows, called *reciprocal inhibition,* causes them to relax and prevents them from resisting (or reversing) the contraction of the stretched muscle caused by the main reflex arc. Additionally, impulses are relayed to higher brain centers (largely via the dorsal white columns) to advise of muscle length, speed of shortening, and the like—information needed to maintain muscle tone and

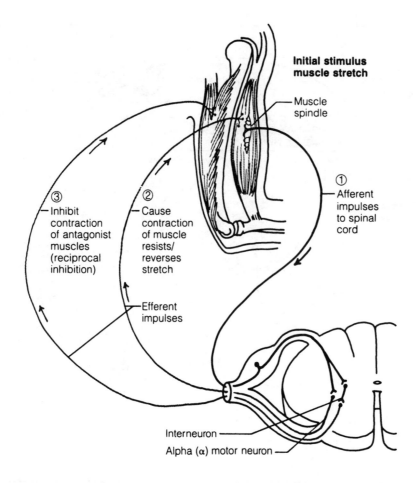

Initial stimulus muscle stretch

Muscle spindle

① Afferent impulses to spinal cord

③ Inhibit contraction of antagonist muscles (reciprocal inhibition)

② Cause contraction of muscle resists/reverses stretch

Efferent impulses

Interneuron

Alpha (α) motor neuron

F22i.2

Events of the stretch reflex by which muscle stretch is damped. The events are shown in circular fashion. **(1)** Stretching of the muscle activates a muscle spindle. **(2)** Impulses transmitted by afferent fibers from muscle spindle to alpha motor neurons in the spinal cord result in activation of the stretched muscle, causing it to contract. **(3)** Impulses transmitted by afferent fibers from muscle spindle to interneurons in the spinal cord result in reciprocal inhibition of the antagonist muscle.

posture. Stretch reflexes tend to be hypoactive or absent in cases of peripheral nerve damage or ventral horn disease, and hyperactive in corticospinal tract lesions. They are absent in deep sedation and coma.

Activity 1: Initiating Stretch Reflexes

We will use computer-driven Intelitool® equipment to demonstrate the stretch reflex in this section. The patellar reflex, which assesses the L2–L4 level of the spinal cord, will be used as the main example of the stretch reflex. Besides simply eliciting the reflex, the effects of a number of factors (mental distraction, exercise, and others) on its expression will be investigated, and the ankle jerk reflex will be elicited for comparison.

Work in groups of 2 to 4 students. During the experiment, all group members should strive to gain experience operating the computer. Because the computer displays the keys that control the program, prior computer experience is not necessary. Each group member will be expected to explain all operations to his or her experimental subject.

1. Prepare the subject. Do not select a subject who has a history of poor reflex responses (that is, in whom a physician has been able to demonstrate reflexes only after repeated tries). Have the subject sit on the edge of the counter or laboratory bench so that the legs are relaxed with feet well above the floor.

⚠ You will attach a transducer, but first loosen its thumbscrew locking tab. *Always loosen the thumbscrew locking tab when the transducer is not being read,* for example, when strapping it on, removing it, or storing it. This will lessen the chance of damage when it is not in actual use. *Also, never force the transducer if it has hit an internal stop!*

2. Start a new data file. (Select **New** from the **File** menu.) If you have not yet calibrated the transducer do so now.

3. Have the subject sit on the edge of a table with his/her leg dangling freely. Strap the transducer to the right thigh and lower leg of the subject so that the transducer box is facing outward and the hinge of

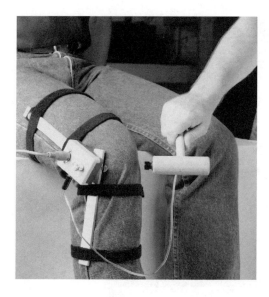

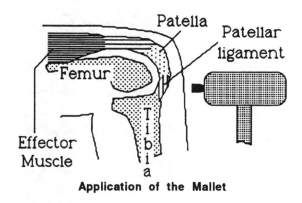

Patella

Patellar ligament

Femur

Effector Muscle

Tibia

Application of the Mallet

F22i.3

(a) Alignment of the force transducer. (b) Application of the mallet.

the transducer is aligned with the hinge of the knee (Figure 22i.3).

4. Click on the **Start** button. NOTE: Data acquisition will not begin until a stimulus is applied.

5. Strike the subject's patellar ligament hard enough to elicit a good response.

6. Wait until the plot reaches the edge of the screen. Notice the automatic calculation of the latent period and the maximum degree of rotation.

7. Repeat the application of the mallet several times. If your technique is good you should get similar results each time.

Record

Maximum degree of rotation _____°

Time to maximum _____ sec

Latent period _____ sec

Which muscles contracted? _____

_____

What nerve is carrying the afferent and efferent impulses?

_____

8. Test the effect of mental distraction on the patellar reflex by having the subject add a column of three-digit numbers while you test the reflex again.

Maximum excursion _____°

Time to maximum _____ sec

Latent period _____ sec

Is the response greater than or less than the first

response? _____

What are your conclusions about the effect of mental

distraction on reflex activity? _____

_____

_____

_____

9. Now test the effect of muscular activity occurring simultaneously in other areas of the body. Have the subject clasp the edge of the laboratory bench and vigorously attempt to pull it upward with both hands. At the same time, test the patellar reflex again.

Maximum excursion _____°

Time to maximum _____ sec

Latent period _____ sec

Is the response more or less vigorous than the first

response? _____

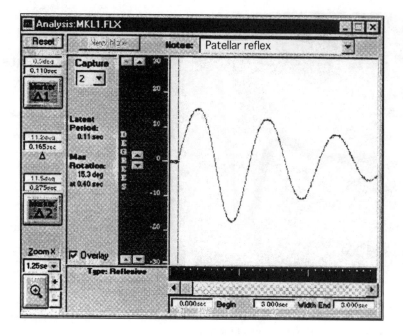

F22i.4

Patellar reflex/Knee jerk data screen.

10. Fatigue also influences the reflex response. After removing the force transducer, the subject should jog in position until she or he is very fatigued (*really* fatigued— no slackers). Attach the transducer and test the patellar reflex again and record whether it is more or less vigorous.

Maximum excursion _____°

Time to maximum _____ sec

Latent period _____ sec

More or less vigorous? _____

Would you say that the nervous system activity *or* muscle function is responsible for the changes you have just observed?

_____

Explain your reasoning. _____

_____

_____

11. Now you are ready to compare the *ankle jerk reflex* (another stretch reflex) to the patellar reflex. To demonstrate the ankle jerk, or Achilles, reflex, loosen the thumbscrew on the transducer, remove it, and kneel on a chair with the feet dangling (relaxed) over the seat edge. Strap the transducer on the leg and foot. Dorsiflex the foot slightly to increase the tension on the gastrocnemius muscle and then tighten the thumbscrew. Have your partner sharply tap the Achilles (calcaneal) tendon with the reflex hammer.

Maximum excursion _____°

Time to maximum _____ sec

Latent period _____ sec

What is the result? _____

_____

Does the contraction of the gastrocnemius normally result in the activity you have observed?

_____

How does the tracing differ from the patellar reflex tracing? _____

_____

Explain: _____

_____

_____

Loosen the thumbscrew and remove the force transducer from the subject.

12. Save your data to an appropriate file.

So far, you have tested the femoral and sciatic nerves. If time allows, and with your instructor's permission, you might want to demonstrate other stretch reflexes. Other possible pathways to test include the following:

- Musculocutaneous nerve (biceps jerk): Attach the transducer to the arm at the elbow. Strike the biceps tendon found in the hollow of the elbow (antecubital fossa).
- Radial nerve (triceps jerk): Keep the transducer attached to the elbow. Strike the triceps tendon about 2 inches above the elbow. The arm should be slightly bent and held in front of the subject (supported by the other arm).

Be sure to use a different file name if you want to save the data for any of these additional reflexes.

Do not exit the program at this time because you will be using the apparatus to record data for the experiment Reaction Time of Basic and Learned or Acquired Reflexes. ■

Crossed Extensor Reflex

The **crossed extensor reflex** is more complex than the stretch reflex. It consists of a flexor, or withdrawal, reflex followed by extension of the opposite limb.

This reflex is quite obvious when, for example, a stranger suddenly and strongly grips one's arm. The immediate response is to withdraw the clutched arm and push the intruder away with the other arm. The reflex is more difficult to demonstrate in a laboratory because it is anticipated, and under these conditions the extensor part of the reflex may be inhibited.

Activity 2: Initiating the Crossed Extensor Reflex

The subject should sit with eyes closed and with the dorsum of one hand resting on the laboratory bench. Obtain a sharp pencil and suddenly prick the subject's index finger. What are the results?

_____

_____

Did the extensor part of this reflex seem to be slow com-

pared to other reflexes you have observed? _____

What are the reasons for this? _____

_____ ■

Superficial Cord Reflexes

The **superficial cord reflexes** (abdominal, cremaster, and plantar reflexes) result from pain and temperature changes. They are initiated by stimulation of receptors in the skin and mucosae. The superficial cord reflexes depend *both* on functional upper-motor pathways and on the cord-level reflex arc. Since only the plantar reflex

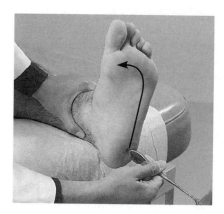

F22i.5

Demonstrating the plantar reflex.

can be tested conveniently in a laboratory setting, we will use this as our example.

The plantar reflex, an important neurological test, is elicited by stimulating the cutaneous receptors in the sole of the foot. In adults, stimulation of these receptors causes the toes to flex and move closer together. Damage to the pyramidal (or corticospinal) tract, however, produces *Babinski's sign,* an abnormal response in which the toes flare and the great toe moves in an upward direction. (In newborn infants, Babinski's sign is due to incomplete myelination of the nervous system.)

Activity 3: Initiating the Plantar Reflex

Have the subject remove a shoe and lie on the cot or laboratory bench with the knees slightly bent and thighs rotated so that the lateral side of the foot rests on the cot. Alternatively, the subject may sit up and rest the lateral surface of the foot on a chair. Draw the handle of the reflex hammer firmly down the lateral side of the exposed sole from the heel to the base of the great toe (Figure 22i.5).

What is the response? _____

_____

Is this a normal plantar reflex or Babinski's sign?

_____ ■

REACTION TIME OF BASIC AND LEARNED OR ACQUIRED REFLEXES

The time required for reaction to a stimulus depends on many factors—sensitivity of the receptors, velocity of nerve conduction, the number of neurons and synapses involved, and the speed of effector activation to name just a few. Some reflexes are *basic* or inborn; others are *learned* or *acquired* reflexes resulting from practice or repetition. If the response involves a reflex arc, the synapses are facilitated and response time will be short.

Learned reflexes involve a far larger number of neural pathways and many types of higher intellectual activities, including choice and decision making, will be involved, which lengthens the response time.

There are various ways of testing reaction time of reflexes. The tests range in difficulty from simple to ultrasophisticated. Since the objective here is to demonstrate the major time difference between simple and learned reflexes, an intermediate approach will suffice.

Activity 4: Testing the Reaction Time for Basic and Acquired Reflexes

1. Once again, have the subject sit on the edge of the counter so that the legs are relaxed with feet well above the floor. Carefully strap the force transducer again to the right knee. Start a new data file. (Select **New** from the **File** menu.)

2. Now test the reaction time for unlearned responses. Have the subject face away and randomly tap the button on the hammer gently on the tabletop. Instruct the subject to respond to the sound of the tap as quickly as possible by gently kicking the right leg away from the table. Record the information for five trials.

Trial	Max. excur.°	Latent (sec)
1		
2		
3		
4		
5		

3. Perform the test again, but this time say a simple word each time you tap the tabletop. Designate a specific word as a signal for the subject to respond. On all other words, the subject is to remain motionless. Trials in which the subject erroneously kicks out the leg are to be disregarded. Record the information for five *successful* trials.

Trial	Max. excur.°	Latent (sec)
1		
2		
3		
4		
5		

4. Perform the test once again to investigate the subject's reaction to word association. As you tap the tabletop, say a word—for example, *hot.* The subject is to respond with a word he or she associates with the stimulus word—for example, *cold*—kicking as he or she responds. If the subject is unable to make a word association, he or she must not kick out the leg. Record the information for five successful trials, as well as the number of times the subject erroneously kicks.

Trial	Max. excur.°	Latent (sec)
1		
2		
3		
4		
5		

The number of times the subject erroneously kicked out.

_____

You should have noticed quite a large variation in reaction time in this series of trials. Why is this so?

_____

_____

_____ ■

5. Save your data to an appropriate file.

Cranial Nerve Reflex Tests

In these experiments, you will be working with your lab partner to illustrate two somatic reflexes mediated by cranial nerves.

CORNEAL REFLEX The **corneal reflex** is mediated through the trigeminal nerve (cranial nerve V). The absence of this reflex is an ominous sign, because it often indicates damage to the brain stem, resulting from compression of the brain or other trauma.

Activity 5: Initiating the Corneal Reflex

Stand to one side of the subject; the subject should look away from you toward the opposite wall. Wait a few seconds and then quickly, but gently, touch the subject's cornea (on the side toward you) with a wisp of absorbent cotton. What is the reaction?

_____

What is the function of this reflex? _____

_____

Was the sensation that of touch or pain? _____

Why? _____

_____ ■

Activity 6: Initiating the Gag Reflex

The **gag reflex** tests the somatic motor responses of cranial nerves IX and X. When the oral mucosa on the side of the uvula is stroked, each side of the mucosa should rise, and the amount of elevation should be equal.*

For this experiment, select a subject who does not have a queasy stomach, because regurgitation is a possibility. Stroke the subject's oral mucosa on each side of the uvula with a tongue depressor. What happens?

_____

_____

Discard the used tongue depressor in the disposable autoclave bag before continuing. Do *not* lay it on the laboratory bench at any time. ■

AUTONOMIC REFLEXES

The autonomic reflexes include the pupillary, ciliospinal, and salivary reflexes, as well as a multitude of other reflexes. Work with your lab partner to demonstrate the four autonomic reflexes described next.

Pupillary Reflexes

There are several types of pupillary reflexes. The **pupillary light reflex** and the **consensual reflex** will be examined here. In both of these pupillary reflexes, the retina of the eye is the receptor, the optic nerve (cranial nerve II) contains the afferent fibers, the occulomotor nerve (cranial nerve III) is responsible for conducting efferent impulses to the eye, and the smooth muscle of the iris is the effector. Many central nervous system centers are involved in the integration of these responses. Absence of the normal pupillary reflexes is generally a late indication of severe trauma or deterioration of the vital brain stem tissue due to metabolic imbalance.

Activity 7: Initiating the Pupillary Reflexes

1.   Conduct the reflex testing in an area that is relatively dim. Before beginning, obtain a metric ruler to measure and record the size of the subject's pupils as best you can.

* The uvula is the fleshy tab hanging from the roof of the mouth just above the root of the tongue.

Right pupil: _____ mm

Left pupil: _____ mm

2.   Stand to the left of the subject to conduct the testing. The subject should shield the right eye by holding a hand vertically between the eye and the right side of the nose.

3.   Shine a flashlight into the subject's left eye. What is

the pupillary response? _____

Measure the size of the left pupil: _____ mm

4.   Observe the right pupil. Has the same type of change (called a consensual response) occurred in the right eye?

_____

Measure the size of the right pupil: _____ mm

The consensual response, or any reflex observed on one side of the body when the other side has been stimulated, is called a **contralateral response.** The pupillary light response, or any reflex occurring on the side that was stimulated, is referred to as an **ipsilateral response.**

When a contralateral response occurs, what does this indicate about the pathways involved?

_____

_____

_____

Was the sympathetic or parasympathetic division of the autonomic nervous system active during the testing of these reflexes?

_____

What is the function of these pupillary responses?

_____

_____

_____ ■

Activity 8: Initiating the Ciliospinal Reflex

The **ciliospinal reflex** is another example of reflex activity in which pupillary responses can be observed. This response may initially seem a little bizarre, especially in view of the consensual reflex just demonstrated. While observing the subject's eyes, gently stroke the skin (or just the hairs) on the left side of the back of the subject's neck, close to the hairline.

What is the reaction of the left pupil?_____

The reaction of the right pupil?_____

If you see no reaction, repeat the test using a gentle pinch in the same area.

The response you should have noted—pupillary dilation—is consistent with the pupillary changes occurring when the sympathetic nervous system is stimulated. Such a response may also be elicited in a single pupil when more impulses from the sympathetic nervous system reach it for any reason. For example, when the left side of the subject's neck was stimulated, sympathetic impulses to the left eye increased, resulting in the ipsilateral reaction of the left pupil.

On the basis of your observations, would you say that the sympathetic innervation of the two irises is closely integrated?

_____

Why or why not?_____

_____

_____

_____ ■

Activity 9: Initiating the Salivary Reflex

Unlike the other reflexes, in which the effectors were smooth or skeletal muscles, the effectors of the **salivary reflex** are glands. The salivary glands secrete varying amounts of saliva in response to reflex activation.

1.   Obtain a small beaker, a graduated cylinder, lemon juice, and wide-range pH paper. After refraining from swallowing for 2 minutes, the subject is to expectorate (spit) the accumulated saliva into a small beaker. Using the graduated cylinder, measure the volume of the expectorated saliva and determine its pH.

Volume: _____ cc   pH: _____

2.   Now place 2 or 3 drops of lemon juice on the subject's tongue. Allow the lemon juice to mix with the saliva for 5 to 10 seconds, and then determine the pH of the subject's saliva by touching a piece of pH paper to the tip of the tongue.

pH: _____

As before, the subject is to refrain from swallowing for 2 minutes. After the 2 minutes is up, again collect and measure the volume of the saliva and measure its pH.

Volume: _____ cc   pH: _____

3.   How does the volume of saliva collected after the

application of the lemon juice compare with the volume

of the first saliva sample?_____

How does the final saliva pH reading compare to the

initial reading? _____

To that obtained 10 seconds after the application of the

lemon juice?_____

What division of the autonomic nervous system mediates the reflex release of saliva?_____

Dispose of the saliva-containing beakers and the graduated cylinders in the laboratory bucket that contains bleach and put the used pH paper into the disposable autoclave bags. Wash the bench down with 10% bleach solution before continuing. ■

Conduction System of the Heart and Electrocardiography

OBJECTIVES

1. To list and localize the elements of the intrinsic conduction, or nodal, system of the heart; and to describe the initiation and conduction of impulses through this system and the myocardium.

2. To recognize that heart contraction results from electrical activity of many muscle cells.

3. To realize that the electrical activity of the heart can be measured at the surface of the body, and that such measurements give different results than intracellular recording.

4. To operate computerized recording equipment.

5. To describe the different parts of the ECG wave form.

6. To realize that ECG patterns can reveal possible heart dysfunction.

7. To explain the results of an ECG recording.

MATERIALS

Windows computer with Cardiocomp7™ software installed as described in section 2 of the User Manual
McADDAM II™ interface with power module and serial port cable set up as described in section 2 of the User Manual
Cardiocomp7™ junction box with its internal biopotential amplifiers
Cardiocomp7™ junction box to McADDAM II™ interface cable
Manual
Cardiocomp7™ electrode cables
Alcohol prep pads, or alcohol and cottonballs to scrub the electrode sites.
Four flat plate electrodes, four rubber attachment straps, and one tube of electrode gel
or
Four disposable electrodes per subject

THE INTRINSIC CONDUCTION SYSTEM

Heart contraction results from a series of electrical potential changes (depolarization waves) that travel through the heart preliminary to each beat. The ability of cardiac muscle to beat is intrinsic. The heart does not depend on nerve impulses to initiate its contraction and will continue to contract rhythmically even if all nerve connections are severed. However, two controlling systems act on the heart. One of these involves nerves of the autonomic nervous system, which accelerate or decrease the heartbeat rate depending on which division is activated. The second system is the intrinsic conduction system, or nodal system, of the heart, consisting of specialized noncontractile myocardial tissue. The intrinsic conduction system ensures that heart muscle depolarizes in an orderly and sequential manner (from atria to ventricles) and that the heart beats as a coordinated unit.

The components of the intrinsic conduction system include the **SA (sinoatrial) node,** located in the upper right atrium just inferior to the entrance to the superior vena cava; the **AV (atrioventricular) node** in the lower atrial septum at the junction of the atria and ventricles; the **AV bundle (bundle of His)** and the right and left **bundle branches,** located in the interventricular septum; and the **Purkinje fibers,** which ramify within the muscle bundles of the ventricular walls. The Purkinje fiber network is much denser and more elaborate in the left ventricle because of the larger size of this chamber (Figure 31i.1).

The SA node, which has the highest rate of discharge, provides the stimulus for contraction. Because it sets the rate of depolarization for the heart as a whole, the SA node is often referred to as the *pacemaker.* From the SA node, the impulse spreads throughout the atria and to the AV node. The electrical wave is immediately followed by atrial contraction. At the AV node, the impulse is momentarily delayed (approximately 0.1 sec), allowing the atria to complete their contraction. It then passes through the AV bundle, the right and left bundle branches, and the Purkinje fibers, finally resulting in ventricular contraction. Note that the atria and the ventricles are separated from one another by a region of electrically inert tissue, so the depolarization wave can be transmitted to the ventricles only via the tract between the AV node and AV bundle. Thus, any damage to the AV node-bundle pathway partially or totally insulates the ventricles from the influence of the SA node. Although autorhythmic cells are found throughout the heart, their rates of spontaneous depolarization differ. The nodal system increases the rate of heart depolarization and synchronizes heart activity.

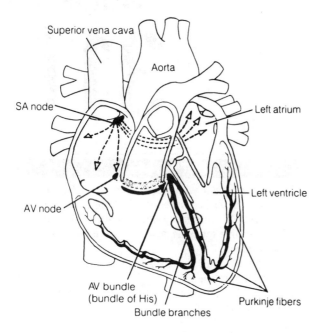

Superior vena cava

Aorta

SA node

Left atrium

AV node

Left ventricle

AV bundle
(bundle of His)

Bundle branches

Purkinje fibers

F31i.1

The intrinsic conduction system of the heart. Dashed-line arrows indicate transmission of the impulse from the SA node through the atria. Solid arrow indicates transmission of the impulse from the AV node to the AV bundle.

ELECTROCARDIOGRAPHY

The conduction of impulses through the heart generates electrical currents that eventually spread throughout the body. These impulses can be detected on the body surface and recorded with an instrument called an *electrocardiograph*. The graphic recording of the electrical changes (depolarization and repolarization) occurring in the cardiac cycle is called an **electrocardiogram (ECG)** (Figure 31i.2). The typical ECG consists of a series of three recognizable waves called *deflection waves*. The first wave, the **P wave,** is a small wave that indicates the depolarization of the atria immediately before atrial contraction. The large **QRS complex,** resulting from ventricular depolarization, has a complicated shape (primarily because of the variability in size of the two ventricles and the time differences required for these chambers to depolarize). It precedes ventricular contraction. The **T wave** results from currents propagated during ventricular repolarization. The repolarization of the atria, which occurs during the QRS interval, is generally obscured by the large QRS complex.

It is important to understand what an ECG does and does not show: An ECG is a record of voltage and time—nothing else. Although we can and do infer that muscle contraction follows its excitation, sometimes it does not. Secondly, an ECG records electrical events occurring in relatively large amounts of muscle tissue (i.e., the bulk of the heart muscle), *not* the electrical activity of nodal tissue which, like muscle contraction, can only be inferred. Nonetheless, abnormalities of the deflection waves and changes in the time intervals of the

ECG are useful in detecting myocardial infarcts or problems with the conduction system of the heart. The P-R (P-Q) interval represents the time between the beginning of atrial depolarization and ventricular depolarization. Thus, it typically includes the period during which the depolarization wave passes to the AV node, atrial systole, and the passage of the excitation wave to the balance of the conducting system. Generally, the P-R interval is about 0.16 to 0.18 sec. A longer interval may suggest a partial AV block caused by damage to the AV node. In total heart block, no impulses are transmitted through the AV node, and the atria and ventricles beat independently of one another—the atria at the SA node rate and the ventricles at their intrinsic rate, which is considerably slower.

If the QRS interval (normally 0.06 to 0.10 sec) is prolonged, it may indicate a right or left bundle branch block in which one ventricle is contracting later than the other. The Q-T interval is the period from the beginning of ventricular depolarization through repolarization and includes the time of ventricular contraction (the S-T segment). With a heart rate of 70 beats/min, this interval is normally 0.31 to 0.41 sec. As the rate increases, this interval becomes shorter; conversely, when the heart rate drops, the interval is longer.

A heart rate over 100 beats/min is referred to as **tachycardia;** a rate below 60 beats/min is **bradycardia.** Although neither condition is pathological, prolonged tachycardia may progress to **fibrillation,** a condition of rapid uncoordinated heart contractions which makes the heart useless as a pump. Bradycardia in athletes is a positive finding; that is, it indicates increased efficiency of cardiac functioning. Because *stroke volume* (the amount of blood ejected by a ventricle with each contraction) increases with physical conditioning, the heart can contract more slowly and still meet circulatory demands.

Twelve standard leads are used to record an ECG for diagnostic purposes. Three of these are bipolar leads that measure the voltage difference between the arms, or an arm and a leg, and nine are unipolar leads. Together the 12 leads provide a fairly comprehensive picture of the electrical activity of the heart.

An important distinction is the difference between the definitions of the terms *electrode* and *lead.*

Electrode: An electrode is a physical piece of wire. The polarity of each wire (electrode) of the cable is labeled by color:

- White—negative
- Black—positive
- Green—ground

Note: Cardiocomp 7 and 12 have labeled interface boxes to allow simultaneous connection of all electrodes.

Lead: A lead measures the electrical potential difference between electrodes.

We will use Intelitool® Cardiocomp ECG recording equipment in this exercise. For this investigation, a total of 4 electrodes are used and results are obtained from

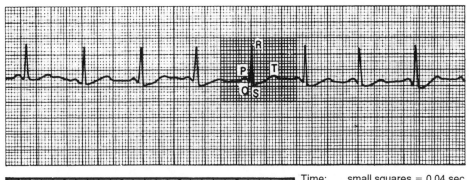

(a)

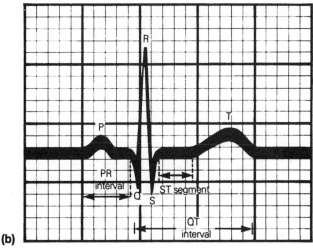

(b)

Time: small squares = 0.04 sec
       1 large square = 0.02 sec
       5 large sqares = 1.00 sec

F31i.2

The normal electrocardiogram. (**a**) Regular sinus rhythm.
(**b**) Waves, segments, and intervals of a normal ECG.

the three bipolar (limb) leads (Figure 31i.3). With each
of the leads, the electrical changes between two of the
electrodes are determined. As shown in the figure, the
potential difference between the right and left arms
(AL-AR) is determined with lead I, between the right
arm and left leg (RA-LL) with lead II, and between the
left arm and left leg (LA-LL) with lead III.

Understanding the Standard Limb Leads

As you might expect, electrical activity recorded by any
lead depends on the location and orientation of the
recording electrodes. Clinically, it is assumed that the
heart lies in the center of a triangle with sides of equal
length (*Einthoven's triangle*) and that the recording connections are made at the vertices (corners) of that triangle. But, in practice, the electrodes connected to each
arm and to the left leg are considered to connect to the
triangle vertices. The standard limb leads record the
voltages generated in the extracellular fluids surrounding the heart by the ion flows occurring simultaneously
in many cells between any two of the connections. A
recording using lead I (AL-AR), which connects the
right arm (RA) and the left arm (LA), is most sensitive
to electrical activity spreading horizontally across the
heart. Lead II (RA-LL) and lead III (LA-LL) record activity along the vertical axis (from the base of the heart
to its apex), but from different orientations. The significance of Einthoven's triangle is that the sum of the voltages of leads I and III equals that in lead II (Einthoven's

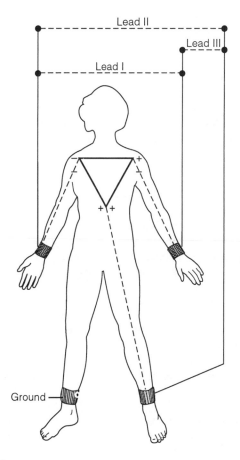

F31i.3

ECG recording positions for the standard limb leads.

law). Hence, if the voltages of two of the standard leads are recorded, that of the third lead can be determined mathematically.

Activity 1: Recording ECGs

Because most common problems encountered with Intelitool® ECG equipment are due to incorrect electrode application, the following instructions should be carefully followed to establish the proper electrical connection.

1. Set up the Cardiocomp7™ amplifier, cables and McADDAM II™ as described in the User Manual.

2. To make the best use of Cardiocomp™, become particularly familiar with the "Auto Save File" and "Auto Print File" features on the data acquisition window, and "Markers", "Automatic Analysis", "Zoom", and "Notes" features of the analysis window.

Electrode Placement

1. All four appendicular electrodes *must* be used at all times.

2. Typical electrode placement is on the inside of the wrists and the inside of the ankles.

If you read a LEAD, for which you have not connected the electrodes, the signal might look legitimate, but don't believe it.

3. The electrode wires should be carefully dressed. Try to keep the wires in use in a tight group or "cable." Taping the wires together is often a good idea. Any wiggling of the wires relative to each together can introduce a lot of noise into the signal. Do not drape any of the wires over a potential noise source such as a power cord.

4. Most of the problems that you might encounter in the quest for a good signal can be avoided with good electrode application procedure. With that in mind, follow these steps carefully.

   Firmly scrub the electrode sites with an alcohol prep pad or alcohol soaked cotton ball. Rub hard enough and long enough to remove oils and dead skin cells.

   Disposable Electrodes: The female snap connector on the end of the wire should be snapped firmly onto the male snap connector on the disposable electrode (see Figure 31i.4).

   Appendicular (Flat Plate Electrodes): Apply a liberal amount of electrode gel between each electrode and the skin. Strap the electrode to the appropriate appendage so the strap is snug, BUT NOT TOO TIGHT. Make sure that the subject is comfortable, and that their circulation is not being cut off. The female snap

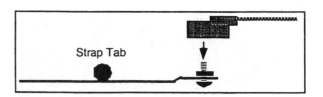

F31i.4

The *flat plate* electrode and its connector.

connector on the end of the wire should be snapped firmly onto the end of the bolt of the flat plate electrode.

Recording the ECG

1. Start the Cardiocomp7™ program.

2. Select **New** from the **File** menu, make sure the setup is correct then click the **OK** button on the setup window.

3. Make sure the subject is lying down very still with all musculature as relaxed as possible. (Muscular tension, particularly in the arms, will introduce noise into the signal.)

4. Leave the data acqustion screen as it appears (accept the defaults) when it comes up. That is:

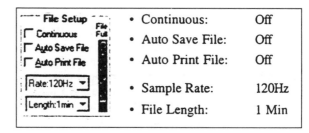

• Continuous:	Off
• Auto Save File:	Off
• Auto Print File:	Off
• Sample Rate:	120Hz
• File Length:	1 Min

5. Click on the **Start** button and collect enough data so that there are several good quality cardiac cycles in the file. This should only take a few seconds.

6. Click on the **Stop** button.

7. Click on the **Analyze** button.

8. Determine where the P wave begins. (Refer to Figure 2.3 and Figure 2.4 in the Cardiocomp™ Electrocardiography Primer.)

9. Put Marker 1 at the very beginning of the P wave of LEAD II.

● Click on the **M1** button.
● Click on the graph where the P wave begins. (After placing the marker you can move it by dragging it around or moving it with the ⊕ ⊕ ⊕ ⊕ keys.)

10. Put Marker 2 at the very top of the R wave of LEAD II.

- Click on the **M2** button.
- Click on the graph at the top of the R wave. (Move the marker back and forth with the ⬆ ⬇ ⬅ ➡ keys while watching the amplitude (voltage). Leave it at the highest voltage value.)

11. Click on the **New Note** button.

- Title the note with the name of the interval between Marker 1 and Marker 2. (Refer to Figure 2.3 and Figure 2.4 in the Cardiocomp™ Electrocardiography Primer.)
- In the text window of the note, explain what the P wave represents.

What is this interval called?

_____

12. Close the **Note** window (this is very important).

13. Put Marker 1 at the very beginning of the Q wave.

14. Put Marker 2 at the end of the S wave.

15. Click on the **New Note** button.

- Title the note with the name of the complex between Marker 1 and Marker 2.
- In the text window of the note, explain what this complex represents.

What does this complex represent?

_____

_____

16. Close the **Note** window (this is very important).

17. Leave Marker 1 at the very beginning of the Q wave.

18. Put Marker 2 at the end of the T wave.

19. Click on the **New Note** button.

- Title the note with the name of the interval between Marker 1 and Marker 2.
- In the text window of the note, explain what the T wave represents.

What is this interval called?

_____

_____

20. Close the **Note** window.

You may want to "Lock" the file at this point (under the **Analysis** menu) and then save it (**File** menu). Remember, if you want to change a note, you will need to "Unlock" it first so make your password easy to remember—like your first name.

21. Compute the heart rate. Place Marker 1 at the beginning of one QRS complex and Marker 2 at the beginning of the next QRS complex. Record the time for one heartbeat:

_____ sec/beat.

22. Now find the beats per minute, or heart rate, by plugging the figure obtained above into the following equation:

Beats/min $= 1/$ _____ sec/beat $\times$ 60 sec/min

Beats/min $=$ _____

Is the value obtained within normal limits? _____

23. Record the following durations you measured using the markers.

P–R interval _____ sec

QRS interval _____ sec

Q-T interval _____ sec

Are the computed values within normal limits? _____

Which of the leads indicates the greatest R-wave deflection (overall height of the wave)? _____

Because the QRS complex represents ventricular depolarization, a greater R-wave magnitude in one of the three bipolar leads means that the greater mass of ventricular tissue is oriented in the axis of that lead. The greatest R-wave deflection is usually recorded by lead II, which indicates that the largest electrical potential (and therefore muscle mass) is in the axis leading from the right shoulder to the left foot. (Notice that the electrode placement for lead II is right arm to left leg.) If a greater R-wave deflection is seen in another lead, then the heart must be oriented less typically, i.e., in the direction indicated by that lead.

How could we determine that the heart is positioned more horizontally than normal by looking at a three-lead ECG tracing?

_____

_____

Compared to the isoelectric line (baseline), we can immediately see if an electrical deflection is positive or negative. What would happen if we switched the polarity of the leads (e.g., positive for negative)?

_____

_____

Describe the differences seen in the tracings for each lead.

_____

_____

_____

_____

_____

24. If your instructor requires you to attach a representative part of your ECG tracing, print the data. ■

Activity 2: Recording an ECG While Running in Place

1. Select the **New** menu from the **File** menu. Click **OK.**

2. Make sure the electrodes are securely attached to the subject to prevent electrode movement while recording the ECG.

3. As before in the baseline recording, prepare the subject and the computer for a lead I recording.

4. With the electrodes in place for lead I recording, have the subject run in place for 3 min.

- In the last 30 sec of running, click on the **Start** button to start recording ECG data.
- After a few cycles have been recorded, press **Stop** to stop data collection.
- Instruct the subject to sit down and relax.
- Record several cycles of ECG data at 1 minute after exercise, and again at 4 minutes after exercise.
- Label with **Notes** and save data.

Do not exit the experiment; continue with the Breath-Holding Recording experiment. ■

Activity 3: Recording the Effects of Breath-Holding

1. Position the subject comfortably in the sitting position.

2. After the subject has fully rested and relaxed, record a few ECG cycles.

3. After approximately 10 seconds, instruct the subject to begin breath-holding and note the time. After another 50 seconds have passed, record for a total of 10 seconds.

At this time, the subjects have been holding their breath for 1 minute; stop the recording and remind the subject to breathe.

4. Save your data as before, using a different file name.

Computerized Data Analysis

1. To open a data analysis window, press the **Analyze** button on the acquisition window, or open a data file using the **Open** selection under the **File** menu.

2. Compute the beats/min during the third minute of running, at 1 minute after exercise, and at 4 minutes after exercise. Record below:

_____ beats/min while running in place

_____ beats/min at 1 minute after exercise

_____ beats/min at 4 minutes after exercise

3. Compare these recordings with the previous (base line) recording from lead I. Which intervals are shorter

in the "running" recording?_____

Does the subject's heart rate return to baseline levels by

4 minutes after exercise?_____

4. Compute the beats/min during the 1-minute experimental (breath-holding) period.

_____ beats/min during breath-holding

5. Compare this recording with the lead I recording obtained under baseline conditions. What differences are seen?

_____

_____

6. Attempt to *explain* the physiological reason for the differences you have seen. (Hint: A good place to start might be to check "hypoventilation" or the role of the *respiratory* system in acid-base balance of the blood.)

_____

_____

_____ ■

Respiratory System Physiology

OBJECTIVES

1. To define the following (and be prepared to provide volume figures if applicable):

   inspiration   *expiratory reserve volume*
   expiration   *expiratory end point*
   tidal volume   *inspiratory reserve volume*
   vital capacity   *minute respiratory volume*

2. To explain the role of muscles and volume changes in the mechanical process of breathing.

3. To demonstrate the proper usage of the spirometer.

4. To explain the relative importance of various mechanical and chemical factors in producing respiratory variations.

5. To describe bronchial and vesicular breathing sounds.

6. To explain the importance of the carbonic acid–bicarbonate buffer system in maintaining blood pH.

MATERIALS

Model lung (bell jar demonstration)
Tape measure
Disposable mouthpieces if available
Alcohol swabs
Spirocomp™ computer interface & cable
Spriocomp™ software
Phipps & Bird student's wet spirometer (6 or 9-L)
One-way valve assembly (supplied with
   Spirocomp™)

PC or compatible computer running Windows® 3.1,
   Windows® 95, or higher
Noseclip
Household disinfectant (such as Lysol™)
Sterile container filled with 75% ethanol solution
   which is large enough to immerse the one way
   valve assembly
Sterile container filled with mild soap solution which
   is large enough to immerse the one way valve as-
   sembly
Stop watch (or clock with second hand)
Printer (if hardcopies of data are desired)
Pneumograph and recording attachments
Recording apparatus
Stethoscope
Paper bag
pH meter (standardized with buffer of pH 7)
Buffer solution (pH 7)
Concentrated HCl and NaOH in dropper bottles
0.01 M HCl in dropper bottle
Straws
0.05 M NaOH in dropper bottles
Phenol red in dropper bottles
100 ml beakers
250- and 50-ml beakers
Graduated cylinder (100 ml)
Glass stirring rod
Plastic wash bottles containing distilled water
Animal plasma
Disposable autoclave bag
Human Respiratory System videotapes*

*Available to qualified adopters from Benjamin Cummings

THE MECHANICS OF RESPIRATION

Pulmonary ventilation, or **breathing,** consists of two phases: **inspiration,** during which air is taken into the lungs, and **expiration,** during which air passes out of the lungs. As the inspiratory muscles (external intercostals and diaphragm) contract during inspiration, the size of the thoracic cavity increases. The diaphragm moves from its relaxed dome shape to a flattened position, increasing the superoinferior volume. The external intercostals lift the rib cage, increasing the anteroposterior and lateral dimensions (Figure 37i.1). Since the lungs adhere to the thoracic walls like flypaper because of the cohesive character of the pleurae, the intrapulmonary volume (volume within the lungs) also increases, lowering the air (gas) pressure inside the lungs.

The gases then expand to fill the available space, creating a partial vacuum that causes air to flow into the lungs—constituting the act of inspiration. During expiration, the inspiratory muscles relax, and the natural tendency of the elastic lung tissue to recoil acts to decrease intrathoracic and intrapulmonary volumes. As the gas molecules within the lungs are forced closer together, the intrapulmonary pressure rises to a point higher than atmospheric pressure. This causes gases to flow from the lungs to equalize the pressure inside and outside the lungs—the act of expiration.

Activity 1: Observing the Model Lung

You will be observing the model lung, which demonstrates the principles involved in gas flows into and out

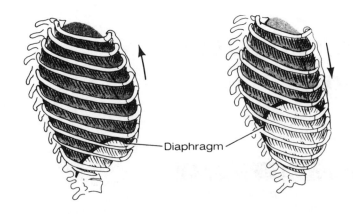

(a) Inspiration   **(b)** Expiration

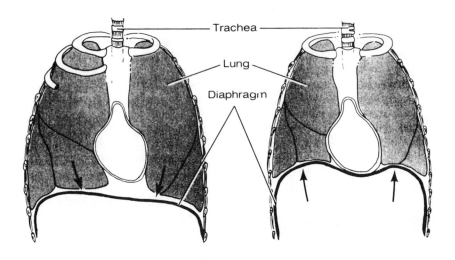

F37i.1

Rib cage and diaphragm positions during breathing. (a) At the end of a normal inspiration; chest expanded, diaphragm depressed. (b) At the end of a normal expiration; chest depressed, diaphragm elevated.

of the lungs. It is a simple apparatus with a bottle "thorax," a rubber membrane "diaphragm," and "balloon lungs."

1. Go to the demonstration area and work the model lung by moving the rubber diaphragm up and down. Notice the changes in balloon (lung) size as the volume of the thoracic cavity is alternately increased and decreased.

2. Check the appropriate columns in the chart concerning these observations in the Exercise 37 Review Sheet.

3. After observing the operation of the model lung, conduct the following tests on your lab partner. Use the tape measure to determine his or her chest circumference by placing the tape around the chest as high up under the armpits as possible. Record the measurements in inches in the appropriate space for each of the conditions below.

Quiet breathing:

inspiration _____ expiration _____

Forced breathing:

inspiration _____ expiration _____

Do the results coincide with what you expected?

_____ ■

RESPIRATORY VOLUMES AND CAPACITIES—SPIROMETRY

A person's size, sex, and physical condition produce variations in respiratory volumes. Normal quiet breathing moves about 500 ml of air in and out of the lungs with each breath. As you have seen in the previous experiment, a person can usually forcibly inhale or exhale much more air than is exchanged in normal quiet breathing. The terms given to the measurable respiratory volumes are defined just below. These terms and their normal values for an adult male should be memorized.

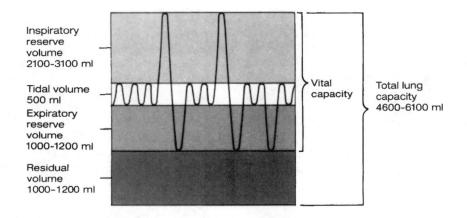

F37i.2

Idealized tracing of the various respiratory volumes.

Tidal volume (TV): amount of air inhaled or exhaled with each breath under resting conditions (500 ml)

Inspiratory reserve volume (IRV): amount of air that can be forcefully inhaled after a normal tidal volume inhalation (3100 ml)

Expiratory reserve volume (ERV): amount of air that can be forcefully exhaled after a normal tidal volume exhalation (1200 ml)

Vital capacity (VC): maximum amount of air that can be exhaled after a maximal inspiration (4800 ml)

$$VC = TV + IRV + ERV$$

An ideal tracing of the various respiratory volumes and their relationships to each other are shown in Figure 37i.2.

Respiratory volumes will be measured with an apparatus called a spirometer. There are two major types of spirometers, which give comparable results—the hand-held dry, or wheel, spirometers (such as the Buhl spirometer 6 or 9-L illustrated in Figure 37i.3) and "wet" spirometers such as the Phipps & Bird spirometers. The somewhat more sophisticated wet spirometer consists of a plastic float within a rectangular (or 9-L round) base; air can be added to or removed from the float (Figure 37i.4). The base contains water and has a tube running through it to carry air above the water level. The plastic float is a "tub" inverted over the water-containing tank and connected to a volume indicator. The Intelitool® equipment connects the wet spirometer to a computer so lung volume recordings can be recorded and analyzed using the included software.

Activity 2: Conducting Spirometer Testing

1. Clean the nose clips with an alcohol swab. While you wait for the alcohol to air dry, count and record your normal respiratory rate.

Respirations per minute _____

2. Set up the Spirocomp™ equipment.
   a. Place all four mouthpieces and the valve assembly into the ethanol solution.

   b. Assemble the spirometer with the Intelitool® supplied scale arm and computer interface box as discussed in sections 2.3 through 2.4 of the user manual.

   c. Fill the spirometer to a little over the fill line with clean tap water. Add disinfectant to the water as per instructions on label for disinfecting.

   d. Load the Spirocomp™ software by double clicking the application icon.

   e. Open or create a Spirocomp™ database if you have not done so already. (To open a file, choose **File » Open** from the menus and then locate and select the database file from the list. To create a new database, choose **File » New**, type in the name of the new database, and then save it.)

   f. Choose **Acquire » New Record** from the menus (or click the **New Record** (lungs) button on the toolbar, or press [CTRL]-R).

   g. Enter the subject data into the data entry window. These data are used by the software to calculate the predicted vital capacity (pVC) for that subject.

      Height can be entered in any of the following ways:
      - to the nearest 0.1 centimeters (e.g., **177.8**)
      - in inches followed by a double quote (e.g., **70"**).
      - in feet and inches, separated by a comma (e.g., **5,10**)

      The value is always converted and displayed in centimeters.

   h. Dip the noseclip in the ethanol solution, then in the mild soap solution, and wipe it off. Put the noseclip on.

   You will not get true results if you have a leaky system, so be sure that the nose is sealed tightly. Also be sure that subject is sealing their lips tightly on the mouthpiece.

F37i.3

The Buhl Spiropet, an example of a hand-held dry spirometer. The dial face of the spirometer is rotated to zero prior to each test.

i. Swish the valve assembly in the ethanol solution, then the mild soap solution.

j. Remove a mouthpiece from the ethanol solution, rinse it in the mild soap solution and wipe it dry. Insert the mouthpiece into the valve assembly.

k. For all spirometry readings, observe the following rules:

- Between subjects, always swish the valve assembly in a 75% ethanol solution and then a mild solution. Leave the mouthpieces in the ethanol to soak, and use them in rotation or use disposable mouthpieces and discard in an autoclave bag.

- The subject should be seated in a straight high-backed chair.

- Before you begin, the subject should have been resting (seated) for several minutes. Normal values can not be obtained if the subject is excited or has been physically active. Various lung volumes will be altered during the data acquisition if the subject changes position, thereby altering the size of the chest cavity.

- Ideally, the subject should not watch his or her lab partner or the computer screen during the TV and ERV measurements. Watching the results could cause the subject to change breathing patterns.

- The nose clip must be secure and the subject's lips must form a good seal around the mouthpiece so as to avoid any air leakage.

F37i.4

Phipps & Bird "wet" recording spirometer.

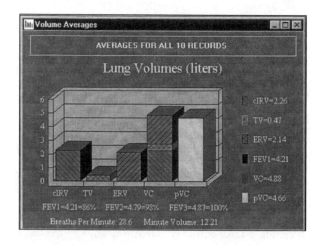

F37i.5

Data collection screen.

CALIBRATION PROCEDURE

The Windows® 95 (32-bit) version and the Macintosh® version 2.0 of the Spirocomp software supports both the 6 and 9-liter Phipps & Bird Wet Spirometers. All previous DOS, Windows, and Macintosh versions of the software supports only the 6-liter spirometer. You must choose either the 6 or 9-liter spirometer when setting up the newer software versions. In the Spirocomp™ software go to **Edit,** then **Spirocomp Preferences,** and choose a **Spirometer Type** (6 or 9-liter). For the 9-liter spirometer, steps 3–5 may not be necessary. The transducer has been "zeroed" at the factory. To calibrate the spirometer:

1.   Attach the valve assembly to the spirometer as shown below.

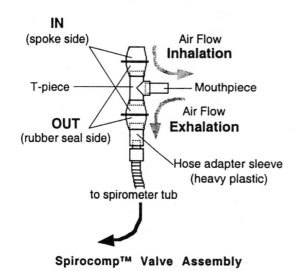

Spirocomp™ Valve Assembly

2.   Be sure the spirometer is completely deflated.

3.   Lift the chain from the assembly (pulling the counterweight side up, not the bell float side). Then turn the pulley until the value displayed at the bottom reads 0 (± 100).

4.   Place the chain back down on the pulley and align the pointer to 0 on the printed scale. Make sure the computer still reads 0 (± 100).

5.   Inflate the spirometer to exactly 6.0 liters (or 9.0) as indicated by the pointer on the scale arm. Click **OK.** If the calibration has been successful, you will get a message from the computer. If not, repeat the procedure. If necessary you can recalibrate at any time while the computer is running.

6.   Since the pressure and temperature inside the spirometer are influenced by room temperature and differ from those in the body, all measured values are to be multiplied by a **BTPS** (body temperature, atmospheric pressure, and water saturation) **factor.** At room temperature, the BTPS factor is typically 1.1 or very close to that value. Hence, measured values are multiplied by the BTPS factor to obtain the corrected respiratory volume values. The Spirocomp™ software automatically factors in the BTPS factor, so additional calculations are not necessary with computerized spirometry.

7.   Repeat the following tests with the first subject until you achieve consistent results.

Measuring the Tidal Volume

If the chain slips at any time during acquisition, be sure to recalibrate the spirometer.

1.   Empty the bell float of the spirometer. To empty the bell float, pull the valve assembly apart as shown. Do not force the bell float down. Allow it to come to rest on its own.

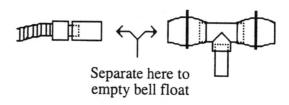

Separate here to
empty bell float

2.   Have the subject breathe normally into the spirometer for one or two cycles. The valve system should cause the spirometer to fill on exhalation, and the subject should be getting fresh air from the room. If the valves are not working correctly, see Chapter 2, section 2.3 in the user manual. The valves work best when wet.

3.   Press the T key *during an inhalation* and follow the instructions on the help line at the bottom of the window. (The computer will also provide verbal instructions if that option has been enabled in the preferences.)

BREATHE NORMAL RESTING CYCLES...

The software will read the changes in the spirometer for three cycles, automatically stop and then graph the average tidal volume. Additionally, the ventilation rate and minute volume will be computed and displayed beneath the graph.

If you felt that you made a mistake or you did not get good results for some reason, repeat the TV reading before you continue.

Measuring the Expiratory Reserve Volume

1.   Empty the spirometer's bell float.

2.   Have the subject breathe normally into the spirometer for one or two cycles.

3.   Press the E key *during an inhalation* and follow the instructions on the help line at the bottom of the window.

BREATHE NORMAL RESTING CYCLES...

After reading two normal cycles, the software will prompt the subject:

PAUSE AT THE END OF THE NEXT EXHALATION...

This means that at the end of the next (3rd) resting exhalation, the subject should stop all air movement and wait for the next prompt. The computer will then instruct:

WITHOUT INHALING, EXHALE MAXIMALLY...

This means that the subject should empty their lungs as completely as possible. *Do not inhale at this point at all.*

When the subject is no longer capable of expelling more air, the software will calculate the expiratory reserve volume and graph it on the screen.

If you felt that you made a mistake or you did not get good results for some reason, repeat the ERV reading before continuing.

Measuring the Vital Capacity

1. Empty the spirometer's bell float.

2. Press the **V** key (or use the menu or toolbar) and follow the computer's instructions:

> INHALE MAXIMALLY, THEN EXHALE
> RAPIDLY AND COMPLETELY...

The subject should first *inhale* maximally and then *exhale* as forcefully, rapidly, and completely as possible into the spirometer. It is very important that the subject exhale rapidly, as the *rate* of air movement is being monitored as well as the volume. The subject should continue to squeeze out every little bit of air until the software stops and graphs the vital capacity on the screen.

Note, also, that the inspiratory reserve volume and predicted vital capacity are computed and graphed. IRV is calculated as VC − (TV + ERV); and pVC is calculated from a regression equation using the subject information entered on the **Subject Data Entry** window.

If you felt that you made a mistake or you did not get good results for some reason, repeat the VC reading before you continue.

Subject Record Is Now Complete

If you have a printer connected to your computer, you can obtain a hardcopy of the subject record by choosing the **File » Print** menu item. First, however, you should make sure of the following:

- the correct printer is selected in your Windows™ environment
- you have chosen **File » Print Setup**

Also compute your **minute respiratory volume (MRV)** using the following formula. (This value, along with the resting respiratory rate, is automatically computed and displayed after the TV measurement in the Windows version.)

$$MRV = TV \times \text{respirations/min}$$

$$MRV = \underline{\hspace{2cm}} \text{liters/min}$$

Forced Expiratory Volume (FEV$_T$) Measurement

While they are not really diagnostic, pulmonary function tests can help the clinician to distinguish between obstructive and restrictive pulmonary diseases. (In obstructive disorders, like chronic bronchitis and emphysema, airway resistance is increased, whereas in restrictive diseases such as polio and tuberculosis, total lung capacity declines.) Two highly useful pulmonary function tests for this purpose are the FVC and FEV$_T$.

The FVC (forced vital capacity) measures the amount of gas expelled when the subject takes the deepest possible breath and then exhales forcefully and rapidly. This volume is reduced in those with restrictive pulmonary disease. The FEV$_T$ (forced expiratory volume) involves the same basic testing procedure, but it specifically looks at the percentage of vital capacity that is exhaled during specific time intervals of the FVC test. FEV$_1$, for instance, is the amount exhaled during the first second. Healthy individuals can expire about 80% of their FVC in the first second; the FEV$_1$ is low in those with obstructive disease. FEV$_1$, FEV$_2$, FEV$_3$ may be read directly off the computer screen after completing the vital capacity reading. Normal FEV values are as follows:

FEV$_1$	75% to 85% of FVC
FEV$_2$	about 94% of FVC
FEV$_3$	about 97% of FVC

The recording is finished for this subject. Before continuing with the next member of your group:

1. Dispose of used cardboard mouthpieces in the autoclave bag.

2. Swish the valve assembly in the ethanol solution, then rinse with water.

3. Put a fresh mouthpiece into the valve assembly.

If you wish to add another record to the database, press (CTRL)-R (or choose **Acquire » New Record** from the menus or click the **New Record** button on the toolbar) and repeat the measurement process.

Continue recording all members of your group using the procedure above.

These are typical values for respiratory volumes and capacities. Values are expressed in liters.

	TV	ERV	IRV	VC
Males	0.5	1.0	3.0	4.5
Females	0.4	0.75	2.25	3.4

FEV1	75%–85% of VC
FEV2	approximately 94% of VC
FEV3	approvimately 97% of VC

Considerable variation is normal.

Computerized Data Analysis

Choose the desired graph from the **Analyze** menu:

> Graph Single Record
> Graph Female Averages
> Graph Male Averages
> Graph Group Averages

1. Compare the average readings for the entire group, for females, and for males to typical average values. If there are any significant variations, try to explain why (think about smoking, illness, asthma, etc.).

male values _____

_____

female values _____

_____

2. Female values tend to be about 20% to 25% less

than male values. Why? _____

_____

_____

3. Bring up your own record by choosing **Graph Single Record** (from the **Analyze** menu) or select **Graph Record** on the toolbar. Record the values below:

Tidal volume (TV)   _____ ml

Expiratory reserve volume (ERV)   _____ ml

Calculated inspiratory reserve vol. (cIRV) _____ ml

Vital capacity (VC)   _____ ml

Predicted vital capacity (pVC)   _____ ml

Forced expiratory volume$_{1second}$ (FEV$_1$)   _____ %

Forced expiratory volume$_{2seconds}$ (FEV$_2$)   _____ %

Forced expiratory volume$_{3seconds}$ (FEV$_3$)   _____ %

4. The normal IRV is substantial, ranging from 2100 ml to 3100 ml. The program calculates the IRV based on the average values obtained for TV, ERV, and VC. How does your cIRV compare to the normal value?

_____

_____

5. Compare your vital capacity reading to the predicted vital capacity displayed on your data screen. If there is any significant difference, explain why:

_____

_____

If you wish to look at the data in a spreadsheet format:

    Choose **Summary Table** from the **Analyze** menu.

6. Record respiratory values as requested in question 2 of Review Sheet for Exercise 37A for later reference. ■

USE OF THE PNEUMOGRAPH TO DETERMINE FACTORS INFLUENCING RATE AND DEPTH OF RESPIRATION*

The neural centers that control respiratory rhythm and maintain a rate of 12 to 18 respirations per minute are located in the medulla and pons. On occasion, input from the stretch receptors in the lungs (via the vagus nerve to the medulla) modifies the respiratory rate, as in the case of extreme overinflation of the lungs (Hering-Breuer reflex).

Death occurs when medullary centers are completely suppressed, as from an overdose of sleeping pills or gross overindulgence in alcohol, and respiration ceases completely. ●

Although these nervous system centers initiate the basic rhythm of breathing, there is no question that physical phenomena such as talking, yawning, coughing, and exercise can modify the rate and depth of respiration. So too can chemical factors, such as changes in oxygen or carbon dioxide concentrations in the blood, or fluctuations in blood pH. Changes in carbon dioxide blood levels seem to act directly on the medullary control centers, whereas changes in pH and oxygen concentrations are monitored by chemoreceptor regions in the aortic and carotid bodies, which in turn send input to the medulla. The experimental sequence in this section is designed to test the relative importance of various physical and chemical factors in the process of respiration.

The pneumograph, an apparatus that records variations in breathing patterns, is the best means of observing respiratory variations resulting from physical and chemical factors. The chest pneumograph is a coiled rubber hose that is attached around the thorax. As the subject breathes, chest movements produce pressure changes within the pneumograph that are transmitted to a recorder.

The instructor will demonstrate the method for setting up the pneumograph and discuss the interpretation of the results. Work in pairs so that one person can mark the record to identify the test for later interpretation. Ideally, the student being tested should face away from the recording apparatus to prevent voluntary modification of the record.

Activity 3: Use of the Pneumograph to Determine Factors Influencing Rate and Depth of Respiration

1. Attach the pneumograph tubing firmly, but not restrictively, around the thoracic cage at the level of the sixth rib, leaving room for chest expansion during testing. If the subject is female, position the tubing above

---

* Note to the instructor: this exercise may also be done without using the recording apparatus by simply having the students count the respiratory rate visually.

the breasts to prevent slippage during testing. Set the pneumograph speed at 1 or 2, and the time signal at 10 second intervals. Record quiet breathing for 1 minute with the subject in a sitting position.

Record breaths per minute: _____

2.   Make a vital capacity tracing: Record a maximal inhalation followed by a maximal exhalation. This should correlate to the vital capacity measurement obtained earlier and will provide a baseline for comparison during the rest of the pneumograph testing. Stop the recording apparatus testing and indicate the following on the graph by marking the graph appropriately: tidal volume, expiratory reserve volume, inspiratory reserve volume, and vital capacity (the total of the three measurements). Also mark, with arrows, the direction the recording stylus moves during inspiration and expiration.

  Measure in millimeters the height of the vital capacity recording. Divide the vital capacity measurement recorded on p. 455 by the millimeter figure to obtain the volume (in milliliters of air) represented by 1 mm on the recording. For example, if your vital capacity reading is 4000 ml and the vital capacity tracing occupies a vertical distance of 40 mm on the pneumograph recording, then a vertical distance of 1 mm equals 100 ml of air.

Record your computed value: _____ ml air/mm

3.   Record the subject's breathing as she or he performs activities from the list below. Make sure the record is marked accurately to identify each test conducted. Record your results on the Exercise 37A Review Sheet.

talking	swallowing water
yawning	coughing
laughing	lying down
standing	running in place

doing a math problem (concentrating)

4.   Without recording, have the subject breathe normally for 2 minutes, then inhale deeply and hold her or his breath for as long as possible.

Time the breath-holding interval: _____ sec

As the subject exhales, turn on the recording apparatus and record the recovery period (time to return to normal breathing—usually slightly over 1 minute):

Time the recovery period: _____ sec

Did the subject have the urge to inspire or expire during

the breath holding? _____

Without recording, repeat the above experiment, but this time have the subject exhale completely and force-

fully *after* taking the deep breath. What was observed this time?

_____

_____

Explain the results. (*Hint:* The vagus nerve is the sensory nerve of the lungs and plays a role here.)

_____

_____

5.   Have the subject hyperventilate (breathe deeply and forcefully at the rate of 1 breath/4 sec) for about 30 seconds.* Record both during and after hyperventilation. How does the pattern obtained during hyperventilation compare with that recorded during the vital capacity tracing?

_____

Is the respiratory rate recorded after hyperventilation faster *or* slower than during normal quiet breathing?

_____

6.   Repeat the above test, but do not record until after the hyperventilation. After hyperventilating, the subject is to hold his or her breath as long as possible. Can the breath be held for a longer or shorter period of time after hyperventilation?

_____

7.   Without recording, have the subject breathe into a paper bag for 3 minutes; then record breathing movements.

⚠ *Caution:* During the bag-breathing exercise, the subject's partner should watch the subject carefully for any untoward reactions.

  Is the breathing rate faster or slower than the rate recorded during normal quiet breathing?

_____

After hyperventilating? _____

8.   Run in place for 2 minutes, then have your partner determine the length of your breath-holding.

_____ sec

* A sensation of dizziness may develop. (As the carbon dioxide is washed out of the blood by overventilation, the blood pH increases, leading to a decrease in blood pressure and reduced cerebral circulation.) The subject may experience a lack of desire to breathe after forced breathing is stopped. (If the period of breathing cessation—**apnea**—is extended, cyanosis of the lips may occur.)

9. To prove that respiration has a marked effect on circulation, conduct the following test. Have your lab partner record the rate and relative force of your radial pulse before you begin.

Rate _____ beats/min   Relative force _____

Inspire forcibly. Immediately close your mouth and nose to retain the inhaled air, and then make a forceful and prolonged expiration. Your lab partner should observe and record the condition of the blood vessels of your neck and face, and again immediately palpate the radial pulse.

Observations _____

_____

Radial pulse _____ beats/min   Relative force _____

Explain the changes observed.

_____

_____

Dispose of the paper bag in the autoclave bag. Keep the pneumograph records to interpret results and hand them in if requested by the instructor. Observation of the test results should enable you to determine which chemical factor, carbon dioxide or oxygen, has the greatest effect on modifying the respiratory rate and depth. ■

RESPIRATORY SOUNDS

As air flows in and out of the respiratory tree, it produces two characteristic sounds that can be picked up with a stethoscope. One is **bronchial sounds,** produced by air rushing through the large respiratory passageways (the trachea and bronchi). The second type, **vesicular breathing sounds,** apparently results from air filling the alveolar sacs and resembles the sound of a rustling or muffled breeze.

Activity 4: Investigating Respiratory Sounds

1. Obtain a stethoscope and clean the earpieces with an alcohol swab. Allow the alcohol to dry before donning the stethoscope. Place the diaphragm of the stethoscope on the throat of the test subject just below the larynx. Listen for bronchial sounds on inspiration and expiration.

2. Move the stethoscope over the following chest areas and listen for vesicular sounds during respiration (heard primarily during inspiration).

- At various intercostal spaces
- At the triangle of auscultation (a small depressed area of the back where the muscles fail to cover the rib cage; located just medial to the inferior part of the scapula)
- Under the clavicle

Diseased respiratory tissue, mucus, or pus can produce abnormal chest sounds such as rales (a rasping sound) and wheezing (a whistling sound). ●

ROLE OF THE RESPIRATORY SYSTEM IN ACID-BASE BALANCE OF THE BLOOD

As you have already learned, pulmonary ventilation is necessary for continuous oxygenation of the blood and removal of carbon dioxide (a waste product of cellular respiration) from the blood. Blood pH must be relatively constant for the cells of the body to function optimally. Therefore the carbonic acid–bicarbonate buffer system of the blood is extremely important, because it helps stabilize arterial blood pH at 7.4 ± 0.02.

When carbon dioxide diffuses into the blood from the tissue cells, much of it enters the red blood cells, where it combines with water to form carbonic acid:

$$H_2O + CO_2 \rightarrow H_2CO_3$$

Some carbonic acid is also formed in the plasma, but its formation there is very slow because of the lack of the carbonic anhydrase enzyme. Shortly after it forms, carbonic acid dissociates to release bicarbonate (HCO_3^-) and hydrogen (H^+) ions. The hydrogen ions that remain in the cells are neutralized, or buffered, when they combine with hemoglobin molecules. If they were not neutralized, the intracellular pH would become very acidic as H^+ ions accumulated. Once formed, the bicarbonate ions diffuse out of the red blood cells into the plasma where they become part of the carbonic acid–bicarbonate buffer system. As HCO_3^- follows its concentration gradient into the plasma, an electrical imbalance develops in the RBCs that draws Cl^- into them from the plasma. This exchange phenomenon is called the *chloride shift.*

Acids (more precisely, H^+) released into the blood by the body cells tend to lower the pH of the blood and cause it to become acidic. On the other hand, basic substances that enter the blood tend to cause the blood to become more alkaline and the pH to rise. Both of these tendencies are resisted in large part by the carbonic acid–bicarbonate buffer system. If H^+ concentration in the blood begins to increase, the H^+ ions combine with bicarbonate ions to form carbonic acid (a weak acid that does not tend to dissociate at physiological or acid pH) and is thus removed.

$$H^+ + HCO_3^- \rightarrow H_2CO_3$$

Likewise, as blood H^+ concentration drops below what is desirable, and blood pH rises, H_2CO_3 dissociates to release bicarbonate ions and H^+ ions to the blood. The released H^+ lowers the pH again. Bicarbonate ions, being weak bases, are poorly functional under alkaline conditions and have little effect on blood pH unless and until blood pH drops toward acid levels.

$$H_2CO_3 \rightarrow H^+ + HCO_3$$

In the case of excessively slow or shallow breathing (hypoventilation) or fast deep breathing (hyperventilation), the amount of carbonic acid in the blood can be greatly modified—increasing dramatically during hypoventilation and decreasing substantially during hyperventilation. In either situation, the buffering ability of the blood may be inadequate, and respiratory acidosis or alkalosis can result. Therefore, maintaining the normal rate and depth of breathing is important for proper control of blood pH.

Activity 5: Demonstrating the Reaction Between Carbon Dioxide and Water in Exhaled Air

1. Fill a beaker with 100 ml of distilled water.

2. Add 5 ml of 0.05 M NaOH and five drops of phenol red. Phenol red is an indicator that turns yellow in acidic solutions.

3. Blow through a straw into the solution.

What do you observe?

_____

_____

What chemical reaction is taking place in the beaker?

_____

_____

4. Discard the straw in the autoclave bag. ∎

Activity 6: Observing the Operation of Standard Buffers

1. To observe the ability of a buffer system to stabilize the pH of a solution, obtain five 250-ml beakers, and a wash bottle containing distilled water. Set up the following experimental samples:

Beaker 1
(150 ml distilled water)   pH _____

Beaker 2
(150 ml distilled water and
1 drop concentrated HCl)   pH _____

Beaker 3
(150 ml distilled water and
1 drop concentrated NaOH)   pH _____

Beaker 4
(150 ml standard buffer solution
[pH 7] and 1 drop concentrated HCl)   pH _____

Beaker 5
(150 ml standard buffer solution
[pH 7] and 1 drop concentrated NaOH)   pH _____

2. Using a pH meter standardized with a buffer solution of pH 7, determine the pH of the contents of each beaker and record above. After *each and every* pH recording, the pH meter switch should be turned to *standby,* and the electrodes rinsed thoroughly with a stream of distilled water from the wash bottle.

3. Add 3 more drops of concentrated HCl to beaker 4,

stir, and record the pH: _____

4. Add 3 more drops of concentrated NaOH to

beaker 5, stir, and record the pH: _____

How successful was the buffer solution in resisting pH changes when a strong acid (HCl) or a strong base

(NaOH) was added? _____ ∎

Activity 7: Exploring the Operation of the Carbonic Acid–Bicarbonate Buffer System

To observe the ability of the carbonic acid–bicarbonate buffer system of blood to resist pH changes, perform the following simple experiment.

1. Obtain two small beakers (50 ml), animal plasma, graduated cylinder, a glass stirring rod, and a dropper bottle of 0.01 M HCl. Using the pH meter standardized with the buffer solution of pH 7.0, measure the pH of the animal plasma. Use only enough plasma to allow immersion of the electrodes, and measure the volume used carefully.

pH of the animal plasma: _____

2. Add 2 drops of the 0.01 M HCl solution to the plasma, stir, and measure pH again.

pH of the plasma plus 2 drops of HCl: _____

3. Turn the pH meter switch to standby, rinse the electrodes, and then immerse them in a quantity of distilled water (pH 7) exactly equal to the amount of animal plasma used. Measure the pH of the distilled water.

pH of distilled water: _____

4. Add 2 drops of the 0.01 M HCl; swirl, and measure pH again.

pH of distilled water plus 2 drops of HCl: _____

Is the plasma a good buffer? _____

What component of the plasma carbonic acid–bicarbonate buffer system was acting to counteract a change in pH when HCl was added?

_____ ∎

PowerLab® Data Acquisition System Exercises

This appendix contains six lab exercises that use Power-Lab® Data Acquisition System equipment. Each Power-Lab® exercise is a complete lab, the same as is found in the lab manual, but with sections involving data acquisition and compilation equipment using PowerLab®. Pages have been perforated to allow for easy tear out and duplication.

PowerLab® exercise numbers correspond to those in the lab manual; however, PowerLab® exercises have an additional letter *b,* which indicates the PowerLab® component. The table below indicates which lab manual exercises are offered for PowerLab®. Use the review sheets for exercises 16A, 22, 31, 33A, 34A, and 37A in the lab manual to review the PowerLab® material. Contact information: ADInstruments, 2205 Executive Circle, Colorado Springs, CO 80906; 888-965-6040; www.adinstruments.com; info@adinstruments.com.

Exercise topic	Lab manual exercise	PowerLab® exercise
Skeletal Muscle Physiology: Frog Experimentation–Wet Lab	Exercise 16A, p. 167	Exercise 16b, p. 481
Human Reflex Physiology	Exercise 22, p. 247	Exercise 22b, p. 489
Conduction System of the Heart and Electrocardiography	Exercise 31, p. 332	Exercise 31b, p. 498
Human Cardiovascular Physiology: Blood Pressure and Pulse Determinations	Exercise 33A, p. 359	Exercise 33b, p. 503
Frog Cardiovascular Physiology: Wet Lab	Exercise 34A, p. 372	Exercise 34b, p. 516
Respiratory System Physiology	Exercise 37A, 399	Exercise 37b, p. 525

Skeletal Muscle Physiology: Frog Experimentation–Wet Lab Using PowerLab® Data Acquisition System

The following lab includes instructions for PowerLab®. This lab uses recording equipment to collect data concerning frog heart activity. The data can be collected with a kymograph, physiograph, or a computerized data collection system. The laboratory manual contains the instructions for BIOPAC® and physiograph, and these instructions are for PowerLab®. It's assumed the students are familiar with the use of the PowerLab® system before beginning the experiments.

Note: For up-to-date versions of this and other experiments, log on to www.powerlab-teaching.com/experiments.

Objectives

1. To observe muscle contraction on the microscopic level and describe the role of ATP and various ions in muscle contraction.

2. To define and explain the physiological basis of the following:
   depolarization
   repolarization
   action potential
   absolute and relative refractory periods
   subthreshold stimulus
   threshold stimulus
   maximal stimulus
   treppe
   wave summation
   tetanus
   muscle fatigue

3. To trace the events that result from the electrical stimulation of a muscle.

4. To recognize that a graded response of skeletal muscle is a function of the number of muscle fibers stimulated and the frequency of the stimulus.

5. To name and describe the phases of a muscle twitch.

6. To distinguish between a muscle twitch and a sustained (tetanic) contraction and to describe their importance in normal muscle activity.

7. To demonstrate how a computer or physiograph can be used to obtain pertinent and representative recordings of various physiological events of skeletal muscle activity.

8. To explain the significance of muscle tracings obtained during experimentation.

Materials

- ATP muscle kits (glycerinated rabbit psoas muscle;* ATP and salt solutions obtainable from Carolina Biological Supply)
- Petri dishes
- Microscope slides
- Cover glasses
- Millimeter ruler
- Compound microscope
- Dissecting microscope
- Pointed glass probes (teasing needles)
- Small beaker (50 ml)
- Distilled water
- Glass-marking pencil
- Copies of textbooks or other heavy books
- Watch or timer
- Frog Ringer's solution
- Scissors
- Metal needle probes
- Medicine dropper
- Cotton thread
- Forceps
- Disposable gloves
- Glass or porcelain plate
- Pithed bullfrog†

Notes to the Instructor:

*At the beginning of the lab, the muscle bundle should be removed from the test tube and cut into ~ 2-cm lengths. Both the cut muscle segments and the entubed glycerol should be put into a petri dish. One muscle *segment* is sufficient for each two to four students making observations.

†Bullfrogs to be pithed by lab instructor as needed for student experimentation. (If instructor prefers that students pith their own specimens, an instructional sheet on that procedure suitable for copying for student handouts is provided in the Instructor's Guide.)

❑ PowerLab® unit and interface cable, Windows PC or Macintosh computer with Chart software installed, Bridge Pod, MLT500/A Force Transducer, transducer cable, transducer stand, micropositioner, bipolar stimulator, S-shaped pin, thread, PowerLab® User's Guide, Chart User's Guide

PhysioEx™ 5.0 Computer Simulation on p. P-17

Muscle Activity

The contraction of skeletal and cardiac muscle fibers can be considered in terms of three events—electrical excitation of the muscle cell, excitation-contraction coupling, and shortening of the muscle cell due to sliding of the myofilaments within it.

At rest, all cells maintain a potential difference, or voltage, across their plasma membrane; the inner face of the membrane is approximately −60 to −90 millivolts (mV) compared with the cell exterior. This potential difference is a result of differences in membrane permeability to cations, most importantly sodium (Na^+) and potassium (K^+) ions. Intracellular potassium concentration is much greater than its extracellular concentration, and intracellular sodium concentration is considerably less than its extracellular concentration. Hence, steep concentration gradients across the membrane exist for both cations. However, because the plasma membrane is slightly more permeable to K^+ than to Na^+, Na^+ influx into the cell is inadequate to balance K^+ outflow. The result of this unequal Na^+-K^+ diffusion across the membrane establishes the cell's **resting membrane potential.** The resting membrane potential is of particular interest in excitable cells, like muscle cells and neurons, because changes in that voltage underlie their ability to do work (to contract or to signal in muscle cells and neurons, respectively).

Action Potential

When a muscle cell is stimulated, the sarcolemma becomes temporarily permeable to sodium, which rushes into the cell. This sudden influx of sodium ions alters the membrane potential. That is, the cell interior becomes less negatively charged at that point, an event called **depolarization.** When depolarization reaches a certain level and the sarcolemma momentarily changes its polarity, a depolarization wave travels along the sarcolemma. Even as the influx of sodium ions occurs, the sarcolemma becomes impermeable to sodium and permeable to potassium ions. Consequently, potassium ions leak out of the cell, restoring the resting membrane potential (but not the original ionic conditions), an event called **repolarization.** The repolarization wave follows the depolarization wave across the sarcolemma. This rapid depolarization and repolarization of the membrane that is propagated along the entire membrane from the point of stimulation is called the **action potential.**

While the sodium gates are still open, there is no possibility of another response and the muscle cell is said to be in

the **absolute refractory period.** The **relative refractory period** is the period after the sodium gates have closed when potassium gates are open and repolarization is ongoing. Especially strong stimuli may provoke a contraction during this part of the refractory period. Repolarization restores the muscle cell's excitability. Temporarily, the sodium-potassium pump, which actively transports K^+ into the cell and Na^+ out of the cell, need not be "revved up." But if the cell is stimulated to contract again and again in rapid-fire order, the loss of potassium and gain of sodium occurring during action potential generation begins to reduce its ability to respond. And so, eventually the sodium-potassium pump must be activated to reestablish the ionic concentrations of the resting state.

Contraction

Propagation of the action potential along the sarcolemma causes the release of calcium ions (Ca^{2+}) from storage in the tubules of the sarcoplasmic reticulum within the muscle cell. When the calcium ions bind to regulatory proteins on the actin myofilaments, they act as an ionic trigger that initiates contraction, and the actin and myosin filaments slide past each other. Once the action potential ends, the calcium ions are almost immediately transported back into the tubules of the sarcoplasmic reticulum. Instantly the muscle cell relaxes.

The events of the contraction process can most simply be summarized as follows: muscle cell contraction is initiated by generation and transmission of an action potential along the sarcolemma. This electrical event is coupled to the sliding of the myofilaments—contraction—by the release of Ca^{2+}. Keep in mind this sequence of events as you conduct the experiments.

Activity 1:
Observing Muscle Fiber Contraction

In this simple observational experiment, you will have the opportunity to review your understanding of muscle cell anatomy and to watch fibers respond to the presence of ATP and/or a solution of potassium and magnesium ions.

This experiment uses preparations of glycerinated muscle. The glycerination process denatures troponin and tropomyosin. Consequently, calcium, so critical for contraction in vivo, is not necessary here. The role of magnesium and potassium salts as cofactors in the contraction process is not well understood, but magnesium and potassium salts seem to be required for ATP-ase activity in this system.

1. Talk with other members of your lab group to develop a hypothesis about muscle fiber contraction for this experiment. The hypothesis should have three parts: (a) salts only, (b) ATP only, and (c) salts and ATP.

2. Obtain the following materials from the supply area: 2 glass teasing needles, 6 glass microscope slides and 3 cover glasses, millimeter ruler, dropper vials containing the following solutions: (a) 0.25% ATP in triply distilled water; (b) 0.25% ATP plus 0.05 M KCl plus 0.001 M $MgCl_2$ in distilled water; and (c) 0.05 M KCl plus 0.001 M $MgCl_2$ in distilled water; a petri dish, a beaker of distilled water, a glass-marking pencil, and a small portion of a previously cut muscle bundle segment. While you are at the supply area, place the muscle fibers in the petri dish and pour a small

Salts only	Muscle fiber 1	Muscle fiber 2	Muscle fiber 3	Average
Initial length (mm)				
Contracted length (mm)				
% Contraction				
ATP only				
Initial length (mm)				
Contracted length (mm)				
% Contraction				
Salts and ATP				
Initial length (mm)				
Contracted length (mm)				
% Contraction				

amount of glycerol (the fluid in the supply petri dish) over your muscle cells. Also obtain both a compound and a dissecting microscope and bring them to your laboratory bench.

3. Using clean fine glass needles, tease the muscle segment to separate its fibers. The objective is to isolate *single* muscle cells or fibers for observation. Be patient and work carefully so that the fibers do not get torn during this isolation procedure.

4. Transfer one or more of the fibers (or the thinnest strands you have obtained) onto a clean microscope slide with a glass needle, and cover it with a cover glass. Examine the fiber under the compound microscope at low- and then high-power magnifications to observe the striations and the smoothness of the fibers when they are in the relaxed state.

5. Clean three microscope slides well and rinse in distilled water. Label the slides A, B, and C.

6. Transfer three or four fibers to microscope slide A with a glass needle. Using the needle as a prod, carefully position the fibers so that they are parallel to one another and as straight as possible. Place this slide under a *stereomicroscope* and measure the length of each fiber by holding a millimeter ruler adjacent to it. Alternatively, you can rest the microscope slide *on* the millimeter ruler to make your length determinations. Record the data on the chart at the top of the page.

7. Flood the fibers (situated under the dissecting microscope) with several drops of the solution containing ATP, potassium ions, and magnesium ions. Watch the reaction of the fibers after adding the solution. After 30 seconds (or slightly longer), remeasure each fiber and record the observed lengths on the chart. Also, observe the fibers to see if any width changes have occurred. Calculate the degree (or percentage) of contraction by using the following simple formula, and record this data on the chart above.

$$\frac{\text{Initial}}{\text{length (mm)}} - \frac{\text{contracted}}{\text{length (mm)}} = \frac{\text{degree of}}{\text{contraction (mm)}}$$

then:

$$\frac{\text{Degree of contraction (mm)} \times 100}{\text{initial length (mm)}} = \underline{\hspace{1cm}} \text{ % contraction}$$

8. Carefully transfer one of the contracted fibers to a clean microscope slide, cover with a cover glass, and observe with the compound microscope. Mentally compare your initial observations with the view you are observing now. What differences do you see? (Be specific.)

_____

_____

_____

What zones (or bands) have disappeared?

_____

9. Repeat steps 4 to 8 twice more, using clean slides and fresh muscle cells. On slide B use the solution of ATP in distilled water (no salts). Then, on slide C use the solution containing only salts (no ATP) for the third series. Record data on the chart above.

10. Collect the data from all the groups in your laboratory and use this data to prepare a lab report. (See Getting Started: Writing a Lab Report, p. xii.) Include in your discussion the following questions on the following page.

What degree of contraction was observed when ATP was applied in the absence of potassium and magnesium ions?

_____

_____

What degree of contraction was observed when the muscle fibers were flooded with a K^+- and Mg^{2+}-containing solution that lacked ATP?

_____

_____

What conclusions can you draw about the importance of ATP and potassium and magnesium ions to the contractile process?

_____

_____

_____

Can you draw exactly the same conclusions from the data provided by each group? List some variables that might have been introduced into the procedure and that might account for any differences.

_____

_____ ∎

Activity 2:
Demonstrating Muscle Fatigue in Humans

1.   Work in small groups. In each group select a subject, a timer, and a recorder.

2.   Obtain a copy of the laboratory manual and a copy of the textbook. Weigh each book separately and then record the weight of each in the chart above.

3.   The subject is to extend an upper limb straight out in front of him or her, holding the position until the arm shakes or the muscle begins to ache. Record the time to fatigue on the chart.

4.   Allow the subject to rest for several minutes. Now ask the subject to hold the laboratory manual while keeping the arm and forearm in the same position as in step 3 above. Record the time to fatigue on the chart.

5.   Allow the subject to rest again for several minutes. Now ask the subject to hold the textbook while keeping the upper limb in the same position as in steps 3 and 4 above. Record the time to fatigue on the chart.

6.   Each person in the group should take a turn as subject and all data should be recorded.

Load	Weight of object	Time elapsed until fatigue		
		Subject 1	Subject 2	Subject 3
Appendage	N. A.			
Lab Manual				
Textbook				

7.   What can you conclude about the effect of load on muscle fatigue? Explain.

_____

_____

_____ ∎

Activity 3:
Inducing Contraction in the Frog Gastrocnemius Muscle

Physiologists have learned a great deal about the way muscles function by isolating muscles from laboratory animals and then stimulating these muscles to observe their responses. Various stimuli—electrical shock, temperature changes, extremes of pH, certain chemicals—elicit muscle activity, but laboratory experiments of this type typically use electrical shock. This is because it is easier to control the onset and cessation of electrical shock, as well as the strength of the stimulus.

Preparing a Muscle for Experimentation

The preparatory work that precedes the recording of muscle activity tends to be quite time-consuming. If you work in teams of two or three, the work can be divided. While one of you is setting up the recording apparatus, one or two students can dissect the frog leg (Figure 16b.1). Experimentation should begin as soon as the dissection is completed.

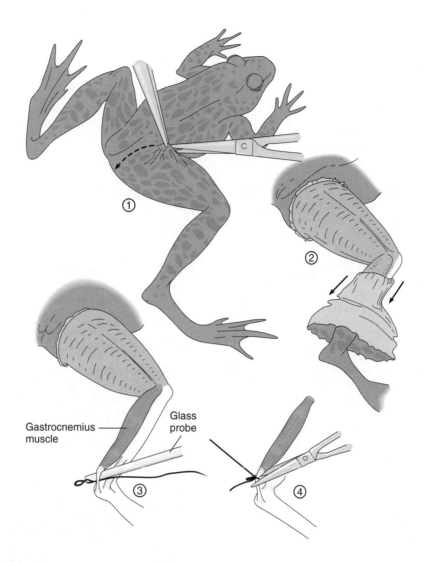

Figure 16b.1 Preparation of the frog gastrocnemius muscle. Numbers indicate the sequence of manipulation.

Dissection:
Frog Hind Limb

1. Before beginning the frog dissection, have the following supplies ready at your laboratory bench: a small beaker containing 20 to 30 ml of frog Ringer's solution, scissors, a metal needle probe, a glass probe with a pointed tip, a medicine dropper, cotton thread, forceps, a glass or porcelain plate, and disposable gloves. While these supplies are being accumulated, one member of your team should notify the instructor that you are ready to begin experimentation, so that the frog can be prepared (pithed). Preparation of the frog in this manner renders it unable to feel pain and prevents reflex movements (like hopping) that would interfere with the experiments.

2. All students that will be handling the frog should obtain and don disposable plastic gloves. Obtain a pithed frog and place it ventral surface down on the glass plate. Make an incision into the skin approximately midthigh (Figure 16b.1), and then continue the cut completely around the thigh. Grasp the skin with the forceps and strip it from the leg and hindfoot. The skin adheres more at the joints, but a careful, persistent pulling motion—somewhat like pulling off a nylon stocking—will enable you to remove it in one piece. From this point on, the exposed muscle tissue should be kept moistened with the Ringer's solution to prevent spontaneous twitches.

3. Identify the gastrocnemius muscle (the fleshy muscle of the posterior calf) and the calcaneal (Achilles) tendon that secures it to the heel.

4. Slip a glass probe under the gastrocnemius muscle and run it along the entire length and under the calcaneal tendon to free them from the underlying tissues.

5. Cut a piece of thread about 10 in. long and use the glass probe to slide the thread under the calcaneal tendon. Knot the thread firmly around the tendon and then sever the tendon distal to the thread. Alternatively, you can bend a common pin into a Z-shape and insert the pin securely into the tendon. The thread is then attached to the opposite end of the pin.

6. Cut away the fibulotibial bone just distal to the knee. Expose the femur of the thigh and cut it completely through at midthigh. Remove as much of the thigh muscle tissue as possible by carefully cutting it away with the scissors.

Recording Muscle Activity

Skeletal muscles consist of thousands of muscle cells and react to stimuli with graded responses. Thus muscle contractions can be weak or vigorous, depending on the requirements of the task. Graded responses (different degrees of shortening) of a skeletal muscle depend on the number of muscle cells being stimulated. In the intact organism, the number of motor units firing at any one time determines how many muscle cells will be stimulated. In this laboratory, the frequency and strength of an electrical current determines the response.

A single contraction of skeletal muscle is called a **muscle twitch.** A tracing of a muscle twitch (Figure 16b.2) shows three distinct phases: latent, contraction, and relaxation. The **latent phase** is the interval from stimulus application until the muscle begins to shorten. Although no activity is indicated on the tracing during this phase, important electrical and chemical changes are occurring within the muscle. During the **contraction phase,** the muscle fibers shorten; the tracing shows an increasingly higher needle deflection and the tracing peaks. During the **relaxation phase,** represented by a downward curve of the tracing, the muscle fibers relax and lengthen. On a slowly moving recording surface, the single muscle twitch appears as a spike (rather than a bell-shaped curve, as in Figure 16b.2), but on a rapidly moving recording surface, the three distinct phases just described become recognizable.

Using PowerLab® to Record Frog Muscle Activity

Setting Up the Equipment

Use the detailed instructions provided with Figure 16b.3 in order to properly set up the PowerLab® equipment. Note that for up-to-date PowerLab® experiments concerning frog muscle activity, log on to www.powerlab-teaching.com/experiments.

Determining the Threshold Stimulus

1. Make sure the muscle is moist, and make sure the stimulator is contacting it.

2. From the Macro menu, select "Graded Response."

3. Follow the on-screen instructions; the recording will proceed automatically.

4. The PowerLab® will stimulate the muscle with increasing strength.

5. Determine the threshold and maximal stimulus voltage from the data recording, then record your values.

6. When the recording stops, add a comment to your Chart data file named "Treppe."

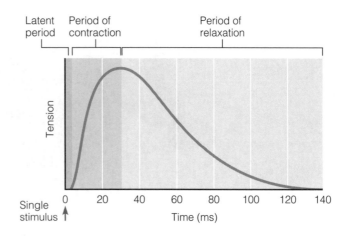

Figure 16b.2 Tracing of a muscle twitch.

Inducing Treppe, or the Staircase Phenomenon

As a muscle is stimulated to contract, a curious phenomenon is observed in the tracing pattern of the first few twitches. Even though the stimulus intensity is unchanged, the height of the individual spikes increases in a stepwise manner, producing a sort of staircase pattern called **treppe** (Figure 16b.4). This phenomenon is not well understood, but the following explanation has been offered: in the muscle cell's resting state, there is much less Ca^{2+} in the sarcoplasm and the enzyme systems in the muscle cell are less efficient than after it has contracted a few times. As the muscle cell begins to contract, the intracellular concentration of Ca^{2+} rises dramatically, and the heat generated by muscle activity increases the efficiency of the enzyme systems. As a result, the muscle becomes more efficient and contracts more vigorously. This is the physiological basis of the warm-up period prior to competition in sports events.

1. Make sure the muscle is moist by applying frog Ringer's solution.

2. From the Macro menu, choose "Tetanus."

3 Follow the on-screen instructions.

4. The PowerLab® will automatically stimulate the muscle for one-second blocks at the following stimulus intervals: 400, 200, 100, 50, and 20ms.

5. When the recording stops, add a comment to your Chart data file named "Treppe."

Observing Graded Muscle Response to Increased Stimulus Frequency

Muscles subjected to frequent stimulation, without a chance to relax, exhibit two kinds of responses—wave summation and tetanus—depending on the level of stimulus frequency (Figure 16b.4).

Wave Summation: If a muscle is stimulated with a rapid series of stimuli of the same intensity before it has had a chance to relax completely, the response to the second and subse-

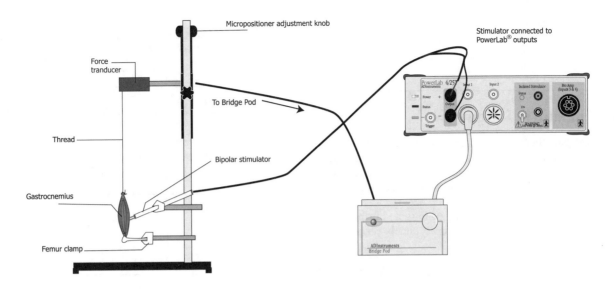

Figure 16b.3 PowerLab® setup for frog gastrocnemius experiments.

Setting Up the Equipment

1. Attach a femur clamp to the lower part of the ring stand.

2. Attach the micropositioner to the ring stand, and mount the force transducer in its holder.

3. Clamp the femur to the femur clamp.

4. Insert an S-shaped pin into the muscle tendon.

5. Tie a thread to the pin, and attach the other end of the thread to the force transducer. Adjust the height of the micropositioner so it is at its lowest position and the thread is just slack.

6. Connect the force transducer cable to the Bridge Pod.

7. Plug the Bridge Pod into the Pod Port on Input 1 of the PowerLab® unit.

8. Mount the bipolar stimulator handle onto the ring stand so its tips are touching the muscle.

9. Connect the BNC plugs to the positive and negative connectors on the Output ports of the PowerLab® unit.

10. Make sure the computer is turned on; turn on the Power-Lab® unit.

11. Open the Chart settings file called "Frog Muscle Settings."

12. A two-channel data file will appear. Channel 1 is named "Force," and Channel 2 is labeled "Stimulus Marker."

13. From the Force channel pull-down menu, select "Bridge Pod."

14. Using the knob on the front of the Bridge Pod, adjust the signal in the dialog box so that it reads zero.

15. Click OK.

---

quent stimuli will be greater than to the first stimulus. This phenomenon, called **wave,** or **temporal, summation,** occurs because the muscle is already in a partially contracted state when subsequent stimuli are delivered.

1. Make sure the muscle is moist by applying frog Ringer's solution.

2. From the Macro pull-down menu, select "Stimulus Amplitude."

3. Input the supra-maximal stimulus value that you calculated earlier in the Amplitude (Output Level) field. *Do not modify the other settings.* When you are finished, close the Stimulator window.

4. From the Macro menu, choose "Stimulus Frequency."

5. Follow the on-screen instructions. The PowerLab® will stimulate the muscle with twin pulses at several intervals, and each interval will appear in a separate data block.

6. When the recording stops, add a comment to your Chart data file called "Graded Response."

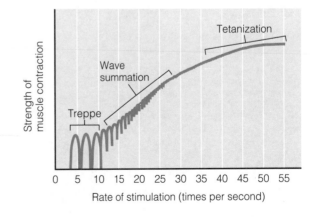

Figure 16b.4 Treppe, wave summation, and tetanization. Progressive summation of successive contractions occurs as the rate of stimulation is increased. Tetanization occurs when the rate of stimulation reaches approximately 35 per second, and maximum contraction force occurs at a stimulation rate of approximately 50 per second.

Appendix B **487**

What did you observe?

_____

_____

Inducing Muscle Fatigue

Muscle fatigue, the loss of the ability to contract, is believed to be a result of the oxygen debt that occurs in the tissue after prolonged activity (through the accumulation of such waste products as lactic acid as well as the depletion of ATP). True muscle fatigue rarely occurs in the body because it is most often preceded by a subjective feeling of fatigue. Furthermore, fatigue of the neuromuscular junctions typically precedes fatigue of the muscle.

1. Make sure the muscle is moist by applying frog Ringer's solution.

2. From the Macro menu, choose "Fatigue."

3. Follow the on-screen instructions.

4. The PowerLab® will stimulate the muscle continuously for 30 seconds with a stimulus interval of 20ms.

5. When the recording stops, add a comment to your Chart data file called "Fatigue."

Determining the Effect of Stretch on Skeletal Muscle

When the fibers of a skeletal muscle are slightly stretched by a weight or tension, the muscle responds by contracting more forcibly and thus is capable of doing more work. When the actin and myosin barely overlap, sliding can occur along nearly the entire length of the actin filaments. If the load is increased beyond the optimum, the latent period becomes longer, contractile force decreases, and relaxation (fatigue) occurs more quickly. With excessive stretching, the muscle is unable to develop any tension and no contraction occurs. Since the filaments no longer overlap at all with this degree of stretching, the sliding force cannot be generated.

Stretch (mm)	Force generation (N)	
	Trial 1	Trial 2
0		
1		
2		
3		
4		
5		
6		
7		
8		
9		
10		

1. Make sure the muscle preparation is moist, and the stimulator leads are contacting it.

2. Note the position of the micropositioner. This is your reference position.

3. From the Macro menu, select "Muscle Tension."

4. Follow the on-screen instructions to record your data.

5. At the end of the recording, lower the micropositioner to its original position.

6. When the recording stops, add a comment to your Chart data file called "Stretch." ■

Human Reflex Physiology Using PowerLab® Data Acquisition System

The following lab includes instructions for using PowerLab® to measure reaction time. This lab uses recording equipment to collect data concerning reaction time from a human subject. The laboratory manual contains the instructions for using BIOPAC®, and these instructions are for PowerLab®. It is assumed the students are familiar with the use of the PowerLab® system before beginning the experiments.

Note: For up-to-date versions of this and other experiments, log on to www.powerlab-teaching.com/experiments.

Objectives

1. To define *reflex* and *reflex arc.*
2. To name, identify, and describe the function of each element of a reflex arc.
3. To indicate why reflex testing is an important part of every physical examination.
4. To describe and discuss several types of reflex activities as observed in the laboratory; to indicate the functional or clinical importance of each; and to categorize each as a somatic or autonomic reflex action.
5. To explain why cord-mediated reflexes are generally much faster than those involving input from the higher brain centers.
6. To investigate differences in reaction time of reflexes and learned responses.

Materials

❑ Reflex hammer
❑ Sharp pencils
❑ Cot (if available)
❑ Absorbent cotton (sterile)
❑ Tongue depressor
❑ Metric ruler
❑ Reaction time ruler (if available)
❑ Flashlight
❑ 100- or 250-ml beaker

❑ 10- or 25-ml graduated cylinder
❑ Lemon juice in dropper bottle
❑ Wide-range pH paper
❑ Large laboratory bucket containing freshly prepared 10% household bleach solution (for saliva-soiled glassware)
❑ Disposable autoclave bag
❑ Wash bottle containing 10% bleach solution
❑ PowerLab® unit and interface cable, Windows PC or Macintosh computer with Chart software installed, MLA92 Timing Push-button Switch, ML1110 Finger Pulse Transducer, PowerLab® User's Guide, Chart User's Guide

The Reflex Arc

Reflexes are rapid, predictable, involuntary motor responses to stimuli; they are mediated over neural pathways called **reflex arcs.**

Reflexes can be categorized into one of two large groups: autonomic reflexes and somatic reflexes. **Autonomic** (or visceral) **reflexes** are mediated through the autonomic nervous system, and we are not usually aware of them. These reflexes activate smooth muscles, cardiac muscle, and the glands of the body and they regulate body functions such as digestion, elimination, blood pressure, salivation, and sweating. **Somatic reflexes** include all those reflexes that involve stimulation of skeletal muscles by the somatic division of the nervous system. An example of such a reflex is the rapid withdrawal of a hand from a hot object.

Reflex testing is an important diagnostic tool for assessing the condition of the nervous system. Distorted, exaggerated, or absent reflex responses may indicate degeneration or pathology of portions of the nervous system, often before other signs are apparent.

If the spinal cord is damaged, the easily performed reflex tests can help pinpoint the area (level) of spinal cord injury. Motor nerves above the injured area may be unaffected, whereas those at or below the lesion site may be unable to participate in normal reflex activity. ●

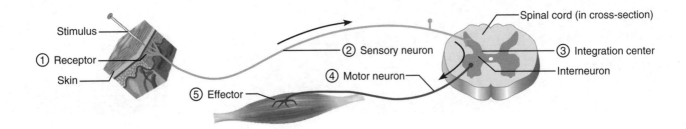

Figure 22b.1 Simple reflex arcs. Components of all human reflex arcs: receptor, sensory neuron, integration center (one or more synapses in the CNS), motor neuron, and effector.

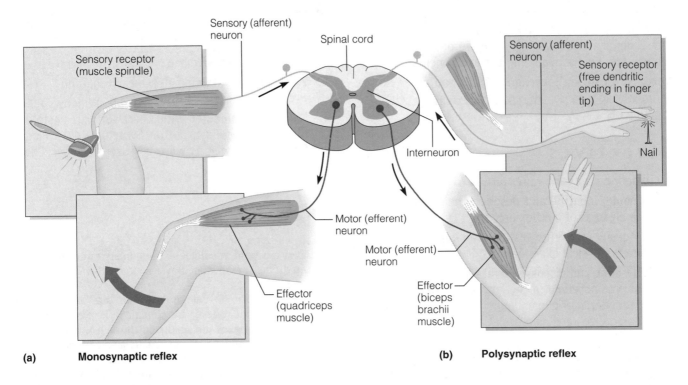

(a)   Monosynaptic reflex

(b)   Polysynaptic reflex

Figure 22b.2 Monosynaptic and polysynaptic reflex arcs. The integration center is in the spinal cord, and in each example the receptor and effector are in the same limb. **(a)** The patellar reflex, a two-neuron monosynaptic reflex. **(b)** A flexor reflex, an example of a polysynaptic reflex.

Components of a Reflex Arc

All reflex arcs have five essential components (Figure 22b.1):

① The *receptor* is the site of stimulus action.

② The *sensory neuron* transmits the afferent impulses to the CNS.

③ The *integration center* consists of one or more synapses in the CNS.

④ The *motor neuron* conducts efferent impulses from the integration center to an effector organ.

⑤ The *effector*, muscle fibers or glands, responds to efferent impulses characteristically (by contracting or secreting, respectively).

The simple patellar or knee-jerk reflex shown in Figure 22b.2a is an example of a simple, two-neuron, *monosynaptic* (literally, "one synapse") reflex arc. It will be demonstrated in the laboratory. However, most reflexes are more complex and *polysynaptic*, involving the participation of one or more association neurons in the reflex arc pathway. A three-neuron reflex arc (flexor reflex) is diagrammed in Figure 22b.2b. Since delay or inhibition of the reflex may occur at the synapses, the more synapses encountered in a reflex pathway, the more time is required to effect the reflex.

Reflexes of many types may be considered programmed into the neural anatomy. Many *spinal reflexes* (reflexes that are initiated and completed at the spinal cord level, such as the flexor reflex) occur without the involvement of higher brain centers. These reflexes work equally well in decerebrate animals (those in which the brain has been destroyed), as long as the spinal cord is functional. Conversely, other

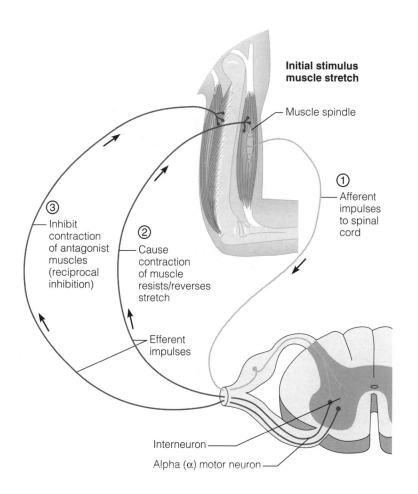

Initial stimulus muscle stretch

Muscle spindle

③ Inhibit contraction of antagonist muscles (reciprocal inhibition)

② Cause contraction of muscle resists/reverses stretch

① Afferent impulses to spinal cord

Efferent impulses

Interneuron

Alpha (α) motor neuron

Figure 22b.3 Events of the stretch reflex by which muscle stretch is damped. The events are shown in circular fashion. **(1)** Stretching of the muscle activates a muscle spindle. **(2)** Impulses transmitted by afferent fibers from muscle spindle to alpha motor neurons in the spinal cord result in activation of the stretched muscle, causing it to contract. **(3)** Impulses transmitted by afferent fibers from muscle spindle to interneurons in the spinal cord result in reciprocal inhibition of the antagonist muscle.

reflexes require the involvement of the brain, since many different inputs must be evaluated before the appropriate reflex is determined. Superficial cord reflexes and pupillary responses to light are in this category. In addition, although many spinal reflexes do not require the involvement of higher centers, the brain is "advised" of spinal cord reflex activity and may alter it by facilitating or inhibiting the reflexes.

Somatic Reflexes

There are several types of somatic reflexes, including several that you will be eliciting during this laboratory session—the stretch, crossed extensor, superficial cord, corneal, and gag reflexes. Some require only spinal cord activity; others require brain involvement as well.

Spinal Reflexes

Stretch Reflexes Stretch reflexes are important postural reflexes, normally acting to maintain posture, balance, and locomotion. Stretch reflexes are initiated by tapping a tendon, which stretches the muscle the tendon is attached to. This stimulates the muscle spindles and causes reflex contraction of the stretched muscle or muscles, which resists further stretching. Even as the primary stretch reflex is occurring, impulses are being sent to other destinations as well. For example, branches of the afferent fibers (from the muscle spindles) also synapse with association neurons (interneurons)

controlling the antagonist muscles (Figure 22b.3). The inhibition of those interneurons and the antagonist muscles that follows, called *reciprocal inhibition,* causes them to relax and prevents them from resisting (or reversing) the contraction of the stretched muscle caused by the main reflex arc. Additionally, impulses are relayed to higher brain centers (largely via the dorsal white columns) to advise of muscle length, speed of shortening, and the like—information needed to maintain muscle tone and posture. Stretch reflexes tend to be hypoactive or absent in cases of peripheral nerve damage or ventral horn disease, and hyperactive in corticospinal tract lesions. They are absent in deep sedation and coma.

Activity 1:
Initiating Stretch Reflexes

1. Test the **patellar,** or knee-jerk, **reflex** by seating a subject on the laboratory bench with legs hanging free (or with knees crossed). Tap the patellar ligament sharply with the reflex hammer just below the knee to elicit the knee-jerk response, which assesses the L_2–L_4 level of the spinal cord (Figure 22b.4). Test both knees and record your observations. (Sometimes a reflex can be altered by your actions. If you encounter difficulty, consult your instructor for helpful hints.)

_____

_____

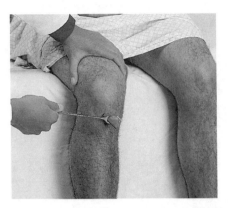

Figure 22b.4 Testing the patellar reflex. The examiner supports the subject's knee so that the subject's muscles are relaxed, and then strikes the patellar ligament with the reflex hammer. The proper location may be ascertained by palpation of the patella.

Which muscles contracted? _____

_____

What nerve is carrying the afferent and efferent impulses?

_____

2. Test the effect of mental distraction on the patellar reflex by having the subject add a column of three-digit numbers while you test the reflex again. Is the response greater than *or* less than the first response?

_____

What are your conclusions about the effect of mental distraction on reflex activity?

_____

_____

3. Now test the effect of muscular activity occurring simultaneously in other areas of the body. Have the subject clasp the edge of the laboratory bench and vigorously attempt to pull it upward with both hands. At the same time, test the patellar reflex again. Is the response more or less vigorous than the first response?

_____

4. Fatigue also influences the reflex response. The subject should jog in position until she or he is very fatigued (really fatigued—no slackers). Test the patellar reflex again and record whether it is more or less vigorous than the first response.

_____

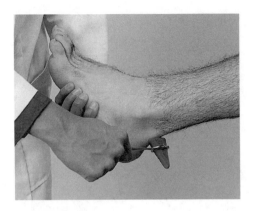

Figure 22b.5 Testing the Achilles reflex. The examiner slightly dorsiflexes the subject's ankle by supporting the foot lightly in the hand, and then taps the Achilles tendon just above the ankle.

Would you say that nervous system activity *or* muscle function is responsible for the changes you have just observed?

_____

Explain your reasoning. _____

_____

_____

_____

5. The **Achilles,** or ankle-jerk, **reflex** assesses the first two sacral segments of the spinal cord. With your shoe removed and your foot dorsiflexed slightly to increase the tension of the gastrocnemius muscle, have your partner sharply tap your calcaneal (Achilles) tendon with the reflex hammer (Figure 22b.5).

What is the result? _____

_____

Does the contraction of the gastrocnemius normally result in the activity you have observed?

_____ ■

Crossed Extensor Reflex The **crossed extensor reflex** is more complex than the stretch reflex. It consists of a flexor, or withdrawal, reflex followed by extension of the opposite limb.

This reflex is quite obvious when, for example, a stranger suddenly and strongly grips one's arm. The immediate response is to withdraw the clutched arm and push the intruder away with the other arm. The reflex is more difficult to demonstrate in a laboratory because it is anticipated, and under these conditions the extensor part of the reflex may be inhibited.

Activity 2:
Initiating the Crossed Extensor Reflex

The subject should sit with eyes closed and with the dorsum of one hand resting on the laboratory bench. Obtain a sharp pencil and suddenly prick the subject's index finger. What are the results?

_____

_____

_____

Did the extensor part of this reflex seem to be slow compared to the other reflexes you have observed?

_____

What are the reasons for this? _____

_____

_____

_____ ▪

The reflexes that have been demonstrated so far—the stretch and crossed extensor reflexes—are examples of reflexes in which the reflex pathway is initiated and completed at the spinal cord level.

Superficial Cord Reflexes The **superficial cord reflexes** (abdominal, cremaster, and plantar reflexes) result from pain and temperature changes. They are initiated by stimulation of receptors in the skin and mucosae. The superficial cord reflexes depend *both* on functional upper-motor pathways and on the cord-level reflex arc. Since only the plantar reflex can be tested conveniently in a laboratory setting, we will use this as our example.

The **plantar reflex,** an important neurological test, is elicited by stimulating the cutaneous receptors in the sole of the foot. In adults, stimulation of these receptors causes the toes to flex and move closer together. Damage to the pyramidal (or corticospinal) tract, however, produces *Babinski's sign,* an abnormal response in which the toes flare and the great toe moves in an upward direction. (In newborn infants, Babinski's sign is seen due to incomplete myelination of the nervous system.)

Activity 3:
Initiating the Plantar Reflex

Have the subject remove a shoe and lie on the cot or laboratory bench with knees slightly bent and thighs rotated so that the lateral side of the foot rests on the cot. Alternatively, the subject may sit up and rest the lateral surface of the foot on a chair. Draw the handle of the reflex hammer firmly down the lateral side of the exposed sole from the heel to the base of the great toe (Figure 22b.6).

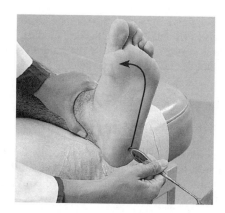

Figure 22b.6 Testing the plantar reflex.
Using a moderately sharp object, the examiner strokes the lateral border of the subject's sole, starting at the heel and continuing toward the big toe across the ball of the foot.

What is the response? _____

_____

Is this a normal plantar reflex or Babinski's sign?

_____ ▪

Cranial Nerve Reflex Tests

In these experiments, you will be working with your lab partner to illustrate two somatic reflexes mediated by cranial nerves.

Corneal Reflex The **corneal reflex** is mediated through the trigeminal nerve (cranial nerve V). The absence of this reflex is an ominous sign because it often indicates damage to the brain stem resulting from compression of the brain or other trauma.

Activity 4:
Initiating the Corneal Reflex

Stand to one side of the subject; the subject should look away from you toward the opposite wall. Wait a few seconds and then quickly, *but gently,* touch the subject's cornea (on the side toward you) with a wisp of absorbent cotton. What reflexive reaction occurs when something touches the cornea?

_____

What is the function of this reflex?

_____

_____

_____ ▪

Gag Reflex The **gag reflex** tests the somatic motor responses of cranial nerves IX and X. When the oral mucosa on the side of the uvula is stroked, each side of the mucosa should rise, and the amount of elevation should be equal.*

Activity 5:
Initiating the Gag Reflex

For this experiment, select a subject who does not have a queasy stomach, because regurgitation is a possibility. Stroke the oral mucosa on each side of the subject's uvula with a tongue depressor. What happens?

_____

_____

⚠ Discard the used tongue depressor in the disposable autoclave bag before continuing. Do *not* lay it on the laboratory bench at any time. ∎

Autonomic Reflexes

The autonomic reflexes include the pupillary, ciliospinal, and salivary reflexes, as well as a multitude of other reflexes. Work with your partner to demonstrate the four autonomic reflexes described next.

Pupillary Reflexes

There are several types of pupillary reflexes. The **pupillary light reflex** and the **consensual reflex** will be examined here. In both of these pupillary reflexes, the retina of the eye is the receptor, the optic nerve (cranial nerve II) contains the afferent fibers, the oculomotor nerve (cranial nerve III) is responsible for conducting efferent impulses to the eye, and the smooth muscle of the iris is the effector. Many central nervous system centers are involved in the integration of these responses. Absence of normal pupillary reflexes is generally a late indication of severe trauma or deterioration of the vital brain stem tissue due to metabolic imbalance.

Activity 6:
Initiating Pupillary Reflexes

1. Conduct the reflex testing in an area where the lighting is relatively dim. Before beginning, obtain a metric ruler to measure and record the size of the subject's pupils as best you can.

Right pupil: _____ mm   Left pupil: _____ mm

* The uvula is the fleshy tab hanging from the roof of the mouth just above the root of the tongue.

2. Stand to the left of the subject to conduct the testing. The subject should shield his or her right eye by holding a hand vertically between the eye and the right side of the nose.

3. Shine a flashlight into the subject's left eye. What is the pupillary response?

_____

Measure the size of the left pupil: _____ mm

4. Observe the right pupil. Has the same type of change (called a *consensual response*) occurred in the right eye?

_____

Measure the size of the right pupil: _____ mm

The consensual response, or any reflex observed on one side of the body when the other side has been stimulated, is called a **contralateral response**. The pupillary light response, or any reflex occurring on the same side stimulated, is referred to as an **ipsilateral response.**

When a contralateral response occurs, what does this indicate about the pathways involved?

_____

_____

Was the sympathetic *or* the parasympathetic division of the autonomic nervous system active during the testing of these reflexes?

_____

What is the function of these pupillary responses?

_____

_____

_____ ∎

Ciliospinal Reflex

The **ciliospinal reflex** is another example of reflex activity in which pupillary responses can be observed. This response may initially seem a little bizarre, especially in view of the consensual reflex just demonstrated.

Activity 7:
Initiating the Ciliospinal Reflex

1. While observing the subject's eyes, gently stroke the skin (or just the hairs) on the left side of the back of the subject's neck, close to the hairline.

What is the reaction of the left pupil? _____

The reaction of the right pupil? _____

2. If you see no reaction, repeat the test using a gentle pinch in the same area.

The response you should have noted—pupillary dilation—is consistent with the pupillary changes occurring when the sympathetic nervous system is stimulated. Such a response may also be elicited in a single pupil when more impulses from the sympathetic nervous system reach it for any reason. For example, when the left side of the subject's neck was stimulated, sympathetic impulses to the left iris increased, resulting in the ipsilateral reaction of the left pupil.

On the basis of your observations, would you say the sympathetic innervation of the two irises is closely integrated?

_____Why or why not? _____

_____

_____ ■

Salivary Reflex

Unlike the other reflexes, in which the effectors were smooth or skeletal muscles, the effectors of the **salivary reflex** are glands. The salivary glands secrete varying amounts of saliva in response to reflex activation.

Activity 8:
Initiating the Salivary Reflex

1. Obtain a small beaker, a graduated cylinder, lemon juice, and wide-range pH paper. After refraining from swallowing for 2 minutes, the subject is to expectorate (spit) the accumulated saliva into a small beaker. Using the graduated cylinder, measure the volume of the expectorated saliva and determine its pH.

Volume: _____ cc   pH:_____

2. Now place 2 or 3 drops of lemon juice on the subject's tongue. Allow the lemon juice to mix with the saliva for 5 to 10 seconds, and then determine the pH of the subject's saliva by touching a piece of pH paper to the tip of the tongue.

pH: _____

As before, the subject is to refrain from swallowing for 2 minutes. After the 2 minutes is up, again collect and measure the volume of the saliva and determine its pH.

Volume: _____ cc   pH:_____

3. How does the volume of saliva collected after the application of the lemon juice compare with the volume of the first saliva sample?

_____

How does the final saliva pH reading compare to the initial reading?

_____

To that obtained 10 seconds after the application of lemon juice?

_____

What division of the autonomic nervous system mediates the reflex release of saliva?

_____

⚠ Dispose of the saliva-containing beakers and the graduated cylinders in the laboratory bucket that contains bleach and put the used pH paper into the disposable autoclave bag. Wash the bench down with 10% bleach solution before continuing. ■

Reaction Time of Basic and Learned or Acquired Reflexes

The time required for reaction to a stimulus depends on many factors—sensitivity of the receptors, velocity of nerve conduction, the number of neurons and synapses involved, and the speed of effector activation, to name just a few. Some reflexes are *basic* or inborn; others are *learned* or *acquired* reflexes, resulting from practice or repetition. There is no clearcut distinction between basic and learned reflexes, as most reflex actions are subject to modification by learning or conscious effort. In general, however, if the response involves a specific reflex arc, the synapses are facilitated and the response time will be short. Learned reflexes involve a far larger number of neural pathways and many types of higher intellectual activities, including choice and decision making, which lengthens the response time.

There are various ways of testing reaction time of reflexes. The tests range from simple to ultrasophisticated. The following activities provide an opportunity to demonstrate the major time difference between simple and learned reflexes and to measure response time under various conditions.

Activity 9:
Testing Reaction Time for Basic and Acquired Reflexes

1. Using a reflex hammer, elicit the patellar reflex in your partner. Note the relative reaction time needed for this basic reflex to occur.

2. Now test the reaction time for learned reflexes. The subject should hold a hand out, with the thumb and index finger extended. Hold a metric ruler so that its end is exactly 3 cm above the subject's outstretched hand. The ruler should be in the vertical position with the numbers reading from the

bottom up. When the ruler is dropped, the subject should be able to grasp it between thumb and index finger as it passes, without having to change position. Have the subject catch the ruler five times, varying the time between trials. The relative speed of reaction can be determined by reading the number on the ruler at the point of the subject's fingertips.* (Thus if the number at the fingertips is 15 cm, the subject was unable to catch the ruler until 18 cm of length had passed through his or her fingers; 15 cm of ruler length plus 3 cm. to account for the distance of the ruler above the hand.)[†] Record the number of cm that pass through the subject's fingertips (or the number of seconds required for reaction) for each trial:

Trial 1:_____ cm or sec   Trial 4:_____ cm or sec

Trial 2:_____ cm or sec   Trial 5:_____ cm or sec

Trial 3:_____ cm or sec

3.   Perform the test again, but this time say a simple word each time you release the ruler. Designate a specific word as a signal for the subject to catch the ruler. On all other words, the subject is to allow the ruler to pass through his fingers. Trials in which the subject erroneously catches the ruler are to be disregarded. Record the distance the ruler travels (or the number of seconds required for reaction) in five *successful* trials:

Trial 1:_____ cm or sec   Trial 4:_____ cm or sec

Trial 2:_____ cm or sec   Trial 5:_____ cm or sec

Trial 3:_____ cm or sec

Did the addition of a specific word to the stimulus increase or decrease the reaction time?

_____

4.   Perform the testing once again to investigate the subject's reaction to word association. As you drop the ruler, say a word—for example, *hot*. The subject is to respond with a word he or she associates with the stimulus word—for example, *cold*—catching the ruler while responding. If unable to make a word association, the subject must allow the ruler to pass through his or her fingers. Record the distance the ruler travels (or the number of seconds required for reaction) in five successful trials, as well as the number of times the ruler is not caught by the subject.

* Distance (d) can be converted to time (t) using the simple formula

   d (in cm) = $(1/2)(980 \text{ cm/sec}^2)t^2$

   $t^2 = d/(490 \text{ cm/sec}^2)$

   $t = \sqrt{d/(490 \text{ cm/sec}^2)}$

[†]An alternative would be to use a reaction time ruler, which converts distance to time (seconds).

Trial 1:_____ cm or sec   Trial 4:_____ cm or sec

Trial 2:_____ cm or sec   Trial 5:_____ cm or sec

Trial 3:_____ cm or sec

The number of times the subject was unable to catch the ruler:

_____

You should have noticed quite a large variation in reaction time in this series of trials. Why is this so?

_____

_____

_____ ∎

Activity 10:
Using PowerLab® to Measure Reaction Time

1.   Make sure the PowerLab® is connected to your computer via the USB cable.

2.   Connect the Timing Push-button Switch to the BNC connector on Input 1 of the PowerLab®.

3.   Connect the Finger Pulse Transducer to the BNC socket on Input 2 of the PowerLab® (Figure 22b.7a).

4.   Turn on the PowerLab®, and open the Chart settings file called "Reaction Settings."

5.   Chart will automatically configure the PowerLab® to record from two channels. Channel 1 is called "Reaction," while Channel 2 is hidden from view (Figure 22.7b).

6.   Position the subject so he or she cannot see the computer screen or the PowerLab®. Give the subject the Timing Push-button Switch.

7.   Wrap the Velcro strap around the diaphragm of the pulse transducer to protect its sensitive mechanism, and place it on the table out of sight from the volunteer.

8.   The tester will use a rolled up piece of paper to tap the pulse transducer, which will produce an audible cue. Instruct the subject to depress the Timing Push-button Switch when he or she hears the tapping.

9.   To conduct the experiment, click Start. The PowerLab® will not start recording until it detects a signal from the pulse transducer. Repeat the experiment ten times. After the tenth record, Chart will stop recording.

10. Analyze the data by placing the waveform cursor at the beginning of the deflection visible in the Response channel. The time between the start of each data block and the response signal is the reaction time.

11. Drop the longest and shortest times, and average the remaining values. Record your data in the chart on the following page.

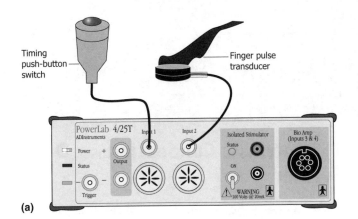

(a)

Reaction Times	
Description of test	**Average response time**
1. Response to random sound production:	
2. Experimental control:	
3. Experimental variable:	

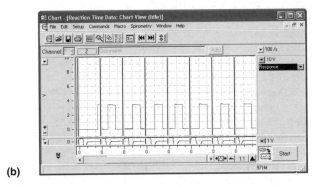

(b)

Figure 22b.7 The PowerLab® setup. (a) The equipment used to measure reaction time. **(b)** Reaction time data. Tapping the pulse transducer triggers PowerLab® to start recording, and the signal in Channel 1 (Response) indicates when the subject responded by pushing the accessory switch.

Conduction System of the Heart and Electrocardiography Using PowerLab® Data Acquisition System

The following lab includes instructions for using PowerLab® to record the ECG. The data can be collected with a physiograph, ECG recording equipment, or a computerized data collection system. The laboratory manual contains instructions for using BIOPAC®, and these instructions are for using PowerLab®. It is assumed the students are familiar with the use of the PowerLab® system before beginning this experiment.

Note: For up-to-date versions of this and other experiments, log on to www.powerlab-teaching.com/experiments.

Objectives

1. To list and localize the elements of the intrinsic conduction, or nodal, system of the heart; and to describe how impulses are initiated and conducted through this system and the myocardium.

2. To interpret the ECG in terms of depolarization and repolarization events occurring in the myocardium; and to identify the P, QRS, and T waves on an ECG recording using an ECG recorder or BIOPAC®.

3. To calculate the heart rate, QRS interval, P-R interval, and Q-T interval from an ECG obtained during the laboratory period.

4. To define *tachycardia, bradycardia,* and *fibrillation.*

Materials

❑ PowerLab® unit and interface cable, Windows PC or Macintosh computer with Chart software installed, ECG recording apparatus, bio amp patient cable, electrodes, electrode gel, alcohol swabs, abrasive pad, PowerLab® User's Guide, Chart User's Guide

The Intrinsic Conduction System

Heart contraction results from a series of electrical potential changes (depolarization waves) that travel through the heart preliminary to each beat. Because cardiac muscle cells are electrically connected by gap junctions, the entire myocardium behaves like a single unit, a **functional syncytium** (sin-sih'shum).

The ability of cardiac muscle to beat is intrinsic—it does not depend on impulses from the nervous system to initiate its contraction and will continue to contract rhythmically even if all nerve connections are severed. However, two types of controlling systems exert their effects on heart activity. One of these involves nerves of the autonomic nervous system, which accelerate or decrease the heartbeat rate depending on which division is activated. The second system is the **intrinsic conduction system,** or **nodal system,** of the heart, consisting of specialized noncontractile myocardial tissue. The intrinsic conduction system ensures that heart muscle depolarizes in an orderly and sequential manner (from atria to ventricles) and that the heart beats as a coordinated unit.

The components of the intrinsic conduction system include the **SA (sinoatrial) node,** located in the right atrium just inferior to the entrance to the superior vena cava; the **AV (atrioventricular) node** in the lower atrial septum at the junction of the atria and ventricles; the **AV bundle (bundle of His)** and right and left **bundle branches,** located in the interventricular septum; and the **Purkinje fibers,** which ramify within the muscle bundles of the ventricular walls. The Purkinje fiber network is much denser and more elaborate in the left ventricle because of the larger size of this chamber (Figure 31b.1).

The SA node, which has the highest rate of discharge, provides the stimulus for contraction. Because it sets the rate of depolarization for the heart as a whole, the SA node is often referred to as the *pacemaker.* From the SA node, the impulse spreads throughout the atria and to the AV node. This electrical wave is immediately followed by atrial contraction. At the AV node, the impulse is momentarily delayed (approximately 0.1 sec), allowing the atria to complete their contraction. It then passes through the AV bundle, the right and left bundle branches, and the Purkinje fibers, finally resulting in ventricular contraction. Note that the atria and ventricles are separated from one another by a region of electrically inert connective tissue, so the depolarization wave can be transmitted to the ventricles only via the tract between the AV node and AV bundle. Thus, any damage to the AV node-bundle pathway partially or totally insulates the ventricles from the influence of the SA node. Although autorhythmic cells are found throughout the heart, their rates of spontaneous depolarization differ. The nodal system increases the rate of heart depolarization and synchronizes heart activity.

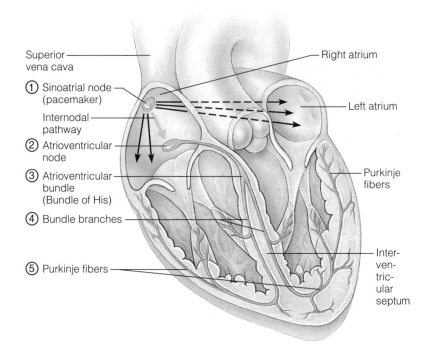

Superior vena cava

① Sinoatrial node (pacemaker)

Internodal pathway

② Atrioventricular node

③ Atrioventricular bundle (Bundle of His)

④ Bundle branches

⑤ Purkinje fibers

Right atrium

Left atrium

Purkinje fibers

Interventricular septum

Figure 31b.1 The intrinsic conduction system of the heart. Dashed-line arrows indicate transmission of the impulse from the SA node through the atria. Solid arrows indicate transmission of the impulse from the SA node to the AV node via the internodal pathway.

Electrocardiography

The conduction of impulses through the heart generates electrical currents that eventually spread throughout the body. These impulses can be detected on the body's surface and recorded with an instrument called an *electrocardiograph*. The graphic recording of the electrical changes (depolarization followed by repolarization) occurring during the cardiac cycle is called an **electrocardiogram (ECG)** (Figure 31b.2). The typical ECG consists of a series of three recognizable waves called *deflection waves*. The first wave, the **P wave,** is a small wave that indicates depolarization of the atria immediately before atrial contraction. The large **QRS complex,** resulting from ventricular depolarization, has a complicated shape (primarily because of the variability in size of the two ventricles and the time differences required for these chambers to depolarize). It precedes ventricular contraction. The **T wave** results from currents propagated during ventricular repolarization. The repolarization of the atria, which occurs during the QRS interval, is generally obscured by the large QRS complex. The relationship between the deflection waves of an ECG and sequential excitation of the heart is shown in Figure 31b.3.

It is important to understand what an ECG does and does not show: First, an ECG is a record of voltage and time—nothing else. Although we can and do infer that muscle contraction follows its excitation, sometimes it does not. Secondly, an ECG records electrical events occurring in relatively large amounts of muscle tissue (i.e., the bulk of the heart muscle), *not* the activity of nodal tissue which, like muscle contraction, can only be inferred. Nonetheless, abnormalities of the deflection waves and changes in the time intervals of the ECG are useful in detecting myocardial infarcts or problems with the conduction system of the heart. The P–Q interval represents the time between the beginning of atrial depolarization and ventricular depolarization. Thus, it typically includes the period during which the depolarization wave passes to the AV node, atrial systole, and the passage of the excitation wave to the balance of the conducting system. Generally, the P-R interval is about 0.16 to 0.18 sec. A longer interval may suggest a partial AV heart block caused by damage to the AV node. In total heart block, no impulses are transmitted through the AV node, and the atria and ventricles beat independently of one another—the atria at the SA node rate and the ventricles at their intrinsic rate, which is considerably slower.

If the QRS interval (normally 0.08 sec) is prolonged, it may indicate a right or left bundle branch block in which one ventricle is contracting later than the other. The Q-T interval is the period from the beginning of ventricular depolarization through repolarization and includes the time of ventricular contraction (the S-T segment). With a heart rate of 70 beats/min, this interval is normally 0.31 to 0.41 sec. As the rate increases, this interval becomes shorter; conversely, when the heart rate drops, the interval is longer.

A heart rate over 100 beats/min is referred to as **tachycardia;** a rate below 60 beats/min is **bradycardia.** Although neither condition is pathological, prolonged tachycardia may progress to **fibrillation,** a condition of rapid uncoordinated heart contractions which makes the heart useless as a pump. Bradycardia in athletes is a positive finding; that is, it indicates an increased efficiency of cardiac functioning. Because *stroke volume* (the amount of blood ejected by a ventricle with each contraction) increases with physical conditioning, the heart can contract more slowly and still meet circulatory demands.

Twelve standard leads are used to record an ECG for diagnostic purposes. Three of these are bipolar leads that measure the voltage difference between the arms, or an arm and a leg, and nine are unipolar leads. Together the 12 leads provide a fairly comprehensive picture of the electrical activity of the heart.

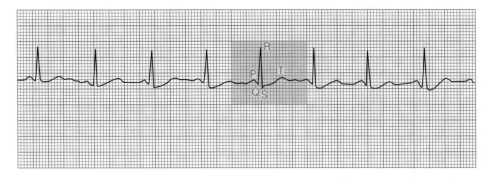

(a)

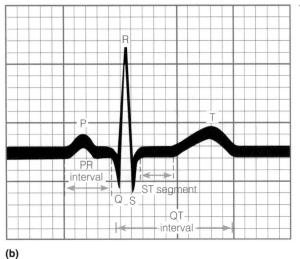

(b)

Time: small squares = 0.04 sec
1 large square = 0.20 sec
5 large squares = 1.00 sec

Figure 31b.2 The normal electrocardiogram.
(a) Regular sinus rhythm. **(b)** Waves, segments, and intervals of a normal ECG.

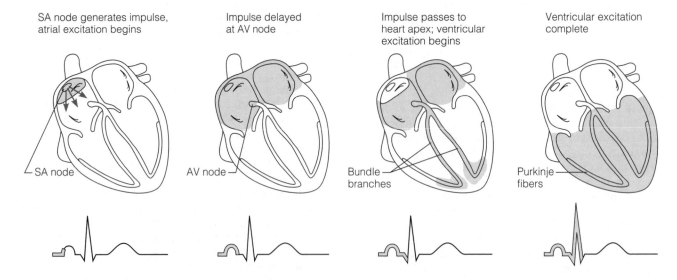

SA node generates impulse, atrial excitation begins

Impulse delayed at AV node

Impulse passes to heart apex; ventricular excitation begins

Ventricular excitation complete

SA node

AV node

Bundle branches

Purkinje fibers

Figure 31b.3 The sequence of excitation of the heart related to the deflection waves of an ECG tracing.

For this investigation, four electrodes are used (Figure 31b.4), and results are obtained from the three *standard limb leads*. Several types of physiographs or ECG recorders are available. Your instructor will provide specific directions on how to set up and use the available apparatus.

Understanding the Standard Limb Leads

As you might expect, electrical activity recorded by any lead depends on the location and orientation of the recording electrodes. Clinically, it is assumed that the heart lies in the

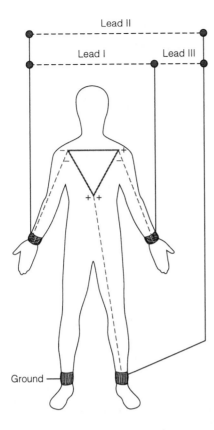

Figure 31b.4 ECG recording positions for the standard limb leads.

center of a triangle with sides of equal lengths (*Einthoven's triangle*) and that the recording connections are made at the vertices (corners) of that triangle. But in practice, the electrodes connected to each arm and to the left leg are considered to connect to the triangle vertices. The standard limb leads record the voltages generated in the extracellular fluids surrounding the heart by the ion flows occurring simultaneously in many cells between any two of the connections. A recording using lead I (RA-LA), which connects the right arm (RA) and the left arm (LA), is most sensitive to electrical activity spreading horizontally across the heart. Lead II (RA-LL) and lead III (LA-LL) record activity along the vertical axis (from the base of the heart to its apex), but from different orientations. The significance of Einthoven's triangle is that the sum of the voltages of leads I and III equals that in lead II (Einthoven's law). Hence, if the voltages of two of the standard leads are recorded, that of the third lead can be determined mathematically.

Activity:
Recording ECGs

Once the subject is prepared, the ECG will be recorded first under baseline (resting) conditions and then under conditions of fairly strenuous activity. Finally, recordings will be made while the subject holds his or her breath. The activity and breath-holding recordings will be compared to the baseline recordings, and you will be asked to determine the reasons for the observed differences in the recordings.

Using PowerLab® to Record the ECG

Making a Baseline Recording

1. Make sure the PowerLab® is turned off. Connect the USB cable from the PowerLab to the computer.

2. Connect the shielded bio amp patient cable to the PowerLab®. Connect three snap lead wires to Earth, CH1 negative, and CH1 positive on the bio amp patient cable (Figure 31b.5).

3. Turn on the PowerLab®. On your computer, open the Chart settings file called "ECG Settings."

4. If alcohol swabs are available, firmly swab the skin with them in each area where electrodes will be placed (Figure 31b.5). Using a pen, mark each area with a small cross and lightly abrade the skin at these areas with an abrasive pad. This decreases the electrical resistance of the outer layer of skin and ensures good electrical contact.

5. If you are using the reusable clamp electrodes, apply a small amount of electrode gel to the electrodes, attach the electrodes to the subject as shown in Figure 31b.5, and connect the electrodes to the leads. If you are using disposable electrodes that have electrode gel on them already, attach the electrodes to the subject using the peel and stick adhesive.

6. Be sure that the subject is relaxed and sits as still as possible to minimize any signal from unwanted movement.

7. From the ECG (Channel 3) pop-up menu, select Input Amplifier. Examine the ECG trace in the dialog box. If the trace is too big or too small, adjust the Range up or down so the signal is 1/3 to 1/2 of the window height (Figure 31b.6). Click OK to return to the Chart view window.

8. Begin recording by clicking Start. Input the subject's name into the comment field, and press the return key. A comment with the subject's name will be entered on the trace.

9. When you are done, click Stop.

10. Save the data with an appropriate filename.

Analyzing the Data

Note: To use the marker, move the cursor to the marker box, click and drag the marker to a location on the ECG, and release the mouse. As the cursor is moved, measurements relative to the position of the marker are given.

1. Use the marker and cursor to measure the following:

   a. The time interval from the beginning of one QRS complex to the beginning of the next; to convert that meaurement to heart rate, use the equation:

   Heart rate (beats/minute) = 60/time intervals

   Heart rate: _____ beats/minute

   b. The QRS interval: QRS _____

   c. The Q-T interval: Q-T _____

   d. The P-R interval: P-R _____

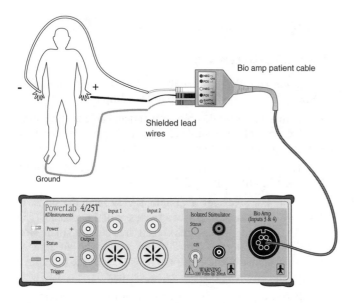

Figure 31b.5 Recording ECG from a subject using PowerLab®.

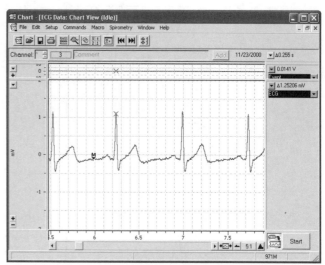

Figure 31b.6 A Chart recording of an ECG trace. The P, QRS, and T waves are visible; the marker and wave form cursor are positioned to measure the amplitude (in volts) of the QRS wave.

2. Evaluate the data. Are all the measurements within normal range or limits?

Recording the ECG after Running in Place

Secure the lead wires to the subject with the clips provided to increase the stability of the recording. If the recording is unstable:

1. Ask the subject to run in place for 3 minutes and then have the subject sit down.

2. Immediately attach the electrodes and begin recording the ECG. Label the first recording *Immediately after exercise*.

3. Record the ECG at 1 and 4 minutes after exercise and label the recordings appropriately.

4. Save the data to an appropriate file.

5. Calculate and compare the subject's heart rates.

_____ beats/minute immediately after running in place

_____ beats/minute 1 minute after exercise

_____ beats/minute 4 minutes after exercise

6. Compare the subject's resting ECG to the ECG after exercise. Which intervals are shorter in the *Immediately after running* recording?

_____

Does the subject's heart rate return to resting level by 4 minutes after exercise? _____

Recording the ECG after Breath-Holding

1. Position the subject comfortably in the sitting position.

2. Begin the recording, and after approximately 10 seconds, instruct the subject to begin breath-holding. Mark the record to indicate the onset of the 1-minute breath-holding interval.

3. Stop recording after 1 minute, and remind the subject to breathe. Compute the beats/minute during the 1-minute experimental (breath-holding) period.

Beats/minute during breath-holding _____

4. Compare this recording with the recording obtained during resting conditions.

What differences are seen? _____

Attempt to explain the physiological reason for the differences you have seen. (Hint: A good place to start might be to check hypoventilation or the role of the *respiratory* system in the acid-base balance of the blood.)

_____

_____

_____ ■

Human Cardiovascular Physiology— Blood Pressure and Pulse Determinations Using Powerlab® Data Acquisition System

The following lab includes instructions for using PowerLab® to measure pulse rate. This lab uses recording equipment to collect data concerning pulse rate from a human subject. The laboratory manual contains the instructions for using BIOPAC®, and these instructions are for PowerLab®. It is assumed the students are familiar with the use of the PowerLab® system before beginning the experiments.

Note: For up-to-date versions of this and other experiments, log on to www.powerlab-teaching.com/experiments.

Objectives

1. To define *systole, diastole,* and *cardiac cycle.*

2. To indicate the normal length of the cardiac cycle, the relative pressure changes occurring within the atria and ventricles during the cycle, and the timing of valve closure.

3. To use the stethoscope to auscultate heart sounds and to relate heart sounds to cardiac cycle events.

4. To describe the clinical significance of heart sounds and heart murmurs.

5. To demonstrate the thoracic locations where the first and second heart sounds are most accurately auscultated.

6. To define *pulse, pulse deficit, blood pressure,* and *sounds of Korotkoff.*

7. To accurately determine a subject's apical and radial pulse.

8. To accurately determine a subject's blood pressure with a sphygmomanometer, and to relate systolic and diastolic pressures to events of the cardiac cycle.

9. To investigate the effects of exercise on blood pressure, pulse, and cardiovascular fitness.

10. To indicate factors affecting and/or determining blood flow and skin color.

A ny comprehensive study of human cardiovascular physiology takes much more time than a single laboratory period. However, it is possible to conduct investigations of a few phenomena such as pulse, heart sounds, and blood pressure, all of which reflect the heart in action and the function of blood vessels. (The electrocardiogram

Materials

❑ Stethoscope
❑ Alcohol swabs
❑ Watch (or clock) with second hand
❑ Record, audiotape, or compact disc of "Interpreting Heart Sounds" (available on free loan from local chapters of the American Heart Association) and appropriate player
❑ Sphygmomanometer
❑ Felt marker
❑ Cot (if available)
❑ Step stools (0.4 m [16 in.] and 0.5 m [20 in.] in height)
❑ Small basin suitable for immersion of one hand
❑ Ice
❑ Hot water
❑ Laboratory thermometer
❑ PowerLab® unit and interface cable, Windows PC or Macintosh computer with Chart software installed, ML1110 Finger Pulse Transducer, PowerLab® User's Guide, Chart User's Guide

PhysioEx 5.0™ Computer Simulation on p. P-60

A1A See Appendix B, Exercise 33 for links to A.D.A.M.® Interactive Anatomy.

is studied separately in Exercise 31.) A discussion of the cardiac cycle will provide a basis for understanding and interpreting the various physiological measurements taken.

Cardiac Cycle

In a healthy heart, the two atria contract simultaneously. As they begin to relax, simultaneous contraction of the ventricles occurs. However, according to general usage, the terms **systole** and **diastole** refer to events of ventricular contraction and relaxation, respectively. The **cardiac cycle** is equivalent to one complete heartbeat—during which both atria and ventricles contract and then relax. It is marked by a succession of changes in blood volume and pressure within the heart.

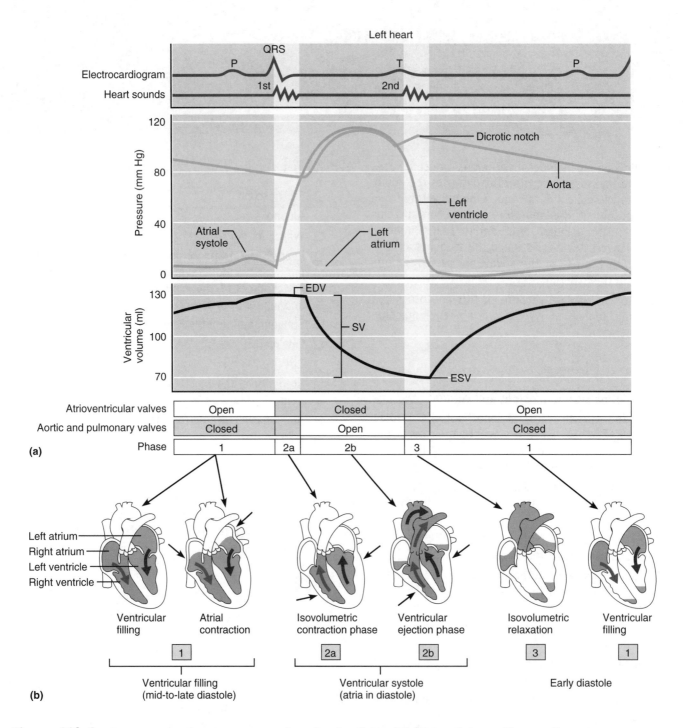

Figure 33b.1 Summary of events occurring in the heart during the cardiac cycle. (a) Events in the left side of the heart. An ECG tracing is superimposed on the graph (top) so that pressure and volume changes can be related to electrical events occurring at any point. Time occurrence of heart sounds is also indicated. **(b)** Events of phases 1 through 3 of the cardiac cycle are depicted in diagrammatic views of the heart.

Figure 33b.1 is a graphic representation of the events of the cardiac cycle for the left side of the heart. Although pressure changes in the right side are less dramatic than those in the left, the same relationships apply.

We will begin the discussion of the cardiac cycle with the heart in complete relaxation (diastole). At this point, pressure in the heart is very low, blood is flowing passively from the pulmonary and systemic circulations into the atria and on through to the ventricles; the semilunar valves are closed, and the AV valves are open. Shortly, atrial contraction occurs and atrial pressure increases, forcing residual blood into the ventricles. Then ventricular systole begins and intraventricular pressure increases rapidly, closing the AV valves. When ventricular pressure exceeds that of the large arteries leaving the heart, the semilunar valves are forced open; and the blood in the ventricular chambers is expelled through the valves. During this phase, the aortic pressure reaches approximately 120 mm Hg in a healthy young adult male. During ventricular systole, the atria relax and their chambers fill with blood, which results in gradually increasing atrial pressure. At the end of ventricular systole, the ventricles relax; the semilunar valves snap shut, preventing backflow, and momentarily, the ventricles are closed chambers. When the aortic semilunar valve snaps shut, a momentary increase in the aortic pressure results from the elastic recoil of the aorta after valve closure. This event results in the pressure fluctuation called the *dicrotic notch* (see Figure 33b.1a). As the ventricles relax, the pressure within them begins to drop. When intraventricular pressure is again less than atrial pressure, the AV valves are forced open, and the ventricles again begin to fill with blood. Atrial and aortic pressures decrease, and the ventricles rapidly refill, completing the cycle.

The average heart beats approximately 75 beats per minute, and so the length of the cardiac cycle is about 0.8 second. Of this time period, atrial contraction occupies the first 0.1 second, which is followed by atrial relaxation and ventricular contraction for the next 0.3 second. The remaining 0.4 second is the quiescent, or ventricular relaxation, period. When the heart beats at a more rapid pace than normal, this last period decreases.

Notice that two different types of phenomena control the movement of blood through the heart: the alternate contraction and relaxation of the myocardium, and the opening and closing of valves (which is entirely dependent on the pressure changes within the heart chambers).

Study Figure 33b.1 carefully to make sure you understand what has been discussed before continuing with the next portion of the exercise.

Heart Sounds

Two distinct sounds can be heard during each cardiac cycle. These heart sounds are commonly described by the monosyllables "lub" and "dup"; and the sequence is designated lub-dup, pause, lub-dup, pause, and so on. The first heart sound (lub) is referred to as S_1 and is associated with closure of the AV valves at the beginning of ventricular systole. The second heart sound (dup), called S_2, occurs as the semilunar valves close and corresponds with the end of systole. Figure 33b.1a indicates the timing of heart sounds in the cardiac cycle.

• Listen to the recording "Interpreting Heart Sounds" so that you may hear both normal and abnormal heart sounds.

Abnormal heart sounds are called **murmurs** and often indicate valvular problems. In valves that do not close tightly, closure is followed by a swishing sound due to the backflow of blood (regurgitation). Distinct sounds, often described as high-pitch screeching, are associated with the tortuous flow of blood through constricted, or stenosed, valves. ●

Activity 1:
Auscultating Heart Sounds

In the following procedure, you will auscultate your partner's heart sounds with an ordinary stethoscope. A number of more sophisticated heart-sound amplification systems are on the market, and your instructor may prefer to use one such if it is available. If so, directions for the use of this apparatus will be provided by the instructor.

1. Obtain a stethoscope and some alcohol swabs. Heart sounds are best auscultated (listened to) if the subject's outer clothing is removed, so a male subject is preferable.

2. With an alcohol swab, clean the earpieces of the stethoscope. Allow the alcohol to dry. Notice that the earpieces are angled. For comfort and best auscultation, the earpieces should be angled in a *forward* direction when placed into the ears.

3. Don the stethoscope. Place the diaphragm of the stethoscope on your partner's thorax, just to the sternal side of the left nipple at the fifth intercostal space, and listen carefully for heart sounds. The first sound will be a longer, louder (more booming) sound than the second, which is short and sharp. After listening for a couple of minutes, try to time the pause between the second sound of one heartbeat and the first sound of the subsequent heartbeat.

How long is this interval? _____ sec

How does it compare to the interval between the first and second sounds of a single heartbeat?

_____

_____

4. To differentiate individual valve sounds somewhat more precisely, auscultate the heart sounds over specific thoracic regions. Refer to Figure 33b.2 for the positioning of the stethoscope.

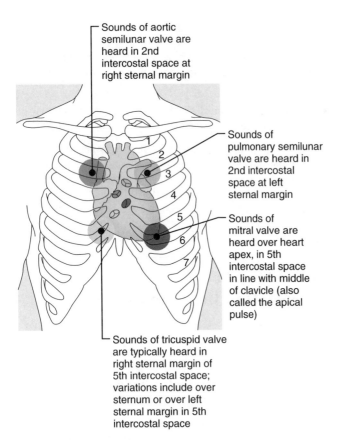

Sounds of aortic semilunar valve are heard in 2nd intercostal space at right sternal margin

Sounds of pulmonary semilunar valve are heard in 2nd intercostal space at left sternal margin

Sounds of mitral valve are heard over heart apex, in 5th intercostal space in line with middle of clavicle (also called the apical pulse)

Sounds of tricuspid valve are typically heard in right sternal margin of 5th intercostal space; variations include over sternum or over left sternal margin in 5th intercostal space

Figure 33b.2 Areas of the thorax where valvular sounds can best be detected.

Auscultation of AV Valves

As a rule, the mitral valve closes slightly before the tricuspid valve. You can hear the mitral valve more clearly if you place the stethoscope over the apex of the heart, which is at the fifth intercostal space, approximately in line with the middle region of the left clavicle. Listen to the heart sounds at this region; then move the stethoscope medially to the right margin of the sternum to auscultate the tricuspid valve. Can you detect the slight lag between the closure of the mitral and tricuspid valves?

There are normal variations in the site for "best" auscultation of the tricuspid valve. These range from the site depicted in Figure 33b.2 (right sternal margin over fifth intercostal space) to over the sternal body in the same plane, to the left sternal margin over the fifth intercostal space. If you have difficulty hearing closure of the tricuspid valve, try one of these other locations.

Auscultation of Semilunar Valves

Again there is a slight dissynchrony of valve closure; the aortic semilunar valve normally snaps shut just ahead of the pulmonary semilunar valve. If the subject inhales deeply but gently, filling of the right ventricle will be delayed slightly

(due to the compression of the thoracic blood vessels by the increased intrapulmonary pressure); and the two sounds can be heard more distinctly. Position the stethoscope over the second intercostal space, just to the *right* of the sternum. The aortic valve is best heard at this position. As you listen, have your partner take a deep breath. Then move the stethoscope to the *left* side of the sternum in the same line; and auscultate the pulmonary valve. Listen carefully; try to hear the "split" between the closure of these two valves in the second heart sound.

Although at first it may seem a bit odd that the pulmonary valve issuing from the *right* heart is heard most clearly to the *left* of the sternum and the aortic valve of the left heart is best heard at the right sternal border, this is easily explained by reviewing heart anatomy. Because the heart is twisted, with the right ventricle forming most of the anterior ventricular surface, the pulmonary trunk actually crosses to the right as it issues from the right ventricle. Similarly, the aorta issues from the left ventricle at the left side of the pulmonary trunk before arching up and over that vessel. ■

The Pulse

The term **pulse** refers to the alternating surges of pressure (expansion and then recoil) in an artery that occur with each contraction and relaxation of the left ventricle. This difference between systolic and diastolic pressure is called the **pulse pressure.** Normally the pulse rate (pressure surges per minute) equals the heart rate (beats per minute), and the pulse averages 70 to 76 beats per minute in the resting state.

Parameters other than pulse rate are also useful clinically. You may also assess the regularity (or rhythmicity) of the pulse, and its amplitude and/or tension—does the blood vessel expand and recoil (sometimes visibly) with the pressure waves? Can you feel it strongly, or is it difficult to detect? Is it regular like the ticking of a clock, or does it seem to skip beats?

A c t i v i t y   2 :
Palpating Superficial Pulse Points

The pulse may be felt easily on any superficial artery when the artery is compressed over a bone or firm tissue. Palpate the following pulse or pressure points on your partner by placing the fingertips of the first two or three fingers of one hand over the artery. It helps to compress the artery firmly as you begin your palpation and then immediately ease up on the pressure slightly. In each case, notice the regularity of the pulse, and assess the degree of tension or amplitude. Figure 33b.3 illustrates the superficial pulse points to be palpated.

Common carotid artery: At the side of the neck

Temporal artery: Anterior to the ear, in the temple region

Facial artery: Clench the teeth, and palpate the pulse just anterior to the masseter muscle on the mandible (in line with the corner of the mouth)

Brachial artery: In the antecubital fossa, at the point where it bifurcates into the radial and ulnar arteries

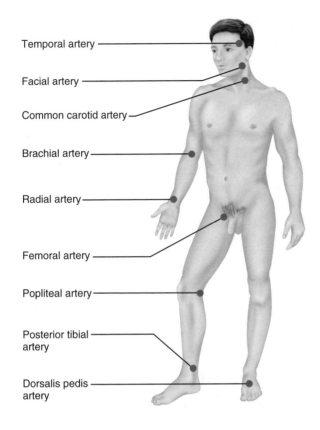

Temporal artery

Facial artery

Common carotid artery

Brachial artery

Radial artery

Femoral artery

Popliteal artery

Posterior tibial artery

Dorsalis pedis artery

Figure 33b.3 Body sites where the pulse is most easily palpated.

Radial artery: At the lateral aspect of the wrist, above the thumb

Femoral artery: In the groin

Popliteal artery: At the back of the knee

Posterior tibial artery: Just above the medial malleolus

Dorsalis pedis artery: On the dorsum of the foot

Which pulse point had the greatest amplitude?

_____

Which the least? _____

Can you offer any explanation for this? _____

_____

_____

_____

Because of its easy accessibility, the pulse is most often taken on the radial artery. With your partner sitting quietly, practice counting the radial pulse for 1 minute. Make three counts and average the results.

count 1 _____   count 2 _____

count 3 _____   average _____ ■

Due to the elasticity of the arteries, blood pressure decreases and smooths out as blood moves farther away from the heart. A pulse, however, can still be felt in the fingers. A device called a plethysmograph or a piezoelectric pulse transducer can measure this pulse.

Activity 3:
Measuring the Pulse Using a Plethysmograph and PowerLab®

1. Make sure your PowerLab® unit is connected to the computer via the USB cable. Turn the PowerLab® unit on.

2. From your PowerLab® folder, choose the ECG and Peripheral Circulation folder, and double-click on the Chart settings file called "ECG and Pulse Settings". Chart will start, and after a few seconds you should see a blank data file with three channels.

3. From the ECG channel pop-up menu (Channel 3), click "Turn Channel Off." You will not be recording an ECG in this exercise.

4. Connect the finger pulse transducer to the Input 2 BNC socket on the front of your PowerLab® unit (Figure 33b.4).

5. Secure the finger pulse transducer to the distal segment of the subject's index finger. Instruct the subject to place his or her hands in his or her lap for the experimental measurement.

6. Click Start and record for 15 seconds.

7. Click Stop.

8. Click the Autoscale button in the Chart toolbar menu.

9. Click the File menu and save your data with an appropriate filename.

10. Select two or more pulse beats from the Volume Pulse channel using the mouse. Click the Zoom view button, and look for the presence of a dicrotic notch (Figure 33b.5).

11. Use the marker and waveform cursor to measure the time in seconds from peak to peak. Calculate and record your

pulse rate _____.

12. If there is time, investigate the effects of hot and cold on pulse rate.

Place a bag of ice and water on the subject's forearm and record the pulse rate after 2 minutes.

Place a bag of hot water on the subject's forearm and record the pulse rate after 2 minutes.

Record your observations.

Effect of cold on pulse rate _____

Effect of heat on pulse rate _____ ■

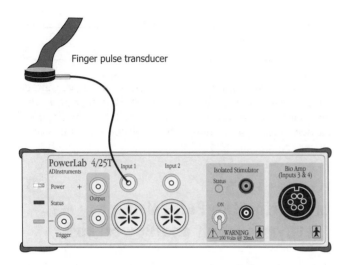

Figure 33b.4 Connecting the finger pulse transducer to the PowerLab® unit.

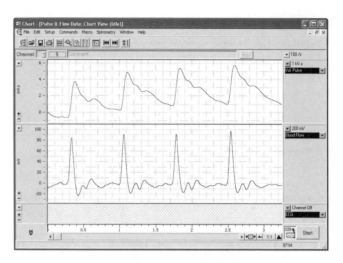

Figure 33b.5 A Chart view window showing finger pulse trace. The Blood Flow channel is the raw data from the pulse transducer. The Volume Pulse channel shows a distinct dicrotic notch.

Apical-Radial Pulse

The correlation between the apical and radial pulse rates can be determined by simultaneously counting them. The **apical pulse** (actually the counting of heartbeats) may be slightly faster than the radial because of a slight lag in time as the blood rushes from the heart into the large arteries where it can be palpated. However, any *large* difference between the values observed, referred to as a **pulse deficit,** may indicate cardiac impairment—a weakened heart that is unable to pump blood into the arterial tree to a normal extent—low cardiac output, or abnormal heart rhythms. In the case of atrial fibrillation or ectopic heartbeats, for instance, the second beat may follow the first so quickly that no second pulse is felt even though the apical pulse can still be heard (auscultated). Apical pulse counts are routinely ordered for those with cardiac decompensation.

Activity 4:
Taking an Apical Pulse

With the subject sitting quietly, one student, using a stethoscope, should determine the apical pulse rate while another simultaneously counts the radial pulse rate. The stethoscope should be positioned over the fifth left intercostal space. The person taking the radial pulse should determine the starting point for the count and give the stop-count signal exactly 1 minute later. Record your values below.

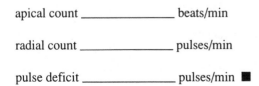

apical count _____ beats/min

radial count _____ pulses/min

pulse deficit _____ pulses/min ∎

Blood Pressure Determinations

Blood pressure is defined as the pressure the blood exerts against any unit area of the blood vessel walls, and it is generally measured in the arteries. Because the heart alternately contracts and relaxes, the resulting rhythmic flow of blood into the arteries causes the blood pressure to rise and fall during each beat. Thus you must take two blood pressure readings: the **systolic pressure,** which is the pressure in the arteries at the peak of ventricular ejection, and the **diastolic pressure,** which reflects the pressure during ventricular relaxation. Blood pressures are reported in millimeters of mercury (mm Hg), with the systolic pressure appearing first; 120/80 translates to 120 over 80, or a systolic pressure of 120 mm Hg and a diastolic pressure of 80 mm Hg. Normal blood pressure varies considerably from one person to another.

In this procedure, you will measure arterial and venous pressures by indirect means and under various conditions. You will investigate and demonstrate factors affecting blood pressure, the rapidity of blood pressure changes, and the large differences between arterial and venous pressures.

Activity 5:
Using a Sphygmomanometer to Measure Arterial Blood Pressure Indirectly

The **sphygmomanometer,** commonly called a *blood pressure cuff*, is an instrument used to obtain blood pressure readings by the auscultatory method (Figure 33b.6). It consists of an inflatable cuff with an attached pressure gauge. The cuff is

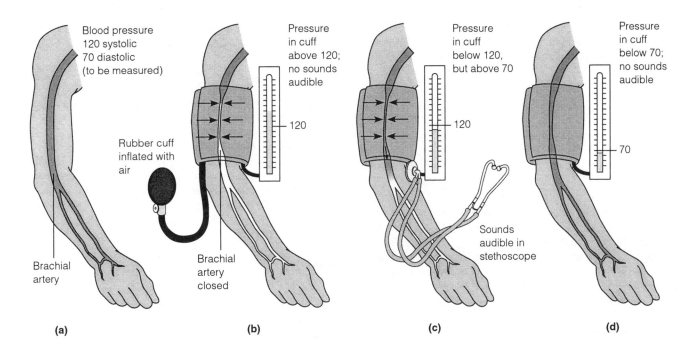

Figure 33b.6 Procedure for measurement of blood pressure. (a) The course of the brachial artery of the arm. Assume a blood pressure of 120/70. **(b)** The blood pressure cuff is wrapped snugly around the arm just above the elbow and inflated until blood flow into the forearm is stopped and a brachial pulse cannot be felt or heard. **(c)** The pressure in the cuff is gradually reduced while the examiner listens (auscultates) carefully for sounds (of Korotkoff) in the brachial artery with a stethoscope. The pressure read as the first soft tapping sounds are heard (the first point at which a small amount of blood is spurting through the constricted artery) is recorded as the systolic pressure. **(d)** As the pressure is reduced still further, the sounds become louder and more distinct, but when the artery is no longer restricted and blood flows freely, the sounds can no longer be heard. The pressure at which the sounds disappear is routinely recorded as the diastolic pressure.

placed around the arm and inflated to a pressure higher than systolic pressure to occlude circulation to the forearm. As cuff pressure is gradually released, the examiner listens with a stethoscope for characteristic sounds called the **sounds of Korotkoff,** which indicate the resumption of blood flow into the forearm. The pressure at which the first soft tapping sounds can be detected is recorded as the systolic pressure. As the pressure is reduced further, blood flow becomes more turbulent, and the sounds become louder. As the pressure is reduced still further, below the diastolic pressure, the artery is no longer compressed; and blood flows freely and without turbulence. At this point, the sounds of Korotkoff can no longer be detected. The pressure at which the sounds disappear is recorded as the diastolic pressure.

1. Work in pairs to obtain radial artery blood pressure readings. Obtain a stethoscope, alcohol swabs, and a sphygmomanometer. Clean the earpieces of the stethoscope with the alcohol swabs, and check the cuff for the presence of trapped air by compressing it against the laboratory table. (A partially inflated cuff will produce erroneous measurements.)

2. The subject should sit in a comfortable position with one arm resting on the laboratory table (approximately at heart level if possible). Wrap the cuff around the subject's arm, just above the elbow, with the inflatable area on the medial arm surface. The cuff may be marked with an arrow; if so, the arrow should be positioned over the brachial artery (Figure 33b.6). Secure the cuff by tucking the distal end under the wrapped portion or by bringing the Velcro areas together.

3. Palpate the brachial pulse, and lightly mark its position with a felt pen. Don the stethoscope, and place its diaphragm over the pulse point.

⚠ *The cuff should not be kept inflated for more than 1 minute.* If you have any trouble obtaining a reading within this time, deflate the cuff, wait 1 or 2 minutes, and try again. (A prolonged interference with BP homeostasis can lead to fainting.)

4. Inflate the cuff to approximately 160 mm Hg pressure, and slowly release the pressure valve. Watch the pressure gauge as you listen carefully for the first soft thudding sounds of the blood spurting through the partially occluded artery. Mentally note this pressure (systolic pressure), and continue to release the cuff pressure. You will notice first an increase, then a muffling, of the sound. Note, as the diastolic pressure, the pressure at which the sound becomes muffled or disappears. Controversy exists over which of the two points should be recorded as the diastolic pressure; so in some cases you may see readings such as 120/80/78, which indicates the systolic pressure followed by the *first* and *second diastolic end points.* The first diastolic end point is the pressure at which the sound muffles; the second is the pressure at which the

sound disappears. It makes little difference here which of the two diastolic pressures is recorded, but be consistent. Make two blood pressure determinations, and record your results below.

First trial: Second trial:

systolic pressure _____   systolic pressure _____

diastolic pressure _____   diastolic pressure _____

5. Compute the **pulse pressure** for each trial. The pulse pressure is the difference between the systolic and diastolic pressures, and indicates the amount of blood forced from the heart during systole, or the actual "working" pressure. A narrowed pulse pressure (less than 30 mm Hg) may be a signal of severe aortic stenosis, constrictive pericarditis, or tachycardia. A widened pulse pressure (over 40 mm Hg) is common in hypertensive individuals.

Pulse pressure:

first trial _____   second trial _____

6. Compute the **mean arterial pressure (MAP)** for each trial using the following equation:

$$\text{MAP} = \text{diastolic pressure} + \frac{\text{pulse pressure}}{3}$$

first trial _____   second trial _____ ■

It is not possible to measure venous pressure with the sphygmomanometer. The methods available for measuring it produce estimates at best, because venous pressures are so much lower than arterial pressures. However, the difference in pressure becomes obvious when these vessels are cut. If a vein is cut, the blood flows evenly from the cut. A lacerated artery produces rapid spurts of blood.

Activity 6:
Observing the Effect of Various Factors on Blood Pressure and Heart Rate

Arterial blood pressure is directly proportional to cardiac output (amount of blood pumped out of the left ventricle per unit time) and peripheral resistance to blood flow, that is

$$\text{BP} = \text{CO} \times \text{PR}$$

Peripheral resistance is increased by blood vessel constriction (most importantly the arterioles), by an increase in blood viscosity or volume, and by a loss of elasticity of the arteries (seen in arteriosclerosis). Any factor that increases either the cardiac output or the peripheral resistance causes an almost immediate reflex rise in blood pressure. A close examination of these relationships reveals that many factors—age, weight, time of day, exercise, body position,

emotional state, and various drugs, for example—alter blood pressure. The influence of a few of these factors is investigated here.

The following tests are done most efficiently if one student acts as the subject; two are examiners (one taking the radial pulse and the other auscultating the brachial blood pressure); and a fourth student collects and records data. The sphygmomanometer cuff should be left on the subject's arm throughout the experiments (in a deflated state, of course) so that, at the proper times, the blood pressure can be taken quickly. In each case, take the measurements at least twice. For each of the following tests, students should formulate hypotheses, collect data, and write lab reports. (See Getting Started: Writing a Lab Report, p. xii.) Conclusions should be shared with the class.

Posture

To monitor circulatory adjustments to changes in position, take blood pressure and pulse measurements under the conditions noted in the chart above. Record your results on the chart also.

Exercise

Blood pressure and pulse changes during and after exercise provide a good yardstick for measuring one's overall cardiovascular fitness. Although there are more sophisticated and more accurate tests that evaluate fitness according to a specific point system, the *Harvard step test* described here is a quick way to compare the relative fitness level of a group of people.

You will be working in groups of four, duties assigned as indicated above, except that student 4, in addition to recording the data, will act as the timer and call the cadence.

⚠ Any student with a known heart problem should refuse to participate as the subject.

All four students may participate as the subject in turn, if desired, but the bench stepping is to be performed *at least twice* in each group—once with a well-conditioned person acting as the subject, and once with a poorly conditioned subject.

Bench stepping is the following series of movements repeated sequentially:

1. Place one foot on the step.

2. Step up with the other foot so that both feet are on the platform. Straighten the legs and the back.

3. Step down with one foot.

4. Bring the other foot down.

The pace for the stepping will be set by the "timer" (student 4), who will repeat "Up-2-3-4, up-2-3-4" at such a pace that each "up-2-3-4" sequence takes 2 sec (i.e., 30 cycles/min).

1. Student 4 should obtain the step (0.5 m or 20-in. height for male subject, or 0.4 m or 16 in. for a female subject) while baseline measurements are being obtained on the subject.

2. Once the baseline pulse and blood pressure measurements have been recorded on the exercise chart on the following page, the subject is to stand quietly at attention for 2 min to allow his or her blood pressure to stabilize before beginning to step.

Posture

	Trial 1		Trial 2	
	BP	Pulse	BP	Pulse
Sitting quietly	_____	_____	_____	_____
Reclining (after 2 to 3 min)	_____	_____	_____	_____
Immediately on standing from the reclining position ("at attention" stance)	_____	_____	_____	_____
After standing for 3 min	_____	_____	_____	_____

Exercise

Harvard step test for 5 min at 30/min	Baseline		Interval Following Test							
			Immediately		1 min		2 min		3 min	
	BP	P	BP	P	BP	P	BP	P	BP	P
Well-conditioned individual	___	___	___	___	___	___	___	___	___	___
Poorly conditioned individual	___	___	___	___	___	___	___	___	___	___

3. The subject is to perform the bench stepping for as long as possible, up to a maximum of 5 min, according to the cadence called by the timer. The subject is to be watched for and warned against crouching (posture must remain erect). If he or she is unable to keep the pace for a span of 15 sec, the test is to be terminated.

4. When the subject is stopped by the pacer for crouching, stops voluntarily because he or she is unable to continue, or has completed 5 min of bench stepping, he or she is to sit down. The duration of exercise (in seconds) is to be recorded, and the blood pressure and pulse are to be measured immediately and thereafter at 1-min intervals for 3 min post-exercise.

Duration of exercise: _____ sec

5. The subject's *index of physical fitness* is to be calculated using the formula given below:

$$\text{Index} = \frac{\text{duration of exercise in seconds} \times 100}{2 \times \text{sum of the 3 pulse counts in recovery}}$$

Scores are interpreted according to the following scale:

below 55	poor physical condition
55 to 62	low average
63 to 71	average
72 to 79	high average
80 to 89	good
90 and over	excellent

6. Record the test values on the chart, and repeat the testing and recording procedure with the second subject.

When did you notice a greater elevation of blood pressure and pulse?

_____

Explain: _____

_____

Was there a sizable difference between the after-exercise values for well-conditioned and poorly conditioned individuals?

_____ Explain: _____

_____

Did the diastolic pressure also increase? _____

Explain: _____

_____

A Noxious Sensory Stimulus (Cold)

There is little question that blood pressure is affected by emotions and pain. This lability of blood pressure will be investigated through use of the **cold pressor test,** in which one hand will be immersed in unpleasantly (even painfully) cold water.

Measure the blood pressure and pulse of the subject as he or she sits quietly. Obtain a basin and thermometer, fill the basin with ice cubes, and add water. When the temperature of the ice bath has reached 5°C, immerse the subject's other hand (the noncuffed limb) in the ice water. With the hand still immersed, take blood pressure and pulse readings at 1-min intervals for a period of 3 min, and record the values on the chart on the following page.

How did the blood pressure change during cold exposure?

_____

_____

Was there any change in pulse? _____

Subtract the respective baseline readings of systolic and diastolic blood pressure from the highest single reading of systolic and diastolic pressure obtained during cold immersion. (For example, if the highest experimental reading is 140/88 and the baseline reading is 120/70, then the differences in blood pressure would be systolic pressure, 20 mm Hg, and diastolic pressure, 18 mm Hg.) These differences are called the index of response. According to their index of response, subjects can be classified as follows:

Hyporeactors (stable blood pressure): Exhibit a rise of diastolic and/or systolic pressure ranging from 0 to 22 mm Hg; or a drop in pressures

Hyperreactors (labile blood pressure): Exhibit a rise of 23 mm Hg or more in the diastolic and/or systolic blood pressure

Is the subject tested a hypo- or hyperreactor?

_____ ■

Skin Color as an Indicator of Local Circulatory Dynamics

Skin color reveals with surprising accuracy the state of the local circulation, and allows inferences concerning the larger blood vessels and the circulation as a whole. The experiments on local circulation outlined below illustrate a number of factors that affect blood flow to the tissues.

Clinical expertise often depends upon good observation skills, accurate recording of data, and logical interpretation of the findings. A single example will be given to demonstrate this statement: A massive hemorrhage may be internal and hidden (thus, not obvious) but will still threaten the blood delivery to the brain and other vital organs. One of the earliest compensatory responses of the body to such a threat is constriction of cutaneous blood vessels, which reduces blood flow to the skin and diverts it into the circulatory mainstream to serve other, more vital tissues. As a result, the skin of the face and particularly of the extremities becomes pale, cold, and eventually moist with perspiration. Therefore, pale, cold, clammy skin should immediately lead the careful diagnostician to suspect that the circulation is dangerously inefficient. Other conditions, such as local arterial obstruction and venous congestion, as well as certain pathologies of the heart and lungs, also alter skin texture, color, and circulation in characteristic ways.

Activity 7:
Examining the Effect of Local Chemical and Physical Factors on Skin Color

The local blood supply to the skin (indeed, to any tissue) is influenced by (1) local metabolites, (2) oxygen supply, (3) local temperature, (4) autonomic nervous system impulses, (5) local vascular reflexes, (6) certain hormones, and (7) substances released by injured tissues. A number of these factors are examined in the simple experiments that follow. Each experiment should be conducted by students in groups of three or four. One student will act as the subject; the others will conduct the tests and make and record observations.

Vasodilation and Flushing of the Skin Due to Local Metabolites

1. Obtain a blood pressure cuff (sphygmomanometer) and stethoscope. You will also need a watch with a second hand.

2. The subject should bare both arms by rolling up the sleeves as high as possible and then lay the forearms side by side on the bench top.

3. Observe the general color of the subject's forearm skin, and the normal contour and size of the veins. Notice whether skin color is bilaterally similar. Record your observations:

_____

_____

_____

A Noxious Sensory Stimulus (Cold)

Baseline		1 min		2 min		3 min	
BP	P	BP	P	BP	P	BP	P
___	___	___	___	___	___	___	___

4. Apply the blood pressure cuff to one arm, and inflate it to 250 mm Hg. Keep it inflated for 1 min. During this period, repeat the observations made above and record the results:

_____

_____

5. Release the pressure in the cuff (leaving the deflated cuff in position), and again record the forearm skin color and the condition of the forearm veins. Make this observation immediately after deflation and then again 30 sec later.

Immediately after deflation _____

_____

30 sec after deflation _____

_____

The above observations constitute your baseline information. Now conduct the following tests.

6. Instruct the subject to raise the cuffed arm above his or her head and to clench the fist as tightly as possible. While the hand and forearm muscles are tightly contracted, rapidly inflate the cuff to 240 mm Hg or more. This maneuver partially empties the hand and forearm of blood, and stops most blood flow to the hand and forearm. Once the cuff has been inflated, the subject is to relax the fist and return the forearm to the bench top so that it can be compared to the other forearm.

7. Leave the cuff inflated for exactly 1 min. During this interval, compare the skin color in the "ischemic" (blood-deprived) hand to that of the "normal" (non-cuffed-limb) hand. Quickly release the pressure immediately after 1 min.

What are the subjective effects* of stopping blood flow to the arm and hand for 1 min?

_____

_____

*Subjective effects are sensations—such as pain, coldness, warmth, tingling, and weakness—experienced by the subject. They are "symptoms" of a change in function.

What are the objective effects (color of skin and condition of veins)?

_____

_____

How long does it take for the subject's ischemic hand to regain its normal color?

_____

Effects of Venous Congestion

1. Again, but with a different subject, observe and record the appearance of the skin and veins on the forearms resting on the bench top. This time, pay particular attention to the color of the fingers, particularly the distal phalanges, and the nail beds. Record this information:

_____

_____

2. Wrap the blood pressure cuff around one of the subject's arms, and inflate it to 40 mm Hg. Maintain this pressure for 5 min. Make a record of the subjective and objective findings just before the 5 min are up, and then again immediately after release of the pressure at the end of 5 min.

Subjective (arm cuffed) _____

_____

Objective (arm cuffed) _____

_____

Subjective (pressure released) _____

_____

Objective (pressure released) _____

_____

3. With still another subject, conduct the following simple experiment: Raise one arm above the head, and let the other hang by the side for 1 min. After 1 min, quickly lay both arms on the bench top, and compare their color.

Color of raised arm _____

Color of dependent arm _____

From this and the two preceding observations, analyze the factors that determine tint of color (pink or blue) and intensity of skin color (deep pink or blue as opposed to light pink or blue). Record your conclusions.

_____

_____

_____

_____

Collateral Blood Flow

In some diseases, blood flow to an organ through one or more arteries may be completely and irreversibly obstructed. Fortunately, in most cases a given body area is supplied both by one main artery and by anastomosing channels connecting the main artery with one or more neighboring blood vessels. Consequently, an organ may remain viable even though its main arterial supply is occluded, as long as the **collateral vessels** are still functional.

The effectiveness of collateral blood flow in preventing ischemia can be easily demonstrated.

1. Check the subject's hands to be sure they are *warm* to the touch. If not, choose another, "warm-handed" subject, or warm the subject's hands in 35°C water for 10 min before beginning.

2. Palpate the subject's radial and ulnar arteries approximately 2.5 cm or 1 in. above the wrist flexure, and mark their locations with a felt marker.

3. Instruct the subject to supinate one forearm and to hold it in a partially flexed (about a 30° angle) position, with the elbow resting on the bench top.

4. Face the subject and grasp his or her forearm with both of your hands, the thumb and fingers of one hand compressing the marked radial artery and the thumb and fingers of the other hand compressing the ulnar artery. Maintain the pressure for 5 min, noticing the progression of the subject's hand to total ischemia.

5. At the end of 5 min, release the pressure abruptly. Record the subject's sensations, as well as the intensity and duration of the flush in the previously occluded hand. (Use the other hand as a baseline for comparison.)

_____

_____

_____

6. Allow the subject to relax for 5 min; then repeat the maneuver, but this time *compress only the radial artery.* Record your observations.

_____

_____

How do the results of the first test differ from those of the second test with respect to color changes during compression, and the intensity and duration of reactive hyperemia (redness of the skin)?

_____

_____

_____

_____

7. Once again allow the subject to relax for 5 min. Then repeat the maneuver, *with only the ulnar artery compressed.* Record your observations:

_____

_____

What can you conclude about the relative sizes of, and hand areas served by, the radial and ulnar arteries?

_____

_____

_____

Effect of Mechanical Stimulation of Blood Vessels of the Skin

With moderate pressure, draw the blunt end of your pen across the skin of a subject's forearm. Wait 3 min to observe the effects, and then repeat with firmer pressure.

What changes in skin color do you observe with light-to-moderate pressure?

_____

_____

With heavy pressure? _____

The redness, or *flare,* observed after mechanical stimulation of the skin results from a local inflammatory response promoted by chemical mediators released by injured tissues. These mediators stimulate increased blood flow into the area and leaking of fluid (from the capillaries) into the local tissues. (Note: People differ considerably in skin sensitivity. Those most sensitive will show **dermographism,** a condition in which the direct line of stimulation will swell quite obviously. This excessively swollen area is called a *wheal.*) ∎

Frog Cardiovascular Physiology: Wet Lab Using PowerLab® Data Acquisition System

The following lab includes instructions for using PowerLab® recording equipment to collect data concerning frog heart activity. The data can be collected with a kymograph, physiograph, or a computerized data collection system. The laboratory manual contains the instructions for BIOPAC® and physiograph, and these instructions are for PowerLab®. It's assumed the students are familiar with the use of the PowerLab® system before beginning the experiments.

Note: For up-to-date versions of this and other experiments, log on to www.powerlab-teaching.com/experiments.

Objectives

1. To list the properties of cardiac muscle as automaticity and rhythmicity and define each property.

2. To explain the statement "Cardiac muscle has an intrinsic ability to beat."

3. To compare the intrinsic rate of contraction of the "pacemaker" of the frog heart (sinus venosus) to that of the atria and ventricle.

4. To compare the relative length of the refractory period of cardiac muscle with that of skeletal muscle, and explain why it is not possible to tetanize cardiac muscle.

5. To define *extrasystole* and to explain at what point in the cardiac cycle (and on an ECG tracing) an extrasystole can be induced.

6. To describe the effect of the following on heart rate: cold, heat, vagal stimulation, pilocarpine, digitalis, atropine sulfate, epinephrine, and potassium, sodium, and calcium ions.

7. To define *vagal escape* and discuss its value.

8. To define *ectopic pacemaker*.

9. To define *partial* and *total heart block*.

10. To describe how heart block was induced in the laboratory and explain the results, and to explain how heart block might occur in the body.

11. To list the components of the microcirculatory system.

12. To identify an arteriole, venule, and capillaries in a frog's web, and to cite differences between relative size, rate of blood flow, and regulation of blood flow in these vessels.

13. To describe the effect of heat, cold, local irritation, and histamine on the rate of blood flow in the microcirculation, and to explain how these responses help maintain homeostasis.

Materials

☐ Frogs*
☐ Dissecting instruments and tray
☐ Disposable gloves
☐ Petri dishes
☐ Medicine dropper
☐ Millimeter ruler
☐ Disposable container for organic debris
☐ Frog Ringer's solutions (at room temperature, 5°C, and 32°C)
☐ Thread
☐ Large rubber bands
☐ Fine common pins
☐ Frog board
☐ Cotton balls
☐ Dropper bottles of freshly prepared solutions (using frog Ringer's solution as the solvent) of the following:

    2.5% pilocarpine
    5% atropine sulfate
    1% epinephrine
    2% digitalis
    2% calcium chloride ($CaCl_2$)
    0.7% sodium chloride (NaCl)
    5% potassium chloride (KCl)
    0.01% histamine
    0.01 N HCl

☐ Dissecting pins
☐ Paper towels
☐ Compound microscope

*Instructor will double-pith frogs as required for student experimentation.

❏ PowerLab® unit and interface cable, Windows PC or Macintosh computer with Chart software installed, Bridge Pod, MLT500/A Force Transducer, transducer cable, micropositioner, transducer stand, S-hook, thread, PowerLab® User's Guide, Chart User's Guide

PhysioEx 5.0™ Computer Simulation on p. P-71

Investigations of human cardiovascular physiology are very interesting, but many areas obviously do not lend themselves to experimentation. It would be tantamount to murder to inject a human subject with various drugs to observe their effects on heart activity, or to expose the human heart in order to study the length of its refractory period. However, this type of investigation can be done on frogs or small laboratory animals and provides valuable data, because the physiological mechanisms in these animals are similar if not identical to those in humans.

In this exercise, you will conduct the cardiac investigations just mentioned and others. In addition, you will observe the microcirculation in a frog's web and subject it to various chemical and thermal agents to demonstrate their influence on local blood flow.

Special Electrical Properties of Cardiac Muscle: Automaticity and Rhythmicity

Cardiac muscle differs from skeletal muscle both functionally and in its fine structure. Skeletal muscle must be electrically stimulated to contract. In contrast, heart muscle can and does depolarize spontaneously in the absence of external stimulation. This property, called **automaticity,** is due to plasma membranes that have reduced permeability to potassium ions, but still allow sodium ions to slowly leak into the cells. This leakage causes the muscle cells to gradually depolarize until the action potential threshold is reached and *fast calcium channels* open, allowing Ca^{2+} entry from the extracellular fluid. Shortly thereafter, contraction occurs.

Also, the spontaneous depolarization-repolarization events occur in a regular and continuous manner in cardiac muscle, a property referred to as **rhythmicity.**

In the following experiment, you will observe these properties of cardiac muscle in an *in vitro* (outside, or removed from the body) situation. Work together in groups of three or four. (The instructor may choose to demonstrate this procedure if time or frogs are at a premium.)

Activity 1:

Investigating the Automaticity and Rhythmicity of Heart Muscle

1. Obtain a dissecting tray and instruments, disposable plastic gloves, two petri dishes, frog Ringer's solution, and a medicine dropper, and bring them to your laboratory bench.

⚠ 2. Don the gloves, and then request and obtain a doubly pithed frog from your instructor. Quickly open the thoracic cavity and observe the heart rate *in situ* (at the site or within the body).

Record the heart rate: _____ beats/min

3. Dissect out the heart and the gastrocnemius muscle of the calf and place the removed organs in separate petri dishes containing frog Ringer's solution. (Note: Just in case you don't remember, the procedure for removing the gastrocnemius muscle is provided on pp. 170–173 in Exercise 16A of the laboratory manual. The extreme care used in that procedure for the removal of the gastrocnemius muscle need not be exercised here.)

4. Observe the activity of the two organs for a few seconds.

Which is contracting? _____

At what rate? _____ beats/min

Is the contraction rhythmic? _____

5. Sever the sinus venosus from the heart (see Figure 34b.1). The sinus venosus of the frog's heart corresponds to the SA node of the human heart.

Does the sinus venosus continue to beat? _____

If not, lightly touch it with a probe to stimulate it. Record its rate of contraction.

Rate: _____ beats/min

6. Sever the right atrium from the heart; then remove the left atrium. Does each atrium continue to beat?

_____ Rate: _____ beats/min

Does the ventricle continue to beat? _____

Rate: _____ beats/min

7. Continue to fragment the ventricle to determine how small the ventricular fragments must be before the automaticity of ventricular muscle is abolished. Measure these fragments and record their approximate size.

_____ mm × _____ mm × _____ mm

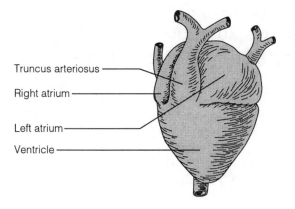

(a)

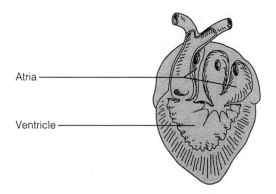

(b)

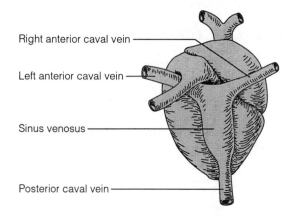

(c)

Figure 34b.1 Anatomy of the frog heart.
(a) Ventral view showing the single truncus arteriosus leaving the undivided ventricle. **(b)** Longitudinal section showing the two atrial and single ventricular chambers. **(c)** Dorsal view showing the sinus venosus (pacemaker).

Which portion of the heart exhibited the most marked automaticity?

_____

Which the least? _____

8. Properly dispose of the frog and heart fragments before continuing with the next procedure. ■

Baseline Frog Heart Activity

The heart's effectiveness as a pump is dependent both on intrinsic (within the heart) and extrinsic (external to the heart) controls. In this experiment, you will investigate some of these factors.

The nodal system, in which the "pacemaker" imposes its depolarization rate on the rest of the heart, is one intrinsic factor that influences the heart's pumping action. If its impulses fail to reach the ventricles (as in heart block), the ventricles continue to beat but at their own inherent rate, which is much slower than that usually imposed on them. Although heart contraction does not depend on nerve impulses, its rate can be modified by extrinsic impulses reaching it through the autonomic nerves. Additionally, cardiac activity is modified by various chemicals, hormones, ions, and metabolites. The effects of several of these chemical factors are examined in the next experimental series.

The frog heart has two atria and a single, incompletely divided ventricle (see Figure 34b.1). The pacemaker is located in the sinus venosus, an enlarged region between the venae cavae and the right atrium. The SA node of mammals may have evolved from the sinus venosus.

Activity 2:
Recording Baseline Frog Heart Activity Using PowerLab®

To record baseline frog heart activity, work in groups of four—two students handling the equipment setup and two preparing the frog for experimentation.

Preparation of the Frog

1. Obtain room-temperature frog Ringer's solution, a medicine dropper, dissecting instruments and pan, disposable gloves, fine common pins, and some thread, and bring them to your bench.

⚠ 2. Don the gloves and obtain a doubly pithed frog from your instructor.

3. Make a longitudinal incision through the abdominal and thoracic walls with scissors, and then cut through the sternum to expose the heart.

4. Grasp the pericardial sac with forceps, and cut it open so that the beating heart can be observed.

Is the sequence an atrial-ventricular one? _____

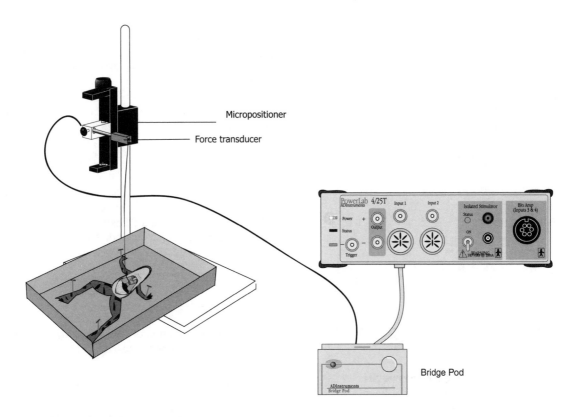

Figure 34b.2 PowerLab® setup for recording the activity of the frog heart.

5. Locate the vagus nerve, which runs down the lateral aspect of the neck and parallels the trachea and carotid artery. (In good light, it appears to be striated.) Slip an 18-inch length of thread under the vagus nerve so that it can later be lifted away from the surrounding tissues by the thread. Then place a saline-soaked cotton ball over the nerve to keep it moistened until you are ready to stimulate it later in the procedure.

6. Using a medicine dropper, flush the heart with the saline (Ringer's) solution. *From this point on the heart must be kept continually moistened with room-temperature Ringer's solution unless other solutions are being used for the experimentation.*

7. Attach the frog to the frog board.

Setting up the Equipment

1. Make sure the PowerLab® unit is turned off and connected to your computer via the USB cable.

2. Connect the MLT500/A Force Transducer to the micropositioner or clamp, and mount it on the ring-stand (Figure 34b.2).

3. Plug the Bridge Pod into the Input 1 Pod Port. Plug the force transducer into the back of the Bridge Pod.

4. Connect the BNC plugs on the stimulator probe handle to the Output connectors on the front of the PowerLab® unit.

5. Turn the PowerLab® unit on. From the computer, open the Chart settings file called "Frog Heart Settings."

6. Connect the frog heart to the force transducer with an S-hook and strong thread. Adjust the position of the transducer on the stand so that the heart is raised slightly from the body cavity.

7. In Chart, choose Input Amplifier from the Force channel pop-up menu.

8. Adjust the Range in the dialog box so that the contraction peaks are 1/3 to 1/2 of the window height and click OK.

9. Click Start to begin your recording.

Making the Baseline Recording

1. Record several normal heartbeats (12 to 15). Be sure you can distinguish atrial and ventricular contractions (see Figure 34b.3). Pay attention to the relative force of heart contractions while recording.

2. Count the number of ventricular contractions per minute and record:

_____ beats/min

3. Compute the A-V interval (period from the beginning of atrial contraction to the beginning of ventricular contraction).

_____ sec

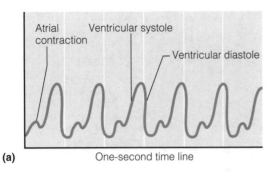

(a)

Atrial contraction   Ventricular systole

Ventricular diastole

One-second time line

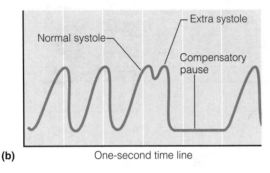

(b)

Normal systole

Extra systole

Compensatory pause

One-second time line

Figure 34b.3 Recording of contractile activity of a frog heart. (a) Normal heartbeat. **(b)** Induction of an extrasystole.

How do the two tracings compare in time?

_____

_____

_____

4.   Mark the atrial and ventricular systoles on the record. *Remember to keep the heart moistened with Ringer's solution.* ▪

Activity 3:
Investigating the Refractory Period of Cardiac Muscle

In conducting Exercise 16A, you saw that repeated rapid stimuli could cause skeletal muscle to remain in a contracted state. In other words, the muscle could be tetanized. This was possible because of the relatively short refractory period of skeletal muscle. In this experiment, you will investigate the refractory period of cardiac muscle and its response to stimulation. During the procedure, one student should keep the stimulating electrodes in constant contact with the frog heart ventricle.

1.   Set the stimulator to deliver 20-V shocks of 2-ms duration, and begin recording.

2.   Deliver single shocks at the beginning of ventricular contraction, the peak of ventricular contraction, and then later and later in the cardiac cycle.

3.   Observe the recording for **extrasystoles,** which are extra beats that show up riding on the ventricular contraction peak. Also note the **compensatory pause,** which allows the heart to get back on schedule after an extrasystole. (See Figure 34b.2b.)

During which portion of the cardiac cycle was it possible to induce an extrasystole?

_____

_____

4.   Attempt to tetanize the heart by stimulating it at the rate of 20 to 30 impulses per second. What is the result?

_____

_____

Considering the function of the heart, why is it important that heart muscle cannot be tetanized?

_____

_____ ▪

Activity 4:
Assessing Physical and Chemical Modifiers of Heart Rate

Now that you have observed normal frog heart activity, you will have an opportunity to investigate the effects of various factors that modify heart activity. In each case, record a few normal heartbeats before introducing the modifying factor. After removing the agent, allow the heart to return to its normal rate before continuing with the testing. On each record, indicate the point of introduction and removal of the modifying agent.

Temperature

1.   Obtain 5°C and 32°C frog Ringer's solutions and medicine droppers.

2.   Bathe the heart with 5°C saline, and continue to record until the recording indicates a change in cardiac activity.

3.   Stop recording, pipette off the cold Ringer's solution (remove the fluid by sucking it into the barrel of a medicine dropper), and flood the heart with room-temperature saline.

4.   Start recording again to determine the resumption of the normal heart rate. When this has been achieved, flood the heart with 32°C Ringer's solution and again record until a change is noted.

5.   Stop the recording, pipette off the warm saline, and bathe the heart with room-temperature Ringer's solution once again.

What change occurred with the cold (5°C) Ringer's solution?

_____

What change occurred with the warm (32°C) Ringer's solution?

_____

6. Count the heart rate at the two temperatures and record below.

_____ beats/min at 5°C; _____ beats/min at 32°C

Vagus Nerve Stimulation

The vagus nerve carries parasympathetic impulses to the heart, which modify heart activity.

1. Remove the cotton placed over the vagus nerve. Using the previously tied thread, lift the nerve away from the tissues and place the nerve on the stimulating electrodes.

2. Using a duration of 0.5 msec at a voltage of 1 mV, stimulate the nerve at a rate of 50/sec. Continue stimulation until the heart stops momentarily and then begins to beat again **(vagal escape).** If no effect is observed, increase stimulus intensity and try again. If no effect is observed after a substantial increase in stimulus voltage, reexamine your "vagus nerve" to make sure that it is not simply strands of connective tissue.

3. Discontinue stimulation after you observe vagal escape, and flush the heart with saline until the normal heart rate resumes. What is the effect of vagal stimulation on heart rate?

_____

The phenomenon of vagal escape demonstrates that many factors are involved in heart regulation and that any deleterious factor (in this case, excessive vagal stimulation) will be overcome, if possible, by other physiological mechanisms such as activation of the sympathetic division of the autonomic nervous system (ANS).

Pilocarpine

Flood the heart with a 2.5% solution of pilocarpine. Record until a change in the pattern of the ECG is noticed. Pipette off the excess pilocarpine solution, and proceed immediately to the next test, which uses atropine as the testing solution. What happened when the heart was bathed in the pilocarpine solution?

_____

Pilocarpine simulates the effect of parasympathetic nerve (hence, vagal) stimulation by enhancing acetylcholine release; such drugs are called parasympathomimetic drugs.

Atropine Sulfate

Apply a few drops of atropine sulfate to the frog's heart and observe the recording. If no changes are observed within 2 minutes, apply a few more drops. When you observe a response, pipette off the excess atropine sulfate and flood the heart with Ringer's solution. What happens when the atropine sulfate is added?

_____

_____

Atropine is a drug that blocks the effect of the neurotransmitter acetylcholine, which is liberated by the parasympathetic nerve endings. Do your results accurately reflect this effect of atropine?

_____

Are pilocarpine and atropine agonists or antagonists in their effects on heart activity?

_____

Epinephrine

Flood the frog heart with epinephrine solution, and continue to record until a change in heart activity is noted.

What are the results? _____

_____

Which division of the autonomic nervous system does its effect imitate?

_____

Digitalis

Pipette off the excess epinephrine solution, and rinse the heart with room-temperature Ringer's solution. Continue recording, and when the heart rate returns to baseline values, bathe it in digitalis solution. What is the effect of digitalis on the heart?

_____

_____

_____

Digitalis is a drug commonly prescribed for heart patients with congestive heart failure. It slows heart rate, providing more time for venous return and decreasing the load on the weakened heart. These effects are thought to be due to inhibition of the Na^+-K^+ pump and enhancement of Ca^{2+} entry into the myocardial fibers.

Various Ions

To test the effect of various ions on the heart, apply the designated solution until you observe a change in heart rate or in strength of contraction. Pipette off the solution, flush with Ringer's solution, and allow the heart to resume its normal rate before continuing. *Do not allow the heart to stop.* If the rate should decrease dramatically, flood the heart with room-temperature Ringer's solution.

Effect of Ca^{2+} (use 2% $CaCl_2$) _____

_____

Effect of Na^+ (use 0.7% NaCl) _____

_____

Effect of K^+ (use 5% KCl) _____

_____

Potassium ion concentration is normally higher within cells than in the extracellular fluid. *Hyperkalemia* decreases the resting potential of plasma membranes, thus decreasing the force of heart contraction. In some cases, the conduction rate of the heart is so depressed that **ectopic pacemakers** (pacemakers appearing erratically and at abnormal sites in the heart muscle) appear in the ventricles, and fibrillation may occur. Was there any evidence of premature beats in the recording of potassium ion effects?

_____

Was arrhythmia produced with any of the ions tested?

_____ If so, which? _____

Intrinsic Conduction System Disturbance (Heart Block)

1. Moisten a 25 cm or 10-inch length of thread and make a Stannius ligature (loop the thread around the heart at the junction of the atria and ventricle).

2. Decrease the scroll speed to achieve intervals of approximately 2 cm between the ventricular contractions, and record a few normal heartbeats.

3. Tighten the ligature in a stepwise manner while observing the atrial and ventricular contraction curves. As heart block occurs, the atria and ventricle will no longer show a 1:1 contraction ratio. Record a few beats each time you observe a different degree of heart block—a 2:1 atria to ventricle, 3:1, 4:1, and so on. As long as you can continue to count a whole number ratio between the two chamber types, the heart is in **partial heart block.** When you can no longer count a whole number ratio, the heart is in **total,** or **complete, heart block.**

4. When total heart block occurs, release the ligature to see if the normal A-V rhythm is reestablished. What is the result?

_____

_____

5. Attach properly labeled recordings (or copies of the recordings) made during this procedure to the last page of this exercise for future reference.

6. Dispose of the frog remains and gloves in appropriate containers, and dismantle the experimental apparatus before continuing. ■

The Microcirculation and Local Blood Flow

The thin web of a frog's foot provides an excellent opportunity to observe the flow of blood to, from, and within the capillary beds, where the real business of the circulatory system occurs. The collection of vessels involved in the exchange mechanism is referred to as the **microcirculation;** it consists of arterioles, venules, capillaries, and vascular shunts called *metarteriole–thoroughfare channels* (Figure 34b.4).

The total cross-sectional area of the capillaries in the body is much greater than that of the veins and arteries combined. Thus, the flow through the capillary beds is quite slow. Capillary flow is also intermittent, because if all capillary beds were filled with blood at the same time, there would be no blood at all in the large vessels. The flow of blood into the capillary beds is regulated by the activity of muscular *terminal arterioles,* which feed the beds, and by *precapillary sphincters* at entrances to the true capillaries. The amount of blood flowing into the true capillaries of the bed is regulated most importantly by local chemical controls (local concentrations of carbon dioxide, histamine, pH). Thus a capillary bed may be flooded with blood or almost entirely bypassed depending on what is happening within the body or in a particular body region at any one time. You will investigate some of the local controls in the next group of experiments.

Activity 5:
Investigating the Effect of Various Factors on the Microcirculation

1. Obtain a frog board (with a hole at one end), dissecting pins, disposable gloves, frog Ringer's solution, 0.01 N HCl, 0.01% histamine solution, 1% epinephrine solution, a large rubber band, and some paper towels.

2. Put on the gloves and obtain a frog (alive and hopping, *not* pithed). Moisten several paper towels with room-temperature Ringer's solution, and wrap the frog's body securely with them. One hind leg should be left unsecured and extending beyond the paper cocoon.

3. Attach the frog to the frog board (or other supporting structure) with a large rubber band and then carefully spread (but do not stretch) the web of the exposed hindfoot over the hole in the support. Have your partners hold the edges of the web firmly for viewing. Alternatively, secure the toes to the board with dissecting pins.

4. Obtain a compound microscope, and observe the web under low power to find a capillary bed. Focus on the vessels in high power. Keep the web moistened with Ringer's solution as you work. If the circulation seems to stop during your observations, massage the hind leg of the frog gently to restore blood flow.

5. Observe the red blood cells of the frog. Notice that, unlike human RBCs, they are nucleated. Watch their movement through the smallest vessels—the capillaries. Do they move in single file or do they flow through two or three cells abreast?

_____

Are they flexible? _____ Explain. _____

Can you see any white blood cells in the capillaries?

_____ If so, which types? _____

6. Notice the relative speed of blood flow through the blood vessels. Differentiate between the arterioles, which feed the capillary bed, and the venules, which drain it. This may be tricky, because images are reversed in the microscope. Thus, the vessel that appears to feed into the capillary bed will actually be draining it. You can distinguish between the vessels, however, if you consider that the flow is more pulsating and turbulent in the arterioles and smoother and steadier in the venules. How does the _rate_ of flow in the arterioles compare with that in the venules?

_____

In the capillaries? _____

What is the relative difference in the diameter of the arterioles and capillaries?

_____

Temperature

To investigate the effect of temperature on blood flow, flood the web with cold saline two or three times to chill the entire area. Is a change in vessel diameter noticeable?

_____ Which vessels are affected? _____

How? _____

Blot the web gently with a paper towel, and then bathe the web with warm saline. Record your observations.

_____

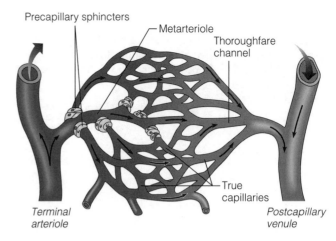

(a) Sphincters open

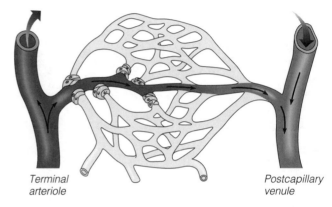

(b) Sphincters closed

Figure 34b.4 Anatomy of a capillary bed. The composite metarteriole–thoroughfare channels act as shunts to bypass the true capillaries when precapillary sphincters controlling blood entry into the true capillaries are constricted.

Inflammation

Pipette 0.01 _N_ HCl onto the frog's web. Hydrochloric acid will act as an irritant and cause a localized inflammatory response. Is there an increase or decrease in the blood flow into the capillary bed following the application of HCl?

_____

What purpose do these local changes serve during a localized inflammatory response?

_____

_____

_____

Flush the web with room-temperature Ringer's solution and blot.

Histamine

Histamine, which is released in large amounts during allergic responses, causes extensive vasodilation. Investigate this effect by adding a few drops of histamine solution to the frog web. What happens?

_____

_____

How does this response compare to that produced by HCl?

_____

Blot the web and flood with warm saline as before. Now add a few drops of 1% epinephrine solution, and observe the web. What are epinephrine's effects on the blood vessels?

_____

Epinephrine is used clinically to reverse the vasodilation seen in severe allergic attacks (such as asthma) which are mediated by histamine and other vasoactive molecules.

Return the dropper bottles to the supply area and the frog to the terrarium. Properly clean your work area before leaving the lab. ■

Respiratory System Physiology Using PowerLab® Data Acquisition System

The following lab includes instructions for using PowerLab® to record respiratory movements. The laboratory manual contains instructions for using a physiograph-pneumograph and for BIOPAC®, and these instructions are for using PowerLab®. It is assumed the students are familiar with the use of the PowerLab® system before beginning this experiment.

Note: For up-to-date versions of this and other experiments, log on to www.powerlab-teaching.com/experiments.

Objectives

1. To define the following (and be prepared to provide volume figures if applicable):
   inspiration   expiratory reserve volume
   expiration   inspiratory reserve volume
   tidal volume   minute respiratory volume
   vital capacity

2. To explain the role of muscles and volume changes in the mechanical process of breathing.

3. To demonstrate proper usage of the spirometer.

4. To explain the relative importance of various mechanical and chemical factors in producing respiratory variations.

5. To describe bronchial and vesicular breathing sounds.

6. To explain the importance of the carbonic acid–bicarbonate buffer system in maintaining blood pH.

Materials

- ❏ Model lung (bell jar demonstrator)
- ❏ Tape measure
- ❏ Stethoscope
- ❏ Alcohol swabs
- ❏ Spirometer
- ❏ Disposable cardboard mouthpieces
- ❏ Nose clips
- ❏ Table (on chalkboard) for recording class data
- ❏ Disposable autoclave bag
- ❏ Battery jar containing 70% ethanol solution
- ❏ Paper bag
- ❏ 0.05 M NaOH
- ❏ Phenol red in a dropper bottle
- ❏ 100 ml beakers
- ❏ Straws
- ❏ Concentrated HCl and NaOH in dropper bottles
- ❏ 250 and 50 ml beakers
- ❏ Plastic wash bottles containing distilled water
- ❏ Graduated cylinder (100 ml)
- ❏ Glass stirring rod
- ❏ Animal plasma
- ❏ pH meter (standardized with buffer of pH 7)
- ❏ Buffer solution (pH 7)
- ❏ 0.01 M HCl
- ❏ *Human Respiratory System* videotape*
- ❏ PowerLab® unit and interface cable, Windows PC or Macintosh computer with Chart software installed, respiratory belt, PowerLab® User's Guide, Chart User's Guide

 PhysioEx™ 5.0 Computer Simulation on p. P–78

*Available to qualified adopters from Benjamin Cummings.

Inspiration

Expiration

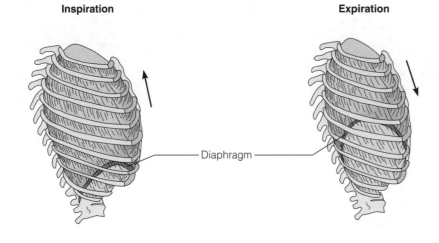

Diaphragm

Figure 37b.1 Rib cage and diaphragm positions during breathing. (a) At the end of a normal inspiration; chest expanded, diaphragm depressed. **(b)** At the end of a normal expiration; chest depressed, diaphragm elevated.

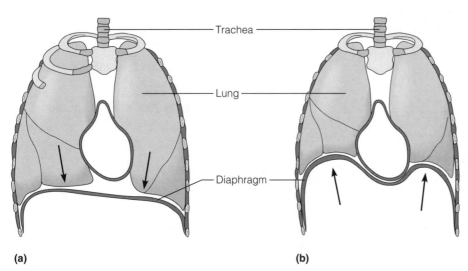

Trachea

Lung

Diaphragm

(a)

(b)

Mechanics of Respiration

Pulmonary ventilation, or **breathing,** consists of two phases: **inspiration,** during which air is taken into the lungs, and **expiration,** during which air passes out of the lungs. As the inspiratory muscles (external intercostals and diaphragm) contract during inspiration, the size of the thoracic cavity increases. The diaphragm moves from its relaxed dome shape to a flattened position, increasing the superoinferior volume. The external intercostals lift the rib cage, increasing the anteroposterior and lateral dimensions (Figure 37b.1). Since the lungs adhere to the thoracic walls like flypaper because of the presence of serous fluid in the pleural cavity, the intrapulmonary volume (volume within the lungs) also increases, lowering the air (gas) pressure inside the lungs. The gases then expand to fill the available space, creating a partial vacuum that causes air to flow into the lungs—constituting the act of inspiration. During expiration, the inspiratory muscles relax, and the natural tendency of the elastic lung tissue to recoil acts to decrease the intrathoracic and intrapulmonary volumes. As the gas molecules within the lungs are forced closer together, the intrapulmonary pressure rises to a point higher than atmospheric pressure. This causes gases to flow from the lungs to equalize the pressure inside and outside the lungs—the act of expiration.

Activity 1:
Operating the Model Lung

Observe the model lung, which demonstrates the principles involved in gas flows into and out of the lungs. It is a simple apparatus with a bottle "thorax," a rubber membrane "diaphragm," and balloon "lungs."

1.   Go to the demonstration area and work the model lung by moving the rubber diaphragm up and down. The balloons will not fully inflate or deflate, but notice the relative size changes in balloon (lung) size as the volume of the thoracic cavity is alternately increased and decreased.

2.   Check the appropriate columns in the chart concerning these observations in the Exercise 37A Review Sheet in the lab manual.

3.   Simulate a pneumothorax. Inflate the balloon lungs by pulling down on the diaphragm. Ask your lab partner to let air into the bottle "thorax" by loosening the rubber stopper.

What happens to the balloon lungs?

_____

_____

4. After observing the operation of the model lung, conduct the following tests on your lab partner. Use the tape measure to determine his or her chest circumference by placing the tape around the chest as high up under the armpits as possible. Record the measurements in inches in the appropriate space for each of the conditions below.

Quiet breathing:

Inspiration _____ Expiration _____

Forced breathing:

Inspiration _____ Expiration _____

Do the results coincide with what you expected on the basis

of what you have learned thus far? _____

How does the structural relationship between the balloon-lungs and bottle-thorax differ from that seen in the human lungs and thorax?

_____

_____

_____ ■

Respiratory Sounds

As air flows in and out of the respiratory tree, it produces two characteristic sounds that can be picked up with a stethoscope (auscultated). The **bronchial sounds** are produced by air rushing through the large respiratory passageways (the trachea and the bronchi). The second sound type, **vesicular breathing sounds,** apparently results from air filling the alveolar sacs and resembles the sound of a rustling or muffled breeze.

A c t i v i t y   2 :
Auscultating Respiratory Sounds

1. Obtain a stethoscope and clean the earpieces with an alcohol swab. Allow the alcohol to dry before donning the stethoscope.

2. Place the diaphragm of the stethoscope on the throat of the test subject just below the larynx. Listen for bronchial sounds on inspiration and expiration. Move the stethoscope down toward the bronchi until you can no longer hear sounds.

3. Place the stethoscope over the following chest areas and listen for vesicular sounds during respiration (heard primarily during inspiration).

- At various intercostal spaces

- At the *triangle of auscultation* (a small depressed area of the back where the muscles fail to cover the rib cage; located just medial to the inferior part of the scapula)

- Under the clavicle ■

H Diseased respiratory tissue, mucus, or pus can produce abnormal chest sounds such as rales (a rasping sound) and wheezing (a whistling sound). ●

Respiratory Volumes and Capacities—Spirometry

A person's size, sex, age, and physical condition produce variations in respiratory volumes. Normal quiet breathing moves about 500 ml of air in and out of the lungs with each breath. As you have seen in the first activity, a person can usually forcibly inhale or exhale much more air than is exchanged in normal quiet breathing. The terms given to the measurable respiratory volumes are defined next. These terms and their normal values for an adult male should be memorized.

Tidal volume (TV): Amount of air inhaled or exhaled with each breath under resting conditions (500 ml)

Inspiratory reserve volume (IRV): Amount of air that can be forcefully inhaled after a normal tidal volume inhalation (3100 ml)

Expiratory reserve volume (ERV): Amount of air that can be forcefully exhaled after a normal tidal volume exhalation (1200 ml)

Vital capacity (VC): Maximum amount of air that can be exhaled after a maximal inspiration (4800 ml)

$$VC = TV + IRV + ERV$$

An idealized tracing of the various respiratory volumes and their relationships to each other are shown in Figure 37b.2.

Respiratory volumes will be measured with an apparatus called a **spirometer.** There are two major types of spirometers, which give comparable results—the handheld dry, or wheel, spirometers (such as the Wright spirometer illustrated in Figure 37b.3) and "wet" spirometers, such as the Phipps and Bird spirometer and the Collins spirometer (which is available in both recording and nonrecording varieties). The somewhat more sophisticated wet spirometer consists of a plastic or metal *bell* within a rectangular or cylindrical tank that air can be added to or removed from (Figure 37b.4). The outer tank contains water and has a tube running through it to carry air above the water level. The floating bottomless bell is inverted over the water-containing tank and connected to a volume indicator.

In nonrecording spirometers, an indicator moves as air is *exhaled,* and only expired air volumes can be measured directly. By contrast, recording spirometers allow both inspired and expired gas volumes to be measured. Directions for both types of apparatus are provided in Activity 3.

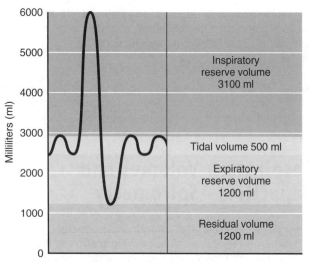

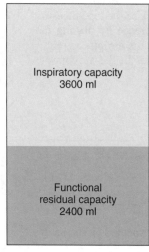

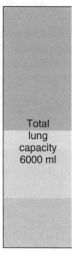

Figure 37b.2 Spirographic record for a male.

Activity 3:
Measuring Respiratory Volumes

The steps for using a nonrecording spirometer and a wet recording spirometer are given separately below.

Using a Nonrecording Spirometer

1. Before using the spirometer, count and record the subject's normal respiratory rate. The subject should face away from you as you make the count.

Respirations per minute _____

Now identify the parts of the spirometer you will be using by comparing it to the illustration in Figure 37b.3 or 37b.4. Examine the spirometer volume indicator *before beginning* to make sure you know how to read the scale. Work in pairs, with one person acting as the subject while the other records the data of the volume determinations. Reset the indicator to zero before beginning each trial.

Obtain a disposable cardboard mouthpiece. Insert it in the open end of the valve assembly (attached to the flexible tube) of the wet spirometer or over the fixed stem of the handheld dry spirometer. Before beginning, the subject should practice exhaling through the mouthpiece without exhaling through the nose, or prepare to use the nose clips (clean them first with an alcohol swab). If you are using the handheld spirometer, make sure its dial faces upward so that the volumes can be easily read during the tests.

2. The subject should stand erect during testing. Conduct the test three times for each required measurement. Record the data where indicated on this page, and then find the average volume figure for that respiratory measurement. After you have completed the trials and computed the averages, enter the average values on the table prepared on the chalkboard

Figure 37b.3 The Wright handheld dry spirometer. Reset to zero prior to each test.

for tabulation of class data,* and copy all averaged data onto the Exercise 37A Review Sheet in the laboratory manual.

3. Tidal volume (TV). The volume of air inhaled and exhaled with each normal respiration is approximately 500 ml. To conduct the test, inhale a normal breath, and then exhale a normal breath of air into the spirometer mouthpiece. (Do not

* Note to the Instructor: The format of class data tabulation can be similar to that shown here. However, it would be interesting to divide the class into smokers and nonsmokers and then compare the mean average VC and ERV for each group. Such a comparison might help to determine if smokers are handicapped in any way. It also might be a good opportunity for an informal discussion of the early warning signs of bronchitis and emphysema, which are primarily smokers' diseases.

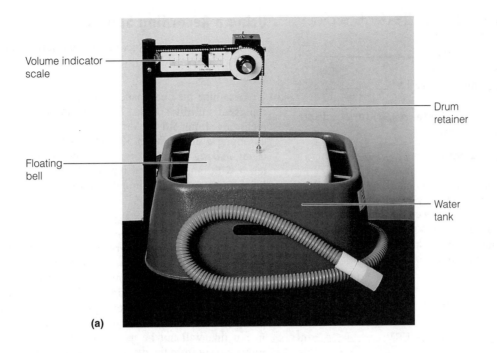

(a)

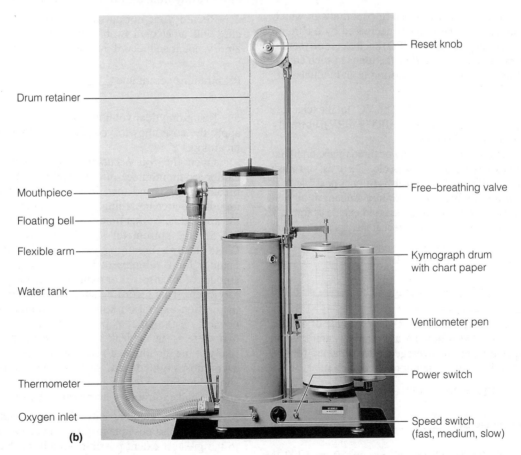

(b)

Figure 37b.4 **Wet spirometers.** **(a)** The Phipps & Bird "wet" spirometer. **(b)** The Collins-9L "wet" recording spirometer.

force the expiration!) Record the volume; repeat the test twice.

trial 1: _____ ml   trial 2: _____ ml

trial 3: _____ ml   average TV: _____ ml

4.   Compute the subject's **minute respiratory volume (MRV)** using the following formula:

$$\text{MRV} = \text{TV} \times \text{respirations/min} = \underline{\hspace{1.5cm}} \text{ml/min}$$

5.   Measuring expiratory reserve volume (ERV). The ERV is the volume of air that can be forcibly exhaled after a normal expiration. Normally, it ranges between 700 and 1200 ml.

Inhale and exhale normally two or three times, then insert the spirometer mouthpiece and exhale forcibly as much of the additional air as you can. Record your results, and repeat the test twice again.

trial 1: _____ ml   trial 2: _____ ml

trial 3: _____ ml   average ERV: _____ ml

ERV is dramatically reduced in conditions in which the elasticity of the lungs is decreased by a chronic obstructive pulmonary disease (COPD) such as **emphysema.** Since energy must be used to *deflate* the lungs in such conditions, expiration is physically exhausting to individuals suffering from COPD. ●

6.   Measuring vital capacity (VC). The VC, total exchangeable air of the lungs (the sum of TV + IRV + ERV), normally ranges from 3600 ml to 4800 ml.

Breathe in and out normally two or three times, and then bend over and exhale all the air possible. Then, as you raise yourself to the upright position, inhale as fully as possible. It is important to *strain* to inhale the maximum amount of air that you can. Quickly insert the mouthpiece, and exhale as forcibly as you can. Record your results and repeat the test twice again.

trial 1: _____ ml   trial 2: _____ ml

trial 3: _____ ml   average VC: _____ ml

7.   Inspiratory reserve volume (IRV), or volume of air that can be forcibly inhaled following a normal inspiration, can now be computed using the average values obtained for TV, ERV, and VC and plugging them into the equation:

$$\text{IRV} = \text{VC} - (\text{TV} + \text{ERV})$$

Record your average IRV: _____ ml

The normal IRV is substantial, ranging from 1900 to 3100 ml. How does your computed value compare?

Steps 8–10, which provide common directions for both nonrecording and recording spirometers, continue after the wet recording spirometer directions.

Using a Recording Spirometer

1.   In preparation for recording, familiarize yourself with the spirometer by comparing it to the equipment illustrated in Figure 37b.4.

2.   Examine the chart paper, noting that its horizontal lines represent milliliter units. To apply the chart paper to the recording drum, lift the drum retainer and then remove the kymograph drum. Wrap a sheet of chart paper around the drum, *making sure that the right edge overlaps the left.* Fasten it with tape, and then replace the kymograph drum and lower the drum retainer into its original position in the hole in the top of the drum.

3.   Raise and lower the floating bell several times, noting as you do so that the *ventilometer pen* moves up and down on the drum. This pen, which writes in black ink, will be used for recording and should be positioned or adjusted so that it records in the approximate middle of the chart paper. This adjustment is made by repositioning the floating bell using the *reset knob* on the metal pulley at the top of the spirometer apparatus. The other pen, the respirometer pen, which records in red ink, will not be used for these tests and should be moved away from the drum's recording surface.

4.   Record your normal respiratory rate. Clean the nose clips with an alcohol swab. While you wait for the alcohol to air dry, count and record your normal respiratory rate.

Respirations per minute _____

5.   Recording tidal volume. After the alcohol has air dried, apply the nose clips to your nose. This will enforce mouth breathing.

Open the *free-breathing valve.* Insert a disposable cardboard mouthpiece into the end (valve assembly) of the breathing tube, and then insert the mouthpiece into your mouth. Practice breathing for several breaths to get used to the apparatus. At this time, you are still breathing room air.

Set the spirometer switch to **SLOW** (32 mm/min). Close the free-breathing valve, and breathe in a normal manner for 2 minutes to record your tidal volume—the amount of air inspired or expired with each normal respiratory cycle. This recording should show a regular pattern of inspiration-expiration spikes and should gradually move upward on the chart paper. (A downward slope indicates that there is an air leak somewhere in the system—most likely at the mouthpiece.) Notice that on an apparatus using a counterweighted pen, such as the Collins Vitalometer shown in Fig. 37b.4b, inspirations are recorded by upstrokes and expirations are recorded by downstrokes.*

6.   Recording vital capacity. To record your vital capacity, take the deepest possible inspiration you can and then exhale to the greatest extent possible—really *push* the air out. The recording obtained should resemble that shown in Figure 37b.5. Repeat the vital capacity maneuver twice again. Then turn off the spirometer and remove the chart paper from the kymograph drum.

---

* If a Collins survey spirometer is used, the situation is exactly opposite: Upstrokes are expirations and downstrokes are inspirations.

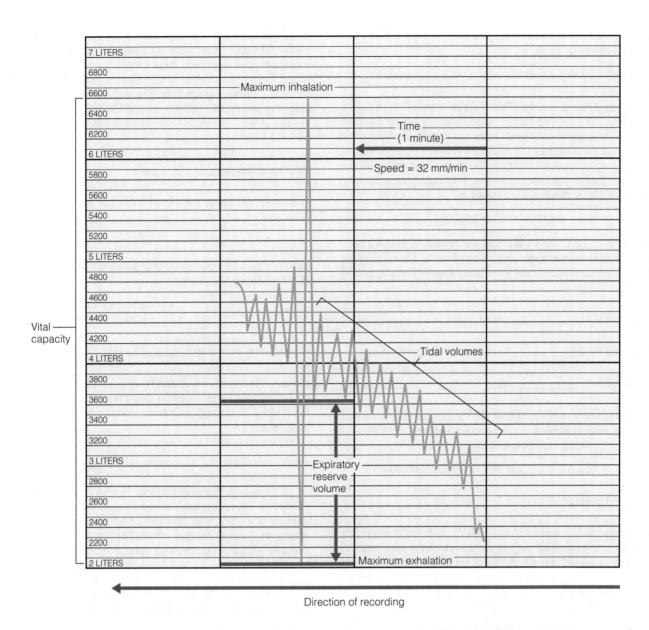

Figure 37b.5 A typical spirometry recording of tidal volume, inspiratory capacity, expiratory reserve volume, and vital capacity. At a drum speed of 32 mm/min, each vertical column of the chart represents a time interval of 1 minute. (Note the downstrokes represent exhalations and upstrokes represent inhalations.)

7. Determine and record your measured, averaged, and corrected respiratory volumes here. Because the pressure and temperature inside the spirometer are influenced by room temperature and differ from those in the body, all measured values are to be multiplied by a **BTPS** (body temperature, atmospheric pressure, and water saturation) **factor.** At room temperature, the BTPS factor is typically 1.1 or very close to that value. Hence, you will multiply your measured values by 1.1 to obtain your corrected respiratory volume values. Copy the averaged and corrected values onto the Exercise 37A Review Sheet.

• Tidal volume (TV). Select a typical resting tidal breath recording. Subtract the millimeter value of the trough (exha-

lation) from the millimeter value of the peak (inspiration). Record this value below as *measured TV 1*. Select two other TV tracings to determine the TV values for the TV 2 and TV 3 measurements. Then, determine your average TV and multiply it by 1.1 to obtain the BTPS-corrected average TV value.

measured TV 1:_____ ml   average TV: _____ ml

measured TV 2:_____ ml   corrected average TV:

measured TV 3:_____ ml   _____ ml

Also compute your **minute respiratory volume (MRV)** using the following formula:

$$\text{MRV} = \text{TV} \times \text{respirations/min} = \underline{\hspace{1.5cm}} \text{ ml/min}$$

• Inspiratory capacity (IC). In the first vital capacity recording, find the expiratory trough immediately preceding the maximal inspiratory peak achieved during vital capacity determination. Subtract the milliliter value of that expiration from the value corresponding to the peak of the maximal inspiration that immediately follows. For example, according to Figure 37b.5, these values would be

$$6600 - 3650 = 2950 \text{ ml}$$

Record your computed value and the results of the two subsequent tests on the appropriate lines below. Then calculate the measured and corrected inspiratory capacity averages and record.

measured IC 1:_____ ml   average IC: _____ ml

measured IC 2:_____ ml   corrected average IC:

measured IC 3:_____ ml   _____ ml

• Inspiratory reserve volume (IRV). Subtract the corrected average tidal volume from the corrected average for the inspiratory capacity and record below.

$$\text{IRV} = \text{corrected average IC} - \text{corrected average TV}$$

corrected average IRV _____ ml

• Expiratory reserve volume (ERV). Subtract the number of milliliters corresponding to the trough of the maximal expiration obtained during the vital capacity maneuver from milliliters corresponding to the last *normal* expiration before the VC maneuver is performed. For example, according to Figure 37b.5, these values would be

$$3650 \text{ ml} - 2050 \text{ ml} = 1600 \text{ ml}$$

Record your measured and averaged values (three trials) below.

measured ERV 1:_____ ml   average ERV: _____ ml

measured ERV 2:_____ ml   corrected average ERV:

measured ERV 3:_____ ml   _____ ml

• Vital capacity (VC). Add your corrected values for ERV and IC to obtain the corrected average VC. Record below and on the Exercise 37A Review Sheet.

corrected average VC: _____ ml

[*Now continue with step 8, whether you are following the procedure for the nonrecording or recording spirometer.*]

8. Figure out how closely your measured average vital capacity volume compares with the *predicted values* for someone your age, sex, and height. Obtain the predicted figure from either Table 37b.1 (male values) or Table 37b.2 (female values). Notice that you will have to convert your height in inches to centimeters (cm) to find the corresponding value. This is easily done by multiplying your height in inches by 2.54.

Computed height: _____ cm

Predicted VC value (obtained from the appropriate table):

_____ ml

Use the following equation to compute your VC as a percentage of the predicted VC value:

$$\% \text{ of predicted VC} = \frac{\text{averaged measured VC}}{\text{predicted value}} \times 100$$

% predicted VC value: _____ %

Figure 37b.2 is an idealized tracing of the respiratory volumes described and tested in this exercise. Examine it carefully. How closely do your test results compare to the values in the tracing?

_____

9. Computing residual volume. A respiratory volume that cannot be experimentally demonstrated here is the residual volume (RV). RV is the amount of air remaining in the lungs after a maximal expiratory effort. The presence of residual air (usually about 1200 ml) that cannot be voluntarily flushed from the lungs is important because it allows gas exchange to go on continuously—even between breaths.

Although the residual volume cannot be measured directly, it can be approximated by using one of the following factors:

For ages 16–34   Factor = 1.250

For ages 35–49   Factor = 1.305

For ages 50–69   Factor = 1.445

Compute your predicted RV using the following equation:

$$\text{RV} = \text{VC} \times \text{factor}$$

⚠ 10. Recording is finished for this subject. Before continuing with the next member of your group:

• Dispose of used cardboard mouthpieces in the autoclave bag.

• Swish the valve assembly (if removable) in the 70% ethanol solution, then rinse with tap water.

• Put a fresh mouthpiece into the valve assembly (or on the stem of the handheld spirometer). Using the procedures outlined above, measure and record the respiratory volumes for all members of your group. ∎

Height in centimeters

Age	146	148	150	152	154	156	158	160	162	164	166	168	170	172	174	176	178	180	182	184	186	188	190	192	194
16	3765	3820	3870	3920	3975	4025	4075	4130	4180	4230	4285	4335	4385	4440	4490	4540	4590	4645	4695	4745	4800	4850	4900	4955	5005
18	3740	3790	3840	3890	3940	3995	4045	4095	4145	4200	4250	4300	4350	4405	4455	4505	4555	4610	4660	4710	4760	4815	4865	4915	4965
20	3710	3760	3810	3860	3910	3960	4015	4065	4115	4165	4215	4265	4320	4370	4420	4470	4520	4570	4625	4675	4725	4775	4825	4875	4930
22	3680	3730	3780	3830	3880	3930	3980	4030	4080	4135	4185	4235	4285	4335	4385	4435	4485	4535	4585	4635	4685	4735	4790	4840	4890
24	3635	3685	3735	3785	3835	3885	3935	3985	4035	4085	4135	4185	4235	4285	4330	4380	4430	4480	4530	4580	4630	4680	4730	4780	4830
26	3605	3655	3705	3755	3805	3855	3905	3955	4000	4050	4100	4150	4200	4250	4300	4350	4395	4445	4495	4545	4595	4645	4695	4740	4790
28	3575	3625	3675	3725	3775	3820	3870	3920	3970	4020	4070	4115	4165	4215	4265	4310	4360	4410	4460	4510	4555	4605	4655	4705	4755
30	3550	3595	3645	3695	3740	3790	3840	3890	3935	3985	4035	4080	4130	4180	4230	4275	4325	4375	4425	4470	4520	4570	4615	4665	4715
32	3520	3565	3615	3665	3710	3760	3810	3855	3905	3950	4000	4050	4095	4145	4195	4240	4290	4340	4385	4435	4485	4530	4580	4625	4675
34	3475	3525	3570	3620	3665	3715	3760	3810	3855	3905	3950	4000	4045	4095	4140	4190	4225	4285	4330	4380	4425	4475	4520	4570	4615
36	3445	3495	3540	3585	3635	3680	3730	3775	3825	3870	3920	3965	4010	4060	4105	4155	4200	4250	4295	4340	4390	4435	4485	4530	4580
38	3415	3465	3510	3555	3605	3650	3695	3745	3790	3840	3885	3930	3980	4025	4070	4120	4165	4210	4260	4305	4350	4400	4445	4495	4540
40	3385	3435	3480	3525	3575	3620	3665	3710	3760	3805	3850	3900	3945	3990	4035	4085	4130	4175	4220	4270	4315	4360	4410	4455	4500
42	3360	3405	3450	3495	3540	3590	3635	3680	3725	3770	3820	3865	3910	3955	4000	4050	4095	4140	4185	4230	4280	4325	4370	4415	4460
44	3315	3360	3405	3450	3495	3540	3585	3630	3675	3725	3770	3815	3860	3905	3950	3995	4040	4085	4130	4175	4220	4270	4315	4360	4405
46	3285	3330	3375	3420	3465	3510	3555	3600	3645	3690	3735	3780	3825	3870	3915	3960	4005	4050	4095	4140	4185	4230	4275	4320	4365
48	3255	3300	3345	3390	3435	3480	3525	3570	3615	3655	3700	3745	3790	3835	3880	3925	3970	4015	4060	4105	4150	4190	4235	4280	4325
50	3210	3255	3300	3345	3390	3430	3475	3520	3565	3610	3650	3695	3740	3785	3830	3870	3915	3960	4005	4050	4090	4135	4180	4225	4270
52	3185	3225	3270	3315	3355	3400	3445	3490	3530	3575	3620	3660	3705	3750	3795	3835	3880	3925	3970	4010	4055	4100	4140	4185	4230
54	3155	3195	3240	3285	3325	3370	3415	3455	3500	3540	3585	3630	3670	3715	3760	3800	3845	3890	3930	3975	4020	4060	4105	4145	4190
56	3125	3165	3210	3255	3295	3340	3380	3425	3465	3510	3550	3595	3640	3680	3725	3765	3810	3850	3895	3940	3980	4025	4065	4110	4150
58	3080	3125	3165	3210	3250	3290	3335	3375	3420	3460	3500	3545	3585	3630	3670	3715	3755	3800	3840	3880	3925	3965	4010	4050	4095
60	3050	3095	3135	3175	3220	3260	3300	3345	3385	3430	3470	3500	3555	3595	3635	3680	3720	3760	3805	3845	3885	3930	3970	4015	4055
62	3020	3060	3110	3150	3190	3230	3270	3310	3350	3390	3440	3480	3520	3560	3600	3640	3680	3730	3770	3810	3850	3890	3930	3970	4020
64	2990	3030	3080	3120	3160	3200	3240	3280	3320	3360	3400	3440	3490	3530	3570	3610	3650	3690	3730	3770	3810	3850	3900	3940	3980
66	2950	2990	3030	3070	3110	3150	3190	3230	3270	3310	3350	3390	3430	3470	3510	3550	3600	3640	3680	3720	3760	3800	3840	3880	3920
68	2920	2960	3000	3040	3080	3120	3160	3200	3240	3280	3320	3360	3400	3440	3480	3520	3560	3600	3640	3680	3720	3760	3800	3840	3880
70	2890	2930	2970	3010	3050	3090	3130	3170	3210	3250	3290	3330	3370	3410	3450	3480	3520	3560	3600	3640	3680	3720	3760	3800	3840
72	2860	2900	2940	2980	3020	3060	3100	3140	3180	3210	3250	3290	3330	3370	3410	3450	3490	3530	3570	3610	3650	3680	3720	3760	3800
74	2820	2860	2900	2930	2970	3010	3050	3090	3130	3170	3200	3240	3280	3320	3360	3400	3440	3470	3510	3550	3590	3630	3670	3710	3740

Courtesy of Warren E. Collins, Inc., Braintree, Mass.

Table 37b.1 Predicted Vital Capacities for Males

Height in centimeters

Age	146	148	150	152	154	156	158	160	162	164	166	168	170	172	174	176	178	180	182	184	186	188	190	192	194
16	2950	2990	3030	3070	3110	3150	3190	3230	3270	3310	3350	3390	3430	3470	3510	3550	3590	3630	3670	3715	3755	3800	3840	3880	3920
17	2935	2975	3015	3055	3095	3135	3175	3215	3255	3295	3335	3375	3415	3455	3495	3535	3575	3615	3655	3695	3740	3780	3820	3860	3900
18	2920	2960	3000	3040	3080	3120	3160	3200	3240	3280	3320	3360	3400	3440	3480	3520	3560	3600	3640	3680	3720	3760	3800	3840	3880
20	2890	2930	2970	3010	3050	3090	3130	3170	3210	3250	3290	3330	3370	3410	3450	3490	3525	3565	3605	3645	3695	3720	3760	3800	3840
22	2860	2900	2940	2980	3020	3060	3095	3135	3175	3215	3255	3290	3330	3370	3410	3450	3490	3530	3570	3610	3650	3685	3725	3765	3800
24	2830	2870	2910	2950	2985	3025	3065	3100	3140	3180	3220	3260	3300	3335	3375	3415	3455	3490	3530	3570	3610	3650	3685	3725	3765
26	2800	2840	2880	2920	2960	3000	3035	3070	3110	3150	3190	3230	3265	3300	3340	3380	3420	3455	3495	3530	3570	3610	3650	3685	3725
28	2775	2810	2850	2890	2930	2965	3000	3040	3070	3115	3155	3190	3230	3270	3305	3345	3380	3420	3460	3495	3535	3570	3610	3650	3685
30	2745	2780	2820	2860	2895	2935	2970	3010	3045	3085	3120	3160	3195	3235	3270	3310	3345	3385	3420	3460	3495	3535	3570	3610	3645
32	2715	2750	2790	2825	2865	2900	2940	2975	3015	3050	3090	3125	3160	3200	3235	3275	3310	3350	3385	3425	3460	3495	3535	3570	3610
34	2685	2725	2760	2795	2835	2870	2910	2945	2980	3020	3055	3090	3130	3165	3200	3240	3275	3310	3350	3385	3425	3460	3495	3535	3570
36	2655	2695	2730	2765	2805	2840	2875	2910	2950	2985	3020	3060	3095	3130	3165	3205	3240	3275	3310	3350	3385	3420	3460	3495	3530
38	2630	2665	2700	2735	2770	2810	2845	2880	2915	2950	2990	3025	3060	3095	3130	3170	3205	3240	3275	3310	3350	3385	3420	3455	3490
40	2600	2635	2670	2705	2740	2775	2810	2850	2885	2920	2955	2990	3025	3060	3095	3135	3170	3205	3240	3275	3310	3345	3380	3420	3455
42	2570	2605	2640	2675	2710	2745	2780	2815	2850	2885	2920	2955	2990	3025	3060	3100	3135	3170	3205	3240	3275	3310	3345	3380	3415
44	2540	2575	2610	2645	2680	2715	2750	2785	2820	2855	2890	2925	2960	2995	3030	3060	3095	3130	3165	3200	3235	3270	3305	3340	3375
46	2510	2545	2580	2615	2650	2685	2715	2750	2785	2820	2855	2890	2925	2960	2995	3030	3060	3095	3130	3165	3200	3235	3270	3305	3340
48	2480	2515	2550	2585	2620	2650	2685	2715	2750	2785	2820	2855	2890	2925	2960	2995	3030	3060	3095	3130	3160	3195	3230	3265	3300
50	2455	2485	2520	2555	2590	2625	2655	2690	2720	2755	2785	2820	2855	2890	2925	2955	2990	3025	3060	3090	3125	3155	3190	3225	3260
52	2425	2455	2490	2525	2555	2590	2625	2655	2690	2720	2755	2790	2820	2855	2890	2925	2955	2990	3020	3055	3090	3125	3155	3190	3220
54	2395	2425	2460	2495	2530	2560	2590	2625	2655	2690	2720	2755	2790	2820	2855	2885	2920	2950	2985	3020	3050	3085	3115	3150	3180
56	2365	2400	2430	2460	2495	2525	2560	2590	2625	2655	2690	2720	2755	2790	2820	2855	2885	2920	2950	2980	3015	3045	3080	3110	3145
58	2335	2370	2400	2430	2460	2495	2525	2560	2590	2625	2655	2690	2720	2750	2785	2815	2850	2880	2920	2945	2975	3010	3040	3075	3105
60	2305	2340	2370	2400	2430	2460	2495	2525	2560	2590	2625	2655	2685	2720	2750	2780	2810	2845	2875	2915	2940	2970	3000	3035	3065
62	2280	2310	2340	2370	2405	2435	2465	2495	2525	2560	2590	2620	2655	2685	2715	2745	2775	2810	2840	2870	2900	2935	2965	2995	3025
64	2250	2280	2310	2340	2370	2400	2430	2465	2495	2525	2555	2585	2620	2650	2680	2710	2740	2770	2805	2835	2865	2895	2925	2955	2990
66	2220	2250	2280	2310	2340	2370	2400	2430	2460	2495	2525	2555	2585	2615	2645	2675	2705	2735	2765	2800	2825	2860	2890	2920	2950
68	2190	2220	2250	2280	2310	2340	2370	2400	2430	2460	2490	2520	2550	2580	2610	2640	2670	2700	2730	2760	2795	2820	2850	2880	2910
70	2160	2190	2220	2250	2280	2310	2340	2370	2400	2425	2455	2485	2515	2545	2575	2605	2635	2665	2695	2725	2755	2780	2810	2840	2870
72	2130	2160	2190	2220	2250	2280	2310	2335	2365	2395	2425	2455	2480	2510	2540	2570	2600	2630	2660	2685	2715	2745	2775	2805	2830
74	2100	2130	2160	2190	2220	2245	2275	2305	2335	2360	2390	2420	2450	2475	2505	2535	2565	2590	2620	2650	2680	2710	2740	2765	2795

Courtesy of Warren E. Collins, Inc., Braintree, Mass.

Table 37b.2 Predicted Vital Capacities for Females

Forced Expiratory Volume (FEV$_T$) Measurement

While they are not really diagnostic, pulmonary function tests can help the clinician to distinguish between obstructive and restrictive pulmonary diseases. (In obstructive disorders, like chronic bronchitis and asthma, airway resistance is increased, whereas in restrictive diseases, such as polio and tuberculosis, total lung capacity declines.) Two highly useful pulmonary function tests used for this purpose are the FVC and the FEV$_T$.

The **FVC** (forced vital capacity) measures the amount of gas expelled when the subject takes the deepest possible breath and then exhales forcefully and rapidly. This volume is reduced in those with restrictive pulmonary disease. The **FEV$_T$** (forced expiratory volume) involves the same basic testing procedure, but it specifically looks at the percentage of the vital capacity that is exhaled during specific time intervals of the FVC test. FEV$_1$, for instance, is the amount exhaled during the first second. Healthy individuals can expire 75% to 85% of their FVC in the first second. The FEV$_1$ is low in those with obstructive disease.

Activity 4:
Measuring the FVC and FEV$_1$

Directions provided here for the FEV$_T$ determination apply only to the recording spirometer.

1. Prepare to make your recording as described in steps 1–5 of Using a Recording Spirometer on p. 530.

2. At a signal agreed upon by you and your lab partner, take the deepest inspiration possible and hold it for 1 to 2 seconds. As the inspiratory peak levels off, your partner is to change the drum speed to **FAST** (1920 mm/min) so that the distance between the vertical lines on the chart represents a time of 1 second.

3. Once the drum speed has been changed, exhale as much air as rapidly and forcibly as possible.

4. When the tracing plateaus (bottoms out), stop recording and determine your FVC. Subtract the milliliter reading in the expiration trough (the bottom plateau) from the preceding inhalation peak (the top plateau). Record this value.

FVC = _____ ml

5. Prepare to calculate the FEV$_1$. Draw a vertical line intersecting with the spirogram tracing at the precise point that exhalation began. Identify this line as *line 1*. From line 1, measure 32 mm horizontally to the left, and draw a second vertical line. Label this as *line 2*. The distance between the two lines represents 1 second, and the volume exhaled in the first second is read where line 2 intersects the spirogram tracing. Subtract that milliliter value from the milliliter value of the inhalation peak (at the intersection of line 1), to determine the volume of gas expired in the first second. According to the values given in Figure 37b.6, that figure would be 3400 ml (6800 ml − 3400 ml). Record your measured value.

Milliliters of gas expired in second 1: _____ ml

6. To compute the FEV$_1$ use the following equation:

$$FEV_1 = \frac{\text{volume expired in second 1}}{\text{FVC volume}} \times 100\%$$

Record your calculated value below and on the Exercise 37A Review Sheet.

FEV$_1$ = _____ % of FVC ∎

Using PowerLab® to Determine Factors Influencing Rate and Depth of Respiration*

The neural centers that control respiratory rhythm and maintain a rate of 12 to 18 respirations/min are located in the medulla and pons. On occasion, input from the stretch receptors in the lungs (via the vagus nerve to the medulla) modifies the respiratory rate, as in cases of extreme overinflation of the lungs (Hering-Breuer reflex).

Death occurs when medullary centers are completely suppressed, as from an overdose of sleeping pills or gross overindulgence in alcohol, and respiration ceases completely. ●

Although the nervous system centers initiate the basic rhythm of breathing, there is no question that physical phenomena such as talking, yawning, coughing, and exercise can modify the rate and depth of respiration. So too can chemical factors such as changes in oxygen or carbon dioxide concentrations in the blood or fluctuations in blood pH. Changes in carbon dioxide blood levels seem to act directly on the medulla control centers, whereas changes in pH and oxygen concentrations are monitored by chemoreceptor regions in the aortic and carotid bodies, which in turn send input to the medulla. The experimental sequence in this section is designed to test the relative importance of various physical and chemical factors in the process of respiration.

Activity 5:
Visualizing Respiratory Variations

1. Make sure your computer is turned on, and connect the PowerLab® unit to your computer with the USB cable.

2. Connect the BNC plug on the respiratory belt to Input 1 on the PowerLab® unit.

3. Open the settings file called "Breathing Settings."

4. Chart will open and a blank data file with two channels will be displayed. Channel 1 is the raw data from the respiratory belt, and Channel 2 will display a real-time rate calculation in breaths per-minute.

* Note to the Instructor: This exercise may also be done without using the recording apparatus by simply having the students count the respiratory rate visually.

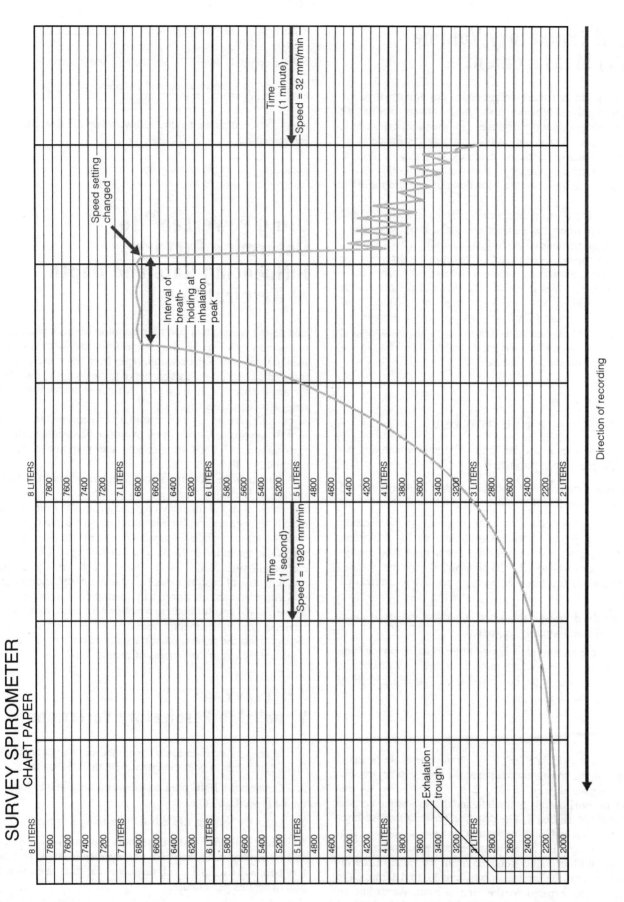

Figure 37b.6 A recording of the forced vital capacity (FVC) and forced expiratory volume (FEV) or timed vital capacity test.

5. Using the Velcro strap, fasten the respiratory belt around the lower abdomen of the subject (Figure 37b.7). The transducer should be at the front of the body, level with the navel. The belt should be firm but not uncomfortably tight.

6. Choose the Input Amplifier command from the Breath Channel Function pop-up menu.

7. Ask the subject to take deep, strong breaths and observe the signal in the Input Amplifier dialog box (Figure 37b.8)

8. Adjust the Range pop-up menu of the Input Amplifier dialog box so that the breathing signal occupies about a half to two-thirds of full scale. Click OK to close the dialog box.

9. From the "Rate" Channel Function pop-up menu, select Computed Input. Have the subject breathe normally and observe the left-hand window. The breathing peaks should exceed the threshold bar "T" in the window. If not, click and drag the "T" so that the threshold line intersects the breathing trace.

10. Click Start and record the respiratory movements for 30 seconds. Add a comment to the trace called "quiet breathing" by typing in the comment field and pressing the return key.

11. Continue recording quiet-breathing for one minute with the subject in a sitting position.

Record breaths per minute. _____

12. For instructions on the balance of the required tracings, go to the procedure for Using a Nonrecording Spirometer and continue as indicated through step 10. Be sure to enter comments into your recording as you proceed, and save your data in an appropriately named file. ■

Role of the Respiratory System in Acid-Base Balance of Blood

As you have already learned, pulmonary ventilation is necessary for continuous oxygenation of the blood and removal of carbon dioxide (a waste product of cellular respiration) from the blood. Blood pH must be relatively constant for the cells of the body to function optimally. The carbonic acid–bicarbonate buffer system of the blood is extremely important because it helps stabilize arterial blood pH at 7.4 ± 0.02.

When carbon dioxide diffuses into the blood from the tissue cells, much of it enters the red blood cells, where it combines with water to form carbonic acid (Figure 37b.9):

$$H_2O + CO_2 \xrightarrow[\text{enzyme present in RBC}]{\text{Carbonic anhydrase}} H_2CO_3$$

Some carbonic acid is also formed in the plasma, but that reaction is very slow because of the lack of the carbonic anhydrase enzyme. Shortly after it forms, carbonic acid dissociates to release bicarbonate (HCO_3^-) and hydrogen (H^+) ions. The hydrogen ions that remain in the cells are neutralized, or buffered, when they combine with hemoglobin molecules. If they were not neutralized, the intracellular pH would become very acidic as H^+ ions accumulated. The bicarbonate ions diffuse out of the red blood cells into the plasma, where they become part of the carbonic acid–bicarbonate buffer system. As

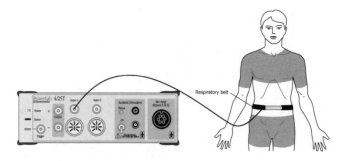

Figure 37b.7 Connecting the respiratory belt to measure breathing with the PowerLab® system.

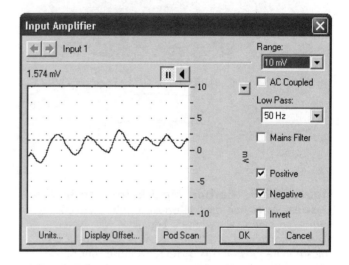

Figure 37b.8 Adjusting the range of the PowerLab® system in Chart. The signal deflections should be 1/3 to 1/2 the window height.

HCO_3^- follows its concentration gradient into the plasma, an electrical imbalance develops in the RBCs that draws Cl^- into them from the plasma. This exchange phenomenon is called the *chloride shift*.

Acids (more precisely, H^+) released into the blood by the body cells tend to lower the pH of the blood and to cause it to become acidic. On the other hand, basic substances that enter the blood tend to cause the blood to become more alkaline and the pH to rise. Both of these tendencies are resisted in large part by the carbonic acid–bicarbonate buffer system. If H^+ concentration in the blood begins to increase, the H^+ ions combine with bicarbonate ions to form carbonic acid (a weak acid that does not tend to dissociate at physiological or acid pH) and are thus removed.

$$H^+ + HCO_3^- \rightarrow H_2CO_3$$

Likewise, as blood H^+ concentration drops below what is desirable and blood pH rises, H_2CO_3 dissociates to release bicarbonate ions and H^+ ions to the blood. The released H^+ lowers the pH again. The bicarbonate ions, being *weak* bases, are

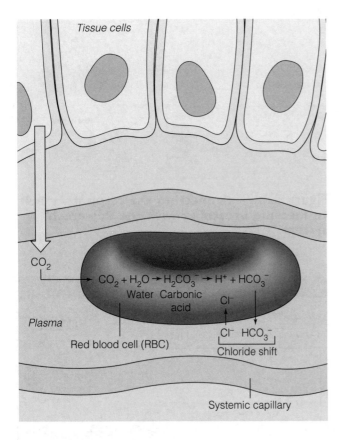

Figure 37b.9 Carbon dioxide loading in the tissues. As carbon dioxide is loaded into the blood, it enters red blood cells where it combines with water to yield carbonic acid, which immediately splits to HCO_3^- (bicarbonate ions) and H^+. HCO_3^- diffuses out of the RBC into the plasma, and chloride ions enter the RBC in exchange (the chloride shift).

poorly functional under alkaline conditions and have little effect on blood pH unless and until blood pH drops toward acid levels.

$$H_2CO_3 \rightarrow H^+ + HCO_3^-$$

In the case of excessively slow or shallow breathing (hypoventilation) or fast deep breathing (hyperventilation), the amount of carbonic acid in the blood can be greatly modified—increasing dramatically during hypoventilation and decreasing substantially during hyperventilation. In either situation, if the buffering ability of the blood is inadequate, respiratory acidosis or alkalosis can result. Therefore, maintaining the normal rate and depth of breathing is important for proper control of blood pH.

Activity 6:
Demonstrating the Reaction Between Carbon Dioxide in Exhaled Air and Water

1. Fill a beaker with 100 ml of distilled water.

2. Add 5 ml of 0.05 M NaOH and five drops of phenol red. Phenol red is a pH indicator that turns yellow in acidic solutions.

3. Blow through a straw into the solution.

What do you observe?

_____

_____

What chemical reaction is taking place in the beaker?

_____

_____

4. Discard the straw in the autoclave bag. ■

Activity 7:
Observing the Operation of Standard Buffers

1. To observe the ability of a buffer system to stabilize the pH of a solution, obtain five 250-ml beakers, and a wash bottle containing distilled water. Set up the following experimental samples:

Beaker 1:
(150 ml distilled water)   pH _____

Beaker 2:
(150 ml distilled water and
1 drop concentrated HCl)   pH _____

Beaker 3:
(150 ml distilled water and
1 drop concentrated NaOH)   pH _____

Beaker 4:
(150 ml standard buffer solution
[pH 7] and 1 drop concentrated HCl)   pH _____

Beaker 5:
(150 ml standard buffer solution
[pH 7] and 1 drop concentrated NaOH)   pH _____

2. Using a pH meter standardized with a buffer solution of pH 7, determine the pH of the contents of each beaker and record above. After *each and every* pH recording, the pH meter switch should be turned to **STANDBY,** and the electrodes rinsed thoroughly with a stream of distilled water from the wash bottle.

3. Add 3 more drops of concentrated HCl to beaker 4,

stir, and record the pH: _____

4. Add 3 more drops of concentrated NaOH to beaker 5, stir, and record the pH: _____

How successful was the buffer solution in resisting pH changes when a strong acid (HCl) or a strong base (NaOH) was added?

_____ ■

Activity 8:
Exploring the Operation of the Carbonic Acid–Bicarbonate Buffer System

To observe the ability of the carbonic acid–bicarbonate buffer system of blood to resist pH changes, perform the following simple experiment.

1. Obtain two small beakers (50 ml), animal plasma, graduated cylinder, glass stirring rod, and a dropper bottle of 0.01 M HCl. Using the pH meter standardized with the buffer solution of pH 7.0, measure the pH of the animal plasma. Use only enough plasma to allow immersion of the electrodes and measure the volume used carefully.

pH of the animal plasma: _____

2. Add 2 drops of the 0.01 M HCl solution to the plasma; stir and measure the pH again.

pH of plasma plus 2 drops of HCl: _____

3. Turn the pH meter switch to **STANDBY,** rinse the electrodes, and then immerse them in a quantity of distilled water (pH 7) exactly equal to the amount of animal plasma used. Measure the pH of the distilled water.

pH of distilled water: _____

4. Add 2 drops of 0.01 M HCl, swirl, and measure the pH again.

pH of distilled water plus the two drops of HCl: _____

Is the plasma a good buffer? _____

What component of the plasma carbonic acid–bicarbonate buffer system was acting to counteract a change in pH when HCl was added?

_____ ■

List of Laboratory Materials

Ordering information is based on a lab size of 24 students, working in groups of 4. Additional information on supply sources may be found in the Advance Preparation section in each exercise chapter of this Instructor's Guide. A list of supply house addresses appears in Appendix D. Multimedia resources are listed in Appendix F, and multimedia resource distributors are listed in Appendix G.

Exercise 1

1–2 human torso models

2 human skeletons, one male and one female

3–4 preserved kidneys (sheep)

scalpels

gelatin-spaghetti molds

Exercise 2

dissectible human torso model

6–12 forceps

6–12 scissors

6–12 blunt probes

disposable gloves, soap, and sponges

6–12 freshly killed or preserved rats

twine or large dissecting pins

dissecting trays

Exercise 3

24 compound microscopes, lens cleaning solution, lens paper, immersion oil

24 stereomicroscopes

24 millimeter rulers

24 slides of the letter e

24 millimeter grids

coins

24 slides of crossed colored threads (threads should cross at a single junction)

filter paper or paper towels

1 box of microscope slides

1 box of coverslips

1 box of flat-tipped toothpicks

8–12 dropper bottles of physiologic saline

8–12 dropper bottles of methylene blue stain

24 slides of cheek epithelial cells

bleach

autoclave bag

Exercise 4

3-D model of composite cell

chart of cell anatomy

24 slides of simple squamous epithelium ($AgNO_3$ stain)

24 slides of teased smooth muscle

24 slides of human blood cell smear

24 slides of sperm

24 slides of whitefish blastulae

24 compound microscopes, lens paper, lens cleaning solution, immersion oil

3-D models of mitotic stages

modeling clay

video of mitosis

Exercise 5A

24 compound microscopes, lens paper, lens cleaning solution, immersion oil

1 box of slides

1 box of coverslips

6 hot plates

6 forceps

6 petri plates with 1.5% agar gel

6 dropper bottles of 3.5% methylene blue solution

6 dropper bottles of 1.6% potassium permanganate solution

1000-milliliter graduated cylinder

6 15-ml graduated cylinders

large beaker

thistle tube osmometer

molasses

6 millimeter rulers

25 dialysis sacs (or small Hefty "alligator" sandwich bags)

6 small funnels

100-ml beaker

carmine dye crystals

6 dropper bottles of yeast
 suspension

6 dropper bottles of silver
 nitrate

6 dropper bottles of Benedict's
 solution

42 test tubes

test tube holders

6 test tube racks

6 wax markers

6 25-milliliter graduated
 cylinders

36 250-milliliter beakers

6 bottles of 40% glucose
 solution

6 bottles of 10% NaCl solution

6 glass stirring rods

6 rolls of fine twine or 48
 dialysis tubing clamps

6 laboratory balances

animal blood (if used)

6 dropper bottles of distilled
 water

6 dropper bottles of physiologic saline (mammalian,
 0.9%)

6 dropper bottles of 1.5% NaCl

container of 10% bleach
 solution

6 wash bottles of 10% bleach

medicine droppers

autoclave bag

disposable gloves

6 ring stands, rings, and clamps

filter paper or paper towels

1 culture of *Amoeba proteus*

1 culture of *Tetrahymena
 pyriformis*

12–24 depression slides

1 box of flat-tipped toothpicks

millimeter-ruled graph paper

Congo Red dye

videotape of phagocytosis

videotape viewing box

Exercise 5B

Part I—See Exercise 5A

Part II—

Minimum computer hardware
 required:

IBM/PC: Windows 95, 98, NT,
 2000, Millennium Edition
 (or higher); Pentium I/266
 MHz (or faster)

Macintosh: Macintosh 8.6
 (and above); 605/300 MHz
 or G3/233 MHz

64 MB RAM (128 MB
 recommended)

800×600 screen resolution,
 millions of colors

Internet Explorer 5.0 (or
 higher) *or* Netscape 4.6 (or
 higher)

Flash 6 plug-in (or higher)

$4 \times$ CD-ROM drive (if using
 CD-ROM)

Printer

Technical Support
 800.677.6337
 Email: media.support@
 pearsoned.com
 Hours: 9 A.M. to 5 P.M. EST,
 Monday–Friday

Software:

Benjamin Cummings
 PhysioEx™ CD-ROM
 (Cell Transport mecha-
 nism and Permeability
 module)

Exercise 6A

24 compound microscopes,
 lens paper, lens cleaning
 solution, immersion oil

24 slides of simple squamous,
 simple cuboidal, simple
 columnar, stratified squamous (nonkeratinized),
 pseudostratified ciliated
 columnar, stratified cu-
 boidal, stratified columnar,
 and transitional epithelium

24 slides of mesenchyme; adipose, areolar, and dense
 connective tissue, regular
 (tendon) and irregular (dermis); elastic connective tissue (wall of large artery),
 hyaline cartilage, elastic
 cartilage, fibrocartilage;
 bone (cross section); and
 blood smear

24 slides of skeletal, smooth,
 and cardiac muscle (longitudinal sections)

24 slides of spinal cord smear

Exercise 6B

Minimum computer hardware
 required:

IBM/PC: Windows 95, 98, NT,
 2000, Millennium Edition
 (or higher); Pentium I/266
 MHz (or faster)

Macintosh: Macintosh 8.6
 (and above); 605/300 MHz
 or G3/233 MHz

64 MB RAM (128 MB
 recommended)

800×600 screen resolution,
 millions of colors

Internet Explorer 5.0 (or
 higher) *or* Netscape 4.6 (or
 higher)

Flash 6 plug-in (or higher)

$4 \times$ CD-ROM drive (if using
 CD-ROM)

Printer

Technical Support
 800.677.6337
 Email: media.support@
 pearsoned.com
 Hours: 9 A.M. to 6 P.M. EST,
 Monday–Friday

Software:

Benjamin Cummings
 PhysioEx™ CD-ROM
 (Histology Tutorial)

Exercise 7

24 compound microscopes, lens paper, lens cleaning solution

24 dissecting microscopes

model of the skin

24 slides of human scalp

24 slides of skin of palm or sole

1 sheet of 20# bond paper

ruler

adhesive tape

24 scissors

24 Betadine swabs or 24 cotton swabs and 6 dropper bottles of Lugol's iodine

24 slides and coverslips

data collection sheets

disposable gloves

Parelon fingerprint pad or portable inking foils

ink cleaning towlettes

index cards (4 in. × 6 in.)

24 magnifying glasses

Exercise 8

24 compound microscopes, lens paper, lens cleaning solution

24 slides of the trachea (x.s.), esophagus (x.s.), and small intestine (x.s.)

24 slides of serous membrane (mesentery)

longitudinally cut fresh beef joint

disposable gloves

Exercise 9

articulated skeleton

numbered disarticulated bones showing four types

24 compound microscopes, lens paper, lens cleaning solution

long bone sawed longitudinally

long bone soaked in 10% HCl or vinegar

long bone baked at 250°F

24 slides of ground bone (x.s.)

disposable gloves

3-D models of microscopic structure of bones

24 slides of developing long bone undergoing endochondral ossification

24 slides of hyaline cartilage, elastic cartilage, and fibrocartilage

Exercise 10

articulated vertebral column

Beauchene skull

6–12 intact skulls

2 articulated skeletons (one male, one female)

X rays of individuals with kyphosis, scoliosis, and lordosis

X ray viewing box

removable vertebral discs

isolated cervical, thoracic, and lumbar vertebrae, sacrum, and coccyx

Exercise 11

6–12 disarticulated skeletons

2 articulated skeletons (one male, one female)

1 articulated male pelvis

1 articulated female pelvis

X rays of bones of the appendicular skeleton

Exercise 12

fetal skull

fetal skeleton

adult skeleton

Exercise 13

articulated skeleton

skull

fresh diarthrotic beef joint or preserved joints

disposable gloves

anatomical charts of joints

X rays of normal and arthritic joints

water balloons and clamps

X ray viewing box

functional models of hip and knee joints

Exercise 14

fresh chicken breast or thigh

physiologic saline (mammalian, 0.9%)

3-D models of skeletal muscle and skeletal muscle cells (if available)

24 compound microscopes, lens paper, lens cleaning solution

microscope slides and coverslips

24 forceps

48 dissecting needles

24 slides of skeletal muscle cross section and longitudinal section

24 slides of neuromuscular junctions

3-D model of skeletal muscle showing neuromuscular junction (if available)

Exercise 15

prosected human cadaver (if available)

human torso models and/or anatomical charts of muscles

disposable gloves

Human Musculature videotape

tubes of body (or face) paint

1-inch wide artists' brushes

Exercise 16A

1 or 2 ATP muscle kits

1 petri dish

1 box of microscope slides and coverslips

24 millimeter rulers

12–24 compound microscopes, lens paper, lens cleaning solution

watch or timer

copies of textbooks or other heavy books

24–48 pointed glass probes (teasing needles)

glass marking pencil

distilled water

12–24 stereomicroscopes

6 small beakers (50 ml)

frog Ringer's solution

6 metal needle probes

6 medicine droppers

6 scissors

cotton thread

6 forceps

6 glass or porcelain plates

6 live frogs (pithed)

disposable gloves

6 sets of recording equipment and accessories (A or B)

A: physiograph (polygraph), paper and ink, myograph, pin electrodes, stimulator output extension cable, transducer stand and cable, straight pins, frog board, laboratory stand, clamp

B: BIOPAC® MP30 (or MP35) data acquisition unit, PC or Macintosh (Mac) computer with at least 4MB of RAM available, BIOPAC® Student Lab Software v3.0 or greater, wall transformer, serial cable, electrode lead set, hand dynamometer, headphones, metric tape measure, disposable vinyl electrodes, conduction gel

Exercise 16B

Minimum computer hardware required:

IBM/PC: Windows 95, 98, NT, 2000, Millennium Edition (or higher); Pentium I/266 MHz (or faster)

Macintosh: Macintosh 8.6 (and above); 605/300 MHz or G3/233 MHz

64 MB RAM (128 MB recommended)

800 × 600 screen resolution, millions of colors

Internet Explorer 5.0 (or higher) *or* Netscape 4.6 (or higher)

Flash 6 plug-in (or higher)

4 × CD-ROM drive (if using CD-ROM)

Printer

Technical Support

    Phone: 800.677.6337

    Email: media.support@ pearsoned.com

    Hours: 9 A.M. to 6 P.M. EST, Monday–Friday

Software:

Benjamin Cummings PhysioEx™ CD-ROM (Skeletal Muscle Physiology module)

Exercise 17

24 compound microscopes, lens paper, immersion oil, lens cleaning solution

model of neuron

24 slides of spinal cord smear, teased myelinated fibers, Purkinje cells (cerebellum), pyramidal cells (cerebrum), dorsal root ganglion, and nerve cross section

Exercise 18A

12 live frogs (*Rana pipiens*)

6 dissecting trays and dissection kits

disposable gloves

12 dropper bottles of frog Ringer's solution

6 small ice baths

12 glass rods or probes

cotton thread

6 laboratory stands and 12 clamps

12 glass slides or glass plates

6 platinum electrodes

6 stimulators

6 pieces of filter paper

6 dropper bottles of 0.01% HCl

NaCl crystals

6 slide holders or heat-resistant mitts

oscilloscope (optional)

nerve chambers

Bunsen burners

absorbent cotton

ether

disposable pipettes

1-cc syringes with small-gauge needle

serum bottle of 0.5% tubocurarine

frog boards

24 safety glasses

filter paper

6 forceps

Exercise 18B

Minimum computer hardware required:

IBM/PC: Windows 95, 98, NT, 2000, Millennium Edition (or higher); Pentium I/266 MHz (or faster)

Macintosh: Macintosh 8.6 (and above); 605/300 MHz or G3/233 MHz

64 MB RAM (128 MB recommended)

800 × 600 screen resolution, millions of colors

Internet Explorer 5.0 (or higher) *or* Netscape 4.6 (or higher)

Flash 6 plug-in (or higher)

4 × CD-ROM drive (if using CD-ROM)

Printer

Technical Support

Phone: 800.677.6337

Email: media.support@ pearsoned.com

Hours: 9 A.M. to 6 P.M. EST, Monday–Friday

Software:

Benjamin Cummings PhysioEx™ CD-ROM (Neurophysiology of Nerve Impulses module)

Exercise 19

human brain models (dissectible)

3-D model of ventricles

preserved human brains

coronally sectioned human brain slice

12 preserved sheep brains with meninges and cranial nerves intact

12 dissecting trays

12 dissecting kits

disposable gloves

24 pairs safety glasses

soap, sponges, and disinfectant

disposable gloves

The Human Nervous System: The Brain and Cranial Nerves videotape

Materials as needed for cranial nerves testing: aromatic oils (e.g., vanilla and cloves), eye chart, ophthalmoscope, penlight, safety pin, mall probe (hot and cold), cotton, ammonia, tuning fork, tongue depressor, and solutions of sugar, salt, vinegar, and quinine

Exercise 20

6 oscilloscopes and EEG lead-selector boxes or 6 polygraphs and high-gain amplifiers

6 containers of electrode gel

6 sets of EEG electrodes and leads

6 containers of collodion *or* long elastic EEG straps

Cot (if available) or pillow

BIOPAC® Apparatus: BIOPAC® MP30 (or MP35) data acquisition unit, PC or Macintosh (Mac) computer with at least 4MB of RAM available, BIOPAC® Student Lab Software v3.0 or greater, wall transformer, serial cable, electrode lead set, disposable vinyl electrodes, Lycra® swim cap (such as Speedo® brand) or supportive wrap (such as 3M Coban™ Self-adhering Support Wrap), a cot or lab bench and pillow

Exercise 21

spinal cord model

3-D laboratory charts of spinal cord, spinal nerves, and sympathetic chain

24 red pencils

24 blue pencils

12–24 preserved spinal cord sections (cow, or maybe saved from sheep brains from Ex. 19)

12–24 dissecting trays and dissecting kits

12–24 stereomicroscopes

24 compound microscopes, lens paper, lens cleaning solution

24 slides of spinal cord cross section

disposable gloves

24 pairs safety glasses

soap, sponges, disinfectant

The Human Nervous System: The Spinal Cord and Spinal Nerves videotape

BIOPAC® Apparatus: BIOPAC® MP30 (or MP35) data acquisition unit, PC or Macintosh (Mac) computer with at least 4MB of RAM, BIOPAC® Student Lab Software v3.0 or greater, wall transformer, serial cable, respiratory transducer belt, GSR finger leads, electrode lead set, disposable vinyl electrodes, conduction gel, and nine 8 1/2" × 11" sheets of paper of different colors (white, black, red, blue, green, yellow, orange, brown, and purple)

Exercise 22

6 reflex hammers

6 sharp pencils

6 small pieces of sterile absorbent cotton

6 tongue depressors

6 metric rulers

6 reaction time or 12" rulers

6 flashlights

6 beakers (100- or 250-milliliter)

6 10- or 25-ml graduated cylinders

6 dropper bottles of lemon juice

6 packages of wide-range pH paper

autoclave bag

6 wash bottles of 10% bleach

large bucket of 10% bleach

Cot (if available)

BIOPAC® Apparatus:
BIOPAC® MP30 (or
MP35) data acquisition
unit, PC or Macintosh
(Mac) computer with at
least 4MB of RAM,
BIOPAC® Student Lab
Software v3.0 or greater,
wall transformer, serial
cable, hand switch,
headphones

Exercise 23

24 compound microscopes,
lens paper, lens cleaning
solution, immersion oil

24 slides of Pacinian corpuscles, Meissner's corpuscles, Golgi tendon organs,
and muscle spindles

12 Mall probes

large beaker with chipped ice

hot water bath set at 45°C

6 sets of red, black, and blue
fine-point, felt-tipped
markers

6 Von Frey's hairs

6 calipers or esthesiometers

6 millimeter rulers

18 large finger bowls

24 coins (nickels or quarters)

Exercise 24

dissectible eye model

chart of eye anatomy

12–24 preserved cow or sheep
eyes

12–24 dissecting pans and dissecting kits

6 laboratory lamps or penlights

Snellen eye chart

6–12 Ishihara's color-blindness
plates

ophthalmoscopes

6 metric rulers

6 test tubes

common straight pins

24 compound microscopes,
lens paper, lens cleaning
solution

24 slides of the eye showing
retinal layers

disposable gloves

24 pairs safety glasses

soap, sponges, and disinfectant

Exercise 25

3-D dissectible ear models

25 compound microscopes,
lens paper, lens cleaning
solution

24 slides of the cochlea

1 slide of crista ampullaris receptor of a semicircular
canal

6 sets of tuning forks

6 rubber mallets

absorbent cotton

otoscopes and alcohol swabs

disposable otoscope tips

6 metric rulers

6 ticking pocket watches or
clocks

white chalk and blackboard

audiometer

red and blue pencils

Exercise 26

24 compound microscopes,
lens paper, lens cleaning
solution

24 slides of the tongue showing
taste buds

24 slides of the nasal epithelium

paper towels

6 small mirrors

6 small packets of granulated
sugar

24 paper cups

96 cotton-tipped swabs

6 dropper bottles of oil of
cloves, oil of wintergreen,
and oil of peppermint (or
corresponding condiment
flavors)

6 vials of 10% NaCl, 0.1% quinine or Epsom salt solution, 5% sucrose solution,
and 1% acetic acid solution, and monosodium glutamate (MSG) crystals
dissolved in distilled water

absorbent cotton

toothpicks

plastic gloves

5 numbered vials containing
common household substances with strong odors
(herbs, spices, etc.)

6 flasks of distilled water

6 paper plates

chipped ice

opaque containers of like-sized
food cubes of cheese, apple, raw potato, dried
prunes, banana, raw carrot,
and hard-cooked egg white
(at least 6 of each)

6 nose clips

autoclave bag

Exercise 27

human torso model

anatomical chart of human endocrine system

24 compound microscopes,
lens paper, lens cleaning
solution

colored pencils

24 slides of anterior pituitary
and posterior pituitary (differential-staining), thyroid
gland, parathyroid glands,
adrenal gland, pancreas tissue, ovaries, testes

Exercise 28A

spring or pond water

18 female frogs

12 20- to 25-gauge needles

12 2-milliliter syringes

12 battery jars

6 wax markers

6 small bottles of amphibian physiologic saline

6 vials of frog pituitary extract

6 bottles of 20% glucose (250-milliliter)

dropper bottle of commercial insulin, 400 IU/100 milliliters H_2O

6 small (1.5–2") freshwater fish (guppy, bluegill, or sunfish, listed in order of preference)

12 finger bowls

6 dissecting pans and dissecting kits

6 dropper bottles of 1:1000 epinephrine

6 dropper bottles of frog Ringer's solution

6 glass desiccators

6 manometers

6 two-hole rubber stoppers

6 T-valves

6 glass syringes (20-milliliter)

18 feet of rubber tubing

6 tubing clamps

soda lime (desiccant)

6 hardware cloth squares or porcelain platforms

animal balances

6 young rats of the same sex

4 kilograms rat chow

80 grams desiccated thyroid

0.02% 6-n-propylthiouracil

6 jars of petrolatum

animal handling gloves

disposable gloves

12 3-inch pieces of glass tubing

6 scissors

chalkboard and chalk

500- or 600-ml beakers

Exercise 28B

Minimum computer hardware required:

IBM/PC: Windows 95, 98, NT, 2000, Millennium Edition (or higher); Pentium I/266 MHz (or faster)

Macintosh: Macintosh 8.6 (and above); 605/300 MHz or G3/233 MHz

64 MB RAM (128 MB recommended)

800×600 screen resolution, millions of colors

Internet Explorer 5.0 (or higher) *or* Netscape 4.6 (or higher)

Flash 6 plug-in (or higher)

$4 \times$ CD-ROM drive (if using CD-ROM)

Printer

Technical Support

  Phone: 800.677.6337

  Email: media.support@ pearsoned.com

  Hours: 9 A.M. to 6 P.M. EST, Monday–Friday

Software:

Benjamin Cummings PhysioEx™ CD-ROM (Endocrine System Physiology module)

Exercise 29A

24 compound microscopes, lens paper, lens cleaning solution

immersion oil

24 slides of macrocytic, hypochromic anemia; microcytic, hypochromic anemia; sickle-cell anemia; lymphocytic leukemia (chronic); and eosinophilia.

assorted slides of WBC pathologies labeled "unknown sample number ____"

2 boxes of clean microscope slides

3-D models of blood cells

autoclave bag

laboratory bucket and 6 beakers of 10% bleach solution

6 spray bottles of 10% bleach solution

6–12 dropper bottles of Wright stain

6–12 dropper bottles of distilled water

6 packages of wide-range pH paper

24 test tubes and test tube racks

6 animal plasma samples

24 pairs of disposable gloves

24 heparinized capillary tubes

4–6 sets of pipette cleaning solutions: (1) 10% household bleach solution, (2) distilled water, (3) 70% ethyl alcohol, (4) acetone

microhematocrit centrifuge and (optional) reading gauge

24 millimeter rulers

6 containers capillary sealer

6–12 hemoglobinometers and hemolysis applicators

24 Landau Sed-rate pipettes with tubing and 6 racks

designated lancet (sharps) disposal container

6 boxes sterile lancets, alcohol swabs, absorbent cotton balls; *or* stained smears of human blood; *or* heparinized animal blood; *or* EDTA-treated red cells with blood type labels obscured

glass stirring rods

6 timers

Rh typing box

medicine dropper

6 bottles of 5% sodium citrate

24 mechanical suction devices *or* supplies for Westergren ESR method

24 nonheparinized capillary tubes

6–12 fine triangular files

6 bottles of each blood typing sera (anti-A, anti-B, anti-Rh[anti-D])

paper towels

24 wax markers

toothpicks and 24 clean glass slides or 24 test cards and blood mixing sticks

24 safety glasses

24 cholesterol test cards and color scale

Exercise 29B

Minimum computer hardware required:

IBM/PC: Windows 95, 98, NT, 2000, Millennium Edition (or higher); Pentium I/266 MHz (or faster)

Macintosh: Macintosh 8.6 (and above); 605/300 MHz or G3/233 MHz

64 MB RAM (128 MB recommended)

800 × 600 screen resolution, millions of colors

Internet Explorer 5.0 (or higher) *or* Netscape 4.6 (or higher)

Flash 6 plug-in (or higher)

4 × CD-ROM drive (if using CD-ROM)

Printer

Technical Support
800.677.6337

Email: media.support@pearsoned.com

Hours: 9 A.M. to 5 P.M. EST, Monday–Friday

Software:

Benjamin Cummings PhysioEx™ CD-ROM (Blood Analysis module)

Exercise 30

3-D torso model

heart anatomy chart

24 red pencils

24 blue pencils

6–12 preserved sheep hearts (with pericardial sacs intact if possible)

6–12 pointed glass rods for probes

6–12 dissection trays

6–12 dissection kits

disposable gloves

24 pairs safety glasses

3-D heart model

3-D model of cardiac muscle

X ray viewing box

X ray of human thorax

24 compound microscopes, lens paper, lens cleaning solution, immersion oil

24 slides of cardiac muscle (longitudinal section)

3-D model of skeletal muscle

container for disposal of organic debris

laboratory detergent

spray bottle with 10% household bleach solution

Human Cardiovascular System: The Heart videotape

Exercise 31

millimeter ruler

cot or lab table

A: ECG recording apparatus, electrode paste, alcohol swabs, rubber straps

B: BIOPAC® MP30 (or MP35) data acquisition unit, PC or Macintosh (Mac) computer with at least 4MB of RAM, BIOPAC® Student Lab Software v3.0 or greater, wall transformer, serial cable, electrode lead set, disposable vinyl electrodes, pillow

Exercise 32

anatomical charts of human arteries and veins (or a three-dimensional model of the human circulatory system)

anatomical charts of the following specialized circulations: pulmonary circulation, hepatic portal circulation, arterial supply and circle of Willis of the brain (or a brain model showing this circulation), fetal circulation

24 compound microscopes, lens paper, lens cleaning solution

24 prepared microscope slides showing cross sections of an artery and vein

Human Cardiovascular System: The Blood Vessels videotape

Exercise 33A

12 stethoscopes (bell and diaphragm)

12 sphygmomanometers

6 watches with second hands

alcohol swabs

6 felt-tipped pens

6 small basins or large finger bowls

6 laboratory thermometers

ice

phonograph or tape deck

record, audiotape, or compact disc of "Interpreting Heart Sounds" (available on free loan from local chapters of the American Heart Association)

BIOPAC® MP30 (or MP35)
data acquisition unit, PC or
Macintosh (Mac) computer
with at least 4MB of RAM,
BIOPAC® Student Lab
Software v3.0 or greater,
wall transformer, serial
cable, electrode lead set,
BIOPAC® pulse plethys-
mograph

cot (if available)

step stools (0.4 m [16 in.] and
0.5 m [20 in.] in height)

Exercise 33B

Minimum computer hardware
required:

IBM/PC: Windows 95, 98, NT,
2000, Millennium Edition
(or higher); Pentium I/266
MHz (or faster)

Macintosh: Macintosh 8.6
(and above); 605/300 MHz
or G3/233 MHz

64 MB RAM (128 MB
recommended)

800 × 600 screen resolution,
millions of colors

Internet Explorer 5.0 (or
higher) *or* Netscape 4.6 (or
higher)

Flash 6 plug-in (or higher)

4 × CD-ROM drive (if using
CD-ROM)

Printer

Technical Support

Phone: 800.677.6337

Email: media.support@
pearsoned.com

Hours: 9 A.M. to 6 P.M. EST,
Monday–Friday

Software:

Benjamin Cummings
PhysioEx™ CD-ROM
(Cardiovascular Dynamics
module)

Exercise 34A

6 frogs

disposable gloves

6 sets of recording equipment
and accessories (A or B)

A: physiograph (polygraph),
paper, ink, myograph transducer, transducer cables,
stimulator output extension
cable, electrodes

B: BIOPAC® MP30 (or MP35)
data acquisition unit, PC or
Macintosh (Mac) computer
with at least 4MB of RAM,
wall transformer, serial
cable, BIOPAC® SS12LA
force transducer, S-hook
with thread, transducer (or
ring) stand

disposable container for
organic debris

dissecting pins

12 right-angle clamps

18 bottles of frog Ringer's solution

water bath at 32°C

12 petri dishes

6 medicine droppers

6 dissecting pans and dissecting kits

6 millimeter rulers

thread

6 large rubber bands

box of common pins

6 frog boards

cotton balls

paper towels

6 compound microscopes,
lens paper, lens cleaning
solution

6 dropper bottles of each of the
following (in frog
Ringer's):
5% atropine sulfate
2% digitalis
1% epinephrine
2.5% pilocarpine
5% potassium chloride
2% calcium chloride

0.7% sodium chloride
0.01% histamine
0.01 N HCl

Exercise 34B

Minimum computer hardware
required:

IBM/PC: Windows 95, 98, NT,
2000, Millennium Edition
(or higher); Pentium I/266
MHz (or faster)

Macintosh: Macintosh 8.6
(and above); 605/300 MHz
or G3/233 MHz

64 MB RAM (128 MB
recommended)

800 × 600 screen resolution,
millions of colors

Internet Explorer 5.0 (or
higher) *or* Netscape 4.6 (or
higher)

Flash 6 plug-in (or higher)

4 × CD-ROM drive (if using
CD-ROM)

Printer

Technical Support

Phone: 800.677.6337

Email: media.support@
pearsoned.com

Hours: 9 A.M. to 6 P.M. EST,
Monday–Friday

Software:

Benjamin Cummings
PhysioEx™ CD-ROM
(Frog Cardiovascular
Physiology module)

Exercise 35

anatomical chart of human
lymphatic system

disposable gloves

24 pairs safety glasses

24 compound microscopes,
lens paper, lens cleaning
solution

24 slides of the lymph nodes

24 wax markers

6 petri plates with saline agar

6 medicine droppers

6 dropper bottles of red food color

6 dropper bottles of green food color

6 dropper bottles of anti-horse serum

6 dropper bottles of anti-bovine serum

6 dropper bottles of bovine serum

6 dropper bottles of horse serum albumin

unknown samples of serum albumin labeled "unknown ____"

24 prepared slides of spleens

24 prepared slides of tonsils

colored pencils

Exercise 36

human torso models

respiratory system model, larynx model, and/or chart of the respiratory system

sheep pluck (preserved or fresh from the slaughterhouse); or inflatable swine lungs kit

source of compressed air and 2-foot length of laboratory rubber tubing or 24 cardboard mouthpieces and autoclave bag

24 histological slides of each of the following (if available): trachea (cross section), normal lung tissue, pathological lung tissues (e.g., with bronchitis, pneumonia, emphysema, or lung cancer)

24 compound and stereomicroscopes, lens paper, lens cleaning solution

resin cast of the respiratory tree (if available)

6 dissecting trays

disposable gloves

autoclave bags

Exercise 37A

model lung

6 tape measures

6 pairs of noseclips

24 disposable mouthpieces

6 100-ml beakers

6 dropper bottles of phenol red

50 milliliters of 0.05 M NaOH

autoclave bag

6 spirometers

alcohol swabs

battery jar of 70% ethanol

6 paper bags

6 stethoscopes

6 pH meters standardized with buffer of pH 7

30 250-milliliter beakers

12 50-milliliter beakers

6 100-milliliter graduated cylinders

6 dropper bottles of concentrated HCl

6 dropper bottles of concentrated NaOH

2 liters standard buffer solution (pH 7)

animal plasma

6 wash bottles of distilled water

6 glass stirring rods

6 dropper bottles of 0.01 M HCl

chart (on chalkboard) for recording class data

straws

A: Physiograph, pneumograph, and recording attachments for physiograph

B: BIOPAC® MP30 (or MP35) data acquisition unit, PC or Macintosh (Mac) computer with at least 4MB of RAM, BIOPAC® Student Lab Software v3.0 or greater, wall transformer, serial cable, BIOPAC® airflow transducer, BIOPAC®

calibration syringe, disposable mouthpiece, nose clip, bacteriological filter

Human Respiratory System videotape

Exercise 37B

Minimum computer hardware required:

IBM/PC: Windows 95, 98, NT, 2000, Millennium Edition (or higher); Pentium I/266 MHz (or faster)

Macintosh: Macintosh 8.6 (and above); 605/300 MHz or G3/233 MHz

64 MB RAM (128 MB recommended)

800 × 600 screen resolution, millions of colors

Internet Explorer 5.0 (or higher) *or* Netscape 4.6 (or higher)

Flash 6 plug-in (or higher)

4 × CD-ROM drive (if using CD-ROM)

Printer

Technical Support

    Phone: 800.677.6337

    Email: media.support@ pearsoned.com

    Hours: 9 A.M. to 6 P.M. EST, Monday–Friday

Software:

Benjamin Cummings PhysioEx™ CD-ROM (Respiratory System Mechanics module)

Exercise 38

24 prepared slides of each of the following: mixed salivary glands, liver, pancreas, longitudinal sections of the gastroesophageal junction and a tooth, and cross sections of the stomach, duodenum, and ileum

24 compound microscopes, lens paper, lens cleaning solution

anatomical charts of the human digestive system

jaw model and/or human skull

dissectible torso model

3-D model of a villus (if available)

3-D model of liver lobules (if available)

Human Digestive System videotape

Exercise 39A

General supply area:

144 test tubes

6 test tube racks

6 wax markers

6 test tube holders

6 250-milliliter beakers

ice water bath

water bath at 37°C

boiling chips

6 hot plates

chart (on chalkboard) for recording class results

Supply area 1:

6 dropper bottles of 1% starch solution

6 dropper bottles of distilled water

6 dropper bottles of 1% amylase solution

6 dropper bottles of 1% maltose solution

6 dropper bottles of Benedict's solution

6 dropper bottles of Lugol's solution

6 spot plates

Supply area 2:

6 dropper bottles of 1% trypsin

6 dropper bottles of 0.01% BAPNA

Supply area 3:

6 dropper bottles of 1% pancreatin

6 dropper bottles of 0.1 *N* HCl

6 dropper bottles of vegetable oil

6 dropper bottles of litmus cream

bile salts

parafilm

Supply area 4:

water pitcher

24 paper cups

12 stethoscopes

alcohol swabs

autoclave bag

watch, clock, or timer

Supply area 5:

VHS player

VHS tape *Passage of Food Through the Digestive Tract* videotape

Exercise 39B

Minimum computer hardware required:

IBM/PC: Windows 95, 98, NT, 2000, Millennium Edition (or higher); Pentium I/266 MHz (or faster)

Macintosh: Macintosh 8.6 (and above); 605/300 MHz or G3/233 MHz

64 MB RAM (128 MB recommended)

800 × 600 screen resolution, millions of colors

Internet Explorer 5.0 (or higher) *or* Netscape 4.6 (or higher)

Flash 6 plug-in (or higher)

4 × CD-ROM drive (if using CD-ROM)

Printer

Technical Support
  Phone: 800.677.6337
  Email: media.support@ pearsoned.com
  Hours: 9 A.M. to 6 P.M. EST, Monday–Friday

Software:

Benjamin Cummings PhysioEx™ CD-ROM (Chemical and Physical Processes of Digestion module)

Exercise 40

6–12 pig or sheep kidneys

24 prepared microscope slides of each of the following: longitudinal section of the kidney, cross section of the bladder

24 compound microscopes, lens paper, lens cleaning solution

dissectible human torso model

3-D model or anatomical chart of the human urinary system

3-D models of kidney and nephron (if available)

6–12 dissection trays

6–12 dissection kits

disposable gloves

24 pairs safety glasses

soap, sponges, and disinfectant

Exercise 41A

prepared "pathological" urine samples

2 laboratory buckets of 10% bleach

autoclave bags

6 flasks of 10% bleach

disposable gloves

120 test tubes and holders

24 glass stirring rods

24 test tube racks

24 medicine droppers

24 urinometer cylinders and floats

24 microscope slides and coverslips

24 of each of the following test strips: Clinistix, Ketostix, Albustix, Hemastix, Bilistix; *or* 24 combination test strips (Chemstrip or Multistix)

24 Clinitest tablets

24 10-CC graduated cylinders

24 Ictotest reagent tablets and mats

25 compound microscopes, lens paper, lens cleaning solution

6 packages of wide-range pH paper

6 hot plates

6 bottles containing 100 milliliters of 10% barium chloride

6 bottles containing 100 milliliters of dilute ammonium molybdate

6 dropper bottles of each of the following: dilute HCl, dilute HNO$_3$, 3.0% silver nitrate, concentrated HNO$_3$

student urine samples collected at the beginning of laboratory *or* "normal" artificial urine

24 50-milliliter beakers

6 Clinitest color charts

timer (watch or a clock with a second hand)

specimen of urine sediment

Exercise 41B

Minimum computer hardware required:

IBM/PC: Windows 95, 98, NT, 2000, Millennium Edition (or higher); Pentium I/266 MHz (or faster)

Macintosh: Macintosh 8.6 (and above); 605/300 MHz or G3/233 MHz

64 MB RAM (128 MB recommended)

800 × 600 screen resolution, millions of colors

Internet Explorer 5.0 (or higher) *or* Netscape 4.6 (or higher)

Flash 6 plug-in (or higher)

4 × CD-ROM drive (if using CD-ROM)

Printer

Technical Support

Phone: 800.677.6337

Email: media.support@ pearsoned.com

Hours: 9 A.M. to 6 P.M. EST, Monday–Friday

Software:

Benjamin Cummings PhysioEx™ CD-ROM (Renal Physiology—The Function of the Nephron module)

Exercise 42

24 prepared microscope slides of each of the following: seminal vesicles, penis, epididymis, uterine tube, and uterus (proliferative endometrium)

24 compound microscopes, lens paper, lens cleaning solution

3-D models and/or large laboratory charts of the male and female reproductive tracts

Exercise 43

3-D models of meiosis, spermatogenesis, and oogenesis

12 sets of CR "pop-it" bead chromosomes in two colors with magnetic centromeres

24 prepared slides of each of the following: testis, ovary, human sperm, uterine endometrium (showing menses, proliferative, and secretory stages)

29 compound microscopes, lens paper, lens cleaning solution, immersion oil

demonstration slides of stages of oogenesis in *Ascaris megalocephala* set up on microscopes to show:

a. primary oocyte with fertilization membrane, sperm nucleus, and aligned tetrads apparent

b. formation of first polar body

c. secondary oocyte with dyads aligned

d. formation of the ovum and second polar body ovum

e. fusion of the male and female pronuclei to form the fertilized egg

Exercise 44

24 compound microscopes, lens paper, lens cleaning solution

3-D models of human development

3-D model of pregnant human torso

dissected pregnant cat, pig, or rat uterus

1–2 dissection kits

disposable gloves

fresh or formalin-preserved placenta

24 microscope slides of placenta

A Colour Atlas of Life Before Birth

24 prepared slides of sea urchin development (zygote through larval stages)

Exercise 45

24 PTC taste strips

24 sodium benzoate taste strips

pennies

24 wax markers

lancets

cotton

alcohol swabs

toothpicks and 24 clean microscope slides; *or* 24 test cards and blood mixing sticks

anti-A and anti-B blood typing sera

2 large beakers of 10% bleach

disposable autoclave bag

disposable gloves

6 plastic baggies

samples of HbA, HbS, HbA HbS mixed solution

6 electrophoresis units and power supplies

6 metric rulers

6 1.2% agarose gels

TGE butter ph 8.4

TBE solubilization buffer with bromophenol blue

Coomassie protein stain solution

Staining tray

6 100-ml graduated cylinders

micropipettes

distilled water

Coomassie de-stain solution

Exercise 46

articulated skeletons

3-D charts and models of skeletal muscles

washable markers

hand mirrors

stethoscopes

alcohol swabs

Exercise 47

Minimum computer hardware required:

IBM/PC: Windows 95, 98, NT, 2000, Millennium Edition (or higher); Pentium I/266 MHz (or faster)

Macintosh: Macintosh 8.6 (and above); 605/300 MHz or G3/233 MHz

64 MB RAM (128 MB recommended)

800 × 600 screen resolution, millions of colors

Internet Explorer 5.0 (or higher) *or* Netscape 4.6 (or higher)

Flash 6 plug-in (or higher)

4 × CD-ROM drive (if using CD-ROM)

Printer

Technical Support
800.677.6337
Email: media.support@ pearsoned.com
Hours: 9 A.M. to 6 P.M. EST, Monday–Friday

Software:

Benjamin Cummings PhysioEx™ CD-ROM (Acid-Base Balance module)

Cat Dissection

General Supplies:

6–12 preserved double injected cats

6–12 dissection trays

24 pairs safety glasses

6–12 dissection kits with metric rulers

6–12 name tags and large plastic storage bags

paper towels

disposable gloves or protective skin cream

embalming fluid

organic debris container

Other Supplies:

6–12 stereomicroscopes (dissection exercise 6)

bone cutters (dissection exercises 3, 4, 7, and 9)

6–12 hand lenses (dissection exercise 7)

6–12 hand magnifying lenses (dissection exercise 8)

scissors

Pig Dissection

General Supplies:

6–12 preserved double injected fetal pigs

6–12 dissection trays

6–12 dissection kits with metric rulers

6–12 name tags and large plastic storage bags

paper towels

disposable gloves

twine

embalming fluid

organic debris container

Other Supplies:

6–12 stereomicroscopes (dissection exercise 6)

6–12 small beakers

bone cutters (dissection exercises 2, 3, 4, 6, 7, and 9)

6–12 hand lenses (dissection exercise 7)

List of Supply Houses

This is a partial list of suppliers of equipment, animals, and chemicals, and should not be considered a recommendation for these companies. Many supply companies have regional addresses. Only one address is listed below.

Aldrich Chemical Company, Inc. *
P.O. Box 2060
Milwaukie, WI 53201
800-558-9160
www.sigma-aldrich.com

Carolina Biological Supply Company
2700 York Road
Burlington, NC 27215
800-334-5551
www.carolina.com

Fisher Scientific
3970 John's Creek Court, Suite 500
Suwanee, GA 30024
800-766-7000/770-871-4726
www.fishersci.com

ICN Biochemicals
1263 South Chillicothe Road
Aurora, OH 44202-8064
800-854-0530
www.icnbiomed.com

Intelitool (Phipps & Bird)
P.O. Box 7475
Richmond, VA 23221-0475
800-955-7621
www.intelitool.com

LabChem, Inc.
200 William Pitt Way
Pittsburgh, PA 15238
412-826-5230
www.labchem.net

Nasco
901 Janesville Avenue
P.O. Box 901
Fort Atkinson, WI 53538-0901
800-558-9595
www.enasco.com

Sigma Chemical Company *
P.O. Box 14508
St. Louis, MO 63178-9974
800-325-3010
www.sigma-aldrich.com

VWR International, Inc.
200 Center Square Road
Bridgeport, NJ 08014
800-932-5000
www.vwrsp.com

Ward's Natural Science
5100 West Henrietta Road
Rochester, NY 14692-9012
800-962-2660/585-359-2502
www.wardsci.com

* The Aldrich and Sigma brands are both sold through Sigma-Aldrich, Inc.

Solution Preparation

This is a complete list of the solutions found in the laboratory manual. Most of the percent solutions are weight/volume (grams/100 milliliters). All solutions should be prepared with distilled water unless otherwise noted. Solutions containing glucose or sucrose should be refrigerated to inhibit bacterial growth.

Acetic Acid, 1%
For 500 milliliters, measure out 50 milliliters of 10% acetic acid.
Add to a small amount of distilled water. Add water to a final volume of 500 milliliters.

Agar Gel, 1.5%
Weigh out 15 grams of dried agar.
Slowly add 1 liter of distilled water while heating.
Bring slowly to a boil, stirring constantly until the agar dissolves.
For immediate use, allow the agar to cool to about 45°C.
Pour into petri dishes to solidify. Refrigerate in an inverted position.
If the plates are to be kept for a longer time (more than one day), autoclave the agar solution in the flask, pour into sterile petri plates, allow the agar to solidify, invert the plates, and store in a refrigerator.

Agarose gel, 1.2%
Weigh out 0.9 gram agarose. Mix with 75 milliliters of electrophoresis buffer in a 250–500 milliliter flask.
Boil over heat source or in a mircowave oven for about 1 minute. Rotate the flask periodically. Stir gently.
The solution should be clear.

Alpha-Amylase, 1%
Weigh out 1 gram alpha-amylase.
Add distilled water to a final volume of 100 milliliters.
For best results, be sure that the enzyme is not standardized with maltose.

Atropine Sulfate in Frog Ringer's Solution, 5%
Weigh out 5 grams of atropine sulfate.
Add frog Ringer's solution to a final volume of 100 milliliters.
Caution! Atropine sulfate is toxic. Label "TOXIC."

BAPNA, 0.01%
Weigh out 0.01 gram BAPNA.
Add distilled water to a final volume of 100 milliliters.

Barium Chloride, 10%
Weigh out 10 grams of barium chloride.
Add distilled water to a final volume of 100 milliliters.

Benedict's Solution
- 173.0 grams sodium citrate
- 100.0 grams sodium carbonate, anhydrous
- 17.3 grams cupric sulfate (pure crystalline)

Add the citrate and carbonate salts to 700–800 milliliters distilled water.
Heat to dissolve. Add the cupric sulfate to 100 milliliters distilled water.
Heat to dissolve. Cool the solutions and then combine.
Add distilled water to make 1 liter of solution.

Bleach (Sodium Hypochlorite) Solution, 10%
Measure out 100 milliliters of household bleach.
Add water to a final volume of 1 liter.

Calcium Chloride in Frog Ringer's Solution, 2%
Weigh out 2 grams of calcium chloride.
Add frog Ringer's solution to a final volume of 100 milliliters.

Carboglycerine Solution
- 30 grams fungicide (Benomyl, sigma)
- 250 milliliters glycerine
- 1 liter water

Mix together and store in a closed container.

Digitalis in Frog Ringer's Solution, 2%
Weigh out 2 grams of digitoxin.
Add frog Ringer's solution to a final volume of 100 milliliters.

Epinephrine (Adrenaline), 1:1000
Weigh out 0.1 gram of epinephrine (Carolina).
Dissolve in 0.5 milliliter of 1 *N* HCl.
Add distilled water to a final volume of 100 milliliters.
Caution! Epinephrine is toxic. Label "TOXIC."

Epinephrine in Frog Ringer's Solution, 1%
Weigh out 1 gram of epinephrine (Carolina).
Dissolve in 0.5 milliliter of 1 *N* HCl.
Add frog Ringer's solution to a final volume of 100 milliliters.
Caution! Epinephrine is toxic. Label "TOXIC."

Epsom Salt Solution, 0.1%
For 500 milliliters, weigh out 0.5 gram of Epsom salts.
Add water to a final volume of 500 milliliters.

Glucose, 40%
Weigh out 40 grams of glucose and bring to 100 milliliters with distilled water.
It may be necessary to heat the mixture to get the glucose into solution.
Refrigerate when not in use.

Glucose, 10%
Weigh out 100 grams of glucose.
Add distilled water to a final volume of 1 liter.

Hemoglobin, HbA and HbS
Weigh out 0.2g HbA or HbS.
Add glycerol to a final volume of 1 milliter.

Histamine in Frog Ringer's Solution, 0.01%
Weigh out 0.01 gram histamine.
Add frog Ringer's solution to a final volume of 100 milliliters.

Hydrochloric Acid (HCl), Dilute, 3 N
Add 258 milliliters of 36% HCl to 700 milliliters distilled water.
Add water to a final volume of 1 liter.

Hydrochloric Acid (HCl), 0.1 N
Add 8 milliliters concentrated HCl to 900 milliliters distilled water.
Add distilled water to a final volume of 1 liter; *or* dilute 100 milliliters of 1 *N* HCl to a final volume of 1 liter with distilled water.

Hydrochloric Acid (HCl), 0.01 M or 0.01 N
Add 0.8 milliliter concentrated HCl to 900 milliliters distilled water.
Add distilled water to make 1 liter of solution; *or* dilute 10 milliliters of 1 *N* HCl to a final volume of 1 liter with distilled water.

Hydrochloric Acid (HCl), 0.01%
Add 0.27 milliliter of 1 *N* HCl to 90 milliliters of distilled water.
Add water to a final volume of 100 milliliters; *or* beginning with 37% HCl (d 1.2), prepare a 1 *N* solution by adding 8 milliliters of 37% HCl to 90 milliliters of water. Add distilled water to a final volume of 100 milliliters.

Hydrochloric Acid (HCl), 10%
Slowly add 100 milliliters of concentrated (37%) HCl to 250 milliliters of distilled water. Add distilled water to a final volume of 370 milliliters.

Hydrochloric Acid (HCl) in Frog Ringer's Solution, 0.01 N
Add 0.8 milliliter of concentrated HCl to 900 milliliters frog Ringer's solution.
Add distilled water to a final volume of 1 liter.

Insulin, 400 IU/100 milliliters H_2O
Weigh out 16 milligrams of zinc-stabilized insulin
(25 IU/milligram dry weight, ICN).
Add water to a final volume of 100 milliliters.

Litmus Cream
Add powdered litmus to fresh cream to achieve a blue color.

Lugol's Iodine (IKI)
• 20 grams potassium iodide
• 4 grams iodine crystals
Dissolve potassium iodide in 1 liter distilled water.
Add the iodine crystals and stir to dissolve. Store in dark bottles.

Maltose, 1%
Weigh out 1 gram maltose.
Add distilled water to a final volume of 100 milliliters.

Nitric Acid (HNO₃), Dilute, 3N
Add 183 milliliters of 69% HNO_3 to 700 milliliters distilled water.
Add water to a final volume of 1 liter.

Pancreatin, 1%
Weigh out 1 gram pancreatin.
Add distilled water to a final volume of 100 milliliters.

Physiologic Saline (Amphibian, 0.75%)
Weigh out 7.5 grams of NaCl. Add water to a final volume of 1 liter.
Make fresh immediately prior to experiment.
(Note: 0.7% saline may also be used.)

Physiologic Saline (Mammalian, 0.9%)
Weigh out 9 grams of NaCl. Add water to a final volume of 1 liter.
Make fresh immediately prior to experiment.

Pilocarpine in Frog Ringer's Solution, 2.5%
Weigh out 2 grams of pilocarpine chloride.
Add frog Ringer's solution to a final volume of 100 milliliters.

Potassium Chloride (KCl) in Frog Ringer's Solution, 5%
Weigh out 5 grams of potassium chloride.
Add frog Ringer's solution to a final volume of 100 milliliters.

Propylthiouracil (PTU), 0.02%
Weigh out 0.2 gram of 6-n-propylthiouracil (Aldrich).
Add distilled water to make 1 liter of solution. Filter and store in light-resistant containers. **Caution! PTU is a possible carcinogen.**
(If it is difficult to dissolve the PTU, add concentrated NaOH to adjust the pH to 8.0.)

Quinine, 0.1%
For 500 milliliters, weigh out 0.5 gram of quinine sulfate.
Add water to a final volume of 500 milliliters.

Rat Chow with Thyroid Extract
Grind up sufficient regular laboratory rat chow to feed the required number of animals for 2 weeks (approximately 40 grams chow/rat/day).
Add 20 grams of desiccated thyroid powder (Carolina) for each 1000 grams of rat chow. Mix thoroughly.

Ringer's Solution, Frog
6.50 grams sodium chloride
0.14 gram potassium chloride
0.12 gram calcium chloride
0.20 gram sodium bicarbonate
Combine salts in flask and add distilled water to make 1 liter of solution.

Saline Agar
Mix together 2 grams agar, 1 gram sodium chloride, and 100 milliters of distilled water. Bring to a gentle boil until the solution becomes clear. Use immediately or steam sterilize or add 0.1 gram sodium azide per 100 milliters to store.

Saline Solution, 0.9%
Weigh out 0.9 gram of sodium chloride.
Add distilled water to a final volume of 100 milliliters.

Silver Nitrate (AgNO₃), 2.9 or 3%
Weigh out 2.9 grams (for 2.9%) or 3 grams (for 3%) of silver nitrate.
Use caution; this is an oxidizing substance. Add distilled water to make 100 milliliters of solution. Store in light-resistant bottles. Make fresh for each use.

Sodium Chloride (NaCl), 10%
Weigh out 10 grams NaCl and bring to 100 milliliters with distilled water.
It may be necessary to heat the mixture to get the NaCl into solution.

Sodium Chloride (NaCl) in Frog Ringer's Solution, 0.7%
Weigh out 0.7 gram of sodium chloride.
Add frog Ringer's solution to a final volume of 100 milliliters.

Sodium Citrate, 5%
Weigh out 25 grams of sodium citrate. Add water to a final volume of 500 milliliters.

Sodium Hydroxide (NaOH), 0.05 M
Weigh out 0.2 gram NaOH. Add distilled water to 100 milliters. **Caution! Caustic.**

Starch Solution, Boiled, 1%
Add 1 gram of starch to 100 milliliters distilled water.
Boil just until it changes from cloudy to translucent. Cool and filter.
Add a pinch of NaCl. Prepare fresh daily.
Best results are obtained with potato starch from a biological supply house.

Starch Solution, Boiled, 0.1%
Weigh out 0.1 gram of starch for each 100 milliliters of solution.
Add distilled water to a final volume of 100 milliliters.
Heat the mixture, stirring constantly, until the starch goes into solution.
Cool and filter. Refrigerate when not in use.

Sucrose, 5%
Weigh out 5 grams of sucrose.
Add distilled water to a final volume of 100 milliliters. Refrigerate when not in use.

Trypsin, 1%
Weigh out 1 gram of trypsin.
Add distilled water to a final volume of 100 milliliters.

Tubocurarine, 0.5%
Weigh out 0.125 gram of D-tubocurarine chloride.
Add distilled water to make 25 milliliters. **Label "Poison. Use extreme care."**
Note: Solution should be placed in a serum bottle (Aldrich) for use.

*Urine Solutions**
Urine, Artificial Normal Human
36.4 grams urea
15 grams sodium chloride
9.0 grams potassium chloride
9.6 grams sodium phosphate
4.0 grams creatinine
100 milligrams albumin
Add urea to 1.5 liters of distilled water. Mix until crystals dissolve.
Add sodium chloride, potassium chloride, and sodium phosphate. Mix until solution is clear.
The pH should be within the 5 to 7 pH range for normal human urine. (Adjust pH, if necessary, with 1 N HCl or 1 N NaOH.)
Place a urine hydrometer in the solution and dilute with water to a specific gravity within the range of 1.015 to 1.025.
This stock solution may be refrigerated for several weeks or frozen for months.
Before use, warm to room temperature and add 4.0 grams creatinine and 100 milligrams of albumin for each 2 liters of solution.

Urine, Glycosuria
For a minimally detectable level of glucose, add a minimum of 600 milligrams of glucose to 1 liter of "normal" urine solution. For moderate to high glycosuria, add 2.5 to 5.0 grams of glucose to each liter of solution.

Urine, Hematuria
Add 1 milliliter of heparinized or defibrinated sheep blood to 1 liter of "normal" urine solution.

Urine, Hemoglobinuria
Add 2 milligrams of bovine hemoglobin to 1 liter of "normal" urine solution.

Urine, Hyposthenuria
Add distilled water to a sample of "normal" urine until the specific gravity approaches 1.005.

Urine, Ketonuria
Add a minimum of 100 milligrams of acetoacetic acid or at least 1 milliliter of acetone to 1 liter of "normal" urine solution.

Urine, Leukocyte Presence
Add 100 to 200 units of pork or rabbit liver esterase to 100 milliliters of the "normal" urine solution. This test must be performed immediately after adding the enzyme.

---

* Reprinted by permission: B. R. Shmaefsky, "Artificial Urine for Laboratory Testing," *American Biology Teacher* 52(3), March 1990, pp. 170–172 (Reston, VA: National Association of Biology Teachers).

Urine, pH Imbalance

Adjust "normal" urine to a pH of 4.0 to 4.5 with 1 N HCl for acid urine.

Adjust "normal" urine to a pH of 8 to 9 with 1 N NaOH for alkaline urine.

Urine, Proteinuria

Add 300 milligrams or more of albumin per liter of "normal" urine solution.

For severe renal damage, add 1 gram of albumin to each liter of solution.

Whole Spectrum Pathological Artificial Human Urine

Mix appropriate amounts of abnormal condition reagents to 1 liter of "normal" urine solution. For diabetes mellitus, use glycosuria and ketonuria solutions.

For glomerular damage, use proteinuria, hemoglobinuria, and hematuria solutions.

Yeast Suspension, 10%

Add 5 grams of dried yeast to 50 milliliters of distilled water and gently stir to form a milky solution. After 15 minutes (no more than 30 minutes), stir again. Prepare suspension immediately before use.

Multimedia Resources

Format Options

VHS
CD-ROM
DVD
Slides

Materials for General Application Throughout the Course

Video

Body Atlas Series (NIMCO, 11-part series, 30 minutes each, VHS, DVD)

In the Womb	*The Skin*
Breath of Life	*Defend and Repair*
Glands and Hormones	*Visual Reality*
Muscle and Bone	*Now Hear This*
Taste and Smell	*The Brain*
Sex	*The Human Pump*
The Food Machine	

Human Biology (FHS, 58 minutes, VHS, DVD)

The Human Body: Systems at Work (FHS, 6-part series, 25 minutes each, VHS, DVD)

Circulatory System: The Plasma Pipeline
Digestive System: Your Personal Power Plant
Skeletal System: The Infrastructure
Brain and Nervous System: Your Information Superhighway
Muscular System: The Inner Athlete
Respiratory System: Intake and Exhaust

The Human Body: The Ultimate Machine (CBS, 27 minutes)

The Incredible Human Machine (CBS, 60 minutes, VHS)

The Living Body (FHS, 26-part series, 26–28 minutes each, VHS, DVD)

Introduction to the Body: Landscapes and Interiors	*The Circulatory System: Two Hearts That Beat as One*
The Senses: Skin Deep	*Breath of Life*
Eyes and Ears	*Life Under Pressure*
Sleep: Dream Voyage	*Hot and Cold*
The Urinary Tract: Water!	*Hormones: Messengers*
Digestion: Eating to Live	*Mechanisms of Defense: Accident*
Breakdown	*Internal Defenses*

The Nervous System: Nerves at Work	*Reproduction: Shares in the Future*
Decision	*Coming Together*
Our Talented Brain	*A New Life*
Cell Duplication: Growth and Change	*Into the World*
Muscles and Joints: Muscle Power	*Aging*
Moving Parts	*Review of Biology: Design for Living*

The New Living Body (FHS, 10-part series, 20 minutes each, VHS, DVD)

Bones and Joints	*Blood*
Muscles	*The Brain*
Skin	*The Senses*
Breathing	*Homeostasis*
Digestion	*Reproduction: Designer Babies*

The World of Living Organisms Part 2 (FHS, 8-part series, 15 minutes each, VHS)

Genetic Transmission	*Respiration*
Genetic Translation	*Circulation*
Bones and Muscles	*The Kidney*
Digestion	*Reproduction*

Software

A.D.A.M.® Interactive Anatomy® 3.0 (AIA, CD-ROM)

A.D.A.M.® MediaPro (AIA, CD-ROM)

A.D.A.M.® Practice (AIA, CD-ROM)

Body Works (WNS, CD-ROM)

The Dynamic Human (CS, CD-ROM)

Netter's Interactive Atlas of Clinical Anatomy (LP, CD-ROM)

The Ultimate Human Body (ED, CD-ROM)

Visible Human Male (VP, CD-ROM)

Materials Specifically Related to Particular Systems
OVERVIEW OF HUMAN ANATOMY
Video

Organ Systems Working Together (WNS, 14 minutes, VHS)

The Incredible Human Machine (CBS, 60 minutes, VHS)

The Cell
Video

A Journey Through the Cell (FHS, DVD)

      Cell Functions: A Closer Look (25 minutes)

      Cells: An Introduction (25 minutes)

An Introduction to the Living Cell (CBS, 30 minutes, VHS)

Inside the Living Cell (WNS, set of 5, VHS)

Mitosis and Meiosis (UL, 23 minutes, VHS)

The Outer Envelope (WNS, 15 minutes, VHS)

Software

Inside the Cell (CE, CD-ROM)

Mitosis (CE, CD-ROM)

The Plasma Membrane and Cellular Transport (CE, CD-ROM)

Homeostasis

Video

Homeostasis (FHS, 20 minutes, VHS)

Homeostasis: The Body in Balance (IM, 26 minutes, VHS)

Homeostasis: The Body in Balance (HRM, 26 minutes, VHS)

Histology

Slides

Basic Human Histology (CBS, microslides, sets of eight related 35-mm slides).

Histology Slides for Life Science (BC, 35-mm slides)

Video

Histology Videotape Series (UL, 26-part series, 30 minutes each, VHS)

Software

Eroschenko's Interactive Histology (UL, CD-ROM)

PhysioEX™: Exercise 6B (BC, CD-ROM)

Wards' Histology Collection (WNS, CD-ROM)

Integumentary System

Video

How the Body Works: Skin, Bones, and Muscles (NIMCO, 19 minutes, VHS)

Skin (FHS, 20 minutes, VHS, DVD)

The Skin (NIMCO, 30 minutes, VHS)

The Senses: Skin Deep (FHS, 26 minutes, VHS, DVD)

Skeletal System

Video

Anatomy of a Runner (Structure and Function of the Lower Limb) (UL, 38 minutes, VHS)

Anatomy of the Hand (FHS, 14 minutes, VHS, DVD)

Anatomy of the Shoulder (FHS, 17 minutes, VHS, DVD)

Bones and Joints (FHS, 20 minutes, VHS, DVD)

Gluteal Region and Hip Joint (UL, 18 minutes, VHS)

Knee Joint (UL, 16 minutes, VHS)

Movement at Joints of the Body (FHS, 40 minutes, VHS, DVD)

Moving Parts (FHS, 27 minutes, VHS, DVD)

Muscle and Bone (NIMCO, 30 minutes, VHS)

Our Flexible Frame (WNS, 20 minutes, VHS)

Skeletal System: The Infrastructure (FHS, 25 minutes, VHS, DVD)

Skeleton: An Introduction (UL, 46 minutes, VHS)

The Skeletal System (WNS, 15 minutes, VHS)

The Skeleton: Types of Articulations (UL, 16 minutes, VHS)

The Skull Anatomy Series (UL, 9-part series, VHS)

The Thoracic Skeleton (UL, 18 minutes, VHS)

Software

Interactive Foot and Ankle (LP, CD-ROM)

Interactive Shoulder (LP, CD-ROM)

Interactive Skeleton: Sports and Kinetic (LP, CD-ROM)

Muscle System

Video

Anatomy of a Runner (Structure and Function of the Lower Limb) (UL, 38 minutes, VHS)

Abdomen and Pelvis (UL, 16 minutes, VHS)

How the Body Works: Skin, Bones, and Muscles (NIMCO, 19 minutes, VHS)

Human Musculature Videotape (BC, 23 minutes, VHS)

Lower Extremity (UL, 28 minutes, VHS)

Lower Extremity (WNS, 28 minutes, VHS)

Major Skeletal Muscles and Their Actions (UL, 19 minutes, VHS)

Movements at Joints of the Body (FHS, 40 minutes, VHS, DVD)

Moving Parts (FHS, 26 minutes, VHS, DVD)

Muscle and Bone (NIMCO, 30 minutes, VHS)

Muscles and Joints: Muscle Power (FHS, 26 minutes, VHS, DVD)

Muscles (FHS, 20 minutes, VHS, DVD)

Muscular System: The Inner Athlete (FHS, 25 minutes, VHS, DVD)

Upper Extremity (UL, 36 minutes, VHS)

Upper Extremity (WNS, 36 minutes, VHS)

Software

Biochemistry of Muscle (ED, CD-ROM)

InterActive Physiology: Muscular System Module (BC, CD-ROM or www.interactivephysiology.com)

> *Anatomy review: skeletal muscle*
>
> *The neuromuscular junction*
>
> *Sliding filament theory*
>
> *Muscle metabolism*
>
> *Contraction of motor units*
>
> *Contraction of whole muscle*

Nervous System and Special Senses

Video

Anatomy of the Human Brain (FHS, 35 minutes, VHS, DVD)

Animated Neuroscience and the Action of Nicotine, Cocaine, and Marijuana in the Brain (FHS, 25 minutes DVD)

The Brain (FHS, 20 minutes, VHS, DVD)

The Brain (NIMCO, 30 minutes, VHS)

Brain Anatomy Series (UL, 6-part series, VHS)

Brain and Nervous System: Your Information Superhighway (FHS, 25 minutes, VHS, DVD)

Decision (FHS, 28 minutes, VHS, DVD)

The Ear: Hearing and Balance (IM, 29 minutes, VHS)

The Eye: Structure, Function, and Control of Movement (FHS, 54 minutes, VHS, DVD)

The Eye: Vision and Perception (UL, 29 minutes, VHS)

Eyes and Ears (FHS, 28 minutes, VHS, DVD)

The Human Brain in Situ (FHS, 19 minutes, VHS, DVD)

The Human Nervous System: Spinal Cord and Nerves Videotape (BC, 28 minutes, VHS)

The Human Nervous System: Human Brain and Cranial Nerves Videotape (BC, 28 minutes, VHS)

Mystery of the Senses (CBS, 5-part series, VHS)

> *Vision* (30 minutes)
>
> *Smell* (30 minutes)
>
> *Taste* (30 minutes)
>
> *Hearing* (30 minutes)
>
> *Touch* (30 minutes)

Nerve Impulse Conduction (IM, 29 minutes, VHS)

Nerves and Nerve Cells (CS, VHS)

Neuroanatomy (UL, 19 minutes, VHS)

Now Hear This (NIMCO, 30 minutes, VHS)

Optics of the Human Eye Series (UL, 4-part series, VHS)

The Peripheral Nervous System (UL, 29 minutes, VHS)

Reflexes and Synaptic Transmission (UL, 29 minutes, VHS)

The Senses (FHS, 20 minutes, VHS, DVD)

The Senses of Smell and Taste (NIMCO, 28 minutes, VHS)

The Senses of Touch (NIMCO, 28 minutes, VHS)

Sheep Brain Dissection (WNS, 22 minutes, VHS)

Sheep Eye Dissection (WNS, 15 minutes, VHS)

The Senses: Skin Deep (FHS, 26 minutes, VHS, DVD)

Smell (FHS, 23 minutes, VHS, DVD)

Smell and Taste (FHS, 30 minutes, VHS, DVD)

Taste (FHS, 23 minutes, VHS, DVD)

Taste and Smell (NIMCO, 30 minutes, VHS)

Visual Reality (NIMCO, 30 minutes, VHS)

Software

InterAactive Physiology: Nervous System I and II Modules (BC, CD-ROM or
www.interactivephysiology.com)

Nervous I	*Nervous II*
Orientation	Orientation
Anatomy review	Anatomy review
Ion channels	Ion channels
The membrane potential	Synaptic potentials and cellular integration
The action potential	Synaptic transmission

Endocrine System
Video
Endocrine Control: Systems in Balance (IM, 30 minutes, VHS)
The Endocrine System (IM, 17 minutes, VHS)
The Endocrine System (UL, 17 minutes, VHS)
The Endocrine System (WNS, 16 minutes, VHS)
Glands and Hormones (NIMCO, 30 minutes, VHS)
Hormonally Yours (FHS, 50 minutes, VHS, DVD)
Hormone Heaven? (FHS, 50 minutes, VHS, DVD)
Hormone Hell (FHS, 50 minutes, VHS, DVD)
Hormones: Messengers (FHS, 27 minutes, VHS, DVD)
The Hypothalamus and Pituitary Glands (UL, 29 minutes, VHS)
The Neuroendocrine System (IM, 29 minutes, VHS)
The Neuroendocrine System (UL, 29 minutes, VHS)
The Pancreas (UL, 29 minutes, VHS)

Cardiovascular System
Video
Bleeding and Coagulation (FHS, 31 minutes, VHS, DVD)
Blood (UL, 22 minutes, VHS)
Blood (FHS, 20 minutes, VHS, DVD)
Blood is Life (FHS, 25 minutes, VHS, DVD)
Circulatory System (WNS, 15 minutes, VHS)
Circulatory System: The Plasma Pipeline (FHS, 25 minutes, VHS, DVD)
Human Biology (FHS, 58 minutes, VHS, DVD)
Human Cardiovascular System: Blood Vessels Videotape (BC, 25 minutes, VHS)
Human Cardiovascular System: The Heart Videotape (BC, 25 minutes, VHS)
Life Under Pressure (FHS, 26 minutes, VHS, DVD)
The Mammalian Heart (AIMS, 15 minutes, VHS)
The Physiology of Exercise (FHS, 15 minutes, VHS, DVD)
Sheep Heart Dissection Video (WNS, 14 minutes, VHS)
The Circulatory System: Two Hearts that Beat as One (FHS, 28 minutes, VHS, DVD)

Software
Blood and Immunity (CE, CD-ROM)
Blood and Immunity (LP, CD-ROM)
InterActive Physiology: Cardiovascular System (BC, CD-ROM or www.interactivephysiology.com)

Anatomy review: the heart	*Anatomy review: blood vessel structure and function*
Intrinsic conduction system	*Measuring blood pressure*
Cardiac action potential	*Factors that affect blood pressure*
Cardiac cycle	*Blood pressure regulation*
Cardiac output	*Autoregulation and capillary dynamic*

Lymphatic/Immune System
Video
Defend and Repair (NIMCO, 30 minutes, VHS)
Organ Systems Working Together (WNS, 14 minutes, VHS)
Internal Defenses (FHS, 28 minutes, VHS, DVD)
The Human Immune System: The Fighting Edge (FHS, 44 minutes, VHS, DVD)

Software
Biochemistry of the Immune System (ED, CD-ROM)
Blood and Immunity (CE, CD-ROM)
Blood and Immunity (LP, CD-ROM)

Respiratory System
Video
Breath of Life (FHS, 26 minutes, VHS, DVD)
Breathing (FHS, 20 minutes, VHS)
The Dissection of the Thorax Series (UL, VHS)
      Part I. The Thoracic Wall (23 minutes)
      Part II. Pleurae and Lungs (24 minutes)
Human Respiratory System Videotape (BC, 25 minutes, VHS)
Lungs (Revised) (AIMS, 10 minutes, VHS)
The Physiology of Exercise (FHS, 15 minutes, VHS)
Respiration (FHS, 15 minutes, VHS)
The Respiratory System (UL, 26 minutes, VHS)
Respiratory System: Intake and Exhaust (FHS, 25 minutes, VHS, DVD)
Thorax (UL, 22 minutes, VHS)

Software
InterActive Physiology: Respiratory System (BC, CD-ROM or www.interactivephysiology.com)
      Anatomy review: respiratory structures
      Pulmonary ventilation
      Gas exchange
      Gas transport
      Control of respiration

Digestive System
Video
Breakdown (FHS, 28 minutes, VHS, DVD)
Digestion (FHS, 20 minutes, VHS, DVD)
Digestion: Eating to Live (FHS, 27 minutes, VHS, DVD)
The Food Machine (NIMCO, 30 minutes, VHS)
The Guides to Dissection Series (UL, VHS)
      Group V. The Abdomen (6 parts, 88.5 minutes total)
Digestive System (WNS, 14 minutes, VHS)
The Human Digestive System (AIMS, 18 minutes, VHS)

Human Digestive System Videotape (BC, 33 minutes, VHS)

Passage of Food Through the Digestive Tract (WNS, 8 minutes, VHS)

Urinary System

Video

Human Urinary System Videotape (BC, 23 minutes, VHS)

Kidney Functions (AIMS, 5 minutes, VHS, DVD)

The Kidney (FHS, 15 minutes, VHS)

The Urinary Tract: Water! (FHS, 28 minutes, VHS, DVD)

Software

InterActive Physiology: Urinary System (BC, CD-ROM or www.interactivephysiology.com)

 Anatomy review

 Glomerular filtration

 Early filtrate processing

 Late filtrate processing

InterActive Physiology: Fluids and Electrolytes (BC, CD-ROM or www.interactivephysiology.com)

 Introduction to body fluids

 Water homeostasis

 Electrolyte homeostasis

 Acid/base homeostasis

Reproductive System

Video

A Dozen Eggs: Time-Lapse Microscopy of Normal Development (IM, 46 minutes, VHS)

A Human Life Emerges (FHS, 33 minutes, VHS, DVD)

A New Life (FHS, 28 minutes, VHS, DVD)

Coming Together (FHS, 28 minutes, VHS, DVD)

Genetics: A Popular Guide to the Principles of Human Heredity (FHS, 3-part series, VHS, DVD)

 Understanding the Basic Concepts of Genetics (30 minutes)

 Genetic Discoveries, Disorders, and Mutations (26 minutes)

 Practical Applications and the Risks of Genetic Science (24 minutes)

The Guides to Dissection Series (UL, VHS)

 Group VI. The Pelvis and Perineum (4 parts, 64 minutes total)

Human Biology (FHS, 58 minutes, VHS, DVD)

The Human Female Reproductive System (UL, 29 minutes, VHS)

The Human Male Reproductive System (UL, 29 minutes, VHS)

Human Embryology Series (UL, VHS)

 Highlights of Reproduction and Prenatal Development (16 minutes)

 Fertilization, Cleavage, and Implantation (17 minutes)

Human Reproductive Biology (FHS, 35 minutes, VHS, DVD)

Human Reproductive System Videotape (BC, 32 minutes, VHS)

In the Womb (NIMCO, 30 minutes, VHS)

Into the World (FHS, 28 minutes, VHS, DVD)

Introduction to Development (IM, 22 minutes, VHS)

Meiosis: The Key to Genetic Diversity (WNS, 30 minutes, VHS)